D1266773

THE AMERICAN MIDLAND NATURALIST

Monograph No. 6

THE AMERICAN MIDLAND NATURALIST

Monograph Series

EDITORIAL STAFF

JOHN D. MIZELLE ....*Zoology*
    Editor, University of Notre Dame, Notre Dame, Ind.

EDWARD A. CHAPIN ....*Entomology*
    U. S. National Museum, Washington, D. C.

ALBERT L. DELISLE ....*Plant Morphology*
    University of Notre Dame, Notre Dame, Ind.

CARROLL LANE FENTON ....*Invertebrate Paleontology*
    404 Livingston Ave., New Brunswick, N. J.

JOHN HOBART HOSKINS ....*Paleobotany*
    University of Cincinnati, Cincinnati, Ohio

GEORGE NEVILLE JONES ....*Plant Taxonomy*
    University of Illinois, Urbana, Ill.

REMINGTON KELLOGG ....*Mammalogy*
    U. S. National Museum, Washington, D. C.

JEAN MYRON LINSDALE ....*Ornithology*
    Hastings Reservation, Monterey, Calif.

GEORGE WILLARD MARTIN ....*Mycology*
    State University of Iowa, Iowa City, Iowa

HUGH M. RAUP ....*Plant Ecology*
    Harvard Forest, Harvard University, Petersham, Mass.

KARL PATTERSON SCHMIDT ....*Ichthyology and Herpetology*
    Chicago Natural History Museum, Chicago, Ill.

HARLEY JONES VAN CLEAVE ....*Invertebrate Zoology*
    University of Illinois, Urbana, Ill.

THE AMERICAN MIDLAND NATURALIST

Monograph No. 6

Edited by John D. Mizelle

Published by the University of Notre Dame
Notre Dame, Indiana

A Manual of the Mosses of Western Pennsylvania
and Adjacent Regions

SECOND EDITION

By O. E. JENNINGS

Director Emeritus, Carnegie Museum
Formerly Head, Department of Biology, University of Pittsburgh and
Curator of Botany, Carnegie Museum; Editor, The Bryologist 1913-1938

University of Notre Dame Press
Notre Dame, Indiana
September, 1951

Copyright, 1951
by
The American Midland Naturalist
University of Notre Dame
Notre Dame, Indiana

Preface to the First Edition*

The aim in the preparation of this *Manual* has been to make it a practical handbook applying particularly to the region of western Pennsylvania and embodying all that is at present known regarding the occurrence and distribution of mosses within that area. As a matter of fact, the *Manual* will be found to apply also to the adjacent regions of central Pennsylvania, extreme southwestern New York, eastern Ohio, and northern West Virginia.

When the present writer took charge of the botanical collections in the Carnegie Museum in 1904 he found that the Herbarium, aside from certain specimens collected by Mr. D. A. Burnett in McKean County, a few years previously, contained but little to represent the rich flora of mosses and liverworts to be expected in the western end of Pennsylvania. One of the aims of the Herbarium of the Carnegie Museum has been to assemble a very complete and comprehensive collection of all the plants to be found in the general region in which Pittsburgh is situated, and, in the prosecution of this work, the writer has been enabled to visit all of the counties in the western half of Pennsylvania and also adjacent portions of Ohio and West Virginia. Certain localities in this general region have been made the subject of detailed ecologic and systematic study and collection—particularly the peninsula of Presque Isle, near Erie, Pennsylvania; the extensive Pymatuning Swamp in Crawford County, Pennsylvania; the mountainous region in the vicinity of Ohio Pyle, Fayette County; and the larger portion of Allegheny County, especially in the vicinity of Pittsburgh. From these and other localities visited, extensive collections of mosses have been made and the amount and representative nature of the herbarium material thus available for study have become such that it has been deemed advisable to prepare a treatise embodying the results of the work accomplished, thus placing within the reach of other students of the mosses within the region a convenient means of identifying and checking their collections. It is hoped that with all its faults this *Manual* may be to some extent the means of stimulating bryological study in a region of whose mosses there is yet much to be learned.

In the preparation of this *Manual* the author has taken as the taxonomic standard the monumental work of Warnstorf, Ruhland, and Brotherus, brought to completion in 1909, in Engler & Prantl's *Die Natürlichen Pflanzenfamilien,* Teil I, Abteilung III. In the characterization of the various orders, families, and genera, these authors have been followed closely, and, while there is much to be said against their arrangement of families in certain cases, it is nevertheless very probable that their work will remain for a long time the standard and that, from the standpoint of convenience at least, a similar sequence of families in this *Manual* is justified. In the determination of the various species the

---

* This work in a more condensed form was submitted as a major thesis in candidacy for the degree of Doctor of Philosophy in the University of Pittsburgh, June, 1911.

author has, naturally, had recourse to the various works of Sullivant, Lesquereux & James, Barnes & Heald, Grout, and others among the American bryologists, and, among the European bryologists, particularly Dixon and Jameson. In the determination of the Sphagnums the works of Warnstorf, Roth, and Braithwaite were found particularly useful, while in the treatment of synonymy the main reliance has been placed on the *Index Bryologicus* of E. G. Paris.

In nomenclature the rulings of the International Botanical Congress, held in Brussels in 1910, have been followed, taking as the starting point the *Species Muscorum* of Hedwig (1801) and the three subsequent "Supplements" by Schwaegrichen, Hedwig's having been the first comprehensive work to deal with the mosses in a modern way. In the present *Manual* the principle of priority has been followed without exception, dating from Hedwig, and a few new combinations have been found necessary. Plant names which have been adopted from pre-Hedwigian sources without important changes in nature or in status are indicated by a double citation of authors, the pre-Hedwigian author being cited first, followed by a comma, and then the name of Hedwig or Schwaegrichen or of the post-Hedwigian author, as the case may be. In case the name of the plant has been derived from pre-Hedwigian sources, but has been used in a different rank or, in the case of species, has been transferred from one genus to another, the name of the pre-Hedwigian author has been enclosed in brackets.

So far as it has been possible to do so, the descriptions of the various species are based entirely on specimens collected in the region covered by the *Manual*. Where specimens of species reported as occurring in the region or thought likely to be eventually discovered in the region, have not been available for description, the description has been in part compiled and in part drawn up from specimens from other regions. It has been the aim to represent by original drawings, completely and in considerable detail every species of which specimens collected in the region of the *Manual* have been available. In the list of specimens, which, in the *Manual*, follows the description of each species, the particular specimen figured has been so indicated and the fact that the specimen is in the Herbarium of the Carnegie Museum. All drawings are the work of the author alone, and, with the exception of a few of the larger habit sketches, all drawings have been first traced by means of the camera lucida, thus insuring a reasonable degree of accuracy in the relative position, shape, and size of the various structures figured. The drawings of most of the dissections have been made from permanent glycerine-jelly mica-covered slides which are to be found in the Herbarium in the proper pocket with the specimen.

Special acknowledgment should be here made to Dr. W. J. Holland, Director of the Carnegie Museum, without whose generous and kindly support the collections could not have been made and properly studied nor the *Manual* prepared. To Professor J. C. Fettermann, of the University of Pittsburgh, is due many thanks for suggestions and criticism, and to Mrs. O. E. Jennings

is due much credit for assistance in the collection of specimens, in the preparation of the manuscript, and in the arrangement of the figures on the plates.—
O. E. JENNINGS, Carnegie Museum, September, 1912.

Preface to the Second Edition

In the thirty-eight years which have elapsed since the publication of the
first edition of this *Manual*, the mosses of the region have been much more
extensively collected and twenty-two species have been found which were not
previously known to occur in western Pennsylvania. Various friends, including a number of the author's former students, especially Mr. Sidney K. Eastwood, have by their field-work extended our knowledge of the moss-flora of
our region. Very special acknowledgment is expressed to Mr. Charles M.
Boardman for contributing the results of his extensive field-work adding much
to our knowledge of the distribution of various species, and for adding several
species to the known flora of our region, including five species of *Sphagnum*.
To him is due in large part the revision of the treatment of the Sphagnales.

In the preparation of this second edition of the *Manual*, particularly with
reference to nomenclature and general range of species, frequent reference has
been had to the second edition of Engler & Prantl, *Die Natürlichen Pflanzenfamilien* (1924-1925); Brotherus, *Die Laubmoos Fennoskandias* (1923);
various articles in *The Bryologist;* and particularly the *Moss Flora of North
America North of Mexico*, A. J. Grout, Vols. I-III, (1928-1940). For
Sphagnum, further reference has been had to Sherrin, W. R., *An Illustrated
Handbook of the British Sphagna* (1927) and to Andrews, A. L., *Sphagnaceae*, in Vol. 15, *North American Flora*.

During the years which have passed since the first edition of the *Manual*
was prepared, bryology has advanced to the point that many changes in nomenclature have become necessary in order to bring this second edition up to date.
As in the first edition, all drawings are original and from specimens collected
in western Pennsylvania.—O. E. JENNINGS, Carnegie Museum, June 1, 1950.

To my wife
for assistance in field and herbarium
and for her never-ending encouragement
this book is affectionately dedicated

CONTENTS

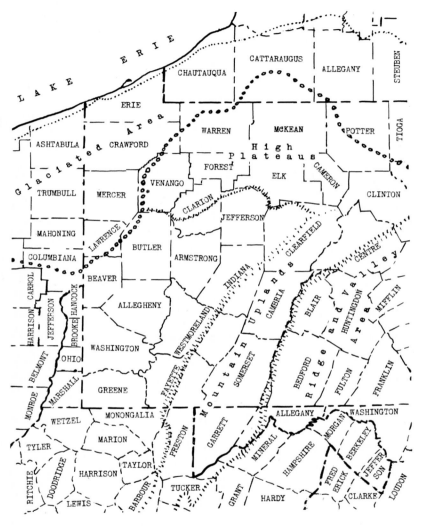

COUNTY MAP OF WESTERN PENNSYLVANIA AND ADJACENT AREAS. Mountain Uplands, mostly 2,000-3,000 ft. altitude, swing across the southeastern quarter, with the Ridge and Valley area to the southeast. The High Plateaus, mostly 1,800-2,400 ft. altitude, occupy the northeastern area; plateaus cut by narrow deep valleys. The Glaciated area in the northwest is bordered southwards by much dissected hilly country. A narrow belt of sandy Lake Plain borders Lake Erie.

A Manual of the Mosses of Western Pennsylvania and Adjacent Regions

Introduction

In a work containing keys and descriptions, so arranged as to make easier the identification of the mosses of any region, it is desirable that a brief sketch of the general life history of the mosses be included. In such a sketch it is not necessary to enter upon a discussion of the many details of minute structure and behavior which, although interesting and important in themselves and also for the light thus thrown upon genetic relationships, are yet of but little practical value in a systematic manual where an easy and quick determination of the identity of the plant is the primary aim.

Speaking broadly, the life history of most of our mosses begins with a minute single-celled *spore*, usually spherical in shape, which, under suitable conditions, germinates and grows out as a slender thread or *filament*, which upon further growth may form a matted felt-like layer, or may flatten out into a more or less lobed body spoken of as a *thallus*, or may simply form a solid cell mass, sometimes consisting of but a few cells. In either case the structure resulting from the growth of the germinated spore is termed the *protonema*. The protonema usually gives rise to buds, which in most mosses grow to be the green leafy shoots which are ordinarily known as moss plants, after which the protonema usually disappears. In a few of the mosses the protonema persists indefinitely as a green felt-like layer on the soil or other substratum. The stems of the green shoots resulting from the growth of protonemal buds usually send out hair-like *rhizoids* which function as roots in holding the plants in place and sometimes act as absorbing organs. The leaves on these green shoots are sessile and with the exception of the midribs (*costae*) are almost uniformly of but one cell in thickness.

This whole phase in the life-history of a moss, beginning with the spore and including the protonema and the leafy shoot, is spoken of as the *gametophyte* or sexual generation. The gametophyte is a sexual plant in that it bears, in definite clusters surrounded by modified leaves called *perichaetial leaves*, the reproductive male and female organs which give rise respectively to the *sperm* and *egg*. These clusters of reproductive organs surrounded by more or less modified perichaetial leaves are known as *perichaetia*. When the sperms and eggs are borne either in the same perichaetium or in different perichaetia on the same plant the plant is spoken of as *monoicous*, but when they are produced upon different plants, *dioicous*. When only male organs are in the cluster the surrounding modified leaves are known as *perigonial leaves*.

The sperms are borne in a globose or more or less club-shaped sac, usually mounted upon a stalk, and this sac is termed the *antheridium*. When ripe the

1

antheridia absorb water and the thin wall, consisting of but a single layer of sterile cells, is ruptured, thus liberating the mass of fertile cells, each of which immediately develops into a sperm. Each sperm consists of a more or less oval or club-shaped and curved body, always free-swimming by means of two long slender *cilia* attached at one end of the body.

The egg is borne in a special organ termed the *archegonium*. The archegonium is usually more or less stalked and is differentiated into a swollen basal portion termed the *venter*, which contains the one fertile egg cell, and the more slender tapering *neck* terminating the archegonium above and containing an axial row of sterile cells termed the *canal cells*, the basal one of which rests directly upon the egg cell. When the archegonium becomes ripe the canal cells break down into a slimy mass of protoplasm, some of which may escape at the tip of the neck. Sperms are attracted in some manner by the slimy protoplasm thus escaping if there is a sufficient film of moisture present so that they may swim about in the perichætium or on the surface of the plant. Having reached the apex of the archegonium the sperms may enter the canal left open by the disintegration of the canal cells and eventually one of the sperms may reach the eggs and, uniting with it, brings about fertilization.

After fertilization the egg immediately begins development as the *sporophyte* but remains enclosed in the venter of the archegonium, which to a considerable extent expands with the development of the young sporophyte but is finally ruptured and usually carried upward on the tip of the sporophyte, where it is then known as the *calyptra* or hood. The ultimate end of the sporophyte is the production of spores which arise entirely by division of cells and are thus known as *asexual* cells. The sporophyte is usually almost devoid of chlorophyll and it develops at its base an absorbing organ termed the *foot* through which its food is obtained from the gametophyte. The sporophyte usually develops more or less of a stalk which is termed the *seta* and which bears at the apex a globose to more or less elongated *capsule* in which the asexual spores form. The method of opening (*dehiscence*) of the capsule and the structures often associated with the dispersal of the spores are varied and are so characteristic for the various systematic groups and species that the capsule becomes highly important for the correct systematic placing of the plants.

Of the mosses there are to be distinguished three well-marked orders known as the *Sphagnales*, the *Andreaeales*, and the *Bryales*. The order *Sphagnales* comprises the one genus *Sphagnum*. These mosses are known as peat mosses or bog mosses, their most characteristic habitat being bogs and the margins of ponds and small lakes. The general color is grayish green, the stems are usually erect in dense tufts or mats and bear at intervals fascicles of short and slender branchlets. The capsules are usually more or less chestnut-colored and globose, while the leaves possess a peculiar and characteristic structure consisting of a meshwork of slender green cells enclosing inflated hyaline cells whose walls are more or less porose.

The *Andreaeales* contain the one genus *Andreaea*, all being small tufted mosses growing on siliceous rocks in mountainous regions. The capsule splits open by four, lateral, vertical slits which, however, do not reach the apex.

The *Bryales* comprise by far the greatest number of the mosses. The capsule in the *Bryales* varies from globose to ovate or pyriform or elongated cylindric. The cells which give rise to the spores are known collectively as *sporogenous tissue* and this tissue occupies but a small portion of the volume of the capsule, being arranged in the form of a hollow tube or cylinder vertically placed and open at both ends. The sterile tissues occupying the hollow part of this tube constitute the *columella*. The outer wall of the capsule usually contains more or less green chlorophyll and the middle portion of this wall is more or less loosely arranged and contains hollow spaces. The capsule is covered by an *epidermis*, perforated by *stomata* in most mosses. The stomata are usually most highly developed on the rounded or tapering base of the capsule which is often more or less distinct and is known as the *collum* or *neck*. In the ripening of the capsule the sterile tissues of the wall and of the columella largely disappear, leaving the capsule filled with a mass of spores. In some species the thin wall of the capsule bursts irregularly, this type of dehiscence being known as *cleistocarpous*. In other species the top of the capsule separates as a *lid* or *operculum*. The separation of the lid is often facilitated by the modification of a series of epidermal cells termed the *annulus*, which usually becomes highly hygroscopic and is often deciduous. The sterile tissues immediately beneath the lid are usually more or less highly modified to form a single or double series of pointed structures known collectively as the *peristome*. The pointed structures constituting the outer series in the double peristome or the single series in a simple peristome are known as *teeth*, while the inner and more delicate series of the double peristome are known as *segments*. Between the individual segments in many species of mosses are very delicate hair-like structures known as *cilia*. Sometimes the cilia are in groups of two or more alternating with the segments. The peristome is usually very hygroscopic, curling inward and closing the mouth of the capsule in damp air and opening outward and allowing the free dispersal of the spores in dry air. Species whose capsules stand vertically are not so likely to have well-developed peristomes as are species whose capsules are inclined or vertical, this variation corresponding to the need for the regulation of spore dispersal.

The *Sphagnales* are most abundant in the cooler parts of the North Temperate Zone, often constituting there large tracts of vegetation. By their aquatic or semi-aquatic manner of life and their apical method of growth, dying away below as they grow upward, they tend to form great tufts or mats, often completely filling depressions and bogs and by the accumulation of the encircling mats around ponds and small lakes tending to fill them also. The mats hold water like a sponge and, being somewhat antiseptic, the dead portions below the mat do not decay but become converted into peat, which, especially in certain parts of Europe, has served a very important purpose as fuel. A considerable number of *Sphagnum* bogs and *Sphagnum* cranberry glades of limited area occur in the mountains of central Pennsylvania. The only other bogs of any considerable extent in our region are those in the

Andreaea Rothii
Astomum Muhlenbergianum
Atrichum crispum
Brachythecium oxycladon
Bruchia Sullivantii
Discelium nudum
Drepanocladus aduncus
Entodon compressus
Ephemerum serratum
Grimmia pilifera
Hookeria acutifolia
Mnium spinulosum
Orthotrichum obtusifolium
Plagiothecium Roeseanum

Astomum Muhlenbergianum
Ptychomitrium incurvum
Rhacomitrium heterostichum
   var. gracilescens
Raphidostegium marylandicum
Rhytidium rugosum
Sphagnum fuscum
Sphagnum Girgensohnii
Sphagnum papillosum
Sphagnum Wulfianum
Splachnum ampullaceum
Tetraplodon angustatus
Thuidium pygmaeum

For some of the mosses included in the first edition no satisfactory material from western Pennsylvania was then available for illustration. Specimens of twenty of these species have since been collected in our region and have now been illustrated in the present edition, as follows:

Bryhnia novae-angliae
Dicranella rufescens
Dicranum rugosum
Drepanocladus fluitans
Encalypta streptocarpa
Entodon compressus
Fissidens hyalinus
Fontinalis gigantea
Hygroamblystegium orthocladon
Isopterygium deplanatum

Isopterygium elegans
Isopterygium geophilum
Mnium hornum
Octodiceras debile
Plagiothecium Roeseanum
Pleuridium subulatum
Sphagnum squarrosum
Stereodon pratensis
Tortula papillosa
Trematodon ambiguus

Including the above additions the present edition contains 18 additional plates covering forty-six species and bringing the number of individual figures to a total of three thousand five hundred and seventeen.

In addition to the 243 kinds of mosses described and illustrated by original drawings by the author from collections made in western Pennsylvania there are included more than 100 descriptions of species reported for the region by various collectors years ago or which are known to occur in territory adjacent to western Pennsylvania. Some of the species reported for our region by T. P. James, Thos. C. Porter, and others are perhaps not now to be found here, while others known from adjoining regions will undoubtedly eventually be found here, although, unlike some of these localities, we do not have extended areas of limestone outcrops such as occur to the east and west, on which certain calciphilous species commonly occur.

The following new combinations occur in the second edition.

Sphagnum palustre var. squarrosulum (Nees & Hornschuch)
Sphagnum palustre var. brachycladum (Schliephacke)
Sphagnum plumulosum f. viride (Warnstorf)
Atrichum undulatum var. allegheniense (Jennings)
Eurynchium pulchellum var. praecox (Hedwig)
Pohlia nutans var. triciliata

The total number of genera, species, and varieties recognized in this *Manual* as having been collected or authoritatively reported in western Pennsylvania is as follows:

	Genera	Species	Varieties
Sphagnales	1	24	7
Andreaeales	1	2	–
Bryales	111	260	26
Total	113	286	33

Directions for Collecting, Preparing, and Preserving Specimens of Mosses

For the benefit of those who may not be familiar with the usual methods of collection and preservation of bryological specimens the following notes may be of use.

Specimens of *Bryales* should be collected in fruit (ripe sporophytes) as far as possible. Specimens of *Sphagnum* are desirable in fruit, but determination is best made in this group from the vegetative characters. Specimens of mosses when collected should be placed at once in envelopes or other suitable paper pockets and the data of collection, especially habitat, should be written upon the envelope. Many collectors prefer to number the envelope and under the corresponding number make note of the data in a note-book. Collections may be carried home in a basket or regular tin collecting case and, if carefully placed in the envelopes in the first place, the specimens need not be taken out of the envelopes but the envelopes should be placed between blotting papers or newspapers and subjected to a slight weight and so placed that they will soon dry. A few books or two or three bricks are usually sufficient weight for drying a package of mosses. Too much weight should be guarded against, as the habit of the plant, i. e., the position assumed by leaves, branches, etc., is often a great help in determining the species, and, if too much weight is used in drying, the specimens will be so flattened as to destroy these characters.

When dry, the specimens may be placed in paper pockets made from a rectangular piece of paper by folding up the lower part of the rectangle to within about one inch of the upper edge and then folding down this inch flap over the first flap. The two ends should now be folded backward for about one inch each and the pocket is then complete and ready for the reception of the moss. The regulation method in most larger herbaria is to glue this pocket in the middle of the back, midway between the two folded ends, to a so-called "herbarium sheet" which is uniformly of white stiff paper measuring 11½ by 16½ inches. For small private collections smaller sizes are sometimes used. On the lower right-hand corner of this sheet is written the name of the species, and the number of specimens which such a sheet will accommodate is, of course, restricted only by the space occupied by the pockets. The label for each specimen should be fastened to the narrow flap at the upper edge of the pocket and should always contain the name of the species, the exact locality and habitat of the specimen, the name of the collector, and the date of the collection.   If material has been collected in sets for distribution the label should so state and a number should be assigned to the various species so that duplicate specimens reaching different botanists may be definitely correlated. It is often advisable to add to the label also the name of the botanist who identified the specimen, especially if he be a specialist.

For any extended study of the mosses, either *Sphagnales* or *Bryales,* it is practically necessary to have at hand besides a pocket lens of some sort, a dissecting lens and a compound microscope. A dissecting lens may be rigged up by providing some sort of a frame for holding the ordinary pocket lens at the right distance above the table. This can be done by some such simple contrivance as knitting needles and corks, in the absence of anything better. The writer has found very satisfactory the ordinary dissecting stand, which may be obtained from any dealer in scientific apparatus, the stand preferably fitted with a rack-and-pinion adjustment for focusing the lens. The writer has used with good results a doublet lens (three-quarter inch) magnifying about four diameters and a one-fourth inch aplanat lens magnifying about seven diameters. The compound microscope should be fitted with a one-inch and also preferably a two-inch eye-piece and the customary two-thirds and one-sixth objectives. A sub-stage condenser is a great convenience and should be provided with diaphragms both above and below.

In preparing a moss for microscopic study the writer proceeds as follows: A portion of the specimen, usually consisting of a whole plant, is selected and soaked in water until it is soft and relaxed. A thin square of mica an inch or more in width is prepared and placed on an ordinary glass miscroscope slide, and upon it is placed a drop of a ten per cent solution of glycerine in water which is kept already prepared in a small bottle with a medicine dropper fastened into the stopper. The glass slide with the mica square and solution in position are placed on the stand of the dissecting microscope. With small forceps and with the aid of needles mounted in wooden handles the moss is now carefully dissected and the parts suitably disposed on the mica square in the film of ten per cent glycerine. It is usually best to place on the mica square some thin cross-sections of the stem of the moss, cut with a scalpel or knife or fine scissors, some stem-leaves, some branch-leaves, some perichætial leaves or, better, the whole perichætium dissected apart but not widely scattered, and then the capsule so dissected as to show a patch of the epidermis from the base of the capsule, the annulus, the peristome, both outer and inner if they are present, and the spores.

Another thin mica square is now selected a little smaller than the first one used and upon it is placed a small chunk of glycerine-jelly, which is melted by holding the square in the forceps over a suitable source of heat—the writer holds the square over the electric bulb of his desk light. The glycerine when melted is smeared over the surface of the mica, which is then inverted and quickly but carefully placed on the square on which the dissections are disposed. To prevent the dissected objects from changing their position too much, and to obviate the inclusion of air-bubbles, it is best to lay the square which is to serve as cover so that one edge only comes into contact with the other square and then let the cover settle down gradually, thus driving the air out in front of the gradually advancing line of contact of the mica and mounting medium. The slide is now ready for study under the compound microscope and after this it may be placed in the paper pocket along with the specimens from one of which the dissections were made. In order to insure greater permanency of the slide, as thus made, some workers advocate sealing the slide by running a little ring of Canada balsam* around the edge of the smaller mica square, thus keeping the air away from the glycerine jelly and preventing any further drying out. The object of placing the dissections in the ten per cent solution of glycerine is to gradually allow the dissections to accommodate themselves to increasing density of solutions; if the dissections were transferred immediately from pure water to the melted glycerine jelly there would in most cases be much shrinkage and curling, thus spoiling the slide for purposes of study. In a few cases even the transferance from water to ten per cent solution and thence to the jelly is too great a change and in such cases it is necessary to pass the dissections through a series of solutions of increasing glycerine per cent, up to a strong solution, before using the glycerine-jelly. Another way is to place the dissections in weak glycerine solution and keep adding more solution as the water evaporates from the first, thus gradually increasing the density.

Another method has been described by Steyaert, R. L. (Science 105: 47-48. 1947). Chloraphenol, consisting of two parts chloral hydrate and one part phenol crystals,** is heated till liquefied and then kept in dropping bottles. This liquid mixes with either water or Canada balsam. Dried material may be placed and dissected directly in a mixture of two drops of chloraphenol to one of balsam dissolved in xylol. After this, place the cover slip on and gently heat to evaporate the chloraphenol, in the meantime placing droplets of balsam at the edge of the cover slip so that it may flow under and ensure a sufficient amount of balsam in the mount. The mount may then be sealed (ringed) with varnish.

Or, material may be dissected in water which may then be drawn out by a blotter while chloraphenol is run under the slip from the opposite edge. Slightly warming the slide helps to get rid of air bubbles. The chloraphenol may then similarly be drawn out with a blotter while balsam is drawn under from the other side of the slip. When thoroughly filled with balsam the amount may be permanently ringed with varnish.

---

* Before applying such a sealing medium, the edges of the slips should be dry. Other sealing media often used are gum dammar, shellac varnish, gold size, or marine glue.

** Care must be taken not to let the phenol come into contact with the skin. It will cause a very severe burn.

cm—Centimeter, equals the one-hundredth part of a meter, or about two-fifths of an inch.
mm—Millimeter, equals one-tenth of a centimeter; about one-twenty-fifth of an inch.
C.M.B.—Charles M. Boardman.
D.A.B.—D. A. Burnett.
S.K.E.—Sidney K. Eastwood.
G.K.J.—Grace K. Jennings (Mrs. O. E. Jennings).
O.E.J.—O. E. Jennings.
J.A.S.—John A. Shafer.

- The hyphen used between figures or between words denotes either an intermediate state or a variation from one to the other extreme.

ANALYTICAL KEY TO THE GENERA OF MOSSES
OF WESTERN PENNSYLVANIA

Order I. **Sphagnales**

Whitish mosses with fasciculate branches, mostly bog plants; leaf-cells of two kinds, —large hyaline ones separated by narrow chlorophyllose ones; ecostate; operculate but with no peristome ....*Sphagnum*, p. 20

Order II. **Andreaeales**

Dark colored or blackish, very fragile, alpine or subalpine plants growing in cushions on granitic, hard sandstone, or slaty rocks; either costate or ecostate; leaf-cells small and quite opaque; capsule dehiscing by 'four longitudinal slits, the valves remaining united at the apex until quite old and empty ....*Andreaea*, p. 43

Order III. **Bryales**

Leaves various but not sphagnoid, costate or ecostate; capsule dehiscing irregularly or, more often, by a deciduous operculum, often furnished with a peristome, never four-valved as in *Andreaea*, plants largely green* I

Haplohymenium triste is not known to fruit in the United States.

I. Sporophyte borne at the apex of the main stem, sometimes appearing lateral by the growth of a branch ....A. (ACROCARPI) p. 44

I. Sporophyte borne at the apex of a usually short lateral branch, or appearing axillary ....B. (PLEUROCARPI) p. 172

I. Sporophytes on rather vigorous, erect, often dendroid secondary branches which rise from a rhizome-like primary stem ....see *Thamnium* or *Climacium*

A. ACROCARPI

1. Capsule non-operculate (or lid not readily separating) 2
1. Capsule operculate 10
   2. Green protonema persistent; plants fruiting in autumn, minute ....
   ....*Ephemerum*, p. 113
   2. Green protonema persistent; plants fruiting in spring ....*Acaulon*, p. 87
   2. Green protonema not persistent, plants fruiting mainly in spring 3

---

* *Hookeria acutifolia* has leaves 4-5 mm long, drying very thin, soft, fluffy, and pale yellow or whitish.

3. Spores few, about 16 to 20, smooth, about 0.2 mm in diameter; leaves linear-lanceolate, with percurrent costa ....*Archidium*, p. 44
3. Spores numerous, rarely exceeding 0.05 mm in diameter 4
    4. Leaf-margins plane or involute 5
    4. Leaf-margins more or less revolute 9
    5. Capsules pyriform, with a distinct neck 6
    5. Capsules globose to ovoid 7
      6. Green protonema occasionally abundant; neck none; capsule acute ....
      ....*Sporledera*, p. 49
      6. Green protonema sparse; usually none; neck more or less well developed; capsule more or less rostrate ....*Bruchia*, p. 46
      7. Leaves crisped when dry, strongly papillose on both sides; operculum rudimentary but persistent ....*Astomum*, p. 78
      7. Leaves not crisped when dry, smooth 8
        8. Calyptra cucullate (mitrate in *Pleuridium palustre*); leaves linear-lanceolate to lanceolate-subulate ....*Pleuridium*, p. 48
        8. Calyptra campanulate; leaves lanceolate-ovate to lanceolate-obovate, dentate or serrate ....*Physcomitrella*, p. 116
9. Capsule apiculate; leaves papillose ....*Phascum*, p. 88
9. Capsule not at all or faintly apiculate; leaves smooth ....*Acaulon*, p. 87
    10. Protonema long persisting; stem-leaves minute; plant looks like a grain of wheat sitting in a tuft of bristles ....*Diphyscium*, p. 155
    10. Protonema brownish, persistent; plant looks like a shriveled, brownish grain of wheat sitting obliquely on a stout seta about 1 cm high ....
    ....*Buxbaumia*, p. 156
    10. Protonema persistent; plants practically stemless, leaves ecostate; calyptra splitting down one side and usually remaining attached to the seta ....
    ....*Discelium*, p. 113
    10. Protonema persistent; plants practically stemless (1-2 mm); costa strongly lamellate in apical portion of the leaf ....*Pogonatum*, p. 165
    10. Protonema not persistent; calyptra not as in *Discelium*. If with hypophysis see *Splachnaceae*, p. 110 11
11. Peristome teeth none, or if present articulate, at least at base 12
11. Peristome teeth not distinctly articulate 60
    12. Peristome present, sometimes imperfect 13
    12. Peristome none 52
13. Leaves distichous, dorsally winged and clasping at the base 127
13. Leaves not distichously clasping and dorsally winged 14
    14. Leaves consisting of costa only, outer cells large and empty, inner small and chlorophyllose ....*Leucobryum*, p. 66
    14. Leaves with a lamina consisting mainly of one layer of more or less uniform cells 15
15. Peristome single, 16- or 32-toothed; teeth without a median longitudinal line on the exterior face 16
15. Peristome double, with 16 outer teeth and an inner variously segmented or almost lacking membrane; teeth mostly with a median longitudinal line on the exterior face 37
    16. Capsules more or less octagonal, the angles with differentiated cells, when dry 8-striate and furrowed ....*Rhabdoweisia*, p. 57
    16. Capsule not octagonal, or, if plicate, the cells uniform 17
17. Exterior face of teeth longitudinally striate. (See also *Ditrichum*) 18
17. Exterior face of teeth smooth or papillose, not longitudinally striate. (See also *Seligeria*) 24
    18. Leaves with differentiated, often enlarged, hyaline or brownish alar cells 12
    18. Leaves without differentiated alar cells 19
19. Leaf-cells strongly and coarsely papillose. (See also *Oncophorus*) ....
....*Oreoweisia*, p. 46

19. Leaf-cells smooth 20
    20. Peristome of 16 broad solid teeth, sometimes somewhat bifid at the apex, smooth and strongly hygroscopic ....*Seligeria*, p. 53
    20. Peristome of 16 narrow, prolonged, more or less two-parted, minutely striate or papillose teeth 21
21. Capsule cernuus, with a long and inflated neck; teeth cleft or perforate ....
    ....*Trematodon*, p. 47
21. Capsule erect or inclined; neck short or none; teeth cleft to the middle into two (or three) filiform divisions; leaves not crisped when dry ....
    ....*Dicranella*, p. 54
21. Capsule erect to horizontal; neck none; teeth cleft about half way; leaves crisped when dry ....*Oncophorus*, p. 58
    22. Monoicous; leaves tufted; capsules strumose, costa with distinctly heterogeneous tissues ....*Oncophorus*, p. 58
    22. Dioicous; leaves flexuose-spreading or secund; capsule more or less distinctly strumose 23
23. Basal auricles of leaves large and inflated; seta cygneous; peristome teeth divided ¾ to base ....*Dicranodontium*, p. 64
23. Basal auricles of leaves small or none; seta not cygneous; peristome teeth divided about half way ....*Dicranum*, p. 59
    24. Peristome distinctly twisted; teeth 32 25
    24. Peristome not distinctly twisted; teeth 16 but often deeply cleft 27
25. Leaves large, oblong to sub-spatulate; costa with two median guides ....
    .... *Tortula*, p. 91
25. Leaves small and narrow, linear-lanceolate; costa with from 4-8 median guides 26
    26. Leaf-margins plane, not revolute; cells papillose ....*Tortella*, p. 83
    26. Leaf-margins revolute, at least below; cells smooth or papillose ....
    ....*Barbula*, p. 85
27. Dark green to brownish or blackish mosses on rocks or sometimes trees; peristome single or none 28
27. Green plants, not blackish nor very dark 30
    28. Calyptra campanulate, plicate, covering most of urn ....
    ....*Orthotrichum*, p. 103
    28. Calyptra covering about half of the capsule, split and plicate; spores large
    ....*Ptychomitrium*, p. 95
    28. Calyptra large cucullate; spores very large; teeth wide, truncate; annulus none ....*Drummondia*, p. 103
    28. Calyptra short, not plicate; annulus usually present; spores medium size to small 29
29. Teeth sub-entire, cribrose or irregular cleft in upper half ....*Grimmia*, p. 95
29. Teeth cleft to near the base into filiform segments ....*Rhacomitrium*, p. 98
    30. Calyptra mitrate, not folded nor torn, complerely covering the capsule; capsule erect; leaves ligulate to spatulate ....*Encalypta*, p. 93
    30. Calyptra cucullate 31
31. Teeth merging below into a more or less continuous basal wall or membrane .. 32
31. Teeth not merging below into a continuous membrane 35
    32. Upper leaf-cells papillose; costa with one or two rows of larger cells ventral to the 2-4 median guides ....*Desmatodon*, p. 90
    32. Upper leaf-cells papillose; costa with 4-6 median guide cells and a well developed stereid region on ventral side ....*Didymodon*, p. 84
    32. Leaves mostly smooth; peristome-teeth mostly medium length to long 33
33. Capsule inclined, distinctly plicate when dry; leaf-cells roundish-quadrate above
    ....*Ceratodon*, p. 52
33. Capsule erect, nearly or entirely smooth when dry; leaf-cells elongated (2:1 or more) above 34
    34. Leaves glaucous ....*(Saelania)*

present; leaf-cells rectangular below, rhomboid-hexagonal above ....
....*Bryum*, p. 127

51. Sporogonia often several in a cluster; stems erect from rhizome-like stolons; annulus present; median leaf-cells rhomboid-hexagonal with pitted walls
....*Rhodobryum*, p. 134

    52. Rock- or crevice-inhabiting mosses 53

    52. Earth-inhabiting plants 58

53. Leaves on the sterile stems in two rows, forming a continuous marginal wing
....*Schistostega*, p. 120

53. Leaves on the sterile stem not thus arranged 54

    54. Leaves distichous, closely imbricate, carinate-plicate; stems radiculose and bulbiform at base ....*Bryoxiphium*, p. 68

    54. Leaves not as above; stem not bulbiferous at base 55

55. Leaves ecostate; seta less than 1 mm long; operculum apiculate ....
....*Hedwigia*, p. 171

55. Leaves costate; operculum rostrate 56

    56. Capsule smooth, terminating the main axis; plants often on calcareous rocks 57

    56. Capsule ribbed, borne on a short lateral branch; plants not often on calcareous rocks ....*Amphidium*, p. 101

57. Leaf-margins revolute on one or both sides; upper leaf-cells clear and pellucid; columella remaining attached to the operculum and falling away with it
....*Hymenostylium*, p. 81

57. Leaf-margins always plane; upper leaf-cells densely papillose and obscure; columella remaining in the capsule after the operculum falls away ....
....*Gymnostomum*, p. 80

57. Leaves canaliculate-subulate from a concave, lanceolate base; basal leaf-cells thin-walled rectangular, upper cells isodiametric incrassate ....*Seligeria*, p. 53

    58. Calyptra cuculate; cells isodiametric above the middle of the leaf (see also *Astomum*) ....*Pottia*, p. 89

    58. Calypra mitrate; cells elongated above the middle of the leaf 59

59. Capsule immersed and sessile, splitting equatorially and without very specially modified cells at the line of dehiscence ....*Aphanorhegma*, p. 115

59. Capsule exserted on a long seta, or, if immersed, operculate with 1-3 rows of denser cells below the line of dehiscence ....*Physcomitrium*, p. 117

    60. Capsule symmetric; peristome single 61

    60. Capsule unsymmetric; peristome double, the inner in the form of a short conical tube 64

61. Peristome teeth 4 ....*Tetraphis*, p. 158

61. Peristome teeth 32 or 64 62

61. Peristome teeth 16 ....*Trichostomum*, p. 82

    62. Capsule usually square or hexagonal; calyptra densely hairy; teeth generally 64 ....*Polytrichum*, p. 166

    62. Capsule cylindrical; teeth 32 63

63. Calyptra densely hairy; leaves not crisped when dry; protonema persistent ......
....*Pogonatum*, p. 165

63. Calyptra cucullate, almost smooth; leaves crisped when dry ....*Atrichum*, p. 159

    64. Leaves green, costate, conspicuous; capsule sessile and immersed ....
....*Diphyscium*, p. 155

    64. Leaves almost microscopic, colorless; capsule exserted on a thick, red stalk
....*Buxbaumia*, p. 156

B. Pleurocarpi

65. Leaves distichous, dorsally winged and clasping at the base ....*Fissidens*, p. 69

65. Leaves pluri-seriate, or, if distichous not clasping at the base 66

    66. Cilia none; segments none, irregular, or rudimentary, or filiform and not

split 67
66. Cilia (none) or often present; segments carinate and often split along the
median line (sometimes adhering to the teeth) 76
66. Inner peristome consisting only of a low papillose basal membrane ....
....*Lindbergia*, p. 202
67. Segments quite rudimentary, sometimes with a distinct carinate basal membrane; leaves smooth to usually more or less papillose 68
67. Leaves smooth 69
68. Leaves deltoid to round-ovate, spinulose-dentate to fimbriate; paraphyllia
none; costa single and usually half the length of the leaf ....*Thelia*, p. 195
68. Leaves oval-elliptic to obovate, entire or cristate-serrate; costa double or
short or almost lacking ....*Pterygynandrum*, p. 278
68. Stem-leaves ovate, sub-cordate, apex abruptly long-acuminate; costa sub-
percurrent; branch-leaves narrower ....*Leskeella*, p. 205
69. Inner peristome lattice-like; leaf-cells narrow and prosenchymatous 70
69. Inner peristome not lattice-like, sometimes none; segments when present free,
sometimes rudimentary 71
70. Ecostate; capsule immersed; plants aquatic ....*Fontinalis*, p. 173
70. Costate; capsule more or less exserted; plants growing on the base of
bushes and shrubs ....*Dichelyma*, p. 178
71. Leaves complanate, more or less transversely undulate ....*Neckera*, p. 187
71. Leaves more or less spreading, not transversely undulate 72
72. Inner peristome none, or, if present, the linear segments without a basal
membrane; teeth flat, thin, distantly articulated, approximate in pairs;
costa simple, often delicate and short, or none 73
72. Inner peristome lacking or the peristome double; basal membrane low 74
73. Costa mostly delicate and short; teeth approximate in pairs, broad and obtuse;
leaves serrate to ciliate-dentate .... *Fabronia*, p. 279
73. Costa strong, ending above the middle of the leaf; peristome deeply inserted;
teeth broadly lanceolate; segments shorter than the teeth, linear, almost
smooth ....*Anacamptodon*, p. 280
74. Calyptra cucullate; capsule exserted; segments of inner peristome rudimentary and narrow or none or adhering to inner surface of teeth 75
74. Calyptra conical-campanulate; capsule immersed; segents linear or very
narrow-carinate ....(*Cryphaea*)
75. Ecostate ....*Leucodon*, p. 183
75. Costate ....*Leptodon*, p. 185
76. Leaves mostly rough-papillose. (*Bryhnia* spp. and *Isopterygium geophilum*
are papillose dorsally by projecting angles of cell-walls)............................. 77
76. Leaves smooth (see also *Helodium*), or sometimes slightly papillose at the
cell angles 89
77. Capsule erect and symmetric 78
77. Capsule usually arcuate, unsymmetric 84
78. Leaves costate, margins papillose-denticulate; cells pluripapillate; operculum
conic-rostrate ....*Rauia*, p. 206
78. Leaves costate, margin usually entire (see also *Myurella*) 79
78. Leaves ecostate 83
79. Costa not more than half the length of the leaf ....*Haplohymenium*, p. 197
79. Costa strong in our species, nearly reaching the apex of the leaf 80
80. Primary stems stoloniform, secondary stems bearing the sporophytes; stem-
leaves minute; paraphyllia none ....*Anomodon*, p. 198
80. Primary stems bearing the sporophytes and not stoloniform; branch and
stem leaves not markedly dissimilar; paraphyllia often present 81
81. Paraphyllia none; leaf-cells compact, oval-oblong to round-hexagonal, nearly
smooth; cilia none; teeth not hygroscopic; dioicous ....*Leskeella*, p. 205
81. Paraphyllia usually present; leaf-cells hexagonal to parenchymatous, mostly
unipapillate; autoicous 82

82. Teeth with well developed lamellae; segments narrow-linear ......*Leskea*, p. 203
82. Teeth with low lamellae; segments none ....*Lindbergia*, p. 202
83. Cilia two; plants glaucous-green with closely imbricated leaves and julaceous
    branches ....*Myurella*, p. 196
83. Cilia none; plants light green with loosely appressed leaves and more or less
    flattened branches ....*Schwetschkeopsis*, p. 281
    84. Plants creeping, one- to three-pinnate 85
    84. Plants erect to ascending, simply pinnate, in large tufts 88
    85. Plants small, delicate, one- to two-pinnate 86
    85. Plants larger, one- to three-pinnate; in large flat mats ....*Thuidium*, p. 209
      86. Costa of stem-leaves one-fifth to one-sixth of the width of the leaf base
      ....*Thuidium*, p. 209
      86. Costa of stem-leaves one-tenth to one-twelfth of the width of the leaf base
      (see also *Thuidium*) 87
    87. Stem and branch leaves dissimilar; leaf-cells each with several minute papillae
    ....*Rauia*, p. 206
    87. Stem and branch leaves similar; leaf-cells each with but one or rarely two
    papillae ....*Haplocladium*, p. 207
      88. Stem and branch leaves rather similar in size and shape ....
      ....(*Helodium*, lvs. costate, p. 214
      ....(*Hookeria*, lvs. ecostate, p. 215
      88. Stem and branch leaves dissimilar ....*Rauia*, p. 206
89. Stems dendroid, upright from a creeping base; capsules clustered 90
89. Stems prostrate or ascending with the capsules borne singly 91
    90. Cilia none; capsules erect and symmetric ....*Climacium*, p. 180
    90. Cilia well developed, appendiculate; capsules inclined, unsymmetric ....
    ....*Porotrichum*, p. 189
91. Cilia none; capsule symmetric and erect, or nearly so (see also 120a) 92
91. Cilia generally present and well developed; capsule unsymmetric, generally
    more or less arcuate and recurved, sometimes almost erect 97
    92. Branches strongly complanate; leaves cultriform ....*Homalia*, p. 188
    92. Branches not strongly complanate; leaves ovate to lanceolate 93
93. Segments adhering to the teeth; basal membrane none or obscure 94
93. Segments free from the teeth 95
    94. Leaves with short single costa; seta rough ....*Homalotheciella*, p. 286
    94. Costa short and double or none; seta smooth ....*Pylaisia*, p. 226
95. Basal membrane broad and distinct ....*Pylaisia*, p. 226
95. Basal membrane none or narrow 96
    96. Stem oval in cross-section; teeth of peristome not hyaline-margined ....
    ....*Entodon*, p. 191
    96. Stem rounded; teeth of peristome hyaline-margined ....*Platygyrium*, p. 229
    96. Small, slender; leaves lance-linear to lanceolate; teeth not margined; cilia
    rudimentary or none ....*Amblystegiella*, p. 223
97. Stem mostly woody, often stoloniferous, irregularly divided, the leafy branches
    often more or less regularly pinnate; leaves erect-spreading to squarrose,
    rarely imbricated; cells narrowly prosenchymatous, rarely parenchymatous,
    towards the base more lax and often punctate; costa various, but rarely
    almost percurrent; alar cells mostly rounded or oval—4- to 6-sided, usually
    forming a well defined but not markedly inflated group; teeth and segments
    same length; basal membrane wide; cilia usually well developed; operculum
    rounded, conical-obtuse to short rostrate ....[*Hypnaceae*] 99
97. Characters not combined as above 93
    98. Slender plants with creeping stems; leaves often secund or somewhat com-
    planate; costa none or double and short; cells narrow, prosenchymatous;
    alar cells 3 to 8, large, inflated and pellucid; capsule small, oval to
    oblong, exothecial cell-walls collenchymatous; operculum mostly long and
    slenderly rostrate ....

....(See also *Hygrohypnum*) *Sematophyllum*, p. 283

98. Stems round, creeping, procumbent or more or less erect, often irregularly stoloniferous; leaves ascending to appressed, often complanate, rarely secund; stem- and branch-leaves dissimilar in the stoloniferous species only, ovate to lanceolate, mostly slenderly ecuminate; costa not often reaching the apex but usually reaching to the middle at least; cells prosenchymatous, long rhomboidal to linear-vermicular; operculum conical, blunt to long rostrate ....[*Brachytheciaceae*] 120

98. Branches somewhat complanate; leaves 4-5 mm long, ovate, soft, thin, drying whitish; leaf-cells parenchymatous ....*Hookeria acutifolia*, p. 215

HYPNACEAE (99-119)

99. Costa single, reaching mid-leaf; stem-leaves lance-ovate, rugose, falcate-secund; robust; ends of stem and branches hooked (falcate-secund): leaf-cells dorsally papillose; lid shortly rostrate ....*Rhytidium*, p. 254

99. If not as above and with costa in our species single; extending to the middle of the leaf or beyond; operculum never rostrate ....[*Amblystegieae*] 102

99. Costa double and usually short, or none; operculum sometimes rostrate 100

100. Stem and branch leaves usually distinctly dissimilar; leaves symmetric, inserted at right angles to the axis of the stem; branches sometimes terete or julaceous ....[*Hylocomieae*] 114

100. Stem and branch leaves quite similar; if minute plants with median leaf-cells oblong-hexagonal to rhomboidal (about 2-8:1); leaves lanceolate to lance-subulate, see *Amblystegiella;* leaves often inserted obliquely and unsymmetrically 101

101. Robust, stiff; branching complanately pinnate and plumose; leaves falcate-secund; costa double and short or none ....*Ptilium*, p. 259

101. Leaves either symmetric and normally inserted or unsymmetric and obliquely inserted and mostly falcate-secund and smooth; operculum sometimes rostrate ....[*Stereodonteae*] 118

101. Leaves obliquely inserted, mostly two-ranked, mostly unsymmetric but little or not at all secund; branches mostly complanate; operculum conic to short rostrate, rarely long-rostrate ....[*Plagiothecieae*] 119

102. Leaves margined ....*Sciaromium*, p. 234

102. Leaves not margined 103

103. Costa strong, ending almost in the apex or sometimes excurrent 104

103. Costa not extending to the apex of the leaf 109

104. Paraphyllia numerous and polymorphic 105

104. Paraphyllia none or very few 106

105. Leaves deeply longitudinally folded, falcate-secund ....*Cratoneuron*, p. 233

105. Leaves not deeply longitudinally folded ....*Hygroamblystegium*, p. 230

106. Leaf-cells linear-vermicular to the leaf-base, mostly with blunt ends, the alar cells forming a small but well defined group of quadrate or rectangular cells ....*Hygrohypnum*, p. 243

106. Leaf-cells hexagonal and 2 to 6 times as long as wide, or prolonged-linear and becoming wider and shorter towards the leaf-base, alar cells forming a larger group often reaching to the costa 107

106. Leaf-cells elongate-hexagonal to rhomboid, about 2-6:1; often a few alar cells inflated, aquatic or sub-equatic ....*Hygroamblystegium*, p. 230

107. Alar cells parenchymatous; leaves falcate-secund to circinate ....*Drepanocladus*, p. 235

107. Alar cells prosenchymatous 108

108. Leaf-cells prolonged; leaves more or less concave ....*Calliergon*, p. 240

108. Leaf-cells prosenchymatous-hexagonal, 2 to 6 times as long as wide ....
....*Hygroamblystegium*, p. 230

109. Leaves cordate- to ovate-lanceolate, more or less acuminate; costa weak, ending

at or beyond the middle of the leaf; cells rarely linear, mostly quadrate and parenchymatous, or hexagonal and short-prosenchymatous ....
....*Amblystegium*, p. 218

109. Aquatic; leaves mostly short and broad, rounded and blunt, soft; median leaf-cells linear-vermicular, the alar forming a distinct group, sub-rectangular or somewhat inflated ....*Hygrohypnum*, p. 243

109. Not with the above combination of characters 110

    110. Leaf-cells narrowly linear; leaves broadly ovate to cordate or lanceolate, prolonged into awl-shaped reflexed squarrose tips ....*Campylium*, p. 247

    110. Not with above combination of characters 111

111. Leaves oval- to oblong-lanceolate, more or less long acuminate; leaf-cells narrow, prosenchymatous; plants shining ....*Homomallium*, p. 225

111. Not with characters combined as above 112

    112. Plants very slender, not shining; leaves usually spreading in all directions, lanceolate to linear-lanceolate; cells rhomboidal to long hexagonal, 2 to 4, or rarely 6-8, times as long as broad ....*Amblystegiella*, p. 223

    112. Leaf-cells prolonged-linear, mostly very narrow 113

113. Leaves erect-spreading or imbricated, oblong-ovate to nearly circular, obtuse or apiculate, often very concave; costa short and double, or none ....
....*Calliergonella*, p. 242

113. Leaves more or less falcate-secund to circinate, from a mostly narrowed and somewhat decurrent base, becoming ovate- to triangular- or cordate-lanceolate, more or less slenderly acuminate; costa weak and reaching above the middle, or rarely even excurrent ....*Drepanocladus*, p. 235

    114. Paraphyllia numerous; leaves more or less concave, from abruptly to gradually acuminate, mostly plicate ....*Hylocomium*, p. 255

    114. Paraphyllia none or few 115

115. Stem-leaves more or less squarrose-spreading to falcate-secund, acuminate 117

115. Stem-leaves more or less crowded, imbricate but with more or less spreading or secund tips 116

115. Stem-leaves elliptic, concave, apex obtuse; branches julaceous ......*Hypnum*, p. 258

    116. Stem-leaves turgidly imbricate and secund, rugose, narrowly lanceolate-acuminate from a broadly oblong base, glossy; apex distinctly serrate; cilia two; annulus present ....*Rhytidium*, p. 254

    116. Stem-leaves close or loosely imbricate, not secund, broadly ovate or rounded with an obtuse apex, olive or grayish-green, apex faintly crenulate; cilia three; annulus none ....*Hypnum*, p. 258

    116. Leaves broad, obtuse, concave; alar cells inflated ....*Calliergonella*, p. 242

117. Alar cells not at all or but very little differentiated; plants distantly and irregularly pinnate; leaves squarrose or spreading-secund ....
....*Rhytidiadelphus*, p. 252

117. Alar cells distinctly differentiated; plants closely pinnate; leaves circinate-secund ....*Ctenidium*, p. 251

    118. Plants large, to 15 cm, closely and regularly pinnate leaves linear-acuminate from a broadly ovate base, stem-leaves plicate, falcate-secund; cilia 3 or 4 ....*Ptilium*, p. 259

    118. Plants large to quite slender, simple or pinnate, mostly irregularly pinnate; leaves ovate- to cordate-lanceolate, shortly to slenderly acuminate, generally circinate-secund in two series ....*Stereodon*, p. 260

    118. Characters not combined as above 128

119. Leaf-cells very narrowly prosenchymatous, alar cells mostly not differentiated; leaves oblong to linear, short pointed, or ovate- to linear-lanceolate, acute to long-acuminate or piliferous ....*Isopterygium*, p. 269

119. Leaf-cells not so narrow, alar cells mostly broader, hyaline and thin-walled; leaves broadly lanceolate to oval, more or less long-acuminate, decurrent
....*Plagiothecium*, p. 274

BRACHYTHECIACEAE (120-126)

120. Capsule erect to horizontal, symmetric to unsymmetric; basal membrane low 120a
120. Capsule generally inclined or horizontal, unsymmetric; basal membrane high 121
    120a. Calyptra hairy; segments adhering to peristome-teeth ....
    ....*Homa'otheciella*, p. 286
    120a. Calyptra smooth; segments not adhering to peristome-teeth (*see* also *Brachythecium*) ....*Chamberlainia*, p. 287
121. Leaves with several deep plications spoon-shaped; branches julaceous ....
    ....*Camptothecium*, p. 287
121. Leaves plane or but shallowly plicate 122
    122. Operculum conic, sometimes short-rostrate; alar cells differentiated, quadrate; capsules usually short, thick, dark chestnut color. (If leaves dorsally papillose, see *Bryhnia*) ....*Brachythecium*, p. 289
    122. Operculum long rostrate; alar cells few or not differentiated 123
123. Autoicous; branches and leaves complanate, leaves mostly only slightly concave, never sulcate, ovate to ovate-lanceolate, more or less acuminate; costa rarely ending in a spine on the back of the leaf; cells narrow, smooth; seta smooth ....*Rhynchostegium*, p. 306
123. Dioicous; seta generally papillose; costa sometimes ending in a spine on the back of the leaf; leaves not complanate 124
    124. Leaves very concave, not at all or but weakly plicate, ovate to oblong, more or less abruptly acuminate or piliferous; costa not ending in a spine; cells narrow and smooth ....*Cirriphyllum*, p. 293
    124. Not with the characters combined as above 125
125. Stem and branch-leaves often dissimilar, stem-leaves ovate- to triangular-cordate or rounded triangular-oval, obtuse to somewhat acuminate; costa often ending in a spine; leaf-cells very narrow and smooth 126
125. Stem-leaves more or less concave, irregularly plicate; cells elongated-rhomboid to elongated-hexagonal; branch-leaves rough on the back by papillae or tooth-like projecting cell-angles; seta very rough ....*Bryhnia*, p. 304
    126. Leaves not or very little concave, never plicate; seta smooth or rough
    ....*Oxyrhynchium*, p. 300
    126. Leaves more or less concave, indistinctly plicate; seta smooth ....
    ....*Eurhynchium*, p. 302
127. Mostly not aquatic, sometimes submerged but yet floating .... *Fissidens*, p. 69
127. Aquatic, filiform, and floating ....*Octodiceras*, p. 75
    128. Leaves obtuse 129
    128. Leaves acute to acuminate 130
129. Aquatic, usually in streams; leaves spreading or somewhat secund, soft and thin; branching irregular ....*Hygrohypnum*, p. 243
129. In bogs or swamps; glossy; regularly pinnate; leaves loosely appressed or descending ....*Calliergonella*, p. 242
    130. Leaves squarrose to squarrose-recurved (see also *Plagiothecium*) ....
    ....*Campylium*, p. 247
    130. Leaves otherwise 131
131. Alar cells inflated; leaves decurrent ....*Plagiothecium striatellum*, p. 275
131. Alar cells not inflated 132
    132. Median leaf-cells linear-hexagonal, about 4-8:1, the apical shorter and sub-rhomboidal, the alar quadrate and green-opaque, incrassate; leaves about 0.6-1.0 mm long ....*Homomallium*, p. 225
    132. Leaves decurrent; median leaf-cells linear, 5-15:1 ....*Plagiothecium*, p. 274
    132. Leaves not decurrent; median leaf-cells linear, 20:1 ....
    ....*Isopterygium pulchellum*, p. 272

Order I. **Sphagnales**—Peat Mosses

Characteristic peat mosses, in bogs, usually either in water or water-soaked, monoicous or dioicous, deeply cespitose, the tufts constantly growing upwards at the same time that the plants are dying from below and often thus giving rise to deep beds of peat, the tufts light grayish-green or sometimes yellowish, often more or less tinted with red above: stems without rhizoids, usually composed of an outer cuticular sheath consisting of one to three or four layers of large lax cells, an intermediate hollow cylinder composed of prosenchymatous cells with usually thickened walls, and a central pith of lax parenchymatous cells; branches symmetrically fascicled, usually partly divergently spreading and partly slender and appressed-pendent; leaves ecostate, unistratose, composed of large, hyaline, more or less elliptic cells with usually perforated and spirally thickened (fibrillose) walls and separated by narrow chlorophyllose cells which meet at their ends to form a continuous network throughout the leaf; stem-leaves usually different in form from the branch-leaves, remote, often lacking entirely the pores and spiral fibrils, while the branch-leaves are usually porose, fibrillose, and more or less densely imbricated; seta none but the capsule is borne upon an outgrowth from the gametophyte termed a pseudopodium; antheridial flowers usually at the apex of specialized branches of the capitulum, the antheridia being pedicillate, globose, and solitary at the base of the bracts; the archegonial flowers gemmiform, axillary in one of the upper fascicles, only one of the three or four archegonia developing, as a rule: capsule globose, castaneous, with a convex operculum, without annulus or peristome; calyptra irregularly lacerate; spores developed from the amphithecium, the columella from the endothecium.

This order is a peculiar one comprising but one family (*Sphagnaceae*) which contains but the one genus (*Sphagnum*) with about 340 known species. The Sphagnums are cosmopolitan in suitable habitats but are most abundant in the cooler temperate regions of Europe and North America, in both of these countries often forming bogs of large areas. In North America there are known about 40 species, at least 30 species or varieties in our range.

The following treatment follows closely that of C. Warnstorf in *Die Natürlichen Pflanzenfamilien* I(3) : 248-262. 1900. Also frequently consulted was Sherrin, W. R. *An Illustrated Handbook of the British Sphagna.* 1927 and Andrews, A. LeRoy. Sphagnales. *North American Flora* 15:1-31. 1913.

I. SPHAGNUM [Dillenius] Hedwig
(Revised with the assistance of Charles M. Boardman)

ANALYTICAL KEY TO THE SPECIES

A. Branches in tufts of 6-12 with 3-5 of them spreading; branch-leaves narrowly ovate-lanceolate, narrowed to an involute-tubulose point ....6. *S. Wulfianum*

A. Branches in tufts of 2-6, with 2 or sometimes 3 of them spreading ....B

    B. Cuticular cells of stems and branches spirally fibrose; branch-leaves cucullate at the apex, which is obtuse and entire, rarely acute ....c. (*Cymbifolia*)

B. Cuticular cells of stem and branches not fibrose ....G

C. Chlorophyllose cells of branch-leaves in cross-section exposed either dorsally or ventrally, or both ....D

C. Chlorophyllose cells of branch-leaves centrally placed and entirely enclosed by the hyaline cells ....5. S. magellanicum

D. Lateral walls of chlorophyllose cells of branch-leaves facing into the hyaline cells either more or less papillose or with comb-fibrils ....E

D. Lateral walls of the chlorophyllose cells smooth ....F

E. Chlorophyllose cells of branch-leaves in cross-section more or less equilaterally triangular and exposed only on the ventral (inner) side of the leaf or, in the upper part of the leaf, usually broadly trapezoidal and exposed on both sides, and, mainly in the lower part of the leaf, the walls facing into the hyaline cells with comb-fibrils ....1. S. imbricatum

E. Chlorophyllose cells of branch-leaves in cross-section narrowly to broadly spindle-shaped or barrel-shaped, usually with thickened outer walls narrowly free on both surfaces or nearly enclosed, the walls facing into the hyaline cells mostly minutely papillose ....2. S. papillosum

F. Chlorophyllose cells of branch-leaves in cross-section very broadly triangular or triangularly trapezoidal, and with the broader face ventral ....3. S. affine

F. Chlorophyllose cells narrowly triangular or trapezoidal, seen in cross-section not more than one-half as wide as long, usually less ....4. S. palustre

G. Chlorophyllose cells of branch-leaves in cross-section elliptical or more or less barrel-shaped or rectangular, but not triangular or trapezoidal ....H

G. Chlorophyllose cells in cross-section triangular or trapezoidal with one or both faces free I

H. Hyaline cells of stem-leaves non-fibrillose; chlorophyllose cells of branch-leaves in cross-section enclosed on both surfaces, with the lumen sub-central, elliptic; branch-leaves squarrose in their upper half; cuticular cells of branches with an apical pore ....7. S. compactum

H. Hyaline cells of stem-leaves fibrillose; chlorophyllose cells of branch-leaves free on both surfaces, their hyaline cells with numerous pores ....N. (Subsecunda)

I. Face of chlorophyllose cells of branch-leaves in cross-section dorsally free; hyaline cells strongly convex ventrally the walls adjoining the chlorophyllose cells smooth or papillose ....J

I. Face of chlorophyllose cells free on the ventral (inner) surface of the leaf, the hyaline cells dorsally strongly convex, the inner walls adjoining the chlorophyllose cells smooth ....s. (Acutifolia)

J. Hyaline cells of median dorsal surface of branch-leaves with about 5 very large pores, but these smaller towards the leaf-apex; chlorophyllose cells with the exterior walls strongly thickened ....K. (Squarrosa)

J. Hyaline cells with pores on median leaf-surface (dorsal) none or very few; chlorophyllose cells with the walls not strongly thickened ....1. (Cuspidata)

K. Stem-leaves with a rounded but narrow apex; branch-leaves at least 2 mm long ......
....8. S. squarrosum

K. Stem-leaves not narrowed but rounded at apex; branch-leaves less than 1.8 mm long
....9. S. teres

L. Cortical cells of stem small and thick-walled not much different from the inner cells ....M

L. Cortical cells of stem distinctly larger in 1-3 layers, thin-walled ....
....11. S. cuspidatum

M. Branch-leaves 1-2 mm long, when dry undulate and with more or less recurved tips and with the dorsal pores of the hyaline cells more or less restricted to the cell-angles ....10. S. recurvum

M. Branch-leaves when dry but weakly undulate, scarcely recurved, about 1 mm long, the upper hyaline cells with pores both in the cell-angles and along the sides ......
....10B. S. recurv. var. tenue

N. Cuticular cells of stem 2-3-stratose ....O

N. Cuticular cells of stem one-stratose ....P
O. Stem-leaves small, not more than 1 mm long, fibrillose only towards the apex; branch-leaves secund ....12. *S. contortum*
O. Stem-leaves large, 1.5-2 mm long, fibrillose to the base or nearly so; branch-leaves not secund ....13. *S. platyphyllum*
    P. Stem-leaves with the hyaline border strongly widened below, fibrils none or only in the upper cells ....15. *S. subsecundum*
    P. Stem-leaves with a uniformly wide border and with fibrils more numerous ....Q
Q. Stem-leaves strongly auriculate, large, 1.5-2 mm long, fibrillose in the upper two-thirds at least, or clear to the base ....14. *S. auriculatum*
Q. Stem-leaves not or but slightly auriculate at the base, usually of medium size, fibrillose in about the upper two-thirds ....R
    R. Stem-leaves about 1-1.5 mm long, with the hyaline cells septate, and in the upper half fibrillose ....16. *S. inundatum*
    R. Stem-leaves 1.3-1.5 (-2) mm long, very little septate, fibrillose in the upper two-thirds, or to the middle ....17. *S. pungens*
S. Stem-leaves erose or lacerate-fimbriate at the broadly rounded apex, non-fibrillose ....T
S. Stem-leaves not fimbriate, but truncate or toothed at the apex, usually more or less fibrillose, at least above ....U
    T. Stem-leaves spatulate, fringed at the apex and around the upper half; plants delicate, with slender branches and never red ....18. *S. fimbriatum*
    T. Stem-leaves lingulate, fringed only at the very broad apex; branches thicker than in *S. fimbriatum* ....19. *S. Girgensohnii*
U. Stem-leaves lingulate V
U. Stem-leaves more or less equilaterally triangular or triangular-lingulate ....W
    V. Pigment red, never brown (green in var.) ....20. *S. Warnstorfii*
    V. Pigment brown ....21. *S. fuscum*
W. Branch-leaves five-seriate, when dry not lustrous ....22. *S. quinquefarium*
W. Branch-leaves not distinctly 5-seriate, when dry more or less lustrous X
    X. Stem-leaves usually non-fibrillose and non-porose; branch-leaves usually lustrous when dry ....23. *S. plumulosum*
    X. Stem-leaves usually fibrillose and porose; branch-leaves usually not glossy when dry ....24. *S. acutifolium*

Section I.   INOPHLOEA

Cuticular cells of stems and branches reinforced with spiral fibers and porose.

Subsection I.   CYMBIFOLIA

Large, with the branch-leaves boat-shaped, cucullate and scabrous at the back of the apex. Stem-leaves not bordered.

1.   SPHAGNUM IMBRICATUM (Hornschuch) Russow
(*S. Austini* Sullivant)
Plate I

This species occurs in bogs and wet moors in Europe and Asia and in North America from Labrador to Alaska and south to Louisiana. In our region it is represented by the following variety. The typical form, as compared with the following variety, has usually more yellowish or brownish denser tufts with the shorter comal branches more erect and the divergent branches more densely-leaved and more ascending; while the hyaline cells of the stem-leaves are sparsely comb-fibrillose on the inside face of the lateral walls; otherwise the characters of variety and species are identical; in fact it may be best to follow Andrews and regard species number three (*S. affine*) as a variety of *S. imbricatum,* the latter possessing comb-fibrils, while *S. imbricatum* var. *affine* entirely lacks them.

1a. SPHAGNUM IMBRICATUM var. SUBLAEVE Warnstorf
(*S. Austini* var. *glaucum* f. *squarrosulum* Roell)

Rather densely cespitose, large, usually more or less glaucous-green, grayish or yellowish below; stems rather stout, with us about 4-8 cm long, the wood-cylinder greenish or yellowish and surrounded by a cuticular sheath of uaually four layers of thin-walled, large, fibrillose, and porose cells, the innermost largest; stem-leaves about 1-1.8 mm long, widely and bluntly lingulate, somewhat concave, the upper half rounded and with an erose-fimbriate margin, the base more or less auriculate; hyaline cells of stem-leaves mostly non-fibrillose and non-porose, a few often septate, the upper median more or less rounded-hexagonal, the basal elongate, the insertion-cells small and brownish-incrassate; branches usually four, two or three spreading, tumid, about 1.5 cm long, the rather shortly tapering apex pendent, the comal branches short and more or less erect-spreading, often obtuse, the pendent branches closely applied to the stem, very slender; branch-leaves 2-3 mm long, broadly ovate, very concave, the margins involute, the apex abruptly and bluntly tapering, cucullate and more or less widely squarrose-spreading; the hyaline cells of the branch-leaves broad, fibrillose, ventrally with a few large round median pores, with small pores in the angles, dorsally with large round or elliptic pores at the cell-angles, the large pores usually equalling about one-third the width of the hyaline cell; the basal hyaline cells of the branch-leaves are distinctly comb-fibrillose on the inner lateral side of the wall adjoining the chlorophyllose cells; in cross-section the chlorophyllose cells are widely trapezoidal, the ventral wall widest and almost or quite as wide as the lateral walls, the dorsal wall exposed between the highly convex dorsal walls of the hyaline cells and usually one-third to one-half the width of the lateral wall; the cuticular sheath of the branches consisting of one layer of rectangular, fibrillose, porose cells: fruit not seen, but spores of *S. imbricatum* are stated to be yellowish, smooth, and about .025 mm in diameter.

This variety is probably well distributed in regions where the typical form occurs.

CRAWFORD CO.: Pymatuning Swamp, near Linesville, May 12, 1908. O.E.J. (figured). FAYETTE CO.: Ohio Pyle and Wiggins. C.M.B. MERCER CO.: Near Houston Junction, July 12, 1902. J.A.S. SOMERSET CO.: Clear Run. C.M.B. WARREN CO.: Columbus, P. 168. Sept. 1948. C.M.B.

2. SPHAGNUM PAPILLOSUM Lindberg
(*S. cymbifolium* var. *papillosum* Schimper)

Plate II

Vigorous, coarse, tufted, yellowish to ochraceous: stems reddish-brown, almost 1 mm in diameter, inflated cuticular cells porose towards apex, scarcely if at all fibrose; divergent branches 1 or 2, pendent 1 or 2; divergent branches

1-1.5 cm long, from a turgid 3 mm-thick portion (wet) rather suddenly tapering to a thin point; branch leaves 2-2.5 mm long, broadly ovoid, cucullate, at
the margin with a border of about 2 rows of liner cells, of which a few project
outwards as minute teeth, the cucullate apex minutely dorsally scabrous by
erosion of the cell walls; median hyaline cells of branch-leaves about 3-4:1,
strongly fibrillose, somewhat porose dorsally, ventrally more so with distinct
pores, the chlorophyllose cells ovoid to triangular-ovoid with the ventral end
flush with the hyaline cells but dorsally being much exceeded by the convex
hyaline cells.

On the sides of the chlorophyllose cell-walls facing the hyaline cells there
are minute papillae in many of the leaves, but apparently not all. These
papillae seem best developed in the basal half of the leaf.

CRAWFORD Co.: Pymatuning Swamp, Linesville. O.E.J. May 26-27, 1934 (Det.,
C.M.B.). MCKEAN Co.: Cathrine Swamp, on plateau, elevation 2080 ft. C.M.B., Sept.
2, 1948 (figured). SOMERSET Co.: Glade Run bog, Negro Mt. Elev. 2470 ft. C.M.B.,
July 15, 1949.

3.   SPHAGNUM AFFINE Renauld and Cardot
(S. imbricatum var. *affine* Warnstorf)*
Plate I

Densely cespitose, usually bluish or glaucous-green above and more or less
yellowish below: stems robust, sometimes as much as a decimeter in length,
usually much less, densely branched; cuticular sheath distinct, three-layered,
the inner layer with the largest cells, the outer cells usually densely spirally
fibrillose and 2-6-pored; stem-leaves large, 1.6-2.2 mm long, about two-thirds
as wide, widely spatulate, the rounded upper half somewhat concave, erose-
fimbriate; hyaline cells of stem-leaves usually weakly fibrillose in their upper
half, porose dorsally, the hyaline cells below non-fibrillose, the pores large and
few; branches usually 4, one or two of these very slender, pendent and rather
closely appressed to the stem, the divergent ones horizontally spreading, with
drooping tips, rather swollen below, tapering towards the apex, the branches
often 2 cm long; branch-leaves 2-3 mm long, broadly ovate, bluntly and cucul-
lately short-pointed, the whole leaf very concave and with more or less involute margins, the apex dorsally scabrous by the erosion of the outer cell-
walls; hyaline cells of the branch-leaves rather wide, spirally fibrillose on both
sides, with large well-defined pores of one-third to one-half the cell-width and
confined mainly to the cell-angles; chlorophyllose cells in cross-section widely
trapezoidal, the wider face being ventrally exposed and more than or at least
half of the width (dorsal-ventral) of the smooth lateral walls, the dorsal face
exposed and rather narrow*; the cuticular cells of the branches porose and
densely fibrillose: fruit not seen.

In bogs and swampy borders of ponds and streams. Europe and in North
America from Canada to Florida. Common in the more northern counties in

---

* The chlorophyllose cells are more nearly equilaterally triangular than appears in our
drawing in Plate I.

our region and in the mountains, but mostly referred in the past to *S. cymbifolium*.

Common and now known from 14 counties in western Pennsylvania. Specimen figured: Open bog, Bear Meadows, Center Co., Pa., Sept. 21, 1909. O.E.J.

3a. **Sphagnum affine** f. *squarrosula* Warnstorf, is merely a strong growing form with the upper half of the leaves of the branches when dry strongly squarrose. All gradations between the typical form and the squarrose form are to be found in our region. A packet of specimens quite characteristically of the squarrose form is as follows:

CAMBRIA CO.: On boggy plateau near St. Lawrence, July 24, 1098. O.E.J. (Mixed with *S. recurvum* Schwaegrichen).

4. SPHAGNUM PALUSTRE Linnaeus

(*S. cymbifolium* Ehrhart; *S. latifolium* of 1st edition)

Plate I

Densely cespitose, usually robust, bluish or glaucous-green to yellowish: stems rather stout, usually 8-10 cm long, sometimes 2-3 dm long, the cuticular sheath composed of 3-4 layers of inflated cells, the innermost of which are the largest, the outer layer being rectangular, fibrillose and porose, the wood-cylinder being usually yellowish or brownish; stem-leaves large, about 2 mm long and 1.25 mm broad, sometimes 3 mm long, spatulate-lingulate, the broadly rounded apex somewhat erose-fimbriate, below narrowly hyaline-bordered, the insertion composed of brownish and incrassate cells; lower hyaline cells of stem-leaves sometimes septate, non-porose, non-fibrillose, those of the upper one-half or two-thirds of the leaf fibrillose and porose as are the branch-leaves also, towards the apex the hyaline cells much broader relatively, often as broad as long; branches in different plants variable, 1-2.5 cm long, more or less turgid below, acutely tapering at the apex, usually two spreading with drooping tips and two pendent and closely appressed to the stem, the comal short, ascending, more or less blunt; the branches in cross-section showing a layer of inflated cuticular cells which are rectangular, porose, and fibrillose; branch-leaves usually about 2 mm long, sometimes 3 mm, widely ovate, very concave, the margins involute, the apex abruptly and bluntly tapering, cucullate, at back somewhat scabrous with the erosion of the outer cell-walls, when dry the leaves being more or less closely imbricate; hyaline cells of branch-leaves broad, fibrillose, ventrally porose with large lateral pores mainly confined to the cell-angles, the pores often equalling one-third the width of the cell, dorsally the pores somewhat smaller and more elliptic and lateral, mostly in the cell-angles; in cross-section the chlorophyllose cells are narrowly barrel-shaped or somewhat trapezoidal, exposed on both faces, being ventrally nearly flush with the ventral surface of the hyaline cells but the latter dorsally very convex and projecting much beyond the chlorophyllose cells, the lateral walls of the chlorophyllose cells smooth; perichætial leaves very large, broadly oval, cucullate, hyaline-bordered, rounded obtuse at apex: capsule at maturity considerably exserted above the comal tuft; spores yellow, .028-.033 mm, mature in mid-summer.

In bogs, margins of quiet rivers and lakes, wet places in woods, etc.; a cosmopolitan, occurring in North America from Labrador and Alaska south to British Columbia, California, Texas, and Florida.

In our region thus far found in Allegheny, Bedford, Butler, Crawford, Erie, Fayette, Lawrence, McKean, Warren, Westmoreland, and Somerset counties.

4a.   Sphagnum palustre var. squarrosulum (Nees and Hornschuch) NEW COMBINATION

(*S. cymbifolium* var. *squarrosulum* Nees and Hornschuch; *S. latifolium* var. *squarrosulum* (Nees and Hornschuch) Jennings, Manual, 1913)

As compared with the typical species this variety has usually a darker or more bluish-green color; the leaves have a more abruptly narrowed apex, the apical third of the leaf especially in the comal branches being rather abruptly squarrulose.

Probably with a world-wide distribution with the typical form but in our region more common and apparently more partial to less decidedly boggy situations.

Now known from the following counties: Beaver, Blair, Centre, Crawford, Fayette, Indiana, Somerset and Westmoreland. Specimen figured: In crevices of rock-bed of river near falls, Ohio Pyle, Fayette Couny, Sept. 1-3, 1906. O.E.J. and G.K.J.

4b.   Sphagnum palustre var. brachycladum (Schliephacke) NEW COMBINATION

(*S. cymbifolium* var. *virescens* f. *brachycladum* Schliephacke; *S. latifolium* var. *brachycladum* (Schliephacke) Jennings)

Bluish-green or glaucous, yellowish below; branches short and closely placed along a short stem, giving the plant a congested appearance; leaves rather loosely imbricated and at their tips slightly squarrulose.

CENTRE Co.: In bog at Scotia, in the "Barrens," Sept. 22, 1909. O.E.J. SOMERSET Co.: Along rivulets in swamp on e. flank of Negro Mt., 3 miles from Salisbury. Paul R. Stewart. July 2, 1944.

5.   SPHAGNUM MAGELLANICUM Bridel

(*S. medium* Limpricht; *S. cymbifolium* var. *compactum* Russow)

Plate III

Deeply cespitose up to 8-10 cm, gray-green to bluish-green, rose-red to purple-red above, brownish or somewhat bleached below; stems rather densely branched, the cuticular sheath consisting of 3-5 layers, distinct, the outer cells smallest, porose and weakly fibrillose, the wood-cylinder castaneous to rose-red, thick-walled; stem-leaves about 1.5 mm. long, (1-2 mm), broadly lingulate-spatulate, the upper margins and the broadly rounded apex fimbriate; the upper hyaline cells of the stem-leaves usually fibrillose and dorsally porose; branches usually short, two slender and appressed to the stem, pendent, and two horizontally spreading or somewhat up-curved, thick-fusiform, the comal and upper more or less obtuse, the lower short-pointed; cuticular cells of branches densely fibrillose, porose; branch-leaves usually densely but sometimes loosely imbricated, 1.5-2.0 mm long, broadly ovate, very concave, cucullate, the apex dorsally rough by erosion of the cell-walls, the margin consisting of one or two very narrow cells which are often eroded away and the edge left more or less dentate; hyaline cells of the branch-leaves rather densely fibrillose, dorsally with a few rather large pores usually confined to the cell-angles; chlorophyllose cells in cross-section small, elliptic, central, enclosed deeply on both sides by the hyaline cells, the lateral walls smooth: capsule considerably exserted; spores stated to be .024-.028 mm, somewhat rust-colored, finely punctulate.

In bogs, etc. Almost cosmopolitan; in North America occurring from Newfoundland to Alaska south to British Columbia and Florida.

Butler Co.: On wet roadside at edge of woods, Semiconon Run, 2½ mi. n. of Conoquenessing. Sidney K. Eastwood, March 24, 1935. Centre Co.: In a sink-hole pond in the Barrens, near Scotia, July 17 and September 22, 1909. O.E.J. (figured). Also from mountain bogs and glades in McKean, Clearfield, Clinton, Somerset, Fayette, Forest, Westmoreland, and Warren counties.

Section II.   Lithophloea

Cuticular cells of the stems and branches not reinforced with spiral fibers. Branch-leaves more or less truncate and toothed at the apex.

Subsection I.   Polyclada

Branches in fascicles of 7-13.   Wood-strand of stem reddish brown. Chlorophyllose cells of branch-leaves elliptical, central, the thick end walls very narrowly exposed on both sides of the leaf.

6.   Sphagnum Wulfianum Girgensohn
Plate II

Loosely tufted, ours rather slender, 7-12 cm high, the uppermost short branchlets congested to form a dense head; stem reddish-brown, in cross-section with an outer layer of rows of somewhat inflated cells, underneath which is a dense reddish-brown layer of small thick-walled cells inside of which the central part of the stem consists of larger thin-walled cells; stem-leaves lingulate-triangular, deflexed, non-fibrillose, border with a margin of several rows of much narrower cells, the apex rather widely erose-denticulate; branchlets in clusters of usually 3-5 spreading and 3-7 pendent, about 1.2-2 cm long, the spreading branchlets slender and gradually tapering, the pendent branchlets linear; their cortical cells non-fibrillose but with an apical pore; branch-leaves about 1 mm long, when dry recurved-spreading, more imbricated when wet but still with somewhat spreading points; branch-leaves ovate-lanceolate, often somewhat incurved-rubulose at apex, bordered with two or three rows of linear cells, the apex often erose-bidentate, the median hyaline cells fibrillose, about 8-10:1 at base, shorter above, dorsally with a few ringed pores; chlorophyllose cells broadly elliptic, thick-walled, the lumen about central, but their thick walls very narrowly exposed on both surfaces, exceeded dorsally by the convex outer walls of the hyaline cells.

This is a far northern species with a reported range south to Connecticut, New York, Minnesota, and British Columbia, hence this collection is a further extension of range southwards.

Columbus Bog, northern Warren County, Pa., Charles M. Boardman, Sept. 1, 1948 (figured).

This species is easily distinguished by the fascicles of 6-12 branchlets and also by the dense capitulum of short apical branchlets.

Subsection II. RIGIDA

With short, densely placed branches, and forming dense tufts. Cortical cells of the branches each with a pore at the upper end. Chlorophyllose cells of branch-leaves small, elliptic, completely enclosed but nearer the dorsal (outer) surface of the leaf. Branch-leaves ovate, ending in an involute, mostly widely spreading or ascending apex.

7. SPHAGNUM COMPACTUM DeCandolle
(*S. rigidum* Schimper)
Plate III

Densely cespitose, gray-green or glaucous-green, brownish above, below whitish or grayish-brown compactly and closely short-branched; stems stout, low, in ours 4-8 cm high, with a cuticular sheath of usually 3 layers of cells, the outermost cells largest, non-fibrillose, the wood-cylinder decidedly castaneous or sometimes yellowish; stem-leaves very small, 0.6-0.8 mm long, broadly to equilaterally triangular-lingulate, the apex concave and broadly rounded or truncate, erose-dentate, the margins rather widely hyaline-bordered; hyaline cells of stem-leaves broadly rhomboidal, non-porose, non-fibrillose; branches short, usually not over 1 cm long, 3 or 4 to a fascicle, horizontally spreading or somewhat upcurved, the others slender and appressed-pendent; branch-leaves when dry with the upper half of the leaf more or less squarrose-spreading, large, 2-3 mm long, ovate, concave, the margins narrowly bordered, the upper margins involute and often slightly erose-ciliate or erose-dentate the apex erose-dentate and cucullate; hyaline cells of branch-leaves rather broadly rhomboidal, fibrillose, dorsally with several large, round pores irregularly scattered and also in the cell-angles, the pores about two-fifths as wide as the cell, sometimes a few oval and lateral, ventrally the pores small, oval, and located in the cell-angles; in cross-section the chlorophyllose cells are elliptic, enclosed both dorsally and ventrally by the moderately convex hyaline cells; cuticuar cells of the branches arge, short-rectangular, with one large apical pore; fruit not seen.

Our plants seem to be the variety *squarrosum* Russow (Roth. Die Europaeischen Torfmoose, p. 14. 1906) (*S. rigidum* var. *squarrosum* Russow. Braithwaite. The Sphagnaceae or Peat Mosses of Europe and North America, p. 58. 1880). In bogs and wet woods, widely distributed in the Northern Hemisphere, in North America occurring from the Arctic regions south to the northern part of the United States.

CENTRE CO.: At margin of pond under *Pinus rigida.* "Barrens," near Scotia. Sept. 22, 1909. (O.E.J. (figured). ERIE CO.: In black ash swamp at head of Conneautte Lake, Edinboro. O.E.J. and J. C. Fetterman. June 23, 1919. WESTMORELAND CO.: Laurel Hill Mt., 9 mi. s.e. of Rector. Hugh Mozingo. Oct. 7, 1945.

Subsection III. SQUARROSA

Branch-leaves squarrose-spreading, their chlorophyllose cells in cross-section trapezoidal to rectangular or barrel-shape, or triangular towards leaf-base, dorsally more widely exposed, thick-walled, their hyaline cells with large pores.

8. SPHAGNUM SQUARROSUM [Persoon] Schwaegrichen
Plate LXX

Loosely cespitose, bluish- to yellow-green: stems long, loosely branched, with wood-cylinder hyaline to greenish or yellowish, cuticular sheath distinctly 2-(3)-layered; stem-leaves broadly oblong-lingulate, the apex broadly rounded and erose-fimbriate, the leaves very narrowly bordered, slightly auriculate, non-fibrillose, the hyaline cells above short and broad; branches 4 or 5, two or three tumid, horizontal, the leaves on the lower two-thirds of the divergent branches with squarrose tips; branch-leaves lanceolate to lance-ovate, very concave, acuminate, with involute margins and usually slightly erose, marginal cells narrower, but not usually forming a hyaline border; hyaline cells of branch-leaves richly fibrillose, on both sides with numerous large round pores of about one-fourth to one-third the width of the cell; in cross-section the chlorophyllose cells free on both surfaces, narrowly rectangular to trapezoidal, when trapezoidal with the wider face dorsal, the faces thick-walled, the lumen more or less elliptic, the hyaline cells strongly convex on both surfaces: spores yellowish and finely roughened, about .022-.025 mm in diameter.

In usually shaded locations in swamps, boggy springs, along woodland streams, etc., in Europe, and, in North America, from the Arctic regions to the northern part of the United States.

Now known from the following eight counties in the northwestern and mountainous parts of our region: Cambria, Carion, Elk, Erie, Huntingdon, McKean, Mercer, and Somerset. Figured from a specimen collected in a wooded swamp in Cook Forest, by Adam M. Barker, Sept. 15, 1935.

9. SPHAGNUM TERES (Schimper) Aongstroem
(*S. squarrosum* var. *teres* Schimper; *S. porosum* Lindberg)

This species is represented in our region by a plant in varying degrees perhaps best regarded as the following variety, which differs from the typical form of the species mainly in having the divergent branches more or less squarrose-leaved rather than distinctly terete.

9a. SPHAGNUM TERES var. SUBTERES Lindberg
(*S. teres* var. *subsquarrosum* Warnstorf)
Plate III

Weakly and loosely but quite deeply cespitose, yellowish-green to distinctly yellowish: stems up to 15 or even 20 cm long, slender, the cuticular sheath usually three-layered, the outer cells perhaps a little the largest, non-fibrillose, usually not distinctly porose, the wood-cylinder strong, yellowish or rarely castaneous; stem-leaves large, about 1.5 mm long, broadly triangular-lingulate, the margin narrowly hyaline-bordered, the rounded to somewhat truncate apex erose-dentate, the base often slightly auriculate; hyaline cells of stem-leaves non-fibrillose, non-porose, in the lateral portions of the basal half of the leaf often septate, the upper hyaline cells about as broad as long; branchs 3 to 5 to a fascicle, usually two appressed-pendent and very slender, the others widely divergent but somewhat recurved, rather slender, about 1-1.5 cm long; branch-leaves when dry imbricate but with the apical half of some of them squarrose, the leaves usually 1.5 mm long, ovate, concave, the narrowly hyaline-bordered margin involute towards the apex; hyaline cells of branch-leaves short, wide, both ventrally and dorsally fibrillose, and with a few large round pores about half as wide as the cell and usually located in the cell-angles; in cross-section the chlorophyllose cells in the apical third of the leaf trapezoidal to barrel-shaped and exposed both dorsally and ventrally, wider on the dorsal face, towards the base of the leaf sometimes triangular and exposed only dorsally; cuticular cells of branches rectangular: spores not seen but said to be brownish, papillose, and about .025 mm in diameter.

In bogs, wooded swamps, etc., in Europe and, in North America, in Canada and the northern United States, probably distributed widely with the type form.

CRAWFORD CO.: In tamarack bog one and one-half miles s.e. of Linesville, June 7, 1904 (figured) and June 12, 1905. O.E. This station is now submerged. ERIE CO.: In swamp near south shore of Presque Isle, August 3, 1935. Nelle Ammons. SOMERSET Co.: Millers Run. O.E.J.

Subsection IV. CUSPIDATA

Chlorophyllose cells of branch-leaves triangular to trapezoidal, exposed on the dorsal (outer) surface, sometimes narrowly on the ventral surface.

10. SPHAGNUM RECURVUM Beauvois
(*S. intermedium* Hoffman; *S. apiculatum* Lindberg)
Plate III

Loosely but deeply tufted, pale green to greenish- or whitish-yellow: stem light green, slender, long, in our region often up to 3 dm long, the cuticular sheath rather indistinct and consisting of 3 or 4 layers of small or medium-sized rather thick-walled cells; stem-leaves small, about 0.5-0 8 (-1.0) mm long, equilaterally triangular to ovate-triangular, obtuse and slightly erose-denticulate; hyaline cells of stem-leaves rather small, mostly non-fibrillose and non-porose, towards the base on each side of the leaf more or less septate and narrowing to form a very wide border, which abruptly narrows above but reaches almost to the apex; branches usually 4, two very slender and appressed-pendent, two somewhat larger and irregularly spreading; cuticular cells of the branches elongate-rectangular, perforate and somewhat recurved at the apex, like those of the stem non-fibrillose; branch-leaves lance-ovate, imbricate, in our region ranging from 1-2 mm long, when dry, with undulate margins, flexuose and with a recurved apex, when moist straight and erect-appressed, tapering to a rather narrowly obtuse apex with two or three teeth, the margin involute above; hyaline cells of branch-leaves fibrillose and porose, above the midde rather narrow, ventrally usually with large pores in the cell-angles of about one-third the width of the cell, dorsally with small end-pores or sometimes a very few rather distinctly ringed lateral ones; in cross-section the hyaline cells are ventrally quite convex, the chlorophyllose cells triangular or rarely trapedoidal, usually exposed only on the dorsal face; perichætical leaves large, broadly oval, concave, pointed: spores smoothish, yellow, about .025 mm in diameter.

A cosmopolitan species occurring in North America from Newfoundland to Labrador and south to the Gulf States.

This is probably our commonest sphagnum, occurring not only around the borders of bogs but out in seepage areas in open/ hillside fields. It is now known from seventeen counties in western Pennsylvania, most of the records being from the southwestern and northwestern parts of our area. The following variety *amblyphyllum* seems to be the commoner form in the central uplands and mountains. Figured from specimens collected May 29-31, 1910, around Mud Lake, Hartstown, Crawford County, O.E.J. & G.K.J.

10a. SPHAGNUM RECURVUM var. AMBLYPHYLLUM (Russow) Warnstorf

(*S. amblyphyllum* Russow)

The variety has the stem-leaves more spatulate-triangular, with a more rounded and somewhat erose-denticulate apex; the cuticular sheath is less plainly differentiated and the cells are more incrassate than in the typical form of the species. All possible intergradations seem to be represented among the specimens examined. It may usually be recognized when dry by the strongly undulate branch-leaves, these usually still remaining undulate when mounted wet for examination under the microscope.

Now known from eight counties from Centre west to Crawford and Allegheny counties through the middle of the area.

10b. SPHAGNUM RECURVUM var. TENUE Klinngraeff

(*S. angustifolium* Jensen; *S. recurvum* var. *parvifolium* Warnstorf; *S. amblyphyllum* var. *parvifolium* Warnstorf; *S. parvifolium* (Sendt.) Warnstorf)

Plate VI

Softly and loosely cespitose, yellowish- to grayish-green, or brownish above: stems slender, usually at least 10-12 cm high, the wood-cylinder yellowish and without any distinctly differentiated cuticular sheath: stem-leaves small, usually 0.5-0.7 mm long, equilaterally triangular to somewhat triangular-lingulate, the apex rounded or somewhat truncate, erose-dentate, the hyaline border narrow above and very wide below; hyaline cells of stem-leaves non-fibrillose, non-porose, a few septate towards the base on each side of the median region; branches 3-5, two being slender and appressed-pendent, two or three short, 5-9 mm long, divergent, recurved at the tips; branch-leaves lanceolate, about 1 mm long, concave, the uniformly narrowly hyaline-bordered margin involute towards the narrowed, slightly truncate-erose apex, leaves when dry more or less undulate, loosely imbricate, with widely spreading or recurved tips; hyaline cells of branch-leaves narrow, fibrillose, ventrally with rounded medium-sized pores in the cell-angles, dorsally with single smaller round pores in the cell-angles or sometimes in rows laterally; in cross-section the chlorophyllose cells triangular and only dorsally exposed, or more usually trapezoidal and free on both faces, the dorsal face wider, the hyaline cells more convex ventrally: fruit not seen.

In bogs, swamps, etc., probably widely distributed. In North America extending from the Arctic south to northern United States.

In our region known from one locality. BLAIR Co.: Springy mountain slope, Rhodo-dendron Park, Llyodsville, October 18, 1901. J.A.S. (figured).

11. SPHAGNUM CUSPIDATUM Ehrhart
(*S. virginianum* Warnstorf)
Plate IV

Usually pale and slender mosses of wet bogs or often submerged in pools. Stem with 2 or 3 layers of non-porose, non-fibrillose, large and thin-walled cortical cells clearly distinct from the wood-cylinder. Stem-leaves isosceles-triangular, about 1-1.4 mm long and about 0.6-1.1 wide, inrolled above, slightly toothed at the narrow truncate tip; the border strong, considerably widened below; the hyaline cells fibrillose and porose. Branches usually 4, two of them drooping or slightly spreading, the other two spreading linear-lanceolate to elongated-lanceolate, about 1.5-3 mm long, the tip toothed, often falcate-secund, the leaves often undulate when dry; the border of 2-4 (3-8) rows of linear cells. Hyaline cells ranging from the basal linear-rhomboidal cells about 15 times as long as wide upwards to those only about 5 times as long as wide, all fibrillose and somewhat porose. Chlorophyllose cells trapezoidal to 4-sided, both surfaces free, but the dorsal (abaxial) surface wider.

In wet bogs and pools, often submerged, Eurasia and from Georgia to Newfoundland.

ALLEGHENY Co.: On springy hillside about one mile west of Thornburg, July 12, 1922. Mrs. Alice B. Lord (figured).

Subsection V. SUBSECUNDA

A difficult group of diverse forms. Branch-leaves mostly more or less secund, the pores of their hyaline cells mostly small and numerous, their chlorophyllose cells truncately elliptic or trapezoidal, mostly central and exposed on both surfaces.

12. SPHAGNUM CONTORTUM Schultz*
(*S. subsecundum* var. *contortum* Huebener: *S. laricinum* Spruce)

Loosely cespitose, green to brownish or yellowish, sometimes more or less

---

* Andrews, A. L. (N. Am. Flora 15: 21-22. 1913) treats *S. contortum, S. platy-phyllum, S. auriculatum, S. subsecundum,* and *S. inundatum* as being a single polymorphic species, *S. subsecundum.*

purplish above: stem about 6-12 cm high, the wood-cylinder reddish to brownish, surrounded by a distinct two-layered sheath of inflated cells; stem-leaves small, about 1 mm long, broadly lingulate or triangular-lingulate, the hyaline border much broader towards the base, the apex broadly rounded and more or less concave, cucullate, and erose-fimbriate; hyaline cells of stem-leaves in upper third fibrillose, short and broad, ventrally with a few cells in the angles, dorsally with more numerous small ringed pores along the sides of the cell, very few of the hyaline cells septate, the lower ones long and narrow; fasciculate branches 3-5 to a fascicle, usually two slender and closely appressed pendent, two divergent and recurved; branch-leaves about 1.5-2 mm long, broadly ovate to lanceolate, more or less sharply acuminate, the upper margin involute and narrowly hyaline-bordered, leaves when dry more or less subsecund and sublustrous; hyaline cells richly fibrillose, slender, ventrally almost poreless, dorsally with small ringed pores more or less completely arranged in bead-like rows, the pores most numerous towards upper margins of leaf; in cross-section the chlorophyllose cells narrowly barrel-shaped, with both faces free and their walls there somewhat thickened; cuticular cells of branches apically porose: spores not seen but reported as .020-.030 mm in diameter, yellowish-brown, finely roughened.

In swampy meadows, along ditches, margins of bogs, etc., in Europe and, in North America from Greenland to Mexico, and along the Pacific Coast

Not heretofore reported from our region but a specimen collected by J. A. Shafer, October 20, 1901, at Ohio Pyle, Fayette County, with stem-leaves about .7-.8 mm long, with the margin uniformly hyaline-bordered and the hyaline cells fibrillose to below the middle of the leaf is now referred here; also a specimen from Centre Co., Neil D. Richmond, June 14, 1950.

13. SPHAGNUM PLATYPHYLLUM (Sullivant) Warnstorf
(*S. auriculatum* Aongstroem; *S. isophyllum* Russow)
Plate V

Loosely cespitose, brownish- to grayish-green: stems in our region up to 10 cm high, slender, rather weak and sparsely branched; stem in cross-section showing a usually brownish wood-cylinder, with a distinct cuticular sheath of rather small, thin-walled, and usually uni-porose cells; stem-leaves large, usually 1.3-2.0 mm long, oval to oblong from an auriculate base, very concave, the apex blunt and a little toothed or erose, the margin narrowly and uniformly bordered; hyaline cells of the stem-leaves in lower half to two-thirds of the leaf non-fibrillose and non-porose but some of them septate, in the upper half or one-third of the leaf the hyaline cells fibrillose and on both sides with lateral rows of small pores; branches usually 3, sometimes 4, usually spreading with recurved tips, one or two being pendent and very slender; branch-leaves broadly ovate, very concave, usually 2-3 mm long, the apex toothed, the margin more or less incurved and with a narrow and uniform border; in cross-section the chlorophyllose cells barrel-shaped, free on both surfaces, the hyaline cells about equally convex on both sides; hyaline cells fibrillose, with numerous small lateral pores on both sides; when dry the leaves towards the base of the spreading branches more or less sub-secund; spores stated by Warnstorf to be .023-.028 mm in diameter, yellowish and finely papillose.

In turfy swamps and bogs in Europe and North America, extending in the latter country from Massachusetts to Louisiana, also to Ohio.

BUTLER CO.: Open swampy pasture, Crider's Corners, Apr. 26, 1908. O.E.J.

14. SPHAGNUM AURICULATUM Schimper

(*S. Gravetti* Russow, p.p.—Warnstorf; *S. subsecundum* var. *intermedium* Warnstorf)

Plate V

Densely cespitose, grayish or glaucous green, light yellow below; stems rather short (In our specimens about 5 cm), densely branched; branches in fascicles 3-5, two or three of these drooping from a horizontally spreading base, terete and rather thick, up to 1 cm long, the other one or two slender, and rather closely appressed to the stem; in cross-section the cortical cells distinct, in one layer, the outer cells of the central axis much thickened and small; stem-leaves large, 1.5-2.0 mm long, about half as wide, concave, from the distinctly auriculate base oval-lingulate, the rounded apex narrowly toothed, somewhat cucullate, the margin narrow and of equal width from base to apex; cells of the stem-leaves fibrillose to the base or nearly so, only rarely septate, ventrally with rather large poorly defined pores in the cell-angles, rarely none, dorsally with numerous distinct pores along each side of the cell, the pores circular to elliptic and about one-fourth the width of the cell; retort cells of the branches with a distinct neck and terminal pore; lower branch-leaves large, about 2 mm long, widely ovate, about 1.5 mm wide, very concave, the margins more or less involute, the apex somewhat spreading, narrowly toothed, the upper leaves more closely imbricated and lanceolate; cells of branch-leaves ventrally with rather few large indistinct angle-pores, dorsally with numerous distinct pores in a row along each side, as in the stem-leaves, the hyaline cells usually with 8-10 spiral fibrils, the border of 2-4 thick-walled, linear-prosenchymatous cells; chlorophyllose cells in cross-section barrel-shaped with both ends exposed: fruit unknown

In wooded swamps and wet shaded places, Europe and North America.

Known from the following collections in our region. FAYETTE CO.: Near Seaton's Lake. Hugh N. Mozingo. April 7, 1946; and in wet cavities in rocks, Ohio Pyle near Falls, O.E.J., June 14, 1908 (figured). SOMERSET CO.: Shafer Run, 2 mi. n. of Bakerville, Hugh N. Mozingo, Sept. 14, 1946. VENANGO CO.: Near Lisbon, Mrs. E. J. Mason, Oct., 1947. WESTMORELAND CO.: Springy hillside, Mellon estate, "Rachelwood," New Florence, Sept. 9-11, 1907, O.E.J.

15. SPHAGNUM SUBSECUNDUM Nees

Plate IX

Moderately densely cespitose, green to yellowish or brownish: stems 5-20 cm long, with a dark or purplish-brown wood cylinder, with a cuticular sheath of one layer of moderately inflated cells; stem-leaves small, about 0.6-0.8 mm long, broadly short-lingulate, somewhat auriculate, the margin broadly hyaline-bordered below, the border narrowing and becoming fimbriate towards the broadly erose-fimbriate apex, the upper half of the stem-leaves often distinctly concave and more or less cucullate; hyaline cells of the stem-leaves broad above, usually all non-fibrillose, rarely a few septate, sometimes porose; of the 3-5 fasciculate branches two or three are variously divergent, short, usually 6-8 mm long, slender and sometimes flagelliform; branch-leaves small, 1-1.5 mm long, very concave, broadly ovate to lanceolate, acuminate to a narrowly truncate or 3-5 toothed apex the margins uniformly narrowly hyaline-bordered, involute, when dry closely imbricate to more or less sub-secund; hyaline cells of branch-leaves narrow, richly fibrillose, ventrally non-porose, or with a few small non-ringed pores in the cell-angles, dorsally with numerous small ringed pores along the sides of the cells; in cross-section the chlorophyl-lose cells narrowly barrel-shaped, relatively rather large as compared with the hyaline cells, free on both faces, the hyaline cells but slightly convex on either side: spores not seen from our region, finely papillose, yellowish, and .025-.028 mm in diameter.

In wet meadows, swamps, ditches, bogs, etc., in Europe and in Asia and, in North America, from Newfoundland to Alabama. In our region frequent; approaching the variety *brachycladum* Warnstorf in having stem-leaves more or less cucullate and the divergent branches often only about 5 mm long.

ERIE CO.: In bog at south end of Cranberry Pond, Presque Isle, May 8-9, 1906. O.E.J. (figured). Also known from Elk, Centre, Clarion, Clearfield, Mercer, Butler, Westmoreland, Fayette, Somerset, and Bedford counties, but not known from the south-western border counties.

16. SPHAGNUM INUNDATUM Russow, Warnstorf

Densely and deeply cespitose, gray or yellowish-green: stems usually 15-30 cm long, more or less completely submerged; branches with moderately densely imbricate leaves; stem-leaves usually somewhat fimbriate at the narrow apex, little or not at all auriculate, fibrillose only above the middle; branch-leaves dorsally richly porose in lateral bead-like rows, ventrally with only a few pores located in the cell-angles. Other characters are as described for the variety *auriculatum*.

In wet meadows, wooded swamps, bogs, etc. In cooler Europe, Asia, and North America. In our region, so far as now known, represented only by the following variety.

16a. SPHAGNUM INUNDATUM var. AURICULATUM (Warnstorf) Roth
(*S. contortum* var. *laxum* Roell)
Plate IX

Only moderately cespitose, green: stems in our specimens only about 6-8 cm high, only occasionally completely submerged; wood-cylinder greenish, sur-rounded by a cuticular sheath of one layer (ossacionally unsymmetrically two) of inflated more or less distinctly porose cells; stem-leaves 1.2-1.5 mm long, about three-fifths as wide, distinctly auriculate, towards the apex somewhat concave, the margins narrowly uniformly hyaline-bordered and toward the apex involute, the narrow apex somewhat dentate but not fimbriate; the hyaline cells of stem-leaves broad, towards the lateral portions of the base becoming narrower, usually septate, fibrillose at least as far down as the middle of the leaf, or farther, and usually also fibrillose at the base of the leaf, above ventrally with rather small distinct pores in the cell-angles and usually other less distinct lateral pores, above dorsally with small pores in cell-angles and numerously along the sides of the cells; of the usually 5 fasciculate branches two are pendent and the others short, usually 6-9 mm long, variously widely divergent; branch-leaves when dry very lax and widely divergent, 1.5-2 mm long, ovate, very concave, with involute, narrowly and uniformly hyaline-bordered margins, the apex narrow and dentate-truncate; hyaline cells of branch-leaves rather long and slender, richly fibrillose, dorsally with laterally-placed bead-like rows of small pores about one-fifth as wide as the cell, ventrally with small ringed pores in the cell-angles, occasionally also a few laterally arranged indistinct pores; cuticular cells of branches large with a short neck and terminal pore; in cross-section the chlorophyllose cells narrowly elliptic with about equally free and thickened faces: for the type of the species the spores are stated to be yellow and about .030-.035 mm in diameter; of the variety the spores have not been seen.

CENTRE Co.: Headwaters of Laurel Run, Tussey Mt., above Shingletown, July 15, 1909. O.E.J. FAYETTE Co.: In pools and wet crevices in rocky bed of river above falls, Ohio Pyle, September 1-4, 1906. O.E.J. and G.K.J. (figured).

17. SPHAGNUM PUNGENS Roth
(S. contortum var. *gracile* Roell)
Plate IX

Rather loosely cespitose, bluish-green, when dry sub-lustrous above, yellowish or brownish below: stems rather stout, often forking, in our specimens up to 6 or 7 cm high; wood-cylinder greenish or pale, enclosed in a one-layered cuticular sheath which in places is unsymmetrically often two-layered; stem-leaves broadly lingulate, about 1-1.5 mm long, at base about three-fifths as wide, somewhat auriculate, the uniformly narrowly hyaline-bordered margin somewhat erose-fimbriate towards the broadly rounded erose dentate apex; the hyaline cells of stem-leaves broad, rarely septate, distinctly fibrillose in upper two-thirds of leaf, ventrally with a few indistinct pores in the angles and along the sides of the cell, dorsally with numerous small pores arranged in lateral bead-like rows; of the usually 4 fasciculate branches, two are slender and appressed-pendent while the other two are horizontally divergent and recurved, about 1-1.5 cm long, the lower and median leaves of the divergent branches more or less widely squarrose, the upper ones imbricate so that the branch ends in a sharply acuminate point; branch-leaves broadly ovate to lanceolate, large, 1.8-2.6 mm long, concave, the uniformly narrowly hyaline-bordered margins involute towards the acuminate few-toothed apex; hyaline cells of branch-leaves narrow, long, richly fibrillose, ventrally with a few indistinct pores in the cell-angles, dorsally with numerous small ringed pores about one-fourth to one-fifth as wide as the cell and arranged in bead like rows along the sides of the cell; in cross-section the chlorophyllose cells relatively large, narrowly barrel-shaped, free on both faces, the hyaline cells not being markedly convex on either face; cuticular cells of branches long-rectangular with a short neck and a large apical pore: spores not known from our region.

More or less intermediate between *S. inundatum* (Russow) Warnstorf, and *S. auriculatum* Schimper, and of doubtful status. Heretofore reported, so far as known to the present writer, only from Europe, where it occurs in swampy meadows.

CENTRE Co.: Bog in sink-hole in pine-barrens near Scotia, July 17, 1909. O.E.J. (figured).

Subsection VI. ACUTIFOLIA

Branch-leaves small to medium size, lanceolate to lance-ovate, acute to narrowly acute and truncate apex, their chlorophyllose cells in cross-section triangular or elliptic-trapezoidal, nearer to and more or less widely exposed on the ventral (inner) side and sometimes narrowly exposed dorsally between the bulging hyaline cells.

18. SPHAGNUM FIMBRIATUM Wilson
Plate VI

Loosely cespitose, grayish-green to yellowish brown: stems rather slender, usually 4-5 cm high, sometimes much longer, in cross-section showing a cuticular sheath of 2-3 layers of cells, the cells of the outer layer largest and porose; stem-leaves very widely obovate-spatulate, about 0.7-0.8 mm, the upper half broadly rounded and erose-fimbriate; hyaline cells of stem-leaves non-fibrose, non-porose, very wide above the middle of the leaf, towards the base often one- to several-septate, the hyaline border towards the base widening to about one-third the width of the leaf on each side; fasciculate branches 3 or 4, usually two slender, arcuate, and decurved, and up to 2.5 cm long, the other one or two pendent, rather closely appressed to the stem, filiform; branch-leaves closely imbricated, shortly ovate-lanceolate below to slenderly lanceolate above, concave, the upper margin incurved, the apex narrowly truncate and dentate; hyaline cells rather small with four to six fibrils, ventrally with a few round pores which are often almost as wide as the cell, dorsally with more numerous lateral pores above one-third as wide as the cell; in cross-section the chlorophyllose cells trapezoidal, free on both surfaces, the inner surface widest, the hyaline cells extending convexly considerably beyond them on the dorsal face; cuticular cells of branches without distinct necks; perichætial leaves large, obtusely ovate: spores stated to be smooth, yellowish-brown, about .025-.030 mm in diameter.

Usually in low-lying bogs and marshes, or along the borders of streams, Europe, Asia, South America, and, in North America, from the Arctic regions through Canada to the northern part of the United States.

Now known from the following counties: Butler, Clearfield, Crawford, Erie, Elk, McKean, Warren, Westmoreland and Somerset. Figured from specimen collected in Pymatuning Swamp, near Linesville, June 7, 1904. O.E.J. Also Forest and Mercer counties. C.M.B.

19. SPHAGNUM GIRGENSOHNII Russow
Plate VII

A tall, slender, loosely cespitose, grayish green or translucent green species with stems up to 10-15 cm in height. Stem in cross-section showing a cuticular sheath of 2-3 layers of thin-walled, non-fibrillose porose, and a zone of much smaller dense cells which in turn surround a central core of larger thinner-walled cells. Stem-leaves about 1-1.2 mm long, short-lingulate, often almost as wide as long, the blunt broad apex partially erose-fimbriate, the sides bordered above by a narrow margin of thick-walled linear cells, the border widening at the base into a triangular patch, each patch about one-fifth the width of the base; the upper middle hyaline cells about 3 times as long as wide, non-fibrillose. Branches usually 4; two of them slenderly attenuate and accumbent to the stem, the other two spreading, about 1.5-2.5 cm long, gradually acuminate, mostly spreading-falcate. Branch-leaves imbricate and in the thicker part of the branch lanceolate to lance-ovate, about 1-1.4 mm long with the apex more or less squarrose-spreading, often involute tubular and sometimes erose at the tip. Branch-leaves narrowly bordered, the median cells ring-fibrillose and with many lateral pores between the fibrils. Chlorophyllose cells triangular-trapezoidal in cross-section, with the broader face nearly flush with the upper (adaxial) surface of the leaf, the lower face nearly enclosed between the strongly convex hyaline cells.

Widely distributed in boreal regions extending south in North America to New Jersey, West Virginia, Ohio, Minnesota, and Oregon. Reported by Boehner as common in swamps and bogs in Cattaraugus County, southwestern New York.

Known/ from Elk, Fayette, McKean, Mercer, Somerset, and Tioga counties, in mountain and upland swamps. Figured from specimen collected by Edmund W. Arthur, in a wooded swamp, Swamp Root, Mercer Co., Sept. 20, 1946.

20. SPHAGNUM WARNSTORFII Russow
(S. acutifolium var. gracile Russow)

In swampy meadows, margins of bogs, etc., in Europe and, in North America, from Greenland to Pennsylvania and westward to the Pacific States and Alaska. The species varies from bright green to yellowish or from red to purplish. The green variety has been found in our region but once, its characters being as follows, but it is doubtfully different enough to merit varietal status.

CRAWFORD Co.: Pymatuning Swamp, Hartstown. O.E.J. May 29-30, 1915 (Det., C.M.B.). FAYETTE Co.: Cranberry-sphagnum glade, 1 mi. w. of Markleysburg P.O. O.E.J. and C.M.B. Aug. 25, 1949.

20a. SPHAGNUM WARNSTORFII var. VIRESCENS Russow
Plate VI

Rather densely cespitose, bright green above, bleached or yellowish below: stems in our specimens from about 5-12 cm high, the wood-cylinder green to red and surrounded by a cuticular sheath of three layers of inflated cells, the middle cells usually being the largest; stem-leaves about 1 mm long, broadly lingulate, not auriculate, rather abruptly rounded to a narrow erose-dentate somewhat concave apex, the margin very broadly hyaline-bordered below but abruptly narrowing above and continuing rather narrow to the apex; hyaline cells in upper half of stem-leaf broad, many of them once (or twice) septate, in the lower half of leaf the hyaline cells broad only in a narrow median strip flnked on both sides by narrow elongate cells, usually all hyaline cells of stem-leaf non-fibrillose and non-porose; fasciculate branches usually 4, two very slender and closely appressed pendent, and two horizontally divergent, rather slender, somewhat recurved, about 1-1.5 cm long, the comal branches short, obtuse, ascending to erect; branch-leaves rather indistinctly five-ranked, when dry with more or less spreading tips, ovate-lanceolate, concave, 1.5-2.0 mm long, the margins uniformly narrowly hyaline-bordered and involute to the quite narrowly acuminate and truncate-erose apex; hyaline cells of branch-leaves richly fibrillose, ventrally with one or two large round median pores of one-half to two-thirds the width of the cell, these pores usually more numerous towards the margin of the leaf, dorsally with quite numerous, small, elliptic, ringed pores in the angles and along the sides of the cell; in cross-section the chlorophyllise cells narrowly trapezoidal with the ventral face wider, both faces usually free, sometimes enclosed dorsally, the hyaline cells being dorsally quite convex; the cuticular sheath of branches with long rectangular cells with indistinct necks and apical pores: spores for the species stated to be dark yellow, minutely roughened, and about .025-.030 mm in diameter.

MERCER Co.: Near Houston Jct. J.A.S. July 12, 1902 (figured).

21. SPHAGNUM FUSCUM (Schimper) Klingr
(*S. acutifolium* var. *fuscum* Schimper)
Plate VIII

Slender plants in dense, soft, deep, brownish tufts. Stems erect, about 5-10 cm tall. Branches usually 3, of which two diverge almost at right angles, then droop; the other branch hanging down alongside the stem. The divergent branches are about 1-1.5 cm long tapering to a slender attenuate tip. Stem in cross-section showing 3-4 layers of larger, rounded-rectangular, thin-walled cells, underlain abruptly by a layer of thick-walled, very much smaller reddish brown cells, these grading abruptly into the central core of somewhat larger colorless cells. Branch-leaves in lower third of divergent branches 1-1.4 (1.5) mm long, somewhat spreading, lance-ovate, with upper margins incurved up to a narrowly truncate toothed apex. Leaves in the attenuate tip lance-linear and clasping at base. Lower central hyaline cells of the branch-leaves about .115 mm long, transversely fibrillose, and with a few large dorsal pores, these being mostly in pairs at the commisures. Chlorophyllose cells narrowly triangular, exposed on both surfaces, but more so on the ventral surface, on the dorsal surface deeply set between the strong convex hyaline cells. Stem-leaves narrowly oblong-lingulate, not much, if any, widened at bas, about 1.1-1.6 mm long, about 2½ to 3 times as long as wide, rounded and with a narrowly erose apex. The border wide at the base, narrowing rapidly towards the apex.

In our region it was collected in Waterman Swamp, Cattaragus Co., southwestern N. Y. (Boehner. Science Studies, Bonaventure College, 9: 4. 1941) and at Mt. Jewett, Potter Co., northern Pennsylvania. O.E.J. Sept. 12, 1922 (figured). CRAWFORD Co.: Pymatuning Swamp, May 29-31, 1915. O.E.J. McKEAN Co.: Cathrine Swamp. C.M.B. Pl. 82. Sept. 2, 1948.

Springy places and swamps, Eurasia and North America, south to northern Pennsylvania, Michigan, Minnesota, Colorado, and Washington.

The brown color of this moss constitutes the most obvious distinction between it and the usually red *S. Warnstorfii*.

22. SPHAGNUM QUINQUEFARIUM (Lindberg) Warnstorf

(Sphagnum acutifolium var. *quinquefarium* Lindberg)

Plate VI

Pale green or yellowish-green, reported as more or less rose-tinted above, but in our region not rose-tinted so far as yet known, deeply and densely cespitose: stems up to 10 cm, often forking, densely fasciculately branched, in cross-section showing a yellowish or pale wood-cylinder, the cuticular sheath composed of 3 or 4 layers of large cells; stem-leaves lingulate-triangular from a wide slightly auriculate base, rather large, about 1.2-1.8 mm long by about three-fifths as wide, rounded above to a narrowly erose-truncate apex, the margins narrowly hyaline-bordered and somewhat involute towards the apex, towards the base widely bordered; hyaline cells of stem-leaves in median portion and towards the apex widely rhomboid, in the upper half of the leaf septate, usually faintly fibrillose and occasionally porose, in the lateral basal portion septate, rapidly becoming very narrow outwards and merging there into the broad hyaline border; branches usually 4 or 5 in a fascicle, usually 2 or 3 widely divergent, the comal short, dense, and widely ascending to erect; branch-leaves oval to ovate, about 1.5 mm long, concave, with involute narrowly hyaline-bordered margins, above quickly narrowed to a rather broad dentate-truncate apex; hyaline cells of branch-leaves large, fibrillose, below ventrally with a few small rounded pores in the cell-angles, the median lateral cells with a few small rounded pores in the cell-angles, the median lateral cells with a few larger indistinct pores, dorsally above with characteristic more or less elliptic pores of about one-third the width of the cell and situated in the cell-angles or along the sides; in cross-section the chlorophyllose cells rather broadly triangular, ventrally free but dorsally enclosed between the highly convex hyaline cells; cuticular cells of branches large, inflated, with a distinct neck and apical pore: spores stated to be smooth, yellowish and about .021-.025 mm in diameter.

In bogs, etc., in Europe and, in North America, from Newfoundland to New England and south along the mountains to the Carolinas.

Rare in our region. CLINTON CO.: Along Hyner's Run above Hyner, July 14, 1908. O.E.J. (figured).

23. SPHAGNUM PLUMULOSUM Roell

(S. subnitens Russow and Warnstorf; *S. acutifolium* var. *subnitens* Dixon)

Plate V

Densely cespitose, pale to grass-green, usually reddish to violet above: stem in typical specimens 10-15 cm high, but in our region usually about 6-8 cm high, the wood-cylinder green to red, the cuticular sheath distinct, 2-4-layered, with the outer cells largest: stem-leaves large, 1-1.5 mm long, broadly triangular lingulate, the apex erose-truncate and toothed, the hyaline border of margin narrow above, very wide below; hyaline-cells of stem-leaves broadly rhomboidal towards the apex and in median basal portion of leaf, towards lateral basal portions rapidly much narrower and septate, all non-fibrillose and non-porose; branches 3-5 in a fascicle, usually two of these variously divergent, rather slender, terete, about 1-1.5 cm long, the others very slender and appressed-pendent; branch-leaves ovate, concave, about 1.5 mm long, the narrowly hyaline-bordered margin towards the apex involute, the blade towards the apex gradually narrowed towards an erose-dentate point, the leaves when dry imbricate with more or less of a metallic lustre, not distinctly 5-seriate; hyaline cells of branch-leaves fibrillose, rather broad, ventrally with usually two or three median, large, round, ringed pores about one-third to one-half as wide as the cell, occasionally a few pores also in the cell-angles, dorsally with about 6-10 elliptic pores about one-third as wide as the cell and situated along the sides and angles of the cell; in cross-section the chlorophyllose cells small and shortly sub-rectangular to triangularly trapezoidal, situated much nearer the ventral leaf-surface with the wider ventral face free, the narrower dorsal face free or enclosed between the dorsally highly convex hyaline cells; cuticular cells of branches inflated, short, with a distinct neck and terminal pore: spores stated to be yellow, papillose, about .025-.030 mm in diameter.

In bogs, swamps, etc., widely distributed in the cooler parts of the Northern Hemisphere, in North America occurring from Greenland and Labrador south to New Jersey and Pennsylvania, and in California and British Columbia. In our region apparently represented only by the following variety, more properly a form, as follows:

23a. Sphagnum plumulosum f. viride (Warnstorf)
New Combination
(*S. subnitens* var. *viride* Warnstorf)

This form differs from the typical species in that the tufts are low and entirely green or often bleached out below.

In deep, shaded swamps and bogs within the range of the type.

CRAWFORD Co.: Shaded boggy margin of Mud Lake, Hartstown, May 29-31, 1909. O.E.J. and G.K.J. (figured).

24. SPHAGNUM ACUTIFOLIUM Ehrhardt
(*S. capillifolium* (Ehrh.) Russ. & Warnst.; *S. capillaceum* (Weiss) Schrank)

The typical form of this species has green to pale or variously reddish to purplish tufts with often short stout stems and a hyaline to yellowish or reddish wood-cylinder; the other characters are as described below for the variety *viride*, to which some of our collections belong, although color differences are here perhaps of not much taxonomic value.

CAMBRIA Co.: Cresson, James. (Porter's Catalogue). ERIE Co.: Lo i·le. L.K.H. 1950. HUNTINGDON Co.: Warrior's Ridge, Porter. (Porter's Catalogue). WARREN Co.: Columbus bog. C.M.B. 1948. It has been found also in Allegheny, Butler, Clearfield, Crawford, Fayette, Forest, McKean, Mifflin, Somerset, and Westmoreland counties.

24a.   SPHAGNUM ACUTIFOLIUM var. VIRIDE Warnstorff

(*S. capillifolium* var. *viride* Jennings)

Plate V

Rather densely cespitose, low, yellowish above, greenish to yellowish-green below, lacking the reddish tinges so often characteristic of the species: stems slender, in our region usually 5-8 cm long, in cross-section showing a yellowish wood-cylinder and a distinct cuticular sheath of 2-4 layers of large but non-porose cells; stem-leaves oval-triangular to lingulate-triangular, 1-2 mm long, always widest at the base, towards the apex abruptly narrowed to a truncate apex with a few teeth, the upper margin usually somewhat involute, the margin narrowly hyaline-bordered, the border sometimes wider at the base; hyaline cells of stem-leaves largely once-septate, especially below the middle, those of the upper half of the leaf usually more or less completely fibrillose and some-times distinctly laterally porose; branches fairly numerous, usually in fascicles of four, two spreading-recurved and two appressed-pendent and very slender; the cuticular sheath of branches composed of cells with a distinct neck and terminal pore; branch-leaves 1-2 mm long, ovate-lanceolate, when dry hardly secund but with slightly spreading tips, concave, with involute margins above, uniformly narrowly hyaline-bordered, the narrow apex somewhat erose-dentate; hyaline cells of branch-leaves rather slender, abruptly fibrillose, with small somewhat elliptic pores at the cell-angles, sometimes also lateral pores of a similar character between the angle-pores on both sides of the leaf, while towards the margin of the leaf the pores are often larger and more numerous; in cross-section the chlorophyllose cells are more or less trapezoidal, unusually short, free on both surfaces but the hyaline cells projecting far beyond them both ventrally and dorsally, especially dorsally; perichaetial leaves said to be very large and broadly ovate: spores yellow, smoothish.

In cool, boggy situations in Europe, Asia, South America, and in the regions of the South Pacific. In North America extending from Greenland and Alaska south to Virginia, Pennsylvania, and Wisconsin.

BUTLER Co.: In boggy place in upland pasture 1 mi. n. of Smith School, Parker Twp. Adam M. Barker. July 5, 1935. FAYETTE Co.: In hollows along rocky river-bed above the falls, Ohio Pyle, July 4, 1908. O.E.J. (figured)

Order II. Andreaeales

Small, monoicous (or dioicous), dark brown to almost black, when dry very brittle, mostly cespitose on granite or slate rocks: stems slender, radiculose below, dichotomous, with fascicled branchlets, no central strand; leaves small, crowded, erect-spreading to often falcate-secund, uni-stratose to partly bi-stratose, thickish, often more or less papillose, costate to ecostate, very opaque; cells small, incrassate: seta none, but represented by a pseudopodium from the gametophore; capsule oval, opening by 4 (-8) vertical slits, the valves remain-ing united both above and below; spores and columella derived from the en-dothecium; no air-cavity between the spore-sac and the capsule-wall; calyptra torn at the base, delicate; spores large, about .034 mm in diameter, chlorophyl-lose.

This peculiar order is represented by but one family, the *Andreaeaceae*, which consists of only one genus, *Andreaea* [Ehrhart] Hedwig. There are about 125 species, alpine and sub-alpine and widely distributed; 19 species occur in North America, only 3 of which, however, are to be expected in our general range.

I.   ANDREAEA [Ehrhart] Hedwig

A. Leaves ecostate ....1. *A. rupestris*
A. Leaves costate ....B
   B. Leaf elongate acuminate from an oval base; costa filling about the middle two-
      thirds of the leaf-apex, not excurrent ....2. *A. Rothii*
   B. Costa practically filling the whole apex of the leaf and excurrent ....
      ....(*A. Rothii* var. *crassinervia* (Bruch) Moenkemeyer)

1.   ANDREAEA RUPESTRIS Hedwig
(*A. petrophila* Ehrhart)

Densely cespitose, dark brown to blackish: stems slender, about 1.5-2.5 cm high, usually branching, more or less erect; leaves when dry very brittle, crowded, small, ovate to lance-ovate, imbricated, often falcate-secund from an erect base, usually obtuse, entire, margin incurved; no costa; (the leaves are so dense that they usually require bleaching in a solution of caustic potash before the leaf-cells can be made out under the microscope); basal leaf-cells narrow-rectangular, very incrassate, sinuose, above becoming shorter, the median and upper cells rounded and angular-oblong, longitudinally seriate, dorsally strongly papillose: fruit similar to that of *Sphagnum* in being enclosed in the perichaetium until mature, when it is quickly exserted on an outgrowth from the tip of the leafy shoot similar in appearance to a short seta and termed the pseudopodium; calyptra very thin and irregularly torn at base; capsule oval, opening usually by four perpendicular slits along the sides but remaining united at apex and base; columella persistent; spores smoothish, mature in late spring.

In mountainous or hilly regions on non-calcareous rocks. In North America from the Arctic regions south to northern United States and south to Georgia, Colorado, and California. Occurs in northeastern Pennsylvania and in northern West Virginia.

2.   ANDREAEA ROTHII Weber and Mohr
(*Andreaea rupestris* Roth)

Plate LX

Small, blackish; stems 1-2 cm. long, branching to form tufts; leaves spreading to falcate-secund, up to 1-1.5 mm long, suddenly elongate acuminate from an oblong or ovate base, entire to faintly crenulate; costa strong, yellowish, more or less plainly percurrent; alar cells rounded-quadrate, the median basal ones variously either rounded or linear-oblong with irregular lumen, the upper rounded, small, all densely incrassate; perichaetial leaves sheathing, suddenly contracted into a short acuminate or linear point; capsule oblong-ovate, dark, about .75 mm long, exserted on a twisted seta, splitting into four valves which in old specimens finally break apart at the apex and coil over each other when dry; spores .030-.040 mm, roughish, ripening in summer.

On non-calcareous rocks. Greenland to Michigan and Georgia; and in Northwestern United States.

FAYETTE CO.: On rocks at White Rock, on Chestnut Ridge above Fairchance. Aug. 9, 1931. John L. Sheldon (figured).

Order III. Bryales—True Mosses

This order comprises numerous mosses of various habit: the endothecium gives rise to the sporogenous tissue, which surrounds an inner sterile tissue, loose in *Archidium*, but forming the columella in the rest of the *Bryales;* the spore-sac is separated from the wall of the capsule by a more or less highly developed air-cavity; there is no pseudopodium but there is a more or less elongated true seta; the outer wall of the archegonium after some growth is ruptured, thus forming a basal vaginule and an apical calyptra; capsule cleistocarpous or, more usually, with a definite operculum and then often with a single or double peristome: the order is conveniently divided, according to the position of the sporogonium upon the leafy shoot of the gametophyte, into the *acrocarpous* mosses (sporogonium at the apex of the leafy shoot) and *pleurocarpous* mosses (sporogonium lateral upon the leafy shoot).

ACROCARPI

The acrocarpous mosses comprise about thirty families of the Bryales widely distributed and numerous in number of species. For the analytical key to the acrocarpous mosses see the general key to the genera of mosses at the beginning of the book, page 10.

Family 1. ARCHIDIACEAE

Autoicous, sometimes paroicous or synoicous, rarely dioicous: small terrestrial plants, closely gregarious and forming broad patches; stems erect, with central strand, below bearing rhizoids; leaves of the shoots and also the basal leaves minute, spreading, distant, linear-lanceolate, acuminate, flat, entire, the costa ending in the point; perichætial leaves much larger, imbricated, more or less linear-acuminate from a lanceolate base; leaf-cells smooth, prosenchymatous or sometimes sub-vermicular to parenchymatous: capsule sessile, spherical, terminal, non-operculate; columella none; spores commonly 16-20, about .2 mm in diameter.

One genus only, the characters being as given for the family, comprising about 25 species, distributed widely in the temperate zones. Six species are native in North America, but only one is likely to be collected in our region.

1. ARCHIDIUM Bridel
1. ARCHIDIUM OHIOENSE Schimper

Occurs on the ground in meadows and fields throughout eastern United States from Quebec and Minnesota to Florida and Louisiana. Not yet reported in our region, but to be expected, as it occurs in eastern Pennsylvania and in Ohio, and its type locality is Harper's Ferry.

Family 2.—DICRANACEAE

Autoicous or dioicous; large to minute, mostly cespitose: stem with a central strand, often thickly covered with rhizoids, mostly densely leafy, branched; leaves often falcate-secund, mostly acuminate to narrowly linear from a broader base, usually more or less smooth and shining, usually costate; costa sometimes dorsally serrate, heterogenous; leaf-cells sometimes mammillate, the basal ones enlarged and mostly transparent, alar cells often much larger and either hyaline or brownish, the central leaf-cells short to rounded, mostly smooth; perichætial leaves often sheathing: seta usually erect and long; capsule mostly unsymmetric, usually cernuous, when dry often curved and sulcate; annulus present or absent; peristome simply or rarely none; when present the peristome teeth are 16 in number, approximate, united below into a basal membrane, usually two parted to the middle, or beyond, into linear or awl-like divisions, no longitudinal lines, but the teeth minutely striate or papillose on the dorsal face, rarely smooth, inner face yellow with one or two longitudinal lines and with more or less projecting trabeculæ, operculum more or less long-rostrate; calyptra usually cucullate.

KEY TO THE GENERA

A. Capsule with a long, slender, usually curved neck; leaves suddenly lanceolate or subulate from a broad, clasping base ....2. *Trematodon*
A. Capsule neck, if any, much shorter than the urn ....B
   B. Cells of costa in cross-section homogeneous; peristome, if present, of 16 flat, smooth, usually entire teeth ....6. *Seligeria*
   B. Cells of costa in cross-section heterogeneous; peristome none, or various   C
   C. Alar cells not conspicuously enlarged or inflated ....D
   C. Alar cells conspicuously enlarged or inflated ....J
      D. Leaf-cells smooth or essentially so in our species ....E
      D. Leaf-cells more or less distinctly mamillose or papillose ....Q
      E. Leaves not crisped when dry ....F
      E. Leaves crisped when dry ....P
         F. Costa more than one-half width of leaf-base ....*Brothera*
         F. Costa less than half as wide as leaf-base ....G
      G. Cleistocarpous ....H
      G. With peristome I
         H. Capsule ovoid, immersed, short-apiculate ....3. *Pleuridium*
         H. Capsule pyriform with a short neck ....1. *Bruchia*
     I. Peristome-teeth unequally subulately 2-3 cleft to the middle or somewhat below, papillose above ....7. *Dicranella*
     I. Peristome-teeth cleft to the base or nearly so into two, linear, filiform papillose divisions ....N
      J. Costa narrow, less than one-third as wide as leaf-base ....K
      J. Costa at least one-third as wide as leaf-base L
      K. Capsule mostly not strumose; peristome at base not forming a deeply inserted tube ....10. *Dicranum*
      K. Capsule strumose; peristome teeth united at base into a deeply inserted tube ....9. *Oncophorus*
         L. No stereid bands in costa; costa filling most of the leaf above the middle ....M

L. Stereid bands above and below the guide-cells; peristome teeth separate to below the mouth of the capsule ....11. *Dicranodontium*

M. Alar cells not definitely inflated ....*Brothera*

M. Inflated alar cells reaching the costa ....10. *Dicranum longifolium*

    N. Basal leaf-cells short-rectangular; the capsules sulcate ....5. *Ceratodon*

    N. Basal leaf-cells somewhat elongated-rectangular ....o

O. Capsules, when dry, sulcate ....4. *Ditrichum pallidum*

O. Capsues not sulcate when dry ....4. *Ditrichum pusillum* and *D. lineare*

    P. Peristome teeth divided one-half way down or more ......9. *Oncophorus Wahlenbergii*

    P. Peristome teeth not divided ....8. *Rhabdoweisia*

Q. Cleistocarpous ....1. *Bruchia*

Q. With peristome ....(*Oreoweisia*)*

I.   BRUCHIA Schwaegrichen

Autoicous or paroicous; gregarious: green protonema persistent but sparse; stem short with a central strand; leaves long-canaliculate-subulate, from an oval to lanceolate base, erect to secund; costa broad and flat, filling the subulate acumen; laminal cells rectangular; seta short; capsule pyriform, more or less cernuous, rostrate; operculum none; calyptra covering one-third or more of the capsule, mitrate, unsymmetrically cleft.

A widely distributed genus of about 25 species, 14 of these being found in North America, one already found and another probably occurring in our region.

KEY TO THE SPECIES

A. Collum less than one-half the whole length of capsule; seta usually longer than capsule ....1. *B. flexuosa*

A. Collum about as long as rest of capsule; seta usually shorter than capsule ....
....2. *B. Sullivantii*

1.   BRUCHIA FLEXUOSA (Swartz) Mueller

Gregarious, the green protonema persistent but not very conspicuous: stems about 2-4 mm long, curved to erect; leaves remote, small, lance-subulate, erect-spreading from a concave base, somewhat serrulate at the apex; leaf-cells rectangular, narrower at the margin, alar not much different; antheridia in axils of comal leaves or in separate buds; seta short, stout, usually shorter than the erect, ovoid-pyriform, partially exserted, apiculate capsule; calyptra narrowly conic, mitrate; spores .030-.040 mm in diameter, decidedly papillose, mature about June.

This and the following species perhaps differ too little to be regarded as distinct. On Clay soil in fields from Minnesota to New England and south to the Gulf States. Occurs in eastern Pennsylvania and in Ohio.

---

* *Oreoweisia serrulata* extends south as far as Tennessee and Kentucky, but is reported thus far in Pennsylvania only from the eastern part of the State. Moist, shaded, cool ledges.

BRUCHIA SULLIVANTII Austin
Plate LX

Very close to B. flexuosa, from which it differs mainly in having shorter stems; the neck about as long as the spore-sac. Leaves suddenly canaliculate-subulate from an ovate concave base, smooth or nearly so, basal cells thin-walled, elongate rectangular, often very irregular, with an indistinct margin of linear somewhat incrassate cells; cells at shoulder much shorter, polygonal, thicker walled; costa strong percurrent: seta curved, 1-1.5 mm long; capsule oblong-pyriform 1-2 mm long, acuminate, the neck about as long as the spore-sac; calyptra about one-half the length of capsule, smooth; spores spinulose, mature in June.

On clay soil in fields from New England to Minnesota, south to the Gulf States. Occurs in eastern Pennsylvania and in Ohio.

BUTLER CO.: One mile north of Moniteau, Cherry Twp., on soil in old cornfield. Sidney K. Eastwood. June 6, 1935 (figured).

2. TREMATODON Richard

Autoicous, rarely dioicous; low, singly disposed: stem with a large central strand and loose ground tissue; leaves yellowish-green, abruptly to gradually lance-subulate from a broad clasping base, more or less crisped when dry; costa ending below the apex or percurrent; cells thin-walled, loosely elongate-hexagonal to rectangular or, above, rhombic-pentagonal or -hexagonal: seta yellow, erect, rarely tortuous to cygneous; capsule with a long tapering neck, moderately arcuate, the urn smooth, annulus differentiated; peristome-teeth united below into a low basal tube, undivided and cribrose or two-parted to the base into filiform divisions, articulate and longitudinally striate, peristome rarely lacking; operculum as long as the urn, obliquely rostrate; calyptra inflated, cucullate, not ciliate.

A cosmopolitan genus of about 70 species, of which about 10 occur in North America, 2 of these in our region.

KEY TO THE SPECIES

A. Collum as long as urn of capsule ....1. T. ambiguus
A. Collum twice as long as urn ....2. T. longicollis

TREMATODON AMBIGUUS (Hedwig) Hornschuch
Plate LXXII

Gregarious, erect, simple or sparingly branched; stems 6-10 mm tall, densely brownish radiculose below; leaves 4-8 mm long, from an ovate or oblong, concave, sheathing base abruptly narrowed to an equally long or somewhat longer linear-subulate, channelled apex, minutely serrulate at the tip; costa at base thin, about one-fifth or one-sixth the width of the leaf, from there percurrent and constituting most of the linear-subulate upper part of the leaf; cells at base of leaf thin-walled, oblong-rectangular, somewhat inflated, about .010-.020 mm wide by 2-5 times as long, at the margin a few rows much narrower, the cells at the shoulder where the sheathing base suddenly tapers into the narrow acumination much smaller, short-rectangular to rounded, .003-.010 mm in diameter, thick-walled: seta bright yellow, slender, 1-2.5 cm long; capsule about 2 mm long, often slightly curved, narrowly ovoid cylindric, abruptly narrowed below into a slender, curved hypophysis, about as long or slightly longer than the urn and strumose at the base with a goiter-like swelling; operculum with a slender beak about two-thirds as long as the urn; annulus large, revoluble peristome dark red, borne on a basal membrane which projects above the mouth of the capsule, the teeth 16, awl-like, more or less irregularly perforate or cleft or entirely divided, striate longitudinally; capsule with a reddish rim of a few rows of small, incrassate, rounded cells, below which the cells become linear and incrassate; spores rough-warty, .023-.024 mm in diameter, mature in June.

On clayey soil in open ground, Virginia to Newfoundland and Alaska.

Cresson, Cambria Co., *James* and *Porter;* and Westmoreland County, on recently disturbed clay soil around sawmill, altitude 1300 ft., two miles north of Darlington, Chestnut Ridge, May 29, 1949, O.E.J. (figured).

2. Trematodon longicollis Richard

Cespitose, light green to brownish-green; stems erect, usually about 5 mm high; leaves abruptly linear-subulate from a concave ovate base, the subulation canaliculate, minutely serrulate at apex; costa scarcely reaching the apex; leaf-cells as in *T. ambiguus;* perichætial leaves quite gradually long-acuminate: seta similar to *T. ambiguus;* collum twice as long as the urn; urn more strictly oblong-cylindric; peristome-teeth 16, narrow-subulate, nodosely articulate, usually perforate rather than cleft. Otherwise very similar to *T. ambiguus.*

In old fields, etc., on sandy or clayey soil, in Europe, Asia, and in North America, from Massachusetts, Pennsylvania, and Ohio southwards to Florida and Mexico. Not yet reported in our region, but to be expected.

3. Pleuridium Bridel

Autoicous or paroicous, rarely synoicous: weak, green or yellowish-green, cespitose or gregarious: stem with a central strand, radiculose at base, perennial by means of fertile shoots below the apex and by means of sterile flagella; leaves mostly terminal, erect-spreading, sometimes secund, linear-subulate from a broader base, upwards weakly denticulate, sometimes thickly imbricated; costa varying from weak and ending below the apex to very broad and filling the whole acumen, often rough-serrate dorsally; seta mostly very short and erect, rather curved; capsule mostly immersed and oval to ovate-globose, short pointed, sometimes obliquely so, cleistocarpous, without a collum; calyptra cucullate, cleft almost to the apex on one side, covering scarcely half the capsule.

About 30 species widely distributed, mainly in temperate regions, on soil. Six species occur in North America, at least one in our region. The following key is adapted from Grout's *Moss Flora.*

KEY TO THE SPECIES

A. Calyptra mitrate; capsule with stomata immersed in middle of wall............................
    (*Sporledera palustris* (Br. & Sch.) Hampe = *P. palustre* (Br. & Sch.) Bryol. Eur.)
A. Capsule split almost to apex ....B
  B. Narrow upper part of leaf shorter than the broadened basal part C
  B. Narrow part of leaf much longer than broad basal part ....D
  C. Leaves gradually narrowed from lance-ovate base to serrulate apex ....
    ....(*P. Ravenellii* Austin)
  C. Leaves abruptly mucronate and smooth above from broad serrulate base ....
    ....(*P. Sullivantii* Austin)
  D. Basal cells of leaf about 2-5:1 ....1. *P. subulatum*
  D. Basal cells of leaf about 5-8:1 ....(*P. acuminatum* Lindberg)

1.   PLEURIDIUM SUBULATUM (Hedwig) Lindberg

(*P. alternifolium* [Dickson; Kaulfuss] Rabenhorst;
Phascum subulatum Schreber)

Plate LX

Densely gregarious to cespitose, yellowish-green: stems usually simple, about 2-6 mm high; lower stem-leaves lance-subulate, short; comal and perichætial leaves much longer, more or less erect or ascending, from a small oval base gradually subulate-setaceous, canaliculate, nearly entirely to minutely denticulate; costa wide, not very well defined, practically filling the apex; basal leaf-cells rectangular to more or less oblong-hexagonal, the upper cells often becoming linear and forming a more or less distinct margin to the costa: seta short, erect, about as long as the capsule; capsule oval or roundish, about 1 mm long, obtusely apiculate, more or less castaneous or yellowish when mature; calyptra cucullate, reaching about halfway down the capsule, short rostrate, split almost to apex; spores large, mature from April to June, minutely roughened; antheridia naked in axils of the upper or median leaves.

On moist clayey or sandy soil in old fields, along banks of ditches, etc., in Europe, Asia and in North America, from New England to Wisconsin and south to Alabama.

BUTLER CO.: In sandy meadow on south slope of hill two miles southwest of Glade Mills, April 20, 1913. O.E.J. and A. R. Hillard. WASHINGTON CO.: On stony ground, near Washington, Linn and Simonton, May 2, 1892, and May 6, 1893. WESTMORELAND CO.: In sandy-clay meadow on gently sloping hillside east of Blackburn, April 24, 1913. O.E.J., G.K.J., and R. J. Sim (figured).

4.   DITRICHUM [Timm] Hampe

Dioicous or autoicous; mostly low, cespitose, not radiculose, green to yellow-green, more or less shining: stem with a central strand, densely foliate, simple or little branched; leaves with a broad base, not sheathing, mostly long-canaliculate-subulate, imbricated to erect-spreading or secund, when dry mostly a little curved or straight; costa broad and flat, percurrent or excurrent, usually filling the upper part of the acumen; leaf-cells rectangular, more or less prolonged, alar cells not inflated: seta elongate, erect; capsule erect or a little cernuous, symmetric or unsymmetric, sometimes weakly arcuate, mostly ovate to oblong-cylindric, sometimes sulcate; peristome with a basal membrane, the 16 teeth mostly cleft to the base or nearly so into two linear-filiform portions, papillose, rarely weakly twisted to the left; articulations not projecting dorsally, some-imes coupled at the base of the teeth; annulus mostly serrate, revoluble; oper-culum mostly obliquely conic; calyptra reaching to below the middle of the capsule.

A cosmopolitan genus of about 50 species, mostly growing on soil, about 10 species in North America, 3 of these occurring in our region.

KEY TO THE SPECIES

A. Dioicous: leaf-margins more or less recurved; seta castaneous ....B
A. Autoicous: awn serrulate; seta bright yellow ....3. *D. pallidum*
    B. Capsule somewhat unsymmetric, subsulcate, somewhat cernuous ....1. *D. lineare*
    B. Capsule symmetric, smooth, erect ....2. *D. pusillum*

1. DITRICHUM LINEARE (Sw.) Lindberg

(*D. tortile* var. *vaginans* Grout; *Trichostomum vaginans* Sullivant; *Leptotrichum vaginans* Schimper; *Ditrichum vaginans* Hampe)

Plate IX

Densely cespitose, yellowish-green, lustrous: stems erect, ascending, about 5 mm. high, usually with erect terete sterile branches, sometimes up to 1.5 cm high; leaves 1-1.5 mm long, close, erect-appressed when dry, not much spread-ing when moist, from an ovate concave base narrowed to a linear deeply canaliculate acumination, margins narrowly recurved, usually entire; costa strong, percurrent or rarely excurrent, comprising from one-third to one-half of the width of the acumination; upper leaf-cells rectangular, mostly about 2:1, rather dense and incrassate, smooth, the basal larger, elongate-rectangular up to 6-8:1, moderately thin-walled, sub-hyaline or yellowish; perichætial leaves larger, convolutely sheathing, above narrowing abruptly into a linear-subulate, canaliculate, entire acumination, the basal cells larger and laxer than in the stem-leaves: seta erect, flexuous, lustrous, yellowish to brownish, sinistrorse, about 1-2 cm long; capsule brownish, about 1.5 mm long, narrowly to oblong-cylindric, rounded at base, little changed when old; lid about one-fourth the length of the urn, conic-rostellate obliquely, castaneous; annulus 2-3-seriate, wide; peristome-teeth linear subulate, imperfect, forked to the base or often united above, or irregularly cleft, deep castaneous, articulate; exothecial cells yellowish-incrassate, irregularly oblong to rectangular, the 4 or 5 uppermost rows much smaller, rounded and obscure; calyptra cucullate, covering about one-half of the capsule; spores yellowish, smooth, about .015-.018 mm, ma-turing in late fall or winter.

Usually on sandy soil in hilly or mountainous districts. In Europe, and in North America, from Maine to Missouri and North Carolina.

Not common in our region. ALLEGHENY Co.: Powers Run, September 14, 1905 (fig-ured). O.E.J. and G.E.K.; Wildwood Road, March 29, 1908. O.E.J. and G.K.J.; Thornhill, December 29, 1908. O.E.J. FAYETTE Co.: Fort Necessity. H. N. Mozingo. April 1, 1945. McKEAN Co.: West Branch, September 6, 1896. D.A.B. WESTMORE-LAND Co.: One mi. n. of Darlington. C.M.B. Oct. 7, 1944.

2. Ditrichum pusillum (Hedwig) E. G. Britton
(*Leptotrichum pusillum* Hampe; *Ditrichum tortile* Brockmueller)

Plate X

Cespitose, yellowish-green, rather dull: stems short, about 5-10 mm high, erect or erect-ascending from a radiculose base, mostly simple, reddish; leaves about 2.5-3.5 mm long, closely appressed-erect to somewhat spreading, usually somewhat secund or twisted, gradually lance-subulate and canaliculate from an ovate-lanceolate concave base, margins more or less narrowly revolute, apex usually denticulate; costa strong, less distinct at base, in the upper portion constituting about one-third to one-half of the leaf-width, percurrent to slightly excurrent; basal cells rectangular to linear-rectangular, alar not different, rather thin-walled and hyaline, smooth, median smaller, mostly about 2:1, rectangular to quadrate, smooth, the apical sometimes bi-stratose; perichætial leaves more or less sheathing, otherwise similar to the stem-leaves: seta reddish-brown, shining, somewhat sinistrorse, erect, about 1 cm. long; capsule oblong to oblong-cylindric, reddish to pale brown, smooth, non-sulcate, not constricted below the mouth, abruptly narrowed to the seta at base, the urn about 1 mm long; annulus uni-seriate; peristome single, rather low, reddish, the 16 teeth cleft into linear-subulate, distinctly trabeculate, somewhat spirally twisted divisions, at base united into a very low membrane; operculum conic-rostellate, usually more or less oblique; calyptra cucullate, pale; spores rather thin-walled, smooth, yellowish-pellucid, about .015-.018 mm, mature in late fall or in winter: dioicous.

On clayey soil in fields, along roadsides, etc., in Europe, Asia, northern Africa, and in the eastern half of North America from Labrador to the Gulf States.

On clay soil, roadside banks, etc., in Fayette, Greene, Allegheny, and southern Butler counties in the extreme southwestern part of the state. Specimen figured: Keown Station, O.E.J. November 14, 1909.

3. Ditrichum pallidum [Schreber] Hampe

Plate X

Loosely cespitose, bright green; stems about 5 mm high, more or less erect, or with a creeping base; leaves erect-spreading, sometimes somewhat secund, from a lance-ovate base, prolonged linear-subulate, concave, channeled towards the apex; costa strong, long-excurrent, denticulate towards the apex; basal leaf-cells laxly oblong-hexagonal, thin-walled, hyaline, up to about .015-.017 mm, the median cells gradually much smaller, rectangular, forming but a narrow margin to the costa; seta erect, yellow, slender, dextrorse and flexuous when dry, about 1-2 cm long; capsule ovate-oblong, yellowish-red, ascending to horizontal, somewhat unsymmetric, usually somewhat strumose at base, about 2 mm long, when dry and empty sub-arcuate and irregularly sulcate; peristome single, the 16 teeth bifid deeply, united at base into a very low basal membrane, the prongs cylindric, nodose-articulate, finely papillose, reddish, about 0.5 mm long; annulus compound, deciduous, bordered by two or three rows of small, rounded, reddish-pellucid cells; spores globose, papillose, about .017 mm, reddish-pellucid, mature in early summer; operculum conic-obtuse, about 0.6 mm long; calyptra smooth, cucullate, slenderly straight-rostrate, about 2.5 mm long, the beak reaching about 1.5 mm beyond the tip of the operculum; antheridial clusters gemmiform in axils of the perichætial leaves.

On bare soil, usually in woods. Europe, Asia, northern Africa, and, in North America, from Nova Scotia to Ontario south to the Gulf of Mexico and westward to Kansas.

Common in our region, and now known from the following counties: Allegheny, Armstrong, Beaver Bedford, Butler, Centre, Crawford, Fayette, Lawrence. McKean, Washington, and Westmoreland. Specimen figured: Blackburn, Westmoreland County, O.E.J. June 13, 1908.

5.   CERATODON Bridel

Dioicous, rarely autoicous; cespitose, green to brown or reddish-brown, somewhat radiculose; stem 3-5-angled, with a central strand, thickly foliate, often bushy-branched; leaves erect-spreading, appressed and more or less twisted when dry, ovate to lance-linear, neither sheathing nor subulate-pointed, margin revolute; costa strong, percurrent or long-excurrent, with median guides; leaf-cells thick-walled, short-rectangular below, the upper quadrate to rounded, smooth; perichætial leaves distinctly sheathing; seta long and erect; capsule inclined to horizontal, elliptic-ovate to oblong, purplish to reddish-brown, shining, when dry sulcate; annulus spirally deciduous, 2-4-seriate; peristome-teeth 16, cleft nearly to the base into filiform divisions, united at the base into a tube, the teeth closely articulated below, less closely above, papillose; operculum conic, much shorter than the capsule; calyptra cucullate.

A cosmopolitan genus consisting of 27 *species; 4 species in North America, only one occurring in our region.

1.   CERATODON PURPUREUS (Hedwig) Bridel

(*Mnium purpureum* Linnaeus; *Dicranum purpurascens* Hedwig;
Dicranum purpureum Hedwig)

Plate X

Densely and often rather deeply brownish- or reddish-cespitose, mostly green above and dark brown below: stems mostly branched, erect, about 1 cm high, dying away below; leaves lanceolate to linear-lanceolate, carinate, the margins revolute to near apex; costa strong, percurrent, at base about one-sixth to one-fourth the width of the leaf; seta about 1.5 cm long, erect, dark-castaneous, lustrous, twisted when dry; capsule oblong-linear, at first erect, later inclined to horizontal and more or less curved, irregularly sulcate, strumose, about 2.5 mm long, dark red-brown, lustrous, annulus distinct, revoluble; peristome-teeth dark red below, basally confluent, papillose, weakly trabeculate to a little above the middle, bordered, hyaline above; operculum conic-elongate, about one-fourth the length of the urn, often somewhat curved, usually darker

---

* Brotherus (Pflanzenfamilien, 1924, 2nd. edit, p. 163) thinks these all can be reduced to two species.

brown than the urn; calyptra cucullate; exothecial cells rather incrassate, irregularly elongate-hexagonal or rectangular-oblong, two or three rows at the rim much smaller and darker; spores smooth, rather thin-walled, yellowish-pellucid, mature in May or June. Quite variable.

Cosmopolitan on burnt-over ground, roadsides, vacant lots, roofs, bare clay soil, etc.

Very common in our region. Now known from Allegheny, Armstrong, Beaver, Bedford, Butler, Cambria, Centre, Clearfield, Clinton, Crawford, Erie, Fayette, Lawrence, McKean, Somerset, Washington, and Westmoreland counties. Specimen figured: Sandplain, Presque Isle, Erie Co., May 8-9, 1906. O.E.J.

6. SELIGERIA Bryologia Europæa

Autoicous: minute, gregarious, or cespitose, rupestral: stem simple or branched at base, rarely with long sterile shoots; leaves in 3 to 5 series, the lower minute and distant, the upper abruptly larger and canaliculate-subulate from a concave lanceolate base; costa often stronger above the base; alar cells not differentiated: seta mostly erect, but little longer than involucral leaves; capsule globose-pyriform, smooth; collum distinct; annulus none; peristome deeply inserted, or rarely none; when present, teeth broadly lanceolate, usually entire, truncate or acute; operculum obliquely rostrate; calyptra cucullate.

A widely distributed genus of about 20 species; 8 occurring in North America; 2 in our region.

KEY TO THE SPECIES

A. Seta arcuate when moist; leaves with a long, acute, subulate acumination ....
....1. *S. recurvata*
A. Seta erect when moist; leaves with a rather short, linear, sub-obtuse subulation ....
....2. *S. calcarea*

1. SELIGERIA RECURVATA (Hedwig) Bryologia Europæa
(*S. setacea* [Wulfen] Lindberg)

Densely gregarious, dark green, very small: stems short, about 1 mm or less, simple or forking; leaves up to 1.5 mm long, erect-spreading, flexuous, with a long, canaliculate, acute subulation from a lance-ovate base, the margins entire; costa long-excurrent, forming much of the subulation; basal leaf-cells thin-walled, pellucid, irregular or rectangular, above becoming quadrate and incrassate; perichætial tubulose-sheathing at base, towards apex lance-subulate; seta long, yellowish, arcuate when moist, but when old and dry often erect, more or less flexuous; capsule oval to subglobose, erect, thin-walled, short-necked, red-mouthed, turbinate when empty; exothecial cells lax; no annulus; operculum about as long as urn (each about 0.4 mm), straight, subulate-rostrate; peristome-teeth 16, lanceolate to linear, obtuse to acute, sometimes irregularly bifid at apex, free, smooth, orange-pellucid, reflexed when dry.

On rocks in shade. Europe, Asia and, in North America, in Ontario, Pennsylvania, New York, New Jersey and in the Rocky Mountains. Occurs on limestone rocks in eastern Pennsylvania and may occur in similar habitats in central Pennsylvania.

2. SELIGERIA CALCAREA [Dickson] Bryologia Europæa

Densely gregarious, dull, dark green: stems short, less than 1 mm, simple; leaves short, less than 1 mm, the lower lanceolate, the upper from an oblong concave base abruptly narrowed to a shorter, linear, obtuse or sub-obtuse, entire subulation; costa rather flat, indistinct below, above obscure and filling the whole apex; basal leaf-cells shortly rectangular, pellucid, thin-walled, above becoming irregularly quadrate to rounded or hexagonal, obscure, chlorophyllose, incrassate: seta straight, erect; capsule erect, oval-pyriform, turbinate when dry and empty, brownish; peristome-teeth 16, broadly lanceolate, rather densely articulate, flat, entire, smooth, orange-pellucid, reflexed when dry; lid subulate-rostrate but considerably shorter than the urn; spores mature in spring or early summer.

On calcareous or chalky rocks. Europe and, in North America, in Ontario, Lake Winnipeg, New York, and Ohio. Rare.

In our region reported but once. HUNTINGTON CO.: Warrior's Ridge. *Porter*. (Porter's Catalogue).

7. DICRANELLA Schimper

Dioicous, rarely pseudautoicous: mainly small, gregarious, or cespitose, terrestrial: stem erect, thickly foliate, sparsely radiculose; leaves somewhat lustrous, from a sheathing base abruptly subulate and squarrose-spreading, or from a non-sheathing base gradually linear to subulate and stiffly erect to falcate-secund, mostly with plane edges; costa strong; mostly percurrent, often filling the acumen; leaf-cells elongate-rectangular to linear: seta erect; capsule cernuous, unsymmetric, short, short-necked, often strumate, or erect and symmetric; peristome-teeth usually present, mostly unequally subulately 2-3-cleft, papillose above, at the extreme base united to form more or less of a basal membrane, exteriorly finely vertically striate; operculum conic-rostrate or obliquely long-rostrate, sometimes as long or even longer than the urn.

A large and cosmopolitan genus of about 60 species; about 30 species in North America; at least 4 species in our region.

KEY TO THE SPECIES

A. Costa wide and flat and not well-defined at base; peristome weakly papillose; annulus often differentiated ....B

A. Costa narrower and fairly well defined at base; peristome distinctly striate-papillose; annulus not differentiated ....D

   B. Seta red ....(D. crispa [Ehrh.] Schimper)

   B. Seta yellowish C

      D. Capsules erect and symmetric ....1. D. Fitzgeraldi

   C. Capsules more or less cernuous ....2. D. heteromalla

      D. Leaves squarrose, with wide clasping base ....(D. Schreberi [Swartz] Schimper)

      D. Leaves not as above ....E

   E. Leaves squarrose, with wide clasping base ....(D. Schreberi [Swartz] Schimper)

   E. Leaves not as above ....E

   E. Capsule usually nodding ....4. D. varia

   E. Capsule erect ....3. D. rufescens

1. DICRANELLA FITZGERALDI Renauld and Cardot

(*D. heteromalla* var. *orthocarpa* (Hedwig) Paris)

Plate X

Rather densely cespitose, yellowish-green: stem 5-10 mm long, mostly simple, erect, leaves crowded, erect-spreading, sometimes subsecund, about 3-3.5 mm long, up to 0.5 mm broad at base, from the lance-ovate base narrowing above into a long, canaliculate-subulate, denticulate apex; costa at base rather indistinct, about one-fourth to one-third the width of the leaf, strong above and constituting most of the acumination; basal leaf-cells elongate-rectangular or sub-rectangular, reaching 8 x 55 microns, hyaline, a few in the extreme alar portion often quadrate, median cells quadrate: seta erect, yellowish-red, becoming quite dark brownish-red when old, about 7-8 mm long, when dry sinistrorse in the lower half and dextrorse above; capsule erect, symmetric, about .6-.9 x .25-.3 mm, oblong, not constricted below mouth, smooth or nearly so even when dry and empty, when ripe brown; peristome single, the teeth very slightly united below, cleft about half-way into linear-subulate prongs, sometimes sub-cribrose along the divisural, articulate, longitudinally striolate-granulose, towards apex hyaline; spores minutely papillose, about .014-.017 mm, mature in late fall or winter; operculum low-conic with an oblique rostrum.

On soil, soil-covered rocks, etc., in the eastern and southeastern parts of the United States.

ALLEGHENY Co.: Schenley Park, Pittsburgh, August 16, 1905, McKees Rocks, August 27, 1905, and Fern Hollow, Pittsburgh, March 8, 1908 (figured). O.E.J.; Wildwood Road, March 29, 1908. O.E.J. and G.K.J. ARMSTRONG Co.: On clay bank, Logansport. C.M.B. Feb. 22, 1943. BUTLER Co.: Frazier's Mill Jefferson Twp., on ground. S. K. Eastwood. FAYETTE Co.: Ohio Pyle "Peninsula." C.M.B. Oct. 13, 1935. INDIANA Co.: Clay roadside ditch, near Crete. O.E.J. & G.K.J. Nov. 2, 1941.

2. DICRANELLA HETEROMALLA [Dillenius] Schimper

(*Dicranum heteromallum* Hedwig)

Plate XI

Cespitose, bright yellowish to dark green; stem erect or ascending, 0.5-3.0 cm tall: leaves numerous, lance-subulate, concave, 2-3 mm long, denticulate towards the apex, usually also denticulate dorsally towards the apex; costa strong, one-fifth to one-third the width of the leaf at base, percurrent, bordered towards the apex by a narrow margin of lamina; leaf-cells parenchymatous, at leaf-base 2-5 times as long as wide, rectangular, brownish, narrower towards the margin, the upper cells shorter and often obliquely quadrilateral; seta 1.5-2.5 cm long, greenish-yellow, dextrorse; capsule smooth, about 1.5 mm long, oblong, castaneous to dark brown, more or less erect, usually slightly curved, when dry bent and curved in at the upper part just below the rim on one side in a very characteristic manner, furrowed; operculum hemispheric, with a linear obliquely inclined beak about 1 mm long; peristome-teeth red, bifid to below the middle or about to the middle, sometimes trifid, with somewhat projecting trabeculæ, articulate, minutely papillose-striate, hyaline and papillose at apex; exothecial cells incrassate, irregularly elongate-rectangular to oblong-hexagonal, the end-walls thinner than the lateral walls, two to four rows of cells at the rim much smaller and rounded; spores .010-.015 mm, yellowish-incrassate, mature in autumn.

Common, especially in hilly or mountainous districts, on rocks, clay banks, soil-covered logs, etc. Europe, Asia, and, in North America, from Canada to the Gulf States.

A very common moss on soil in the southwestern part of the State from Erie to eastern Somerset and Greene counties (13 counties) but as yet known only from Cameron and Centre counties on the elevated plateaus and mountains. Specimen figured: "Rachelwood," slope of Laurel Ridge, southeast of New Florence. Sept. 8-11, 1907, O.E.J.

3. DICRANELLA RUFESCENS [Dickson] Schimper
Plates XI and LX

Rather loosely cespitose, reddish- to yellowish-green: stems erect, in our region generally very short, reddish, about 3 mm or less high, mostly simple; leaves few, linear-lanceolate, sometimes reaching 1.5 mm long, gradually narrowed, minutely denticulate towards apex, plane, erect-spreading or sometimes sub-secund; costa narrow, about one-seventh to one fifth the width of the leaf-base, percurrent; basal leaf-cells large, hyaline, smooth, thin-walled, quadrate-rectangular to linear-rectangular, reaching 8-10 times as long as wide, median cells shorter and smaller but similar, the percurrent costa margined by cells similar to the median: seta erect, red, about 3-5 mm long, dextrorse when dry; capsule globose-ovoid, erect, red, symmetrical, smooth to slightly wrinkled when dry, the urn wide-mouthed and more or less turbinate; operculum obliquely conic-rostrate, nearly as long as urn (0.5 mm); calyptra cucullate, smooth, yellowish-red, narrowly conic, about 0.8 mm long; peristome pellucid red-chestnut in color; teeth bifid about half-way, articulate, irregularly and finely longitudinally striate-papillose; spores globose, smooth, orange-pellucid, about .012-.015 mm, mature in late summer or fall.

Usually on damp, bare soil, in Europe, Asia, and, in North America, from Alaska to Nova Scotia and southwards to Virginia.

Rather common in our region. Now known from the following counties: Allegheny, Beaver, Butler, Cambria (Porter), Elk (Porter), Fayette, Huntingdon (Porter), Indiana, McKean. Specimen figured: Clay soil on upper slope of Laurel Mt., above New Florence, Sept. 8-11, 1907. O.E.J.; and for the perigonial shoots, clay bank of ditch, Elder's Ridge, O.E.J. & G.K.J. Nov. 2, 1941.

4. DICRANELLA VARIA [Hedwig] Schimper
Plate XI

Densely gregarious to cespitose, bright to yellowish-green; stems short, usually about 5-7 mm high, ascending to erect, branching at base; leaves up to 2.5 mm long, linear-lanceolate, gradually narrowed to a long-linear acumination, spreading to recurved, not very secund, when dry somewhat flexuous, margin narrowly revolute, entire, excepting sometimes at the very apex somewhat denticulate; costa wide and not well-defined, percurrent and comprising a large portion of the acumen; basal leaf-cells rather thin-walled, rectangular or with oblique end-walls, 2-6:1, gradually becoming smaller and narrower above, the upper being about 2-4:1 and somewhat incrassate, all smooth and more or less yellowish-pellucid: seta yellowish-brown to castaneous, ascending to erect, about 5-8 mm long, sinistrorse; capsule ovate to oblong, more or less cernuous, reddish to pale castaneous, curved, smooth, together with lid about 1-1.25 mm long; lid about as long as urn, rostellate; peristome-teeth large, lance-subulate, cleft to middle, strongly articulate, finely striate-papillose, rich castaneous below, sub-hyaline above; spores yellowish, rather thick-walled, minutely roughened, .020-.024 mm, mature in late autumn or in winter.

On bare clay soil in fields, on ledges, etc. Widely distributed in the Northern Hemisphere; in North America from Nova Scotia to Alaska and south to Georgia and the subtropics.

ALLEGHENY CO.: In niches on cliff, Powers Run, November 30, 1909 (figured). O.E.J. BUTLER CO.: On moist shale in railroad cut, Wahlville. Sept. 22, 1935. Sidney K. Eastwood. McKEAN CO.: Bennett Brook, October 23, 1897. D.A.B. WASHINGTON CO.: On shale near creek, west of Taylortown. Nov. 5, 1892. A. Linn and J. S. Simonton.

8. RHABDOWEISIA Bryologia Europæa

Autoicous: low, densely cespitose: stem without central strand, in cross-section obtusely pentagonal, densely foliate, radiculose, branched; leaves when dry crisped, decurrent, linear to linear-lanceolate, acute, plane-margined; costa strong, disappearing below the apex; upper leaf-cells chlorophyllose, quadrate to rounded, smooth; basal cells rectangular and hyaline: seta straw-yellow, erect; capsule erect, minute, symmetric, ovate to oblong, obtusely octagonal with darker striæ, 8-costate when dry; annulus none; peristome rarely absent, inserted on the rim; teeth arising from low, broad, more or less united bases, abruptly filiform or subulate, reddish-yellow, trabeculæ prominent ventrally but articulations scarcely projecting dorsally, surface of teeth non-papillose but often obliquely minutely striate; operculum long-subulate, obliquely rostrate, as long or longer than the urn; calyptra cucullate, rostrate, reaching to the middle of the capsule.

About 8 species of the Northern Hemisphere, inhabiting crevices of silicious rocks; 5 species in North America; 2 species in our region.

KEY TO THE SPECIES

A. Leaves entire or nearly so ....1. R. denticulata
A. Leaves rather coarsely denticulate towards the apex ....2. R. denticulata var. americana

1. RHABDOWEISIA DENTICULATA (Bridel) Bryologia Europæa
(Weisia fugax Am. Auth.)
Plate XI

Densely cespitose, usually dark green: stems short, in ours about 5 mm high, radiculose at base; leaves lance-linear, recurved-spreading, numerous, about 2-2.5 mm long, usually somewhat concave, acute to shortly acuminate, margins plane, somewhat denticulate towards apex, leaves crisped when dry; costa strong but not quite reaching apex; upper leaf-cells rounded-hexagonal, about .010-.014 mm, incrassate, chlorophyllose, papillose, rather yellow, arranged in rows, in the upper part of the leaf about 6 or 8 rows on either side of the costa, the apical cells larger and more hyaline, the basal cells pellucid and elongate-rectangular, about 2-8:1: seta erect, 2-3 mm high, yellowish; capsule erect, symmetric, oval; the urn wide-mouthed, about 0.5-0.7 mm high, brownish, when dry and empty 16-striate; operculum about as long as urn, obliquely rostrate from a broad base; peristome-teeth rather abruptly subulate from a broad base, small, not very persistent, articulate, papillose; spores about .018-.020 mm, minutely roughened, yellowish-pellucid, maturing in mid-summer; calyptra cucullate, covering about two-thirds of the urn; exothecal cells yellowish, incrassate, irregularly oblong to rectangular, the upper two to four rows much smaller and rounded.

In crevices in various kinds of rocks, in moist, shady cliffs, mountains from Canada to North Carolina and Missouri.

FAYETTE Co.: On sandstone rocks near Bear Run falls, Oct. 30, 1935. Adam M. Barker. LAWRENCE Co.: Slippery Rock Creek. Wm. James. (Porter's Catalogue). Mc-KEAN Co.: Sandstone rocks between Hawkins and Rutherford hollows, March 12, 1894; and Toad Hollow, July 19, 1896, and August 1, 1897. D.A.B.

This moss occurs on the sandstone cliffs of Chestnut Ridge six miles south of the Pennsylvania-West Virginia state line. July 4, 1909. O.E.J. & G.K.J. (figured).

2. RHABDOWEISIA DENTICULATA var. AMERICANA Culman

Closely similar to the species but with the leaves narrower and narrowly acute, entire or only slightly denticulate.

We have seen no specimens of this variety from our region although Grout reports it as occurring with the species and refers most of the collections to it.

9. ONCOPHORUS Bridel

Autoicous: rather large, cespitose in broad, soft, bright green or yellowish-green tufts, usually radiculose below: stems thickly foliate; leaves when dry crisped, when moist ascending to squarrose, from a sheathing base more or less abruptly long-acuminate or subulate, concave, carinate; costa strong, per-current or excurrent; cells in the sheathing base of the leaf long-rectangular, translucent to hyaline, the alar sometimes somewhat differentiated, the laminal cells small, mostly rounded-quadrate, at the margin bi-stratose; perichætial leaves sheathing to above the middle, abruptly subulate: seta long, erect; capsule unsymmetric, strumose with a short collum, when empty more or less weakly sulcate; annulus indistinct; peristome-teeth 16, deeply inserted, approximate, united below into a tube which is adherent to the wall of the capsule, the teeth 2-(3)-divided to the middle, outwardly minutely papillose in longitudinal lines, the inner surface with 1 (or 2) delicate longitudinal lines and strongly projecting transverse plates; operculum at least half as long as the capsule, obliquely rostrate; calyptra cucullate.

A genus of 5 species widely distributed on damp gravelly soil, on moist non-calcareous rocks, or on decaying logs. Only one known species in our range.

1. ONCOPHORUS WAHLENBERGII Bridel
Plate XII

Densely cespitose, light or yellowish-green above, darker below: stem ascending or erect, forking, up to 3 cm high, sparsely radiculose below; leaves numerous, dense, much crisped when dry, abruptly flexuous-spreading when moist, from a concave, widely obovate base abruptly contracting into a long, carinate, linear-subulate, flexuous, rather acute portion which is low-serrate at the apex both marginally and dorsally; costa strong, ending in the apex; leaf-cells at base mostly pellucid and obliquely elongate-rectangular, about 3-10:1, above at the shoulder and along the subulation quickly becoming much smaller, incrassate, about .005-.007 mm in diameter, smooth, sometimes faintly rounded papillose: seta single, erect, flexuous, yellowish to brownish, when dry strongly dextrorse, 1-1.5 cm long; capsule about 1.2 mm long, arcuate-cernuous, oblong-cylindric, gibbous, distinctly sharply strumose, when old irregularly wrinkled; peristome-teeth united at base into a rather deeply inserted tube, the teeth divided to the middle, lance-linear, castaneous-pellucid, very faintly dorsally articulate below, strongly ventrally trabeculate in a double series separated by a more or less zig-zag divisural line, at the base smooth, towards the middle minutely vertically striate-papillose, at the apex sub-hyaline; annulus narrow with crenulate margin; operculum obliquely rostrate; exothecial cells irregular, rather lax, with medium walls, not much different towards the mouth; spores papillose, castaneous-pellucid, about .028-.030 mm, mature in spring.

On rocks, soil, or mostly on old logs, in cool and moist situations, usually in the mountains in non-calcareous districts. Europe, Asia, and, in North America, from Greenland to Alaska and south to Pennsylvania and Ohio; and Wyoming.

Rare in our region. McKEAN Co.: Broadbow, D.A.B. (figured.)

10. DICRANUM Hedwig

Autoicous or dioicous; mostly large and thickly tufted, often cushion-like: stems mostly erect; leaves mainly falcate-secund, more or less subulate-acuminate from a concave, lanceolate base, and usually canaliculate to tubulose; costa largely excurrent; alar leaf-cells mostly brownish and differentiated; inner perichætial leaves elongate, involute-sheathing, the acumen often short or lacking: seta erect, mostly twisted, sometimes 2 to 5 together in a perichætium; capsule various from cylindric and erect to cernuous and arcuate or even rarely strumose; operculum long-rostrate and by a differentiated annulus always with a notched edge; peristome not inserted below the edge of the capsule; teeth mostly 2-3-parted to the middle, vertically striate below, ventrally trabeculate; calyptra not ciliate at base.

A cosmopolitan genus as here treated of about 150 species, mostly on non-calcareous sub-strata, in the tropics confined to the mountains and rather rare in the Southern Hemipshere. In North America about 40 species are known and at least 6 species occur in our region.

Key to the Species

A. Capsule cernuous, unsymmetric ....B
A. Capsule erect, symmetric ....G
   B. Leaf-cells porose C
   B. Leaf-cells very slightly or not at all porose ....(*D. condensatum* Hedw.)
C. Leaves transversely undulate; costa not reaching, or vanishing in apex ....D
C. Leaves not transversely undulate; costa percurrent to excurrent ....F
   D. Upper leaf-cells elongated ....1. *D. rugosum*
   D. Upper leaf-cells iso-diametric ....E
E. Capsule solitary; costa and lamina dorsally smooth ....(*D. Bergeri* Bland.)
E. Capsules clustered; costa and lamina dorsally rough ....(*D. Drummondii* C. M.)
   F. Capsules clustered; guides of costa in two rows; leaves up to 15 mm long ....
      ....(*D. majus* Smith.)
   F. Capsules solitary; guides of costa in one row; leaves up to 8 or 9 mm long ....
      ....2. *D. scoparium**
G. Costa with median guides ....H
G. Costa without median guides, 2-4 stratose ....6. *D. longifolium*
   H. Entire lamina uni-stratose; costa percurrent I
   H. Upper lamina more or less bi-stratose; costa excurrent ....J
   I. Upper leaf-cells short rectangular and mamillate dorsally ....3. *D. montanum*
   I. Upper leaf-cells less regular, not mamillate ....4. *D. flagellare*
   J. Costa and margin entire, apex usually broken off ....5a. *D. fulvum* var. *viride*
   J. Costa and margin serrulate ....5. *D. fulvum*

1. Dicranum rugosum (Hoffm.) Bridel

(*D. polysetum* Swartz, Schwaegrichen; *D. undulatum* Ehrhart)

Plate LXI

Tall, up to 20 cm. or more, loosely cespitose: stems erect or decumbent, densely radiculose below; leaves undulate, lustrous yellowish-green; 6-9 mm long, lanceolate, the upper half spinosely serrate, the lower half with recurved margin; costa strong, rather narrow, vanishing in the apex, with two serrate dorsal lamellae above; alar cells distinct, brownish, not reaching costa, median and upper leaf-cells elongate-elliptic to linear-fusiform, incrassate and porose: seta long, reddish, usually 2-5 in a cluster; capsule arcuate-cernuous, rather small, when dry and empty striate and brown; spores mature in late summer or early fall.

On moist soil and on humus-covered rocks in moist and shady woods, usually in hilly or mountainous regions. Europe, Asia, and, in North America, in the northern United States and in Canada.

Apparently rare in our region. Huntington Co.: *Porter*. (Porter's Catalogue). Somerset Co.: 12 mi. s.w. of Somerset. C. M. Hepner, Dec. 1, 1933 (figured). Washington Co.: In sandy soils in woods, near Washington. A. Linn and J. S. Simonton.

---

* *Dicranum Bonjeani* DeNot., is regarded by Grout as a subspecies of *D. scoparium*, and separated as follows:

  Leaf-apex slender, strongly serrate, strongly falcate-secund (except some varieties), leaves not undulate ....2. *D. scoparium*

  Leaf-apex broad, often obtuse; leaves laxly spreading, rarely secund (except var. *alatum*), sometimes slightly undulate ....2a. *D. Bonjeani*

2. DICRANUM SCOPARIUM [Linnaeus] Hedwig
(*Bryum scoparium* Linnaeus)
Plate XII

Large, rather loosely tufted, glossy, yellowish-green, often brownish below: stems growing upwards and dying away below, often 7 or 8 cm long, densely felted-radiculose; leaves falcate-secund, often more or less tufted at the upper end of the innovations, about 8-12 mm long, linear-subulate, not undulate, concave, serrate towards apex, little changed when dry; costa strong, flat, one-fourth to one-third the width of the leaf at base, above bearing four serrate dorsal lamellae; leaf-cells at base enlarged, quadrate to rectangular, rather thin-walled, orange-colored, the median elongate rectangular to somewhat linear, incrassate, porose, the apical irregularly oblong, not porose: seta about 3 cm long, erect-sinuose, yellowish to chestnut-brown, lighter below, usually sinistrorse, sometimes dextrose above; capsule 3.5-4 mm long, about 0.8 mm thick, chestnut-brown, cylindric, arcuate, when dry furrowed and slightly constricted below the mouth, tapering below into a short neck, exannulate; operculum low-conic, subulate-rostrate the beak about 2.5 mm long; calyptra about 6-7 mm long, cucullate, conic-rostrate, peristome single; teeth pellucid, reddish-brown, papillose above, below strongly articulate and vertically striate, divided about one-half into 2 or 3 lance-subulate prongs, sometimes more or less cribrose; spores globose, slightly roughened, about .020-.024 mm, mature in late summer or early fall.

On soil, logs, rocks, etc., in woods. Europe, Asia, and, in North America, throughout the cooler and temperate regions.

Quite common in our region. Known from Allegheny, Armstrong, Beaver, Bedford, Butler, Cambria, Cameron, Centre, Clinton, Erie, Fayette, Forest, Greene, Huntingdon, McKean, Somerset, Venango, Warren, Washington, and Westmoreland counties. Specimen figured: Ohio Pyle, Fayette Co., Sept. 1-3, 1907. O.E.J. & G.K.J.

2a. DICRANUM BONJEANI DeNot.

A specimen collected by C. M. Boardman on a talus slide one-half mile north of Sulphur Springs, Bedford Co., Pa., approaches *D. scoparium* very closely.

3. DICRANUM MONTANUM Hedwig
Plate XII

Densely cespitose, bluish to light yellowish-green, lustrous: stems erect, short, up to 1 cm in our region, sparsely branching; leaves much crisped when dry, in the same cushion some of the plants with equally-spreading leaves, others with all secund leaves, from a wider base gradually narrowly linear-lanceolate, up to 5 mm long, concave below and canaliculate above to near the apex, on margin and back of costa serrulate above; costa rather strong, percurrent or almost excurrent, forming about one-fourth to one-fifth of the width of the leaf at base; median leaf-cells shortly rectangular-quadrate to laterally oblong, incrassate, yellowish, the upper somewhat smaller and rounded-quadrate, more or less distinctly papillose, the basal rectangular, thinner-walled, up to 6:1, the alar not much larger but quadrate-inflated, all the basal cells often more or less castaneous in color; perichaetial leaves similar to stem leaves; seta single, erect, yellowish to brownish, about 1.5 cm high; capsule oblong-cylindric, slightly curved, yellowish to finally brownish, plicate when dry and empty, the urn about 2.5 mm long; the lid conic, more or less obliquely rostrate, about 1.5 mm long, castaneous; annulus narrow; peristome-teeth cleft to below the middle or nearly to the base into linear-subulate, deeply castaneous, articulate, faintly trabeculate, striate-papillose divisions; exothecial cells yellowish-incrassate, irregularly oblong to rectangular, the upper 3-6 rows much smaller, more deeply colored and incrassate, rounded-quadrate or hexagonal; spores smoothish, yellowish, about .022-.025 mm, not very thick-walled, maturing in early fall.

Mostly on rotten wood and on roots and trunks of trees, or on rocks. Europe, Asia, and, in North America, from Newfoundland to Tennessee and westward to the Rocky Mountains.

Now known from Bedford, Butler, Elk, Erie, Huntingdon, Indiana, Fayette, and Somerset counties. Figured from specimen from Ohio Pyle, on rotten log, O.E.J. and G.K.J.

4. DICRANUM FLAGELLARE Hedwig

Plate XII

Rather densely cespitose, bright green above, brownish below, tufts about 1 cm high: stem radiculose, often with flagellae in the axils of the upper leaves, erect; leaves crisped and sub-secund when dry, falcate-secund when moist, from an oblong base narrowed gradually into a subulate acumen, strongly involute to near the apex, apex serrate; costa strong, about one-fourth to one-third the width of the leaf-base, percurrent, serrate dorsally at the apex; alar leaf-cells large, distinct, inflated-quadrate, rather thin-walled, colored, reaching nearly to the costa, the leaf-cells above loosely elongate-rectangular, farther above becoming shorter, above the middle rounded-quadrate, incrassate; perichaetial leaves shorter, abruptly subulate-acuminate from a sheathing base: seta erect, sinistrorse when dry; reddish to yellowish-brown, about 2 cm. long; capsule erect, cylindric, symmetric, reddish-brown, about 2.5 mm long, when dry striate and often slightly curved; lid obliquely long-rostrate, lustrous, brown; peristome-teeth trabeculate, articulate, confluent at base, cleft to two-thirds to three-fourths, the lower two-thirds reddish and more or less vertically striate-papillose, hyaline above; annulus delicate; exothecial cells elongate, strongly laterally incrassate with thinner end-walls, several series at the rim much smaller and rounded-quadrate; calyptra reaching to the middle of the capsule, fugacious; spores globose, slightly roughened, yellow-incrassate, .018-.022 mm in diameter, mature in summer.

On decayed logs and stumps and on bases of trees in moist woods. In Europe, Asia, and, in North America, from Nova Scotia to British Columbia and south to the Carolinas and Mexico.

Rather common in our region. Known from Beaver, Bedford, Blair, Butler, Cambria, Cameron, Erie, Fayette, Forest, Huntingdon (Porter), McKean, Somerset, Washington, and Westmoreland counties. Specimen figured: Mellon Estate (Rachelwood) near New Florence. Sept. 8-10, 1907. O.E.J.

5. DICRANUM FULVUM Hooker

(*D. interruptum* Bryologia Europaea)

Plate XIII

Deeply but rather loosely cespitose, fulvous to brownish-green: stem ascending to erect, sparsely branching, radiculose at base; leaves numerous, secund, somewhat crisped when dry, about 5-6 mm long, gradually narrowed, from a concave lanceolate base to a linear-acuminate more or less concave to canaliculate apex, the upper margin serrulate; costa strong, about one-third of leaf-width at base, usually somewhat excurrent, dorsally serrulate above, in the long acumination occupying most of the leaf; median and upper leaf-cells quadrate to shortly rectangular, strongly yellowish-incrassate, the lower rectangular, not porose at base, becoming in the alar portion enlarged, inflated, rectangular to quadrate, thin-walled, brownish, this alar area reaching usually to the costa; perichaetial leaves linear-subulate from a broadly sheathing base: seta single, rather stout, erect, flexuous, yellowish to dark with age, about 1-1.5 cm long; capsule erect, symmetric to slightly curved, the urn about 4 mm long, cylindric, castaneous, sulcate when dry and empty; lid stoutly and more or less obliquely rostrate and about 1.5 mm long; annulus rather narrow; exothecial cells yellowish-incrassate, quadrate to rectangular or oblong-hexagonal, several rows below the mouth much smaller and rounded-quadrate-hexagonal; spores large, .024-.030 mm, smoothish, rather thin-walled, mature in autumn.

Generally on non-calcareous rocks in moist woods among the hills or mountains, often on the face of sandstone cliffs; Europe and North America from Nova Scotia and North Carolina west to the Mississippi River.

Rather common in our region. Now known from Butler, Fayette, Greene, McKean, Warren, and Westmoreland counties. Figured from specimen collected from rock in woods, Ohio Pyle. Sept. 1-3, 1906. O.E.J. & G.K.J.

5a. DICRANUM FULVUM var. VIRIDE (Sull. & Lesq. Grout

(*D. viride* Lindberg)

Plate XIII

Densely cespitose, yellowish-green to dark green or sometimes almost blackish: stems ascending, up to 2 cm high, simple or sparsely branching, radiculose below; leaves 3-4 mm long, spreading or recurved, when dry crisped, the apices usually found broken off, the leaves close, gradually linear-acuminate from a lanceolate base, concave below, the acumination often concave or canaliculate, the margin entire or slightly denticulate at apex; costa strong, percurrent or excurrent, at base comprising from one-fourth to one-third the width of the leaf; median and upper leaf-cells more or less regularly quadrate, small, incrassate, towards base slightly larger, but not much longer than broad, nonporose, suddenly becoming enlarged, thin-walled, brownish, and rectangular up to 3:1, the alar inflated and sometimes extending to the costa: capsule oblong, erect or slightly curved. Not seen in fruit in our region.

On decayed logs and on bases of trees in woods, rarely on rocks, in Europe, Asia, and, in North America, from Newfoundland to the Rocky Mountains, south to Pennsylvania and Ohio.

Known from the following counties: Allegheny, Butler, Cambria (Porter), Fayette, McKean, Washington, and Westmoreland. Specimen figured: Base of *Tilia americana*, Brush Creek Swamp, Crider's Corner's, Allegheny-Butler county line, April 26, 1908. O.E.J.

6. Dicranum longifolium [Ehrhart] Hedwig
(*Paraleucobryum longifolium* (Hedwig) Loeske)

Plate XIII

Densely cespitose, pale green, glossy: stems more or less deeply castaneous, ascending, geniculate at intervals, at least 3-5 cm long, sparingly brownish-tomentose below; leaves lustrous, pale green, yellowish-green and hardly altered when dry, falcate-secund, about 5-8 mm long, linear-subulate, from a short lanceolate base about one-fourth the length of the leaf, at the base reddish or brownish, non-decurrent; costa wide, comprising about one-third the width of the leaf-base, somewhat narrowed at insertion, the upper three-fourths of the leaf consisting entirely of the linear-subulate, canaliculate, more or less spinose-denticulate, excurrent costa; alar leaf-cells lax, rather thin-walled and hyaline, sometimes brownish, rounded and extending to the costa, the laminal cells immediately above with medium walls, obliquely oblong-angular, narrower towards the margin and farther above becoming smaller and rhomboid-quadrate along the margin to elongate-rectangular near the costa: capsule cylindric, erect, nearly straight, smooth, produced but rarely.

On tree-trunks and on non-calcareous rocks in hilly or mountainous regions, in Europe, Asia, and, in North America, from Greenland and British Columbia south to Colorado and North Carolina.

Rare in our region. McKean Co.: Bradford, 1896. Sterile. D.A.B. (figured). Washington Co.: On root of beech tree near Washington. Dec., 1891. Linn & Simonton.

11. Dicranodontium Bryologia Europaea

Dioicous: tall mosses mostly in dense tufts, the stems and often the basal portion of the costa on the under side felted-radiculose: leaves weakly or not at all auriculate, from the lanceolate base long-subulate, canaliculate-tubulose, the acumen often plainly toothed on the margin and dorsal surface of the costa by reason of the mammillate cells; costa broad and flat, long, excurrent, and almost filling the acumen; alar cells reaching the costa, inflated, hyaline, sometimes reddish, delicate, areolation above the alar cells widened towards the costa and rectangular to long-hexagonal, at the margin usually united into a more or less broad border; perichaetial leaves sheathing, abruptly long-subulate: seta arcuate, finally erect-flexuous; capsule symmetric, oblong-cylindric, smooth; annulus not differentiated; peristome inserted below the edge of the capsule-mouth; teeth separate, two-parted deeply, or to the base, the divisions filiform-subulate, below vertically and above obliquely striate-papillose; calyptra cucullate.

A cosmopolitan genus of 21 species; 5 species in North America; 3 species occurring in our region.

KEY TO THE SPECIES

A. Leaves smoothish to serrulate not over half-way down ....B.
A. Leaves serrulate to well below the middle ....(D. asperulum)
  B. Peristome-teeth cleft to the base; leaves with somewhat widened auricles ....
  ....1. D. denudatum
  B. Peristome-teeth not cleft to base; leaves not auriculate c
  C. Leaves easily caducous; seta 1.5-2 cm; urn 1.5-2 mm long ....2. D. virginicum
  C. Leaves rather persistent; seta 5-8 mm; urn 1 mm long ....3. D. Millspaughii

1. DICRANODONTIUM DENUDATUM (Bridel) E. G. Britton
(Didymodon longirostris Starke)
Plate XIII

Densely and softly cespitose, lustrous, pale green, when dried as in herbarium-specimens often a lustrous yellowish-brown: stems erect or ascending, up to 3 or 4 cm high, forking frequently, flexuous, radiculose below; leaves rather numerous, often quickly deciduous, from a more or less sheathing oblong concave base with more or less widened auricles gradually narrowed to a long, flexuous-spreading or falcate-secund, linear-subulate or setaceous, tubulose point, the margin entire to faintly denticulate towards the apex; costa strong, one-fifth to one-third the width of the leaf at base, excurrent in the rough subulation, in cross-section showing a median row of large hyaline cells bordered on either side by minute incrassate cells; alar leaf-cells large, inflated, hyaline to brownish, rectangular, above becoming incrassate and narrower, in the oblong base the upper marginal cells elongate-linear and more or less prosenchymatous, the median and upper rounded-quadrate, varying to short-rectangular or oblong: seta cygneous, dextrorse; capsule oblong-cylindric, small; peristome-teeth cleft to the base or nearly so into two filiform divisions, inserted below the mouth of the urn, reddish; lid as long as the urn, subulate-rostrate, straight; spores mature in late fall or in winter: dioicous.

On sandstone rocks, walls, turfy places, etc., usually in hilly or mountainous regions. Europe, Asia, and, in North America, from New Brunswick and Alaska south to Ohio and Pennsylvania.

Rare and usually sterile in our region, often on the vertical face of heavy conglomerate boulders. FAYETTE Co.: Mouth of Cucumber Run, Ohio Pyle. C.M.B. June 22 and Oct. 20. 1940. FOREST Co.: Vertical face of s.s. block, Blue Jay Creek, 1 mi. n. of Frost. C.M.B. May 28, 1946. McKEAN Co.: Rutherford Rocks, July 7, 1894, Hawkins, October 18, 1895, Langmade Rocks, April 16, 1896, all in the vicinity of Bradford. D.A.B. (figured). SOMERSET Co.: Face of dry rock, Beck Spring, Laurel Mt. C.M.B. July 26, 1947.

2. DICRANODONTIUM VIRGINICUM E. G. Britton

Lustrous, bright green: stems ascending to erect, below red-tomentose; leaves erect-spreading to secund, variously straight to curled or twisted, often 5 mm. long, narrowly concave-subulate from a short, thick, non-auriculate base, often caducous, the caducous leaves usually with smooth points, the persistent ones with serrulate points; alar cells more or less hyaline, the median and upper rectangular to quadrate, incrassate; seta appearing lateral by growth of innovations, flexuous, up to 2 cm long, lustrous, yellow, arcuate to erect;

capsule cylindric, 1.5 to 2 mm long; peristome-teeth deep red, not deeply inserted, split about to the middle, papillose-striate at base, sub-hyaline above; no annulus; lid subulate-rostrate, shorter than the urn, straight or curved; calyptra cucullate, rostrate, covering only the upper third of urn; spores small, mature in summer: dioicous, antheridia terminal.

At the southern border of our region, on sandstone boulder along wooded path, Tibbs Run, Monongalia County, West Virginia. C. F. Millspaugh. Both Williams and Grout regard this as the same as *D. denudatum*.

3.   DICRANODONTIUM MILLSPAUGHII E. G. Britton

Silky, cespitose, yellowish-green; stems rufous-tomentose at base, up to 3 cm long; leaves erect-spreading to secund, up to 5 mm long, from a broad, concave, non-auriculate base narrowly tubulose-subulate; costa strong, excurrent into a linear tip, dentate marginally and dorsally; alar leaf-cells large, hyaline, mainly quadrate to shortly rectangular, extending to the costa, above quickly smaller, incrassate, tending to fusiform-prosenchymatous towards the margin, shorter to quadrate in the upper part of the lamina: seta cygneous, erect when old, 5-8 mm long, stout; capsule pyriform-cylindric, smooth, the urn about 1 mm long; peristome-teeth deeply inserted, red, confluent at base, split to the middle or perforate to the base, papillose-striolate below, paler above; no annulus but the rim of the urn dark colored; lid about as long as the urn (1 mm), straight, subulate-rostrate; spores maturing in summer; dioicous.

At the southern border of our region on sandstone rock in deep woods along Tibbs Run, Monongalia County, West Virginia. C. F. Millspaugh. Both Williams and Grout regard this the same as *D. denudatum*.

Family 3.   LEUCOBRYACEAE

Dioicous, rarely autoicous; densely cespitose and more or less spongy like *Sphagnum*, whitish to glaucous-green: stem without central strand, scarcely radiculose; leaves pluriseriate, close, quite uniform in size; costa very broad, constituting most of the leaf, sometimes narrow with a stereid-bundle, composed of two kinds of cells, the outer large and parenchymatous with perforated inner walls, the inner smaller and chlorophyllose, the lamina hyaline, usually very narrow and mainly basal: seta single, erect; capsule erect and symmetric or inclined, unsymmetric and strumose; annulus none; peristome usually inserted below the edge of the urn, the teeth mostly 16, sometimes only 8, lanceolate, articulate, entire or cleft to the middle; operculum conic, rostrate; calyptra cucullate or sometimes mitrate.

With the exception of the genus *Leucobryum* the species of this family are mostly tropical or sub-tropical in their distribution and occur mainly on trees.   In our region there occurs only the following genus:

1.   LEUCOBRYUM Hampe

Dioicous: thickly to loosely cespitose; whitish or glaucous green, mostly lustrous: leaves erect, when dry appressed and brittle, sometimes spiral, or falcate, or squarrose-spreading, from an ovate base lanceolate- to subulate-acuminate, canaliculate or sometimes almost tubulose above; costa flat, the large parenchymatous outer cells 2-6-layered; lamina mostly narrow, often vanishing below the apex, without a border; perichaetial leaves half-sheathing and long-acuminate: seta terminal, or lateral by the growth of innovations, long; capsule more or less arcuate, unsymmetric, often strumose, with 8 rib-like projecting ridges; peristome on the edge of the urn, the teeth united at base into a tube, cleft to the middle into two lance-subulate prongs, thickly trabeculate, vertically striate and papillose; operculum subulate from a conical base; calyptra inflated, cucullate, covering the urn.

About 100 species, mostly in the tropics, on trees, rocks, or on shaded earth; 8 in North America; 2 species in our range.

KEY TO THE SPECIES

A. Leucocyst on the median line in 3 to 4 layers; leaves 3 to 9 mm long: capsules arcu-
ate, strumose ....1. *L. glaucum*
A. Leucocysts on the median line in 2 layers in 4 to 14 series; leaves 1 to 4 mm long:
capsule almost erect, not strumose ....2. *L. albidum*

1. LEUCOBRYUM GLAUCUM [Linnaeus] W. P. Schimper
(*Dicranum glaucum* Hedwig)
PINCUSHION MOSS —WHITE MOSS
Plate XIV

In dense, rounded, spongy, whitish or glaucous tufts, often 6 or 7 cm deep, only the upper 5 mm or thereabouts alive, the dead inner portion grayish-brown and peaty: leaves crowded, in our region about 3-6 mm long, more or less tubular somewhat more than halfway down, acute, entire, ovate-lanceolate, narrowed at base, erect-appressed, consisting almost wholly of the broad, thick costa, the lamina extending about half-way up the leaf as a narrow margin of 2-5 rows of hyaline, thin-walled, long-rectangular to linear cells: seta about 10 mm long, sinistrorse, castaneous, erect; capsule 1.5 to 2 mm long, castaneous, when dry arcuate, oblong-cylindric, distinctly strumose, furrowed; lid long-rostrate, nearly as long as the urn; calyptra longer than the capsule; peristome slightly inserted, deep reddish-brown, dicranoid; spores rather thin-walled, slightly roughened, .015-.020 mm in diameter, slightly roughened, mature in autumn. Capsules are produced infrequently.

Almost cosmopolitan on soil or on rocks in woods. In North America it occurs from Newfoundland to Florida and westward to the Mississippi River. Common in our region, especially preferring the somewhat acid soil of exposed white oak wooded upper slopes, often thus associated with *Kalmia* and some of the wild huckleberries.

Now known from 19 counties in western Pennsylvania and probably occurs in all. Specimen figured; Barrens, Scotia, Centre County. Sept. 23, 1909. O.E.J.

2. LEUCOBRYUM ALBIDUM [Bridel] Lindberg
(*L. minus* Hampe; *Dicranum albidum* Bridel)

Much smaller than *L. glaucum;* tufts very dense, about 1-3 cm deep; leaves acute, narrower, shorter (about 1-4 mm long), closely imbricated and but little spreading at the tip, the tubulose apex usually shorter than the broad base: capsule almost symmetric, little or not at all inclined, slightly or not at all strumose.

On stumps, logs, or on the ground, Europe and in the eastern part of the United States.

Rare in our region. HUNTINGDON CO.: *Porter.* (Porter's Catalogue). WESTMORE-LAND CO.: A sterile specimen from near Bear Cave, Chestnut Ridge, Hillside. September 17, 1909. O.E.J. and G.K.J.

Family 4.   FISSIDENTACEAE

Autoicous or dioicous: minute to large, gregarious to cespitose, mostly green: stem oval, mostly with central strand, basally radiculose, or with reddish rhizoids from the leaf-axils; leaves distichous, mostly vertically placed, so that they stand edgewise to the stem with a clasping sheath at the base, or extending well up the leaf, and a dorsal lamina which is often somewhat decurrent, the apical lamina being lacking in the perichaetial and lowest stem leaves and little developed in *Bryoxiphium;* costa usually present; leaf-cells small, uniform, rounded hexagonal, chlorophyllose: seta erect or cygneous, usually elongated; capsule erect and symmetric, or cernuous and unsymmetric or curved, smooth, collum present; annulus present or none; peristome present, except in *Bryoxiphium,* usually inserted, simple, red; teeth articulate, united at base, cleft to the middle or below into two or three filiform divisions, trabeculate with two series of projecting transverse plates, yellowish; spores mostly small; operculum more or less rostrate; calyptra small, narrowly conical, entire or cleft on one side, rarely several times cleft, mostly smooth.

A family of over 700 species, largely tropical, with widely varied habitats, represented in our range by three genera.

KEY TO THE GENERA

A. Dorsal lamina very narrow: peristome none: stem radiculose-bulbiform at base ....
....1. *Bryoxiphium*
A. Dorsal lamina usually broad: peristome present: stem not radiculose-bulbiform at
    base ....B
  B. Mostly not aquatic; sometimes submerged, but floating ....2. *Fissidens*
  B. Aquatic, filiform, floating mosses ....3. *Octodiceras*

1.   BRYOXIPHIUM Mitten
(*Eustichia* Bridel)

Slender, dioicous, more or less densely silky-cespitose, bright green or yellowish: stem stiff, oval in cross-section, with central strand, radiculose at the extreme base, upwardly flattened, with distichous, closely imbricated leaves, simple or irregularly branched; leaves from a linear-lanceolate base, either linear, with a small acumen, or rounded and abruptly more or less long-subulate, denticulate above; costa percurrent, with a very narrow dorsal wing which does not extend to the base of the leaf; basal leaf-cells hyaline, rectangular, upper cells chlorophyllose, triangular to irregularly trapezoidal, smooth, towards the margin linear and forming a distinct border; perichaetium terminal, with two concave, ovate, prolonged-acuminate, serrulate leaves with a complete dorsal wing: seta shorter than the perichaetial leaves, flexuous or cygneous; capsule spherical, oval or obovate, smooth; no peristome or annulus; spores .015-.020 mm; operculum abruptly and irregularly rostrate; calyptra smooth, covering about one-third of the urn; antheridial plants similar in appearance to the archegonial.

Three species; one in Mexico, one in Asia, and one in Europe, Korea, and the United States, rare.

1. BRYOXIPHIUM NORVEGICUM [Bridel] Mitten
(*Eustichia norvegica* Mueller)

Plants 1-2.5 cm long, somewhat flexuous, flat, lustrous, yellow, fastened to vertical sandstone cliffs by a radiculose bulbiform base; stems mostly simple; leaves short-acuminate and as described for the genus; costa vanishing at or near the apex: seta rather thick, about 2 mm long; capsule obovate, pale yellow, mouth reddish, peristome none; operculum reddish at base, attached to columella and long-persistent; calyptra cucullate, large, tipped with a slender beak.

On shaded vertical exposures of sandstone in Greenland, and in a few widely separated localities from Minnesota to western Pennsylvania and Tennessee.

LAWRENCE CO.: "Slippery Rock Creek, Lesquereux." (Porter's Catalogue). The writer has not been able to find this species along Slippery Rock Creek, where Lesquereux found it.

2. FISSIDENS Hedwig

Autoicous or dioicous: stem short to long, erect to procumbent, more or less branched or simple; leaves prominently winged, linear-obovate to lanceolate-obovate; costa usually present; cells rounded-hexagonal, sometimes loosely rhomboidal, rarely prosenchymatous, smooth or papillose: seta erect or ascending, long to short, mostly terminal, sometimes lateral; capsule mostly exserted, erect or inclined, symmetric or unsymmetric; peristome mostly inserted below the mouth of the urn, teeth cleft, exteriorly articulate, often striate-papillose; spores mostly small; operculum conic to rostrate; calyptra entire to once or rarely several times cleft, mostly smooth.

A widely distributed genus of about 700 species, mainly tropical, on soil, rocks, trees, humus, or in water. In our region at least 8 species.

KEY TO THE SPECIES

A. Costa none: minute plants 2-4 mm high ....1. *F. hyalinus*
A. Costa well developed ....B
  B. Leaves bordered, at least on the vaginant lamina of the perichaetial leaves, by a band of linear cells C
  B. Leaves not bordered, or at least the border not composed of linear cells ....G
    C. Costa percurrent, confluent with border at apex and forming a mucro: capsule erect ....2. *F. bryoides*
    C. Costa not usually percurrent, or only so in upper leaves; border not usually reaching apex: capsule curved or erect ....D
      D. Leaves non-bordered, entire, obtuse ....3. *F. obtusifolius*
      D. Leaves bordered, at least on sheath of the perichaetial leaves, acute or apiculate ......E
        E. Leaves bordered to near the apex ....F
        E. Leaves usually bordered only on the sheath of the perichaetial leaves ....5. *F. exiguus*

F. Leaves broadly oblong-lanceolate: capsules usually more or less curved: plants usually more than 2 mm ....2. *F. bryoides* var. *incurvus*

F. Leaves narrowly oblong-lanceolate: capsules usually erect: plants often less than 2 mm high ....4. *F. minutulus*

G. Leaves without a marginal band of several rows of somewhat paler cells, the outer row sometimes paler I

G. Leaves with a marginal band of several rows of paler incrassate cells ....H

H. Upper median leaf-cells rather obscure, about .006-.010 x .006-.014 mm; border distinct ....6. *F. cristatus*

H. Upper median leaf-cells distinct, about .012-.016 x .015-.025 mm; border not very distinct ....7. *F. adiantoides*

I. Costa excurrent into the apiculus ....8. *F. taxifolius*

I. Costa not quite reaching apex ....J

J. Leaves often apiculate: seta terminal: leaf-cells .010-.016 x .014-.020 mm ....9. *F. osmundioides*

J. Leaves more or less rounded at apex: seta lateral in basal half of stem: leaf-cells about .007-.011 mm ....10. *F. subbasilaris*

1.   FISSIDENS HYALINUS Hooker and Wilson

Plate LXI

Gregarious, pale green, minute, 2-4 mm high: stem usually simple, erect; leaves in 3-5 pairs, soft, the upper much larger, lance-oblong, acute, non-costate, margined by a single row of narrow elongate cells, the sheath hardly reaching the middle of the leaf, margin entire; cells large, about .030-.045 x .060-.100 mm, thin-walled, irregularly elongate-hexagonal, hyaline: seta terminal, 1-2 mm long, erect smooth; capsule oblong, erect, thin-walled; teeth closely articulate, red, cleft to the middle; operculum rostrate; calyptra cylindric-conic and covering the rostrum only of the operculum; spores .014-.020 mm.

The original station of this rare moss was "moist, rocky ledges, Bank Lick, on Cassidy's farm, near Cincinnati, Ohio," where it was first collected by T. G. Lea, in 1839. This station has since been lost, but the moss has been found elsewhere in Ohio: on ground in deep ravines near Plainesville,—H. C. Beardslee, and later in Pennsylvania, as follows:

WASHINGTON Co.: On clay banks with *Fissidens taxifolius* on banks in ravines near Washington, September and October, 1892, 1894, and 1898. Linn and Simonton. Bank in shaded ravine near Monongahela Lock No. 4, Linn & Simonton. Sept. 6, 1895 (figured).

2.   FISSIDENS BRYOIDES [Linnaeus] Hedwig

(*Hypnum bryoides* Linnaeus)

Plate XIV

In loose tufts or densely gregarious, rather dark green: stems ascending or erect, 5-15 mm high; leaves numerous, ascending, or the apical erect, oblong-lingulate, usually abruptly and somewhat obliquely acuminate, the sheath reaching about half way to the apex, the dorsal lamina gradually becoming very narrow at base, the border strong and reaching the apex, where it becomes confluent with the costa, margin entire or sometimes faintly denticulate at apex; costa strong; leaf-cells rounded-hexagonal, somewhat incrassate, somewhat smaller at the apex of the sheath, becoming rectangular at the base, the border consisting of two or three rows of linear-prosenchymatous incrassate cells, the border of the vaginant lamina edged below with a row of rectangular cells about two to three times as long as wide: seta erect, flexuous, about 4-9 mm long, yellowish to reddish, smooth, slender, terminal: capsule typically erect and symmetric, sometimes inclined, usually reddish-yellow, smooth, oblong-oval, about 7-8 mm long; peristome-teeth red, the upper two-thirds split into two awl-like prongs with spiral thickenings, pellucid, papillose, the teeth inserted below the mouth; spores smooth, small, about .010-.012 mm in diameter; operculum conic-rostrate. Mature in late fall or winter. Antheridial flowers gemmiform, axillary.

Widely distributed in temperate regions on shaded soil, in our region especially in and about greenhouses. Our specimens show considerable variation in the arrangement of the leaf-cells, either in rows or not so, and in the capsule, the latter varying from erect and symmetric to arcuate. The spores in our specimens are much smaller than is indicated in some descriptions. Most of the specimens from our region have more or less unsymmetric or arcuate capsules and belong to the following variety.

ALLEGHENY Co.: In flower-pots, Phipps Conservatory, Schenley Park, Pittsburgh, March 20, 1910. O.E.J. (figured). ELK Co.: James. (Porter's Catalogue).

2a. FISSIDENS BRYOIDES var. INCURVUS (Weber & Mohr) Hübener
(F. incurvus Schwaegrichen)

Typically this moss is about 2-6 mm high, with rather broadly oblong-lanceolate leaves, which are obtuse-apiculate and narrowly bordered up to near the apex: seta reddish, long, flexuous; capsule oval-cylindric, curved and usually more or less inclined or cernuous; antheridial buds basal.

On rocks, or more rarely clay, usually in shaded brooks and ravines, America from Greenland to Vancouver Island to Texas. Europe, Asia, Africa, New Zealand.

FAYETTE Co.: On muddy rock in bed of mountain rivulet, Ohio Pyle, June 14, 1908. O.E.J. and G.K.J. McKEAN Co.: Hunt's Run, April 28, 1893. D.A.B.

3.   FISSIDENS OBTUSIFOLIUS Wilson
Plate XIV

Small, densely gregarious, sometimes forming cushions, usually growing at right angles to the substratum, pale green: stems comparatively stout, in our specimens about 3-6 mm long, mostly simple; leaves of fertile plants about 4-8 pairs, of sterile shoots about 6-12 pairs, distichous, vertical, in fertile shoots closely placed, the lower small, obovate to oblong, the upper much larger, oblong, ascending to erect, obtuse, the clasping portion extending above the middle, non-margined except for a few elongate cells at the end of the sheathing portion, entire, the apical leaves reaching to 1.5 mm long by 0.3 mm wide; cells rounded to quadrate-hexagonal above, a few at the margin of the base rectangular (up to 4:1), at the apex of the sheath a few marginal cells elongate to linear, all incrassate; costa strong, disappearing shortly below the apex, the dorsal lamina becoming narrow or disappearing at the base: seta comparatively stout, erect, or upcurving, in ours about 1.5-2.0 mm long, brownish, smooth;

the capsule erect, oblong-oval to oblong-obovate, somewhat narrowed below the mouth, smooth, brownish; operculum hemispheric-apiculate to very shortly rostrate; peristome yellowish-pellucid, trabeculate, the teeth lanceolate, acuminate; capsule walls with cells incrassate, quadrate to hexagonal; spores smooth, .018-.023 mm. Mature in autumn.

On wet rocks from New England to Minnesota, Colorado, Texas, and Alabama.

In West Virginia on walls of Lock No. 9, Monongahela River, a short distance south of the West Virginia-Pennsylvania State Line, July 3, 1909. O.E.J.

Rare in our region. BEAVER Co.: Gorge of Little Beaver Creek, on sides of large sandstone rocks in dashing current and often inundated, Smith's Ferry, October 1, 1910. O.E.J. (On the Ohio-Pennsylvania State Line.)

4. FISSIDENS MINUTULUS Sullivant
(*F. incurvus* var. *minutulus* (Sullivant) Austin)
Plate XIV

Plants minute, 0.8-3.0 mm high, gregarious, green, erect: stem simple, reddish; leaves 3-7 pairs, hardly imbricate, the uppermost much larger and incurved-erect and up to 2.5 mm long, narrowly oblong-lanceolate, more or less acute, the border narrow, ceasing below apex, widest at upper part of sheath, margin entire or somewhat undulate, the sheath about one-half the length of the leaf, the inferior lamina narrowing at base but hardly decurrent; costa strong, ending usually a little below apex; leaf-cells incrassate, more or less rounded to hexagonal, rather irregular, the basal becoming rectangular, the border consisting of 1-3 rows of elongate-linear or ascending prosenchymatous cells: seta reddish, smooth, erect, subflexuous, about 3-6 mm long; capsule usually erect, subflexuous, about 3-6 mm long; capsule usually erect, symmetric, 0.7-0.9 mm long, yellowish to dark chestnut color, oval-oblong, tapering abruptly at base; peristome rich red-chestnut, the teeth deeply forked into two awl-like prongs with prominent spiral thickenings, teeth slightly inserted; spores round to oblong, pellucid, pale yellow-red, smoothish, .014-.017 mm in diameter; operculum conic-rostrate. Mature in early autumn.

On damp stones and rocks in shady woods or in stream beds, Europe, and from eastern Canada south to the Gulf States.

Now known from the following counties: Allegheny, Armstrong, Butler, Lawrence, McKean, Warren, Washington, and Westmoreland. Figured from specimens from Mellon Estate (Rachelwood), New Florence, Westmoreland Co., O.E.J. Sept. 8, 1907.

5. FISSIDENS EXIGUUS Sullivant
Plate XV

Plants very small, gregarious, light green: stems, in our specimens, 1-2.5 mm high, erect, or ascending; leaves usually 3-5 pairs, the lower minute, the upper reaching 1.5 mm long, ascending to erect, oblong-lanceolate, acute, only the sheath margined, entire, the dorsal lamina narrowing to none at the base, the sheath about one-half the length of the leaf; costa stout, vanishing a little below apex; cells in apical lamina quadrate to hexagonal, at base of leaf becoming rectangular, the sheath being bordered, especially in its upper part, by a border one to four cells wide, of elongate and more or less prosenchymatous cells, all cells moderately incrassate or more so in border of sheath: capsule on an erect, somewhat flexuous, stout, reddish pedicel 2-5 mm long; capsule oblong-oval, narrowed to pedicel at base, somewhat constricted below mouth, smooth, reddish-yellow, about 0.5-0.7 mm long; operculum conic-rostrate, about two-thirds the length of the capsule; calyptra narrow, dimidiate; teeth red, split to the middle into two awl-like prongs which have spiral thickenings, closely infolded in wet specimens, inserted a little below edge of mouth; spores smooth, about .020 mm in diameter. Mature in September.

On stones and rocks in stream beds, especially in ravines. Southern Canada, United States east of the Rockies, south to North Carolina, England.

ALLEGHENY Co.: On sandstone rocks, ravine of Powers Run, November 30, 1909. O.E.J. FAYETTE Co.: Cheat Haven, September 3-6, 1910. O.E.J. and G.K.J. (figured).

6. FISSIDENS CRISTATUS Wilson
(F. decipiens De Notaris)
Plate XV

Usually tufted, branching from the base, green to dark green; stem erect, 1-2 cm high; leaves numerous, ascending, imbricate, the upper reaching 2.5 mm long, oblong-lingulate, acute, crenulate below, irregularly serrate above, inferior lamina narrowed and somewhat decurrent at base, sheath extending half-way to apex or a little above; costa strong, ending just below or in the apex, sometimes a little excurrent; leaf-cells irregularly angular to rounded-hexagonal, about .008-.012 mm in diameter, some of these next to the costa larger, the marginal 3 or 4 rows paler and forming a rather obscure belt around the leaf, all cells incrassate: seta ascending, usually about 1 cm high, smooth, light chestnut color, arising from the lower half of the stem; capsule oblong, smooth, about 2 mm long, tapering to the seta, ascending to nearly erect, chestnut-brown, constricted below the mouth at least when old; peristome bright red-chestnut, the teeth split at one-third above the base into two very slender, trabeculate, somewhat spirally papillose prongs; operculum conic, rostrate; spores about .020 mm in diameter, smooth, pale yellowish, globose. Mature in winter or early spring.

On moist soil and stones or occasionally at base of trees, Nova Scotia to the Gulf States and the Rocky Mountains, Europe, Asia.

Known from the following counties: Allegheny, Armstrong, Cameron, Crawford, Butler, Elk, Fayette, Lawrence, McKean, Somerset, Warren, Washington, and Westmoreland. Specimen figured: On bark at base of black ash, Linesville, Crawford Co., June 11-12, 1907. O.E.J.

7. FISSIDENS ADIANTOIDES [Linnaeus] Hedwig

This species differs chiefly from F. cristatus in that the cells are larger, .012-.016 x .015-.025 mm, distinct; border none or rather indistinct: seta usually longer than in F. cristatus, about 1-2.5 cm long. The plants are often much larger, 2-15 cm high, and are monoicous instead of dioicous, as in F. cristatus. The two species apparently intergrade.

This spcies is reported as common in the eastern United States but, with the following exceptions, all the specimens we have seen from our region labeled as *F. adiantoides* we have referred to *F. cristatus*.

WASHINGTON Co.: Shaded ravine, McCracken Sta., Sept. 24, 1892; near Washington, Dec. 10, 1892; and ravine near Claysville, Dec. 17, 1892, all A. Linn and J. S. Simonton.

8.   FISSIDENS TAXIFOLIUS [Linnaeus] Hedwig

(*Hypnum taxifolium* Linnaeus)

Plate XV

Plants gregarious, light green, branching at base, usually 5-10 mm high, erect to ascending: stem rather stout and rigid; leaves close, imbricate, oblong-ovate, apiculate, uniformly crenulate, non-bordered, ascending, the middle leaves usually longest and up to 2 mm. long, the inferior lamina ending abruptly at the base, sheath extending to the middle or beyond; costa strong and excurrent in the apiculus; leaf-cells rounded-hexagonal, about .010 mm in diameter, incrassate, one or two rows next the costa larger, the marginal row usually a little paler, the costa at the apex widening and consisting of elongate parenchymatous cells: seta about 8-14 mm long, flexuous-ascending, smooth, yellowish-castaneous, arising near the base of the plant; capsule varying from sub-pendulous to erect, oblong, slightly inflated on the back, smooth, about 1.5 mm long, tapering abruptly to the seta, castaneous to dark brown; peristome bright red-chestnut, the teeth inserted a little below the mouth of the capsule, forked to below the middle, the prongs very slender, trabeculate, somewhat spirally papillose; spores smooth, about .016-.017 mm in diameter, pale yellowish-pellucid; operculum conic, obliquely rostrate to about half the length of the capsule. Mature in late fall or winter.

On damp clayey soil, Canada and eastern United States, south to the Gulf. Europe, Asia, Africa.

Known from Allegheny, Butler, Fayette, McKean, Lawrence, Tioga, and Washington counties. Specimen figured: Bennett, McKean Co., Oct., 26, 1898. D.A.B.

9.   FISSIDENS OSMUNDIOIDES [Swartz] Hedwig

(*Dicranum osmundioides* Swartz)

Densely tufted, 1-5 (-10) cm high, dark green, tomentose below with brown rhizoids: stems simple or sometimes branched basally, erect; leaves numerous, close but hardly imbricated, the apical ones the largest, oblong-lanceolate, serrulate towards the apex, non-bordered, usually rounded and apiculate at apex, the sheath reaching from one-half to two-thirds the leaf-length, inferior lamina often ceasing abruptly at base and not decurrent; costa ending just below the apex; leaf-cells oval- or rounded-hexagonal, large, about .010-.018 x .012-.025 mm, incrassate, a single row at margin often paler, pellucid, and a little smaller: seta terminal, yellowish to chestnut-red, about 5-10 mm long; capsule narrow-oblong, sub-erect, to inclined, thick-walled, chestnut-brown or darker; operculum conic with a needle-like usually straight beak nearly as long as the urn; calyptra cucullate or several-lobed at base; spores smooth about .018-.025 mm. Mature in midsummer.

In swampy woods and along streams, quite widely distributed in the cooler portions of the Northern Hemisphere, reaching the northern United States and south to Missouri, Ohio, North Carolina, Georgia, and Tennessee. It occurs in eastern Pennsylvania and in Ohio but has not yet been found in western Pennsylvania.

10. FISSIDENS SUBBASILARIS Hedwig

Plate XVI

Cespitose in wide mats, 5-10 mm high, erect or ascending, green, brownish tomentulose at base: stems branching at base; leaves usually in 10-18 pairs, crisped when dry, widely spreading to ascending, close, imbricate, those in middle of stem often largest, the largest reaching about 1.5 mm, the sheath reaching about three-fifths the length of the leaf, leaf oblong, rather obtuse, but apiculate with a pointed cell, non-bordered, minutely crenulate below, irregularly serrate above, the inferior lamina ceasing abruptly at the base; leaf-cells incrassate, and rather obscure, small, about .007-.012 mm, roundish-hexagonal; the costa ending considerably below the apex: seta smooth, arising from basal part of stem, ascending, usually about 3-5 mm long and reaching about to the top of stem, light chestnut-color; capsule cylindric-oval, about 1.5 mm long, smooth, chestnut-color to dark brown, tapering at base, erect or very nearly so; calyptra narrowly cucullate; operculum conic, obliquely rostrate to about one-half the length of capsule; peristome rich chestnut-color, strongly trabeculate, not papillose, the teeth slightly inserted, bifid to about the middle into two slender prongs; spores smooth, pale yellowish pellucid, round, about .016-.018 mm in diameter. Mature in late autumn.

On earth and on rocks and bases of trees, Ontario and southwards through our Eastern States to the Gulf.

Now known from the following counties: Allegheny, Butler, Fayette, Indiana, Mc-Kean, Somerset, Tioga, Washington, and Westmoreland. Specimen figured: On base of white oak, Douthett, southern Butler Co., O.E.J. Dec. 27, 1908.

3. OCTODICERAS Bridel

(*Conomitrium* Montagne)

Plants slender, fasciculately branching, floating, filiform: leaves remote, lance-linear, short-auriculate: flowers monoicous, the male axillary, the female on elongated branchlets; seta short; capsule thin-walled, erect, very small, without stomata; calyptra minute, conic, undivided, covering only the rostrum of the operculum; operculum conic-rostrate; peristome-teeth variously laciniate or entire and evidently degenerate; annulus none; spores about .018-.025 mm.

This genus includes about 20 species of aquatic mosses more or less resembling *Fontinalis* in general appearance, widely distributed over the earth,—2 species occurring in eastern United States, one already found and another likely to be found in our region.

KEY TO SPECIES

A. Large much-branched plants, up to 15 cm. long: seta shorter than the capsule ....
....1. *O. debile*

A. Small little-branched plants, up to 4 cm long: seta longer than the capsule ....
....2. *O. Hallianum*

1. OCTODICERAS DEBILE (Schwaegrichen) Jennings
(*Octodiceras julianus* Bridel; *Conomitrium Julianum* Montagne;
Fontinalis Juliana Savi)

Plate LXI

Plants up to 15 cm long, flaccid, floating, blackish-green below, much branched: leaves up to 5 or 6 mm long, distant, spreading, numerous, linear-lanceolate, entire, non-bordered, vaginant lamina one-fourth to one-third the length of the leaf, inferior lamina not quite reaching base, costa ending slightly below the apex; leaf-cells irregular hexagonal or more quadrate below, about .015-.020 x .020-.030 mm, somewhat incrassate, within the border at the lower outer corner of the vaginant lamina several rows of elongated linear-oblong cells: seta shorter than capsule, pale, fragile at base, elliptic, erect, scarcely raised above perichaetical bracts, symmetric; operculum conic-rostrate and about as long as urn; peristome-teeth short, imperfect, 16, yellowish-pellucid, irregularly cleft and perforate in upper part; calyptra conic, dark, erose at base; spores about .020-.022 mm, mature in summer.

Almost cosmopolitan, but rather local, on stones and on wood in creeks and springy swamps.

This species has not been collected in western Pennsylvania except as follows: BUTLER Co.: Walley Mill region, Parker Twp., on submerged rocks in brook. Sidney K. Eastwood, July 14, 1935 (figured). CRAWFORD Co.: On clay bank along Shenango River, west of Lineville. W. R. Van Dersal, Oct. 15, 1933. HUNTINGDON Co.: Porter. (Porter's Catalogue.)

2. OCTODICERAS HALLIANUM (Sullivant and Lesquereux)
Jaeger and Sauerbeck

(*Conomitrium Hallianum* Sullivant and Lesquereux; *Fissidens Hallianus* Mitten)

Plants smaller, up to 3-4 cm long, laxly tufted, dirty-green: stems sparsely fasciculate-branching at base; leaves remote, narrowly linear-lanceolate, usually in 5-10 pairs, entire, the sheath not reaching over one-fourth or one-third the length of the upper pair of leaves, inferior lamina narrowing and reaching almost to the base; cells irregularly hexagonal, tending to quadrate below, about .015-.022 mm: seta longer than capsule, pale; capsule pale, elliptic-oblong; peristome-teeth undivided, reddish, subulate-lanceolate, articulate, inserted below the mouth of urn, papillose; operculum acutely conic-rostrate and about as long as urn; calyptra cucullate, covering the entire operculum; spores smooth, about .018-.024 mm.

On wood and stones, in streams, swamps, etc., New Jersey, New York, Illinois, and Idaho. Not reported for our immediate region, but perhaps overlooked on account of small size.

Family 5. POTTIACEAE

Autoicous or dioicous, rarely par-, syn-, or polyoicous: mostly small or medium-sized, more or less densely cespitose, rarely gregarious: stems mostly with central strand, radiculose below, thickly foliate, simple or more or less branched; leaves pluri-seriate, rarely 3-seriate, lanceolate to broadly ovate or obovate; costa heterogeneous, mostly percurrent, or excurrent, sometimes with longitudinal lamellae or with green branched filaments on the ventral surface above the middle; leaf-cells parenchymatous, the basal rectangular to elongate, mostly pellucid, or hyaline. upper cells always chlorophyllose, on both sides mostly warty papillose, loose, sometimes towards the apex 4-6-angled, or small and rounded-quadrate; seta more or less elongate, mostly straight, rarely almost lacking; capsule erect, symmetric, rarely slightly inclined, straight to slightly arcuate, mostly oblong to cylindric, rarely oval to spherical; collum short, rarely none; peristome various to none, mostly inserted on the mouth of the urn, usually without projecting trabeculae; teeth 16, straight or spirally twisted, often united at base into a tube, entire or 2-3-cleft into filiform-subulate divisions, papillose; operculum mostly conic, rostrate; calyptra mostly cucullate, smooth, rarely papillose or minutely bristly or short-hirsute.

A very large family, mainly confined to the temperate zones, occurring almost entirely on soil or on rocks. The systematic relationships and the scope of the family are variously treated by different bryologists who have taken different characters as the basis for the various classifications. This family was called Tortulaceae in the first edition, but for purposes of uniformity it is here called Pottiaceae, following Brotherus (*Pflanzenfamilien*, 2nd edit., 1924, and Grout, *Moss Flora*, 1938).

KEY TO GENERA

A. Minute, bud-like plants with broadly ovate, concave or carinate leaves; cleistocarpous
.... 9. *Acaulon*
A. Not as above ....B
    B. Leaves mostly narrow, often linear-lanceolate, never broadest above the middle
        except some occasionally lingulate in *Gymnostomum calcareum;* costa with sev-
        eral guides, no accompanying cells, but 2 stereid bands, rarely long-excurrent.. C
    B. Leaves mostly broad, ovate-oblong ot spatulate or lingulate; costa with 2 median
        guides, with accompanying cells, and 1 stereid band, mostly more or less long-
        excurrent ....M
C. Plants minute; areolation dense, strongly papillose: capsules cleistocarpous ....
.... 1. *Astomum*
C. With deciduous operculum ....D
    D. Peristome none ....E
    D. Peristome present, rudimentary or well-developed ....F
E. Operculum deciduous with the columella detached ....4. *Hymenostylium*
E. Columella remaining in the urn after the falling away of the operculum ....
.... 3. *Gymnostomum*
    F. The exterior surface of the teeth more strongly developed and with projecting
        plates; leaves crispate when dry; seta long ....2. *Weisia*
    F. Both surfaces of the teeth equally well-developed and no projecting plates ....G
G. Perichaetial leaves long-convolute-sheathing ....8. *Barbula*
G. Perichaetial leaves not or but little convolute-sheathing .... H
    H. Leaves more or less lingulate, margins plane; cells smooth ....7. *Didymodon*
    H. Leaves more or less lanceolate ....J
J. Leaf-margins plane or involute; cells papillose ....K
J. Leaf-margins more or less revolute; leaf-cells nearly smooth or papillose L
    K. Divisions of peristome erect or slightly dextrorsely twisted ....5. *Trichostomum*

I. ASTOMUM Hampe

Autoicous, rarely polyoicous: small, gregarious to cespitose, dull green: stem with a few-celled central strand, radiculose, thickly foliate; upper leaves tufted, when dry mostly crisped, keeled, from a broad base lanceolate to subulate-lanceolate, margin plane to involute, entire; costa strong, percurrent or excurrent; leaf-cells in upper part of leaf small, rounded-quadrate, papillose both sides, the lower cells elongate-quadrangular, thin-walled and hyaline: capsule mostly immersed, almost spherical to oblong-elliptic, mostly with a small, elongate-conic operculum, which, however, is rarely deciduous; calyptra cucullate, rarely mitrate, smooth.

A widely distributed genus of 21 terrestrial species; 3 species occurring in North America; 2 (3) species in our region.

1. ASTOMUM MUHLENBERGIANUM (Swartz) Grout
(Astomum Sullivantii Schimper; A. crispum Am. Auth.)
Plate LXII

Densely cespitose, pale to dark green: stem about 5 mm high, usually branched above, erect; leaves numerous, close, when dry crispate, the stem-leaves small, lance-linear, the comal and perichaetial much larger, up to 4 mm long, elongate-linear from a narrowly oblong, concave, whitish base, usually narrowly involute or canaliculate above, the apex abruptly acute; costa strong, acutely and shortly excurrent-mucronate, sometimes upturned so as to make the leaf somewhat cucullate; basal leaf-cells laxly and irregularly long-rectangular, hyaline, upper leaf-cells sub-quadrate, densely chlorophyllose, papillose: seta erect, shorter than the capsule; capsule immersed, ovoid, small, brownish, about 1 mm long; lid finally distinct but not separating from the urn of its own accord, minute, obliquely conic-apiculate to short rostellate; exothecial cells laxly hexagonal to oblong-hexagonal, one to three rows of cells being somewhat smaller at the junction of the lid; calyptra cucullate; spores papillose, .021-.027 mm, mature in spring: autoicous; the immature capsule fully grown by late November.

In old sandy or clayey fields and along roadsides, principally in non-calcareous districts, temperate Europe, Japan, Algeria, and, in North America, from Saskatchewan to Massachusetts and southward to the Gulf States.

BEAVER Co.: James. (Porter's Catalogue). INDIANA Co.: James. (Porter's Catalogue). About 3 miles northeast of Saltsburg along abandoned road above Black Leg Creek, Nov. 23, 1941. O.E.J. and G.K.J. (figured). WASHINGTON Co.: Snake Woods, near Washington. Mar. 10, 1894. Linn and Simonton.

2. ASTOMUM NITIDULUM Bryologia Europaea
(*Systegium nitidulum* (Jaeger)

The moss reported in Porter's Catalogue as collected by James in Indiana County, and listed as *Astomum nitidulum* Bry. Eur., is doubtful. It is suggested that *A. nitidulum* is a hybrid of *Astomum Muhlenbergianum* and *Weisia viridula*, or that it is *A. phascoides* (Hook.) Grout from Ohio westward. This latter species has stouter leaves than *A. Muhlenbergianum* with longer seta and a rostrate lid.

INDIANA Co.: Derry. James. (Porter's Catalogue).

2. WEISIA Hedwig

Autoicous, rarely paroicous, polyoicous, or dioicous: low, cespitose, freely branching: upper leaves much larger, relatively to the lower, erect-spreading, crisped when dry, carinate, elongate-lanceolate; costa strong, cuspidate-excurrent; basal leaf-cells rectangular, hyaline, the upper small, rounded, low-papillose on both surfaces: seta erect or sometimes curved, mostly longer than the perichaetial leaves; capsule erect and symmetric or a little inclined and swollen dorsally, round-ovoid to cylindrical, narrow-mouthed, finally usually somewhat plicate, the urn at the rim being several cells thick and the insertion of the peristome thus considerably removed from the exterior border of the rim; peristome-teeth short, often rudimentary, undivided, papillose, the exterior layer more strongly developed and with projecting bars; lid obliquely long-rostrate; calyptra cucullate.

A widely distributed genus of 27 terrestrial species; 7 species occurring in North America; only one in our range.

1. WEISIA VIRIDULA [Linnaeus] Hedwig
Plate XVI

Densely cespitose, yellowish-green: stem erect, often branching, up to 5 mm tall; leaves erect-spreading, the upper much larger and up to 3 mm long and 0.5 mm wide, lance-linear, tapering to an acute or acuminate apex, the margin strongly involute, entire, leaves crispate when dry; costa strong, about .030-.040 mm wide at base, excurrent into a short and more or less hyaline point; upper leaf-cells roundish-hexagonal, strongly papillose, obscure, the basal more or less elongate-rectangular and hyaline: seta slender, up to 1 cm long, lustrous, yellowish, faintly sinistrorse; capsule erect, ovoid, symmetric, slightly narrowed at mouth, reddish-brown, about 0.9 mm long, somewhat plicate when dry and empty; exothecial cells rather thin-walled, irregularly oblong to hexagonal or rounded, those at the mouth in 3-5 rows, much smaller, quadrate and darker in color; peristome-teeth 16, more or less rudimentary, short, irregularly linear, divided, or truncate, papillose; lid conic, obliquely long-rostrate, altogether nearly as long as the urn; calyptra cucullate, covering about two-thirds of the capsule; spores orange-pellucid, papillose, about .016-.019 mm in diameter, mature in spring.

Almost cosmopolitan on bare earth in fields, excavations, along roadsides, etc.

ALLEGHENY Co.: On shale cliffs, Little Sewickley Creek, 2 mi. n. of Edgeworth, C.M.B. BEDFORD Co.: On shale cliff, Gravel Pit Sta. C.M.B. June 15, 1941. FAYETTE Co.: Ohio Pyle, on clay bank, September 1-3, 1906. O.E.J. and G.K.J. (figured.) McKEAN Co.: Bradford, Nov. 21, 1896, Divide, Bolivar and Bennett, Dec. 15, 1896, and Quintuple, Mar. 20, 1898. D.A.B. WASHINGTON Co.: Linn and Simonton. (Porter's Catalogue). WESTMORELAND Co.: Clay bank, Darlington, C.M.B. May 19, 1945.

3. GYMNOSTOMUM Hedwig

Dioicous: densely cespitose, rusty in color below: stem thickly foliate, sparsely radiculose, in cross-section circular, the central strand few-celled, the branching dichotomous; leaves erect-spreading, more or less carinate, not crisped but when dry, more or less appressed and curved; elongate-lanceolate or subulate to sub-lingulate, margin plane; costa strong, vanishing below the apex; upper leaf-cells rounded-quadrate, small, thickly papillose on both sides, as is also the costa, lower cells rectangular, the walls yellow to hyaline; perichaetial leaves somewhat sheathing at the base; seta long, erect; capsule erect, symmetric, oval or oblong, when ripe smooth and shining, the wall of the capsule not distinctly thickened at the mouth; peristome none; operculum conic, long rostrate, easily deciduous; calyptra narrowly cucullate, covering about half of the urn.

A widely distributed genus of 11 species, mainly occurring on calcareous rocks; 3 species occurring in North America; two in our region.

KEY TO THE SPECIES

A. Stems usually less than 2 cm; at least some of the leaves obtuse, narrowly lingulate to ligulate ....1. G. calcareum
A. Stems from 1 to 10 cm; leaves oblong to linear-lanceolate, more or less acute .... 2. G. aeruginosum

1. GYMNOSTOMUM CALCAREUM Nees and Hornschuch
(G. viridulum Bryol. Eur.; G. tenue of L. and J. Manual)

Plate XVI

Densely cespitose, yellowish-green: stems erect, branched, up to 10 mm high; leaves about 1 mm long, spreading, somewhat recurved, elongate-oblong-lanceolate, somewhat concave, usually larger and tufted at the apex of the stem, obtuse, plane-margined; upper leaf-cells densely papillose, small, incrassate, obscure, the interior basal cells hyaline, rectangular or up to 2-3:1; costa strong, ending below the apex: seta erect; capsule oblong, often somewhat constricted below the mouth when dry and empty, erect, symmetric, tapering below; lid conic, obliquely rostrate, the beak one-half to two-thirds as long as the urn; calyptra cucullate; annulus none; peristome none; exothecial cells rectangular to quadrate, at the mouth becoming smaller, darker and quadrate in 3 to 5 rows; spores smooth, .008-.011 mm in diameter, mature in summer.

Cosmopolitan on damp limestone rocks and boulders, but rare in our region.

BRADFORD Co.: On moist shaly limestone cliff. June 25, 1935. S. K. Eastwood. FAYETTE Co.: On wet cliff, one mile up Meadow Run, Ohio Pyle, C. M. Boardman, June 23, 1940. LAWRENCE Co.: Gorge near Rock Point, June 26, 1909 (figured). Sterile. O.E.J.

2. GYMNOSTOMUM AERUGINOSUM Smith
(*G. rupestre* Schleich)

Forms dense cushions; stems slender, branched, 1 to 3 or 4 or occasionally even to 10 cm long; leaves oblong- to linear-lanceolate, about 1-1.5 mm long: capsule thin-walled, brownish; spores about .010-.012 mm in diameter, mature in summer.

On moist limestone rocks, from southern Canada through eastern United States in Texas

HUNTINGDON Co.: Spruce Creek, T. C. Porter.

4. HYMENOSTYLIUM Bridel

Dioicous: densely and deeply cespitose, green to rusty or yellowish-green: stem densely foliate, sparsely radiculose, without a central strand, triangular in cross-section; leaves erect-spreading, rarely squarrose-recurved, when dry involute, sometimes somewhat twisted when dry, not crisped, more or less carinate, elongate-lanceolate, acuminate; costa mostly ending below the apex; laminal leaf-cells thick-walled, smooth or papillose: seta long, erect; capsule erect, symmetric, obovate, firm, when empty smooth and pyriform; peristome none; lid obliquely long-rostrate from a broad base, remaining attached to the columella and deciduous thus attached; calyptra cucullate, covering about half of the urn.

A widely distributed genus of about 25 species, occurring mainly on calcareous rocks; 8 species in North America; only one occurring in our region.

1. HYMENOSTYLIUM RECURVIROSTRUM (Ehrhart, Hedwig) Lindberg
(*Gymnostomum curvirostrum* Bridel; *Weisia curvirostris* Mueller; *Gymnostomum recurvirostrum* Hedwig 1801)
Plate XVI

Closely cespitose, 2-4 cm high, bright green above, darker and more or less ferruginous below: leaves little or not at all twisted when dry, erect to recurved-spreading when moist, narrowly lanceolate-acuminate, 1-1.5 mm long, apex acute, base sub-clasping, margin entire but papillose, as are also the entire upper and lower surfaces of the lamina and costa, one or both lower margins recurved; costa strong, vanishing just below the apex, at base occupying about one-eighth the entire width of the leaf; upper leaf-cells rounded to sub-quadrangular, the lower towards the costa becoming elongate-rectangular: seta 8-10 mm long, lustrous, castaneous; capsule about 1 mm long, rounded ovate, lustrous, castaneous, widest towards the mouth, when dry and empty decidedly urceolate; peristome none; operculum with a long and oblique rostrum at least two-thirds the length of the urn, the operculum often remaining attached to the columella for some time after the spores have been shed; spores yellowish, moderately incrassate, smooth, about .014-.017 mm in diameter, mature in September or October.

Not uncommon on wet cliffs, principally calcareous, in Europe, Asia, northern Africa, and, in North America, from Alaska to Labrador south to California and the Carolinas.

ALLEGHENY Co.: Guyasuta Hollow, Aspinwall, on wet cliff near waterfalls, October 12 and 25 (figured) 1908, and September 8, 1909. O.E.J. BUTLER Co.: On cliff, Winfield Jct., Buffalo Creek. June 8, 1940. C.M.B. LAWRENCE Co.: On wet face of exposure of the Homewood Sandstone, near Rock Point, October 15, 1910. O.E.J. and G.K.J. SOMERSET Co.: Vicinity of Trent. Aug., 1932. Chas. M. Hepner.

5. TRICHOSTOMUM Bruch

Dioicous, rarely autoicous: densely cespitose, medium size, green to yellowish-green: stem with central strand, erect, radiculose, rarely felted, densely leaved, mostly dichotomously branching; leaves spreading, mostly crisped when dry, upper leaves much the larger, long and narrow, more or less concave to canaliculate, margins mostly erect to involute, often undulate, mostly entire; costa well-developed, sometimes ending below the apex or excurrent; upper leaf-cells small, rounded, chlorophyllose, papillose on both faces, towards the base elongated-rectangular, mostly hyaline: seta long, erect; capsule erect, rarely inclined, mostly symmetric, oblong-cylindric to cylindric, short-necked, rarely strumose; basal membrane of peristome low or none, the teeth 16, erect, smooth or papillose, red or yellow, undivided or cleft into two filiform non-articulated divisions which are sometimes approximate in pairs; spore small; lid conic, rostrate, the exothecial cells of the base in vertical series or rarely dextrorsely ascending; calyptra cucullate, smooth.

A genus of about 80 species, widely distributed on earth and rocks. Several species in North America; only one in our region.

1. TRICHOSTOMUM CYLINDRICUM (Bruch) C. Mueller
(*Didymodon cylindricus* Bryologia Europaea; *T. tenuirostre* Lindberg)

Plate XVI

Rather loosely and softly cespitose, yellowish, dark below: stems erect branching, rather flexuous, reaching to 1.5-2 cm in height; leaves about 2-3 mm long, narrowly linear-lanceolate, when dry crisped and contorted, when moist spreading or flexuous, gradually acuminate or sometimes rather abruptly narrowed on an acute apex, the margin papillose-sinuate, plane or involute; basal leaf-cells elongate-rectangular or more or less angular-oblong, somewhat inflated, hyaline in a broad band that does not extend up the margin, above rather abruptly becoming much smaller, incrassate, quadrate to rounded-hexagonal, the median and upper rounded-quadrate to rounded-hexagonal or transversely oblong, densely papillose, much incrassate; costa strong, usually forming the apex of larger pellucid cells: seta single or sometimes in pairs, slender, erect, about 1.5 mm long, yellow; capsule linear-cylindric, brownish; lid conic and obliquely rostrate; peristome-teeth short, untwisted, linear-subulate, fragile, usually more or less irregularly cleft or perforate; spores about .012 mm in diameter, mature in autumn: dioicous: fruit produced but rarely.

On wet non-calcareous stones in brooks or at the base of cliffs in hilly or mountainous districts, in Europe, Asia, South America, and, in North America, from Greenland to Manitoba and southward in the mountains to North Carolina.

Rare in our region. HUNTINGDON Co.: Alexandria. *Porter.* (Porter's Catalogue). McKEAN Co.: Toad Hollow, Bradford, July 19, 1896. Sterile. D.A.B. (figured).

6. TORTELLA (C. Mueller) Limpricht

Dioicous; rarely autoicous: widely and deeply cespitose, the cushions often yellowish-green outside, brownish inside: stem erect, mostly without a central strand, felted-radiculose: leaves tufted at the apex of the stem, widely spreading to recurved-squarrose from a whitish and shining base, cirrhate-crispate when dry, elongate-lanceolate to subulate, margin undulate, entire, usually involute above; costa strong, ending in the apex or excurrent; basal leaf-cells differentiated, hyaline, elongate-rectangular, extending up the margins and forming a Y-shaped area, smooth; upper cells green, small, rounded-quadrangular, thickly papillose on both sides: seta red, long, erect; capsule erect to inclined, oblong to cylindric; annulus rarely differentiated; peristome attached below the rim of the urn, the basal membrane low, teeth 32, filiform, sinistrorsely wound, papillose; spores small; lid small and elongate-conic; calyptra cucullate, smooth, long-rostrate.

A cosmopolitan genus, the 37 species mainly occurring on soil or on rocks; 5 species in North America; 2 in our region.

KEY TO THE SPECIES*

A. Dioicous: leaves long-acuminate ....1. *T. tortuosa*
A. Autoicous: leaves linear-lanceolate to oblong-lanceolate, costa shortly excurrent as an
     abrupt mucro ....2. *T. humilis*

1. TORTELLA TORTUOSA [Linnaeus] Limpricht
(*Barbula tortuosa* Weber and Mohr; *Tortula tortuosa* Ehrhart)

Densely cespitose in rounded tufts, yellowish or pale green above, brownish below: stems stout, branching, up to 6 cm high, red-brown-radiculose; leaves crowded, usually 4-6 mm long, lance-linear, tapering to a gradually acuminate apex, flexuous-spreading, margin crenulate-papillose, more or less undulate, plane at the apex; leaves when dry strongly spirally crispate-contorted; costa strong, pale, excurrent into the fine and sometimes denticulate acumen; basal leaf-cells thin-walled, hyaline, extending obliquely up the mar-

---

* *Tortella nitida* (Lindb.) Brotherus, with leaves (when dry) curling in circles at the tip and with the costa lustrous dorsally; and also *T. fragilis* (H. & W.) Limpricht, with leaves curled only slightly at the tip when dry and frequently broken off, may be expected in the northern part of our range.

gin, above becoming abruptly smaller, chlorophyllose, rounded, incrassate, papillose: seta 1-3 cm long, reddish below, paler above; capsule cylindric, 2.5-3.5 mm long, usually somewhat curved, almost erect; lid obliquely and slenderly conic-rostrate, at least one-half as long as urn; peristome-teeth long and from a low basal membrane, two or three times dextrorsely twisted; spores mature in late spring or early summer.

On rocks, usually calcareous, in hilly or mountainous districts, Europe, Asia, northern Africa, and, in North America, from Greenland to the Gulf and from Idaho to Vancouver Island.

Apparently rare in our region. Cambria Co.: Cresson. James. (Porter's Catalogue).

2. Tortella humilis (Hedwig) Jennings
(*Tortula caespitosa* Hooker and Greville; *Barbula caespitosa* Schwaegrichen)
Plate XVII

Loosely cespitose, green to yellowish-green, about 5 mm high; leaves crispate when dry, erect-spreading when moist, oblong-lanceolate and about 2 mm long below, the upper linear-lanceolate and up to 3.5 mm long, somewhat concave, the margin plane or sometimes involute, the perichaetial leaves similar and sheathing; costa strong, excurrent-cuspidate; the lower one-fourth of the leaf has a large V-shaped patch of hyaline rectangular cells reaching about .018 x .085 mm, the median cells rounded-hexagonal, papillose, rather opaque, much smaller, about .007-.008 mm in diameter, the upper similar: seta yellowish-brown, 15-20 mm long, erect, dextrorse; capsule yellowish-brown; ovoid-cylindric, about 2-2.5 mm long, 0.5 mm thick, erect, symmetric, sometimes arcuate, tapering at the base; peristome single, of 32 filiform, papillose, articulate teeth about 0.6-0.8 mm long, two or three times dextrorse, arising from a low membrane scarcely exserted above the mouth of the capsule; spores globose, somewhat papillose, about .008-.011 mm, mature in early summer; operculum narrowly conic-rostrate; calyptra smooth, cucullate, rostrate, covering about one-half of the capsule.

Almost cosmopolitan in temperate or sub-tropical regions on earth and on the roots of trees in the woods.

Allegheny Co.: Coraopolis, September 11, 1905, and near Carnot, October 11, 1908. O.E.J.) (figured). Cambria Co.: James. (Porter's Catalogue). Fayette Co.: Ohio Pyle, September 1-3, 1906. O.E.J. and G.K.J. Huntingdon Co.: On limestone rocks, Pennsylvania Furnace, July 13, 1909. O.E.J. Lawrence Co.: On VanPort limestone, Squaw Run, n. of Ellwood City. C.M.B. Nov. 26, 1948. McKean Co.: Bolivar Run, September 6, 1897. D.A.B. Somerset Co.: Vicinity of Trent. Aug., 1932. C. M. Hepner. Washington Co.: At root of tree, Snake Woods near Washington. Nov., 1891. Linn & Simonton. Westmoreland Co.: Chestnut Ridge, s.e. of Torrance. C.M.B. June 13, 1943.

7. Didymodon Hedwig

Dioicous, rarely synoicous; paraphyses filiform: mostly slender plants, red or brown, cespitose: stem with central strand, thickly foliate, radiculose, the branches reaching to about the same height; leaves more or less keeled, erect-spreading, mostly lanceolate from a broad base, the margin revolute; costa well developed, upwards cylindrical, rarely excurrent; leaf-cells small, rounded-quadrangular, often smooth, sometimes the basal elongate and pellucid: seta long, erect; capsule erect, oblong to cylindric, sometimes slightly arcuate, short-necked, smooth; no annulus; peristome inserted on the edge of the urn, papillose, the trabeculae projecting; teeth 16, plane, narrow, undivided, or perforate, or cleft to the base into filiform parts approximate in pairs; spores small; operculum conic-rostrate; calyptra smooth.

A widely distributed genus of 90 species, on soil or rock, mainly in temperate regions; 17 species in North America; only one in our region.

1. DIDYMODON RECURVIROSTRIS [Hedwig] Jennings
(*D. rubellus* Bryologia Europaea; *Barbula rubella* Mitten;
Weisia recurvirostra Hedwig)

Cespitose in large, soft patches, bright green above, rusty-red below; stems erect, branched, usually 2-5 cm high, radiculose below; leaves when dry flexuous and somewhat curled, when moist somewhat recurved-spreading from the appressed and whitish base, narrowly lance-linear, the comal longer, abruptly acute, margin narrowly revolute to near apex, apex obscurely denticulate; costa either ending in the apex or minutely apiculate-excurrent; basal leaf-cells elongate, rectangular, pellucid, medium-walled, the median and upper much smaller, papillose, rather obscure, quadrate; perichaetial bracts long-sheathing: seta long, red, slender, sinistrorse; capsule erect, oblong-cylindric, becoming reddish-brown, smooth; annulus fragile, revoluble; peristome-teeth 16, united at base into a very low membrance, linear from a wider base, nodose-articulate, reddish, minutely roughened, with the median line but rarely divided; lid short, obliquely conic-rostrate; spores mature in summer or in early autumn: paroicous or synoicous.

On wet, usually calcareous rocks, stones, walls, etc., widely distributed in the Old World and, in North America, occurring from Greenland to Alaska and south to the northern United States. Although not yet recorded from our region this species is to be expected here.

8. BARBULA Hedwig

Dioicous; paraphyses filiform: more or less slender and densely and deeply cespitose, the tufts green to brownish: stems with central strand, thickly-leaved, forked; leaves erect-spreading, rarely recurved-squarrose, keeled, oblong to prolonged linear-lanceolate; with mostly revolute margins; costa strong, ending in the point, or excurrent; leaf-cells very small, thickened and opaque, papillose both sides; basal leaf-cells enlarged, quadrate to rectangular, colored: seta long, erect; capsule erect, rarely a little inclined, oblong to cylindric, straight or rarely a little arcuate; annulus distinct or none; peristome rarely rudimentary, or none; the teeth united below into a rather low basal membrane which is rather deeply inserted, the 32 teeth spirally one to several times dextrorsely wound, filiform; operculum conic-rostrate; calyptra cucullate, long-rostrate, reaching to about the middle of the urn; spores small.

A genus of 300 species distributed over the whole earth, on soil and rocks, many of these species are poorly defined and probably synonymous; about 20 species in North America; only two species definitely known from our region.

KEY TO THE SPECIES

A. Perichaetial leaves high-convolute-sheathing: seta yellow or later reddish ....
....3. *B. convoluta*
A. Perichaetial leaves not as above: seta red or brown ....B
  B. Stem-leaves obtuse, costa shortly mucronate-excurrent ....2. *B. unguiculata*
  B. Stem-leaves acute, costa not mucronate-excurrent C
C. Costa .070 mm wide at base and tapering gradually; leaves widely spreading or but
  little recurved ....1. *B. acuminata*
C. Costa .050 mm wide at base and of equal breadth to the middle; leaves strongly
  recurved or squarrose ....(*B. reflexa* Bridel)

1.   BARBULA ACUMINATA Hedwig
(*B. fallax* Hedwig)

Loosely and widely cespitose, brownish dull green: stems fastigiately branched, slender, 1-5 cm high; leaves somewhat distant, recurved-spreading or arcuate, appressed and slightly twisted when dry, lanceolate-acuminate from the base, the base ovate, the leaves carinate and often faintly plicate below, the margin revolute in the lower half at least, entire; costa strong, ending in the apex; upper leaf-cells small, rounded to hexagonal, incrassate, strongly papillose, gradually larger below, and at the lowest part of the base a few elongate-rectangular and pellucid: seta reddish, capsule brownish, long-ovoid to sub-cylindric, mostly symmetric and erect; lid long, often as long as the urn, acutely rostrate-subulate; peristome-teeth reddish, long, filiform, dextrorsely much twisted, united at base into a low membrane; annulus none; spores mature from late fall to spring: dioicous.

On moist earth, rocks, walls, etc., usually on calcareous substrata, in Europe, Asia, northern Africa, and, in North America from the Arctic region south to Virginia and Iowa. To be expected in northern Pennsylvania.

2.   BARBULA UNGUICULATA [Hudson] Hedwig
Plate XVII

Densely cespitose, yellowish-green: stems erect, somewhat branching, usu-ally about 1 cm high; leaves about 2 mm long, erect-spreading, somewhat recurved, when dry spirally imbricate and twisted, oblong-lanceolate, sometimes lingulate, obtuse, mucronate, entire, the margin recurved below, plane above; costa strong, excurrent and thus forming the rounded mucro; upper leaf-cells small, about .008-.010 mm, rounded-quadrate, incrassate, strongly papillose, obscure, the basal elongate-rectangular, yellowish-pellucid to more or less hya-line, the marginal not different; perichaetial leaves longer and more erect: seta erect, castaneous, lustrous, about 1 cm high, when dry sinistrorse; capsule oblong-cylindric, deep-castaneous, the urn about 1.8 mm long, erect, exannu-late, rather smooth when dry and empty; lid about one-third as long as urn, conic-rostrate, slightly curved or straight; the 16 peristome-teeth castaneous, pellucid, papillose, cleft to the base into 32 filiform divisions, from a narrow membrane at the base twisted into about two turns dextrorsely; spores smooth-ish, yellowish, about .009-.012 mm, mature from November to spring: dioicous.

A quite variable species occurring on moist earth, banks, stones, walls, etc., in Europe, Asia, northern Africa, and throughout southern Canada and northeastern United States.

Allegheny Co.: Schenley Park, Pittsburgh, August, 1905 (figured); Fern Hollow, Pittsburgh, January 21, 1906, and Powers Run, November 30, 1909. O.E.J. Butler Co.: T. P. James. (Porter's Catalogue). Centre Co.: T. C. Porter. (Porter's Catalogue). Huntingdon Co.: T. C. Porter. (Porter's Catalogue). McKean Co.: West Branch Swamp, Bradford, April 10, 1894. D.A.B. Washington Co.: Grove Sta., near Washington. Nov. 5, 1892. Linn & Simonton. Westmoreland Co.: T. P. James. (Porter's Catalogue).

3. Barbula convoluta Hedwig
Plate XVII

Densely cespitose, yellowish-green: stems 1-3 cm high, usually about 1-1.5 cm, erect, branching; leaves about 1-1.5 mm long, when dry crisped, when moist erect-spreading, often somewhat recurved, lance-oblong to lance-linear or lingulate, rounded to obtuse, sometimes sub-acute, concave, the margins mostly plane or slightly recurved on one side at base, mostly minutely crenu-late with bifid papillae; basal leaf-cells elongate-rectangular, pellucid to hyaline, rather incrassate, smooth, median and upper leaf-cells elongate-rectangular, pellucid to hyaline, rather incrassate, smooth, median and upper leaf-cells small, sub-quadrate, densely papillose, strongly incrassate, often rather ob-scure; costa strong, yellowish-pellucid, ending below apex or rarely shortly apiculate-excurrent; perichaetial leaves high-convolute-sheathing, the inner ecos-tate: seta erect, about 1.5 mm long, yellow, or reddish when old, sinistrorse below, dextrorse above; capsule small, symmetric, erect, reddish-brown, narrow-ly oblong, the urn about 1.5 mm long; lid conic-rostrate, oblique, about 1 mm long, the cells spirally arranged; exothecial cells narrow, elongate-rectangular, brownish or yellowish pellucid, two or three series at the rim much smaller, sub-quadrate and darkly obscure; annulus distinct and narrow; peristome-teeth consisting of 32 filiform articulate divisions several times dextrorsely twisted from a low basal membrane; spores brownish-pellucid, medium-walled, smooth-ish, about .016-.018 mm, mature in spring: dioicous.

On soil, especially in calcareous districts, Europe, Asia, northern Africa, and from southern Canada to Florida, Kansas, and California. In our region occurring at Latshaw, southern New York, near the Pennsylvania State-line (figured) and as follows,—not common:

Lawrence Co.: Enon Valley. T. P. James. (Porter's Catalogue). Lycoming Co.: McMinn. (Porter's Catalogue).

9. Acaulon C. Mueller
(Sphaerangium Schimper)

Dioicous: minute, bud-like, brown, gregarious: stem very short and few-leaved, without central strand, unbranched, green protonema persistent; leaves erect-spreading, broadly ovate, keeled or concave, above with revolute and sinuate-denticulate margin, or plane and entire; costa more or less excurrent-cuspidate; upper cells short-rhombic, below rhomboidal, dorsally strong thickened, smooth, rarely with a few high papillae, the lowest thin-walled, hyaline and rectangular: seta very short; capsule sub-globose, cleistocarpous, immersed; calyptra very small and delicate, conic-mitriform 3-5-cleft; spores small, brown, subglobose, minutely granulose.

A widely distributed genus, on soil, mostly in the temperate zone. Fifteen species in all, 3 in North America, 2 in our region.

KEY TO THE SPECIES

A. Uppermost and perichaetial leaves sharply carinate; costa strongly excurrent ....
....1. *A. triquetrum*
A. Uppermost and perichaetial leaves concave; costa rarely excurrent ....2. *rufescens*

1.   ACAULON TRIQUETRUM (Spruce) C. Mueller
(*Sphaerangium triquetrum* Schimper)

Plants minute, about 1 mm high, bulbiform, pale green or yellowish, distinctly triquetrous; protonema green, persistent; lower leaves small, rounded, the middle leaves larger, broadly ovate, deeply concave, convolute, the upper largest (perichaetial) broadly ovate, deeply carinate, triquetrous, all upper leaves with reflexed margins, erose-denticulate above; costa strong, in upper leaves excurrent in a recurved apiculus; basal leaf-cells elongate-hexagonal, lax, thin-walled, hexagonal to oblong-hexagonal: seta about as long as capsule, arcuate; capsule globose, smooth; calyptra minute, mitrate, cleft-lobed, covering only very apex of capsule; spores papillose, about .025-.030 mm, mature in early spring.

On clayey or sandy soil in fields or on banks, Europe, Algeria, and, in North America, from western Canada to New England south to the Carolinas; occurs in Ohio and in Pennsylvania but not yet reported from our range.

2.   ACAULON RUFESCENS Jaeger
(*Phascum rufescens* Kindb.)

Plants minute, bulbiform, about 1 mm high, yellowish-green, not markedly triquetrous: protonema persistent; lower leaves very small, ecostate, the upper much larger, broadly ovate, deeply concave, convolute, plane-margined, erose-denticulate at apex; in larger leaves the costa thick, excurrent into a squarrose-recurved apiculus; leaf-cells about as in *A. triquetrum*: seta flexuose or arcuate; capsule globose, smooth; calyptra and spores similar to those of *A. triquetrum*.

On bare clayey or sandy soil in moist fields, eastern and central North America.

INDIANA CO.: Derry. James. (Porter's Catalogue, as *Sphaerangium muticum* [Schreber] Schimper).

10.   PHASCUM [Linnaeus] Hedwig

Autoicous or synoicous: very small, closely gregarious: stem short, without central strand, erect, simple or bushy-branched; leaves mostly ovate-lanceolate to elongate-lanceolate, mostly with entire and revolute margins, the upper mostly with a strong excurrent costa; upper leaf-cells quadrate to hexagonal, warty-papillose on both sides, rarely smooth; basal leaf-cells rectangular and hyaline: seta very short, sometimes curved; capsule immersed or slightly emergent, sometimes two in a perichaetium, mostly globose and obtusely apiculate, with no indication of an operculum; calyptra cucullate or rarely mitrate, small, conic.

A widely distributed genus of 15 species, on soil; 5 occurring in North America, one in our range.

1.   PHASCUM CUSPIDATUM [Schreber] Hedwig
(*P. acaulon* Linnaeus)

Cespitose, deep green: stems short, 1-2 mm high, simple or forked; leaves crowded, erect, the comal longest, oblong-lanceolate, acuminate, more or less carinate, entire, revolute towards middle; costa excurrent; basal cells lax, hyaline, the upper rectangular to hexagonal, .015-.030 mm, finely dorsally papillose: seta short, straight or curved; capsule globose, sometimes two or three on the same plant, immersed or rarely emergent, obtusely apiculate, about 1 mm long, cleistocarpous; calyptra cucullate, conic, covering only the upper portion of the capsule; spores large, .028-.035 mm, yellowish-pellucid, finely roughened, mature in spring: autoicous or paroicous, antheridia clustered in the axils of the upper leaves.

On soil in old fields, pastures, etc., usually preferring a sandy soil, in Europe, Asia, Algeria, South America, and from Ontario to Virginia and west to Arizona.

Rare in our region. BEAVER CO.: T. P. James. (Porter's Catalogue).

11.   POTTIA Ehrhart, Fuernrohr

Autoicous or paroicous, rarely synoicous or dioicous: small, gregarious to cespitose, green to brownish or whitish: stem with central strand above, often simple, radiculose at base, leafy; leaves tufted above, spreading to imbricate, carinate to deeply concave, oblong to elongate-lanceolate, or spatulate, acuminate to piliferous, rarely obtuse, margin revolute or plane; costa without lamellae, complete to excurrent, rarely incomplete; lower leaf-cells elongate, pellucid, smooth, the upper rounded-quadrate or rounded-hexagonal, mostly papillose on both sides: seta mostly long and straight; capsule exserted or rarely immersed, erect, symmetric, short-necked; annulus none or deciduous or remaining attached; peristome often none or rudimentary, when present of 16 perforate or upwards 2-3-cleft teeth upon a basal membrane, articulate; operculum mainly obliquely rostrate, rarely conic-obtuse, sometimes not deciduous; calyptra cucullate, papillose or smooth, usually falling away with the operculum; spores large, variously papillose or pitted.

A genus of about 50 species widely distributed, on soil or soil-covered rocks, mainly in the temperate zones; 12 species in North America, 1 species in our region.

1. POTTIA TRUNCATA [Hedwig] Fuernrohr

(*P. truncatula* Lindberg; *Gymnostomum truncatum* Hedwig)

Plate XVII

Densely cespitose, dull green: stems simple or sparingly branched, erect, about 2.5 mm high, radiculose at base; leaves numerous, the upper much larger than the lower, obovate to oblong-spatulate, about 1.5-2.5 mm long, soft, spreading, the margins plane, minutely crenulate with the projecting transverse cell-walls, the leaves when dry become twisted, apex abruptly acute, costa strong and excurrent into a short point; basal leaf-cells quadrate to rectangular, large, lax, hyaline, more or less inflated, above becoming gradually smaller, the median and upper medium- to thin-walled, smooth, hexagonal: seta erect, about 3-4 mm high, mostly yellowish; capsule broadly oval or turbinate, erect, symmetric, about 0.6-0.8 mm high, exannulate, more or less castaneous, when dry and empty smooth and turbinate-hemispheric; lid broadly convex to flattish with a beak about one-half as long as the urn; exothecial cells medium-walled, castaneous, pellucid, irregularly quadrate to rectangular, the upper two or three rows at the rim much smaller, rounded-quadrate, obscure; spores orange-pellucid or brownish-pellucid, minutely punctulate, large, .026-.030 mm, mature from autumn to spring.

On moist soil in grasslands, along streams, etc., Europe, Asia, northern Africa, and from Ontario to New England and Maryland, Pennsylvania, and Michigan.

Rare in our region. McKEAN Co.: Corydon Street, Bradford. D.A.B. (figured).

12. DESMATODON Bridel

Autoicous: slender plants in mostly low, soft, green to yellow-green tufts, dense to loose: stem mostly with central strand, thickly foliate, forking; leaves when dry appressed and more or less plicate, when moist erect-spreading, carinate to concave, obovate to ovate or lance-linear, mostly with recurved margins below, plane above, often serrate, sometimes margined; costa ending below the apex or less often mucronately or aristately excurrent; leaf-cells loose, thin-walled, above rounded-quadrate or more or less hexagonal or rhomboidal, mammillose to papillose, below rectangular and long-hexagonal, hyaline, smooth: seta elongate, mostly straight; capsule erect, inclined, or even pendent, mostly symmetric, ovate to cylindric; annulus persistent or falling away in pieces; peristome inserted below the rim of urn, the basal membrane forming a tube which is slightly exserted from the urn, thickly articulate, the 16 teeth rather broad, divided to the base into two or three flat, filiform, papillose, divisions, united here and there, usually twisted; lid stoutly and obliquely rostrate, with the cells more or less spirally arranged; calyptra cucullate, smooth, long-rostrate; spores large.

A genus of 8 species, mainly on rich humus-soil in the mountains or on mostly limestone rocks; one species in our region.

KEY TO THE SPECIES

A. Costa of at least the upper leaves excurrent into a long smooth point ....
....(*D. plinthobius*)

A. Leaves obtuse to short apiculate ....B
   B. Leaves bordered with a band of lighter colored, elongate cells ....(D. Porteri)
   B. Leaves not bordered ....1. D. obtusifolius

1. DESMATODON OBTUSIFOLIUS (Schwaegrichen) Jur.

(Desmatodon arenaceus Sullivant; D. ohioensis Schimper;
Didymodon arenaceus Kindberg)

Plate XVII

Gregarious to loosely cespitose, bright yellowish-green: stems short, in our specimens about 3 mm. long, radiculose at base; leaves erect-spreading when moist, crisped when dry, very small below but increasing to form a comal tuft above, from ovate to lance-ovate, the comal 2-3 mm long, bluntly acute, short-apiculate, the margin entire and more or less revolute; costa strong, reaching the apex or extending into the apiculation; upper leaf-cells opaque, incrassate, papillose, from rounded to hexagonal or quadrate, towards the base of the leaf becoming elongate, thin-walled and hyaline: seta erect, 6-8 mm high, sub-lustrous, sinistrorse, castaneous; capsule dark-castaneous, oblong, the urn 2-4 mm long; peristome-teeth yellow, slender, divided almost to the base into two slender, minutely-papillose prongs; annulus distinct, revoluble; operculum bluntly and obliquely conic-hexagonal, immediately below the annulus being smaller and incrassate; spores smoothish, yellowish, .012-.015 mm, mature in spring.

On sandy soil, rocks, etc., mainly confined to the drainage-system of the Ohio River.

Rather rare in our region. CRAWFORD CO.: Linesville, May 12, 1908. O.E.J. (figured). FAYETTE CO.: Along river-bank at Ohio Pyle, September 1-3, 1907. O.E.J. and G.K.J. McKEAN CO.: Near Bradford, December 15, 1894. D.A.B.

13. TORTULA Hedwig

Autoicous or dioicous, rarely synoicous or polyoicous: small to robust, in green to brown tufts or cushions: stems mostly with a central strand, below brownish- or red-radiculose, simple or branched; leaves mostly larger at the ends of the shoots, often appearing rosette-like, when dry not crispate but somewhat twisted and contorted, when moist erect-spreading, mostly keeled, obovate or spatulate, rounded at the apex or rarely short-acuate, commonly bordered, usually entire; costa strong, often cylindric, often mucronate-excurrent or, more commonly, excurrent into a hyaline hair-like awn; upper leaf-cells rounded-hexagonal, loose, chlorophyllose, papillose, grading below into the rectangular to elongate hyaline basal cells: seta long, erect; capsule erect, cylindric, symmetric, short-necked, straight or sometimes slightly arcuate; annulus present; peristome single, rarely none, basal membrane low to high, teeth 32, filiform, equally spaced, mostly once to twice dextrorsely wound, papillose and transversely striate, articulate; operculum conic, obliquely rostrate; calyptra cucullate, reaching to the middle of the urn; spores small.

A large genus of more than 200 species, widely distributed in the temperate regions, mainly on calcareous rocks or soils; about 40 species occurring in North America; only one species thus far reported in our region.

KEY TO THE SPECIES

A. Small; leaves when dry contorted and twisted; basal membrane low ....B
A. Medium to robust; basal membrane high and tessellated ....D
   B. Teeth rather short, erect or slightly wound c
   B. Teeth long, once to several times wound ....(T. muralis [Linnaeus] Hedwig)
C. Cells of leaf-margin not distinctly differentiated into a border ....
   ....(T. plinthobia [Sull.] Broth.)
C. Cells distinctly differentiated at margin into a border ....
   ....(T. Porteri [James and Aust.] Broth.)
   D. On trees; leaves deeply concave, margins involute; costa spinulose-aristate ....
   ....1. Tortula papillosa
   D. On soil or stones; leaves not deeply concave; margin not revolute; costa smooth-
   cuspidate ....(T. ruralis [Hedwig] Smith)

1. TORTULA PAPILLOSA Wilson, mss., Spring
(Barbula papillosa C. Mueller)
Plate LXII

Loosely cespitose, green, brownish in drying: stem short, up to 1 cm; leaves erect-spreading, when dry appressed but scarcely twisted, broadly obovate-spatulate, sometimes fiddle-shaped (panduriform), with margins involute, the apex rounded to short-acute; costa thick and spongy, dorsally papillose, above ventrally often bearing numerous shortly pedicellate multicellular gemmae, excurrent-mucronate or cuspidate; basal leaf-cells rectangular, a few hyaline, upper leaf-cells pellucid, incrassate, more or less collenchymatous, large, ventrally smooth, dorsally simply papillose: capsule, known thus far only from Australia and New Zealand, reddish-brown, short, with a short seta.

On tree-trunks (in America often on elms), rarely on rocks in open places. South America, New Zealand, Australia, Europe, and, in North America, ranging south in the Atlantic States to North Carolina and west to Michigan.

Rare and always sterile in our region. BLAIR CO.: Tyrone, T. P. James. (Porter's Catalogue). WASHINGTON CO.: On bark of elm tree near Washington. Linn & Simonton. April 7, 1894 (figured) and March 16, 1894.

Family 6. ENCALYPTACEAE

Autoicous, rarely dioicous: robust, usually densely cespitose, bright green, the inside of the cushion rust-colored: stem 3-5-angled with little or no central strand, erect, brown-radiculose, thickly-leaved, branched dichotomously; leaves erect-spreading, when dry folded and twisted, more or less lingulate, acute to obtuse, margins plane to undulate; costa highly developed, usually percurrent to very shortly excurrent, prominent dorsally and dorsally papillose or toothed; cells in upper two-thirds of leaf rather symmetrically hexagonal, chlorophyllose, opaque, thickly papillose on both sides, in the lower third the cells much larger, without chlorophyll, rectangular to rhombic, hyaline or slightly colored, smooth, bordered by a few rows of narrow, elongate, and yellowish cells: seta 0.5-2.5 cm long, erect; capsule erect, symmetric, cylindric, smooth or plicate, mostly with a short neck; annulus present; peristome varying from none to well-developed, usually of 16 teeth; operculum from a conic base very long and slenderly erect-rostrate; calyptra cylindric-campanulate ("extinguisher-like"), long-rostrate, straight, completely enclosing the capsule, the border fringed; spores large and papillose.

A world-wide family mostly on soil and rocks, occurring in the tropics, however, only on the higher mountains. At least 30 species; 2 in our region. The family embraces but one genus, with characters as given for the family.

1.   ENCALYPTA Schreber, Hedwig

KEY TO THE SPECIES

A. Monoicous: no gemmae; peristome single; capsule smooth; leaf-apex with distinct
    point ....1. *E. ciliata*
A. Dioicous: clusters of slender brown gemmae in axils of leaves: peristome double;
    capsule spirally striate; leaf-apex obtuse to bluntly mucronate ....2. *E. streptocarpa*

1.   ENCALYPTA CILIATA Hedwig
(*Leersia laciniata* Hedwig; *Leersia ciliata* Hedwig)

Loosely cespitose, bright green: stems branched, 1-2.5 cm high, densely radiculose below; leaves large, broadly obovate-oblong to lingulate, rounded at apex, apiculate, plane-margined and narrowly recurved below, spreading when moist, crisped and incurved when dry; costa yellowish, ending just below apex or percurrent; basal cells lax, hyaline, rectangular, walls red, the marginal paler and narrower in several rows, the upper leaf-cells opaque, densely papillose, hexagonal-quadrate, the walls pellucid, cells about .015 mm across: seta long, erect, yellowish to reddish, dextrorse; capsule cylindric, reddish-brown, smooth, constricted below mouth and smooth when dry, at base abruptly tapering into the seta; peristome single, the teeth 16, lanceolate, reddish, inserted below the rim, irregularly divided in some specimens, papillose, articulate, strongly incurved when moist; annulus none; exotherial cells smaller in several rows at the rim; lid erect, nearly as long as urn, narrow, slenderly rostrate-clavate; calyptra straw-colored, mitrate, cylindric, slenderly rostrate, extending below the base of capsule, the lower margin fringed with a row of narrowly lanceolate teeth; spores roughened, mature in late summer or early fall: autoicous.

In crevices or shaded places on rocks and walls, almost cosmopolitan in mountainous or hilly regions; in North America from the Arctic region south to the northern United States. Reported from the adjacent states of New York and Ohio and to be expected from the northern part of our range.

2.   ENCALYPTA STREPTOCARPA Hedwig
(*E. contorta* Lindberg)

EXTINGUISHER MOSS
Plate LXII

Densely cespitose, dull or yellowish-green; stems up to 3 to 6 or 7 cm high, branched, densely radiculose at base; leaves rather crowded, spreading, when dry twisted and crisped, large, 5-6 mm long, oblong-lingulate, sometimes narrowed in the middle, more or less undulate, plane-margined, often incurved and sub-cucullate at apex; costa strong, reddish, ending just below apex, dorsally scabrous; basal leaf-cells hyaline, rectangular to elongate rectangular, 1-4:1, the marginal often forming a distinct border of a few rows of linear-elongate cells, upper leaf-cells hexagonal-quadrate, about .015 mm, multipapillose, incrassate-pellucid, usually regularly seriate; perichaetial leaves oblong, abruptly long lanceolate-acuminate: seta long, red; capsule long, cylindric, dextrorsely orange-striate, furrowed when dry; peristome double, the teeth filiform, papillose, articulate, red, the inner peristome of 16 or 32 filiform pale segments half as long as the teeth and adherent to the latter by the broad puncticulate basal membrane; lid narrow, long, rostrate, erect; calyptra very long, cylindric, scabrous at the tip of the long and slender beak, extending considerably below the capsule and laciniate at the border; spores mature in late summer; dioicous.

On rocks, walls, earth, etc., usually in crevices on calcareous substrata, mainly confined to rough country. Europe, Asia, and from Ontario and Virginia to British Columbia. Not yet found fruiting in North America.

Rare in our region. Cambria Co.: Cresson. T. P. James. (Porter's Catalogue). Westmoreland Co.: In limestone rock on Chestnut Ridge, 2 miles east of Hillside, Charles M. Boardman, May 30, 1936 (figured).

Family 7. Grimmiaceae

Autoicous or dioicous: cespitose, dark green to blackish: stem mostly without central strand, radiculose only at the base, branches mostly of equal height, leaves often hyaline-pointed, often piliferous, but rarely crispate, when damp more or less spreading, rarely secund, mostly lanceolate, rarely and then only upwards denticulate, towards the apex and at the margin two to several cells thick, sometimes papillose; costa complete or nearly so; cells small, often sinuate-walled; above mostly rounded-quadrate, towards the base inflated and mostly pellucid, rectangular to elongate, rarely linear throughout the whole leaf: seta rarely shorter than the capsule; capsule mostly symmetric, globose to cylindric, mostly smooth, often immersed or emergent; annulus present, or none at all; teeth 16, mostly separate to the insertion, red to orange, papillose, plane, undivided or cleft or cribrose, rarely divided to the base into filiform parts, trabeculae mostly projecting only outwards; operculum mostly rostrate, sometimes deciduous with the attached columella; calyptra mostly small, mitrate or cucullate, glabrous, sometimes campanulate and plicate.

A large family, world-wide in distribution, but most abundant in sub-arctic and temperate regions, mostly on stones or rocks, rarely on soil or trees. In Grout's *Moss Flora* the Hedwigiaceae are included as a sub-family of the Grimmiaceae.

Key to the Species

A. Costa with basal guides, or homogeneous; calyptra rarely campanulate; spores small to medium-sized ....B

A. Costa with several median guides; spores small; calyptra campanulate; basal leaf-cells smooth-walled ....1. *Ptychomitrium*

B. Teeth undivided, cribrose, cleft in upper half, or none; branches as high as the stem; basal leaf-cells mostly smooth-walled ....2. *Grimmia*

B. Teeth divided almost to the base into two filiform divisions; branches irregular short; basal leaf-cells with nodulose or sinuose walls ....3. *Rhacomitrium*

1. Ptychomitrium Fuernrohr

Autoicous: cespitose in loose yellowish-green to brownish or blackish cushions; stem with central strand, erect or ascending, radiculose at the base, thickly-leaved; leaves long, narrow, the points not hyaline, crispate when dry, spreading when moist; costa strong, percurrent or ending below the apex; cells not with sinuose walls, smooth, upwards small and rounded-quadrate, below linear to more or less loosely rectangular; perichaetial leaves not sheathing: seta straight, more or less elongate, mostly two or more to a perichaetium; capsule smooth, erect, symmetric, mostly oval to oblong-elliptic; annulus wide, deciduous, rarely none; peristome inserted below the mouth; teeth 16, papillose, usually deeply divided into two subulate prongs, trabeculae more or less distinct; spores small; operculum conic with a long, fine, straight beak; calyptra campanulate, plicate and lobed, reaching about halfway down the capsule.

A widely distributed genus of 62 species, of which at least 9 occur in North America and one in our region. Occurring on rocks and stones,—rarely on trees.

1. Ptychomitrium incurvum (Muhlenberg) Sullivant

Plate LXIII

Densely cespitose, dark green to brownish: stems about 5 mm high, erect; leaves erect-spreading when moist, sometimes incurved, twisted-crispate when dry, the lower small, increasing in size upwards, linear-lanceolate, obtuse, thick, opaque, the margin plane; costa broad, ending in apex; basal leaf-cells rectangular, pellucid, the upper much smaller, rounded to quadrate, incrassate, dense; seta about 2-3 mm high, erect; capsule erect, oval; peristome-teeth 16, long-subulate, articulate, papillose; lid erect, conic-subulate, about as long as urn; calyptra long-rostate, mitrate, plicate-lobed to base of beak, covering a little more than half of the urn; spores mature in spring.

On more or less exposed calcareous rocks from Connecticut to Georgia and Texas. Not uncommon in eastern Pennsylvania, northern Ohio, and western New York.

Westmoreland Co.: On limestone rock, 1½ miles east of Hillside, Chestnut Ridge, C.M.B. May 30, 1936 (figured).

2. Grimmia Ehrhart, Hedwig

Autoicous or dioicous: forming cushions and mats, slender, often hoary by reason of the hyaline leaf-apices: stem erect or ascending, mostly with a central strand, radiculose mainly at the base, thickly-leaved; leaves imbricate when dry, rarely crispate or spirally appressed, spreading to recurved-squarrose when moist, lower often small and bract-like, the upper often suddenly larger, often hyaline-piliferous, carinate, concave, sometimes canaliculate, mostly lanceolate from an oblong or ovate base, acuminate, entire, margins plane or revolute; costa complete or extending to the base of the piliferous apex; upper cells small, rarely papillose, rounded-quadrate, often opaque, looser towards the middle, the basal linear to rectangular, mostly smooth-walled, and sometimes forming a colored border; perichaetial leaves mostly larger, more or less sheathing, areolation looser: seta sometimes shorter than the capsule, rarely much longer than the perichaetial leaves, arcuate or straight, mostly yellow, twisted when dry, capsule mostly symmetric, smooth to ribbed, globose to cylindric; annulus persistent or curling off, sometimes none; peristome rarely absent, when present inserted below the mouth; teeth reddish-brown, broad to subulate, entire to cribrose, sometimes cleft to the middle, the trabeculae projecting outwards; operculum often rostrate, never longer than the urn; calyptra lobed-mitrate to cucullate, long-rostrate, smooth; spores small, .010-.012 mm diameter.

A large genus of world-wide distribution, but mainly confined to the mountains of the tropics, occurring on rocks and stones. About 230 species, of which more than 90 occur in North America and at least 4 in our region.

KEY TO THE SPECIES

A. Seta not longer than the capsule; operculum mostly falling with the columella still attached; hyaline leaf-points decidedly spinulose ....B
A. Seta longer than the capsule ....F
  B. Apices of upper leaves with short hair-points C
  B. Apices of upper leaves long-piliferous ....E
  C. Lower and median leaf-cells with sinuose walls ....4. *G. laevigata*
  C. Lower leaf-cells not with conspicuously sinuose walls ....D
    D. Slender small plants in dense cushions; central strand in stem; teeth decidedly cribrose or cleft ....2. *G. conferta*
    D. More robust, loosely cespitose; with indistinct central strand; teeth slightly cribrose or entire ....1. *G. apocarpa*
  E. Leaf-cells without sinuose walls; capsule oblong; calyptra often cucullate, ...
    ....(*G. ambigua* [Sullivant] Sullivant)
  E. Leaf-cells with somewhat sinuose walls; capsule oblong-ovate ....3. *G. pilifera*
  F. Capsule distinctly ribbed; seta curved; leaf-margins of a single layer of cells ....
    ....(*G. Olneyi* Sullivant)
  F. Capsule smooth, seta straight; upper leaf-margins of more than one layer of cells ....G
  G. Leaves lanceolate, tapering; basal leaf-cells thin-walled and elongate-rectangular, about 1:4 to 1:8, alpine ....(*G. obtusa* Schwaegrichen; *G. Doniana* Smith)
  G. Leaves ovate to oblong-lanceolate, the long apex rough, piliferous; basal leaf-cells more or less quadrate ....4. *G. laevigata*

1. GRIMMIA APOCARPA [Linnaeus] Hedwig

Plate XVIII

Loosely cespitose, more or less erect, branching rather freely, about 2 cm high, dull olive-green, drying stiff and non-crisped: leaves ovate-lanceolate, erecting-spreading, strongly costate and usually more or less carinate, margin narrowly recurved, apex narrowly obtuse, leaves about 2 mm long; perichaetial leaves similar but somewhat longer and thinner; costa ending in or just below the apex, terete dorsally; basal cells rectangular, about .008-.010 x .015.030 mm, upper basal cells quadrate, and in our specimens usually sinuose-walled, the

median and upper cells rounded and .005-.009 mm in diameter, all cells incrassate and more or less opaque: seta erect, stout, about 0.5 mm long; capsule
immersed, oval-oblong, about 1 mm long, reddish-brown, rather thick-walled,
smooth; calyptra short, lobed; operculum low-conic, rostrate; peristome single,
teeth 16, lance-linear, trabeculate, somewhat cribrose, reddish-brown, faintly
papillose, when dry reflexed-revolute; spores reddish-brown, in our specimens
about .012-.018 mm in diameter; columella falling away with the operculum
and remaining attached to it; spores mature in late spring.

On stones, hard earth, etc., with a wide distribution over the colder regions
of the earth. In America occurring from Alaska and Newfoundland to the
Northern States and south in the mountains to Georgia.

G. apocarpa var. gracilis (Schleicher) Weber and Mohr occurs on rocks
from lower Canada to West Virginia and Tennessee. It grows in loose, slender
mats up to 10 cm long; leaves lanceolate, acuminate, 1.5-2 mm long.

Now known from the following counties: Butler, Erie, Fayette, Greene, McKean
(Porter), Washington (Porter), and Westmoreland. Specimen figured: Shaly bank of
stream, Shades Ravine, east of Trafford, Westmoreland Co., March 25, 1910. O.E.J.

2. GRIMMIA CONFERTA Funck
(G. apocarpa var. conferta (Funck) Sprengel)

Densely cespitose, in gray-green rounded cushions: stems slender; leaves
1 mm or less long, keeled, margins revolute, lance-ovate to oblong, acuminate,
opaque, apex hyaline, denticulate; costa strong, dorsally prominent, ending at
apex; basal leaf-cells rectangular to quadrate, the upper smaller and rounded,
all incrassate and dense: seta short; capsule immersed, ovate-globose, wide-
mouthed, hemispheric and somewhat wrinkled when dry; peristome-teeth light
reddish-brown to orange, fragile, markedly cribrose; annulus said to be none;
lid wide, low-convex, apiculate; spores mature in spring.

On rugged exposed rocks, Europe, Asia, and Africa, and, in North America, from Nova Scotia to British Columbia south to Idaho and North Carolina.

WASHINGTON CO.: Linn and Simonton. (Porter's Catalogue).

3. GRIMMIA PILIFERA Beauvois
(Grimmia pennsylvanica Schwaegrichen)
Plate LXIII

Densely cespitose, dark green: stems 1 to 3 cm high, robust, rigid, branching; leaves close, narrowly ovate-lanceolate, acuminate, concave, the hyaline
point usually distinctly spinulose; margins somewhat recurved below and
thickened above; basal leaf-cells linear-rectangular 3-6:1, thin-walled, hyaline
to yellow-pellucid, shortly above base the cells incrassate-sinuous, short-rectangular, the upper rounded-quadrate to hexagonal, small, piliferous: seta about
half as long as urn, capsule more or less completely immersed, oblong-ovate,
smooth, even when dry, lid conic-rostrate, about three-fifths as long as urn,
erect; annulus large; peristome-teeth large, broadly lanceolate, irregularly split
and cribrose to about the middle, castaneous pellucid; calyptra lobed, mitrate;
spores mature in the autumn but often not shed till spring: dioicous.

On moist rocks in woods, Japan and, in North America, from Nova Scotia to Georgia and Minnesota, and in Mexico. Reported from Painesville, Ohio (W. C. Werner) and in Pennsylvania.

FAYETTE CO.: Meadow Run, Ohio Pyle, June 23, 1940, C. M. Boardman (figured). WASHINGTON CO.: On sandstone rock on high hill, near Grier's Station. A. Linn and J. S. Simonton. Oct. 5, 1898.

4. GRIMMIA LAEVIGATA (Bridel) Bridel
(*G. campestris* Burch.; *G. leucophaea* Greville)

Cespitose loosely in wide, dull gray-green tufts; hoary above: stems stout; leaves close, larger towards top of stem, when dry imbricate-appressed, very concave, oblong-oval to rather widely ovate, 1-1.5 mm long, plane-margined, at the apex abruptly terminating in a hyaline, flattened, finely denticulated hair; the smaller lower leaves acuminate but without the hair-point; costa narrow, ending in the apex; basal leaf-cells quadrate, except a few rectangular ones near the costa, the upper smaller and rounded, all incrassate, non-sinuose, the upper quite chlorophyllose; seta erect; capsule included, or emergent, 1-2 mm long, elliptic, broadly oblong, brownish smooth when dry; annulus large; lid conic-rostellate, short, peristome-teeth cleft to about the middle, cribrose below, castaneous-pellucid; calyptra mitrate, lobed; spores mature in spring.

On rocks, mainly non-calcareous, often granite or sandstone, almost cosmopolitan. In North America from New York and Pennsylvania to Alabama and northwestward to Oklahoma; also in the west. Rare in our region.

BLAIR CO.: Tyrone, T. P. James. (Porter's Catalogue).

3. RHACOMITRIUM Bridel

Dioicous: robust plants, loosely and widely cespitose, the mats green to yellowish or blackish-green: stem without central strand, procumbent to erect, radiculose at the base only, uniformly foliate, often with numerous short branches giving the shoot a nodose appearance; leaves spreading to recurved-spreading or sometimes secund, when dry appressed, from an ovate to oblong base mostly lanceolate to lance-linear, more or less long-acuminate, often piliferous, sometimes lingulate and obtuse, margins sometimes 2-layered and sometimes recurved; costa mostly broad flat, and complete; cells nearly all with sinuose or nodulose walls, often papillose, towards the base or sometimes all over linear: seta long, straight, rarely curved, twisted; capsule erect, oblong to cylindric, narrow-mouthed, smooth; annulus broad, curling off; teeth united at the base but mostly cleft deeply into 2 (-3-4) filiform divisions, often very long, trabeculate; spores small; operculum conic with a long subulate apex from one-third to more than the length of the urn; calyptra mitrate, lobed, not folded, subulate-rostrate, glabrous or rough.

A world-wide genus of about 90 species, mostly on siliceous rocks; about 10 in North America; probably 2 species in our region.

KEY TO THE SPECIES

A. Upper leaf-cells quadrate, lower ones linear; shoots not appearing nodose by arrange-
ment of short lateral branches .... .B

A. Upper leaf-cells elongate; shoots appearing nodose with short lateral branchlets ....D
   B. Leaves lingulate; leaf-apex broad and rounded ....1. *R. aciculare*
   B. Leaves lanceolate-acuminate C
C. Leaf-apex hyaline-acuminate ....2. *R. microcarpum*
C. Leaf-apex obtuse, not hyaline ....3b. *R. heterostichum* var. *gracilescens*
   D. Leaf-apex acute, not hyaline; seta 4-5 mm long ....(*R. fasciculare*)
   D. Upper leaves with hyaline points; seta 4-10 mm long ....
   ....3a. *R. heterostichum* var. *ramulosum*

1. RHACOMITRIUM ACICULARE [Linnaeus] Bridel

(*Dicranum aciculare* Hedwig)

Plate XVIII

Cespitose in coarse tufts, dark dull green to blackish; stems long, up to 6 or 8 cm long, stout, branching by short innovations, radiculose below; leaves erect-spreading, stiffly imbricate when dry, large, up to 1 mm wide by 2.5 mm long, broadly ovate-oblong, usually somewhat plicate at the base, the margin usually revolute, the apex broadly obtuse, denticulate to entire, non-hyaline, the upper margin usually thickened; costa strong, ending below apex; leaf-cells densely yellowish-pellucid, incrassate, sub-papillose, the upper sub-quadrate to rounded-hexagonal and in two layers at the margin, the basal elongate-rectangular to linear, markedly sinuose-incrassate, at the margin sub-quadrate, the alar a little larger, quadrate: seta erect, straight, about 10-12 mm long; capsule dark brown, erect, oblong-cylindric to elliptic, smooth, with narrow mouth; peristome-teeth cleft to below the middle into 2 or 3 unequal divisions; lid aciculate-rostrate or subulate, almost as long as urn; calyptra smooth, long-rostrate, mitrate, lobed, covering only the top of capsule; annulus rather large, revoluble; spores mature in spring; fruit rarely found.

On wet, shaded, non-calcareous rocks in hilly or mountainous country, in Europe, Africa, and, in North America, from Alaska and Labrador south to California and Alabama. Occurs in northern West Virginia and Pennsylvania.

Now known from Butler, Cambria (Porter), Clearfield, Fayette, Somerset, and Westmoreland counties. Specimen figured: Ohio Pyle, Fayette Co., in crevices of rock along the river near the falls. Sept. 1-3, 1906. O.E.J. & G.K.J.

2. RHACOMITRIUM MICROCARPUM (Hedwig) Bridel, not Schrader

(*Rhacomitrium sudeticum* Bryologia Europaea; *Trichostomum microcarpum* Hedwig; *R. heterostichum* var. *sudeticum* (Funck)

Loosely cespitose, dull or yellowish-green above: stem slender with ascending branches, 2-5 cm high; leaves divaricately spreading, erect when dry, narrowly lanceolate, linear-acuminate, apex hyaline, denticulate, margin more or less bistratose above, usually revolute below; costa strong, ending in apex; basal leaf-cells linear, sinuose, incrassate, upper leaf-cells rounded-quadrate: seta short, light-colored, often curved or flexuose; capsule relatively very small, elliptic, pale brown, thin-walled; annulus large, revoluble; peristome-teeth brownish, irregularly divided; lid conic-rostrate, shorter than the urn; spores mature in spring.

On wet rocks or cliffs, principally granite or gneiss, Europe, Asia, and, in

North America, from Greenland to British Columbia, south to Oregon and northeastern United States. Perhaps to be expected in the eastern or northeastern part of our region.

3.   RHACOMITRIUM HETEROSTICHUM var. RAMULOSUM (Lindberg) Jones

(*R. ericoides* (Schwaegrichen) Jennings; *Trichostemum ericoides* Schwaegrichen)

Cespitose in low, green to yellow-green tufts: stems slender, markedly nodose with obtuse lateral innovations; leaves crowded, spreading to falcate-secund, lanceolate from an ovate base, acuminate, the apex hyaline, flat, denticulate, not very narrow, margin revolute, not thickened; costa strong, ending in the apex; leaf-cells all linear, the upper 3-6:1, incrassate, sinuose, the marginal shorter and in the alar portion often a few larger, rectangular, pellucid, and not sinuose-walled: seta yellowish, short; capsule small, elliptic-cylindric to oblong, pale yellow-brown, thin-walled; annulus large, revoluble; peristome-teeth short, divided almost to the base; calyptra somewhat papillose at the apex; lid short-rostrate; spores mature in spring.

On exposed rocks and stones in hilly or mountainous regions, Europe, and, in North America, from Greenland to British Columbia south to Oregon, eastern Pennsylvania and Georgia. Perhaps will be found in the eastern part of our region.

3b.   RHACOMITRIUM HETEROSTICHUM var. GRACILESCENS Bry. eur.

Plate LII

When dry forming crisped, blackish-green, dense tufts about 1 cm deep, the prostrate stems 1-3 cm long and sending up short, irregularly spaced upcurved branchlets which, when dry have closely appressed leaves and are less than 1 mm thick; when wet the leaves spreading-ascending or somewhat recurved-spreading; leaves about 2 mm long, concave, from a broader base slenderly lanceolate to a narrow, obtuse, entire apex, the base sub-clasping, the margins entire, thickened and imperfectly bi-stratose, narrowly revolute; costa 50-60 μ thick, prominent dorsally, percurrent into the somewhat cucullate leaf-apex, bi-stratose with usually 2-3 smaller interior cells; basal cells enlarged, somewhat colored in a narrow basal band, with a few somewhat larger rounded alar cells, above these the cells rapidly becoming strongly incrassate and sinuose, the median lower about 3-3.5 by 8-10 μ, these at the apex roughly rounded and about 2.5μ in diameter. Some of the upper cells appear faintly papillose.

The specimen here described and figured was collected by Charles M. Boardman on rocks at Beck Spring, Laurel Ridge, Somerset Co., s.w. Pa., July 26, 1947, and seems best placed under the polymorphic *R. heterostichum*, nearest to var. *gracilescens*, although were the cells papillose it might as well be referred to *R. protensum* Braun. The variety *gracilescens* is a very rare alpine moss found in the U. S. on Bald Mountain, near Camden, Maine.

Family 8.   ORTHOTRICHACEAE

Dioicous or autoicous, rarely heteroicous or polyoicous: cespitose, light green to yellowish- or blackish-green outside the tufts, inside brown to black:

stem mostly with no central strand, erect to ascending, or creeping with erect or ascending branches, radiculose below, or along the creeping stem, with reddish or brownish filaments; leaves spreading to squarrose, carinate, mostly from a decurrent base more or less lanceolate, sometimes oblong-lingulate to linear, mostly entire, usually papillose both sides; costa strong, sometimes excurrent-aristate or piliferous; upper cells generally rich in chlorophyll, round-quadrate to round-hexagonal, basal mostly elongate rectangular to linear, pellucid; perichaetial usually more or less sheathing: seta erect; capsule erect, symmetric, collum distinct, oval to pyriform or cylindric, smooth or striate, deeply plicate when dry and empty; annulus persistent; peristome mostly double, rarely none; teeth 16 united or approximate in 8 pairs, lanceolate, flat, whitish to yellowish or reddish, reflexed when dry, exteriorly papillose or transversely, obliquely, or longitudinally striate, rarely smooth, rather delicately trabeculate; inner peristome of 8 or 16, filiform, or lanceolate; glabrous or papillose segments alternating with the teeth; spores small to very large; operculum long-rostrate; calyptra cucullate and sometimes smooth to campanulate, often plicate and hairy.

A rather large family of mostly tree-inhabiting species, mostly of temperate regions.

KEY TO THE GENERA

A. Calyptra cucullate, not plicate; stems erect or creeping ....B
A. Calyptra mostly campanulate, plicate; stems mostly erect C
  B. Stem erect: peristome none; leaves crispate when dry ....1. *Amphidium*
  B. Stem creeping with erect or ascending branches: peristome single ....2. *Drummondia*
  C. Leaves when dry crispate, at the base ovate and mostly with a hyaline border; capsule exserted in our species ....4. *Ulota*
  C. Leaves not ovate at the base nor with hyaline border: capsule immersed or emergent in our species ....3. *Orthotrichum*

1. AMPHIDIUM (Nees) Schimper

(*Amphoridium* Schimper; *Zygodon* Authors)

Autoicous or dioicous: tufts cushion-like, soft, often extensive, yellowish olive-green to blackish, inside rusty brown: stem furcately branching, uniformly foliate, radiculose to the apex with smooth filaments; leaves linear-lanceolate, papillose both sides, when dry contorted or crispate; costa practically complete, with median guides; leaf-cells thick-walled, angular to roundish, green, towards the base generally elongate, rectangular, thin-walled to hyaline; perichaetial leaves erect, longer, sheathing or half-sheathing: seta short, generally erect, thickening above and grading into the long collum; capsule emergent to exserted, mostly erect, pyriform, with 8 projecting, reddish-brown ribs, when empty much widened at the mouth and urceolate; annulus none; peristome none; operculum obliquely rostrate from a low-conic base; calyptra cucullate, glabrous, not plicate.

A world-wide genus of 12 species, on mainly non-calcareous rocks; 5 species in North America; 2 in our range.

KEY TO THE SPECIES

A. Autoicous: leaf-margins plane: seta 1.5 mm long or less; beak of operculum shorter than radius of capsule ....1. *A. lapponicum*

A. Dioicous: leaf-margins recurved below: seta about 3 mm, long; beak of operculum longer than radius of capsule ....2. *A. Mougeotii*

1. AMPHIDIUM LAPPONICUM (Hedwig) Schimper

(*Anictangium lapponicum* Hedwig; *Zygodon lapponicus* Bryologia Europaea)

Densely cespitose, dark olive-green above, blackish below: stems dichotomously branching, usually 1-3 cm high; leaves flexuous-spreading, lance-oblong to lance-linear, 1.5-2.0 mm long, margins plane, acute, crisped when dry; costa strong, ending below apex; basal cells large, thin-walled, pellucid to hyaline, the upper small, quadrate-hexagonal, rather obscure, incrassate, papillose; perichaetial leaves sheathing: seta very short, usually not over 1.5 mm; capsule oval with distinct collum about as long as sporangium, partially immersed, brownish, when dry constricted below mouth, urceolate, with 8 reddish striae, the mouth forming a deep red, thickened rim; no peristome; lid red, lustrous, small, low-conic, obliquely rostellate, the length of the beak not more than one-half the diameter of the capsule; calyptra cucullate, small, reaching about half-way down the urn, brownish; spores mature in early summer: autoicous, the antheridial flowers axillary along the stem.

In crevices of shaded rocks, rarely in calcareous habitats; Europe, Asia, and, in North America, from Greenland to British Columbia south to northern United States and to California.

Rare in our region. HUNTINGDON CO.: Porter. (Porter's Catalogue).

2. AMPHIDIUM MOUGEOTII (Bryologia Europaea) Schimper

(*Zygodon Mougeotii* Bryologia Europaea; *Anoectangium Mougeotii* Lindberg)

Densely cespitose, in large tufts, yellowish-green above, rusty to blackish below: stems usually 2-6 cm high, dichotomously branching; leaves spreading or erect-spreading, crisped when dry, elongate lance-linear, acuminate, carinate, margin narrowly revolute below, slightly irregular above; costa strong, vanishing at apex; basal leaf-cells narrowly rectangular, rather thick-walled, above shorter, sub-quadrate to rounded, incrassate, hardly papillose, pellucid; perichaetial leaves sheathing only the base of seta: seta about 2-3 mm long; capsule shortly exserted, narrowly oval with a distinct neck, when dry urceolate, only slightly contracted below mouth, 8-striate: peristome none; lid low, obliquely rostrate, the length of the beak at least one-half the radius of the capsule: calyptra cucullate; spores mature in summer or early autumn: dioicous: fruit rare.

On damp, shaded, usually non-calcareous rocks, in mountains or hilly regions; in Europe, Asia, and in North America, from Newfoundland to Alaska south to Alabama and Oregon. To be looked for in the eastern part of our range.

2. DRUMMONDIA Hooker

Autoicous or dioicous: slender, in low, dense, green, scarcely shining, often extensive mats: stem long, creeping, brown-radiculose, thickly covered with short, erect, simple or furcate branches; leaves when dry stiffly appressed, when moist erect-spreading to spreading, ovate-lanceolate to linear-oblong, acute or obtuse, entire; costa strong, almost percurrent; cells uniformly rounded, smooth, chlorophyllose: seta erect, long; capsule erect, symmetric, oval, smooth, when dry shriveled; annulus none; peristome simple, inserted below urn-mouth; teeth 16, very short, truncate, entire, smooth, densely trabeculate; spores very large (.08-.10 mm); round or oval, several-celled, green, smoothish; operculum obliquely rostrate; calyptra cucullate, large.

A small genus of 7 species, on trees, rarely on rocks; mostly Asiatic, one in our region.

1. DRUMMONDIA PROREPENS [Bridel] Jennings

(*Anodontium prorepens* Bridel; *Gymnostomum prorepens* Hedwig; *Hypnum clavellatum* Dillenius; *Orthotrichum clavellatum* Hooker)

Plate XVIII

Stems creeping, radiculose on the under side, with numerous short, erect branches, 6-10 mm, forming dark green or blackish tufts: leaves erect to spreading, oblong to ovate-lanceolate, 1 to 1.5 mm long, obtuse to acute, concave, carinate, firm; costa strong, almost percurrent; cells small, thick-walled, rounded; the alar often quadrate-inflated and hyaline in the stem-leaves, the whole lower fourth of the perichaetial leaves elongate-rectangular and hyaline: seta erect, about 2.5 mm long, sinistrorse; capsule ovate-globose, smooth, about 1 mm high; operculum low-conic, obliquely long-rostrate; peristome of 16 very short, wide, truncate, smooth, trabeculate teeth, often more or less confluent; annulus none; calyptra, at first conic, large, cucullate; spores minutely roughened, chlorophyllose, about .080-.095 mm, moderately incrassate, mature in summer.

On tree-trunks in woods, Japan, and in North America from New England to Alabama, Missouri, and Ontario.

ERIE Co.: Presque Isle, May 8-9, 1906. O.E.J. (figured). McKEAN Co.: Quintuple, Bradford, November 10, 1893. D.A.B. WASHINGTON Co.: Linn and Simonton. (Porter's Catalogue).

3. ORTHOTRICHUM Hedwig

Autoicous, rarely dioicous: cespitose in cushions sometimes on rocks, mostly on trees: stems erect and ascending, radiculose at the base, thickly leaved, branched; leaves when dry never crispate but straight and appressed, ovate-or linear-lanceolate, mostly acute, margins usually revolute; costa quite strong, mostly not quite percurrent; basal leaf-cells rectangular to elongate, pellucid to hyaline, the marginal often shorter and green: seta generally shorter than the scarcely or non-sheathing perichaetial leaves; capsule oval to cylindric, usually with 8 or 16 colored striae, when dry usually 8 (-16)-furrowed; annulus persistent; peristome mostly double, sometimes single, rarely none, usually with 16 broadly lanceolate teeth in pairs, and 8 to 16 filiform segments; operculum conic to convex, rostrate; calyptra campanulate, plicate, covering most of the urn, glabrous, hirsute or papillose.

A cosmopolitan genus of about 200 species, on trees or rocks, rare, however, in the Tropics; about 60 species occur in North America; at least 5 in our region.

KEY TO THE SPECIES

A. Peristome simple, teeth 16, erect or erect-spreading when dry ....B
A. Peristome double, teeth more or less reflexed when dry ....D
  B. Capsule half-emergent, 16-striate ....(*O. cupulatum* [Hoffmann] Schwaegrichen)
  B. Capsule immersed to half-emergent, 8-striate C
  C. Capsule ovate-cylindric, half-emergent when leaves are dry ....1. *O. strangulatum*
  C. Capsule much shorter, ovate-globose, practically immersed in the dry leaves ....
  ....2. *O. Lescurii*
    D. Capsule smooth when dry, immersed ....E
    D. Capsule plicate when dry ....F
  E. Teeth 16, in pairs; segments 8, short, filiform ....(*O. pusillum* Mitten)
  E. Teeth 16, not in pairs; segments 16, comparatively broad ....
  ....(*O. elegans* Hooker & Greville)
    F. Leaves more or less obtuse at the extreme apex ....G
    F. Leaves usually distinctly acute at the extreme apex I
  G. Capsule strongly contracted below the mouth when dry and very decidedly plicate with reddish-brown folds ....3. *O. stellatum*
  G. Not very strongly contracted nor very decidedly plicate ....H
    H. Stomata immersed; leaf-margins revolute ....4. *O. ohioense*
    H. Stomata not immersed; leaf-margins erect; leaves short and broad, oblong-ovate to lingulate, obtuse, usually with brood-bodies ....6. *O. obtusifolium*
  I. Capsule but little contracted below mouth when dry, ribs orange, segments 8; leaves oblong-lanceolate ....5. *O. pumilum*
  I. Capsule strongly contracted under the mouth when dry ....J
    J. Capsule with very prominent reddish-brown ribs when dry, half-emergent ....
    ....3. *O. stellatum*
    J. Capsule with less prominent light colored ribs, usually immersed (or emergent) ....
    ....(*O. sordidum* Sullivant)

1.   ORTHOTRICHUM STRANGULATUM Schwaegrichen

(*O. Porteri* Austin; *O. cupulatum* var. *Porteri* Venturi)

Plate XVIII

Densely cespitose, about 1 cm high: stems densely leaved, branched; upper leaves lanceolate, about 3 mm long, the lower ovate, shorter, acute, margins entire or papillose, more or less revolute, lamina often somewhat bi-stratose at margins and apex; costa strong, almost percurrent; basal leaf-cells quadrate at margin to rectangular (2:1) towards costa, smooth, hyaline, the median rounded-hexagonal, dense, papillose, becoming towards apex densely incrassate-rounded, arranged in quite regular rows: seta short, about 0.5 mm, capsule about 1.5 mm long, oblong-cylindric, tapering rather gradually to the seta, when dry often only partly immersed, when wet always immersed, dark reddish-brown, deeply 8-costate and 8-furrowed, the costae with about 3 rows of rectangular cells with thicker longitudinal walls, stomata few, immersed, calyptra mitrate, quite densely erect-hirsute; operculum low with a rounded apiculation; peristome single, teeth paired, papillose, erect-spreading when dry, irregularly triangular-lanceolate, about 8-articulate, the divisural distinct and the teeth often split; the three or four upper rows of cells of the capsule densely incrassate, brown, pellucid like the costal and laterally oblong; spores globose, papillose, .017-.020 mm, mature in summer.

On rocks, mostly limestone, from Alabama to Missouri, Minnesota, and New England.

Rare in our region. CAMBRIA CO.: Cresson. James. (Porter's Catalogue). CENTRE Co.: On limestone 2 mi. w. of Scotia, Sept. 22, 1909. O.E.J. (figured). WESTMORELAND Co.: On rocks, Chestnut Ridge above Hillside. Sept. 23, 1910. O.E.J. & G.K.J.

2. ORTHOTRICHUM LESCURII Austin
(O. cupulatum var. minus Sullivant)
Plate XIX

Rather densely cespitose, about 5 mm high: stems thickly-foliate, branched; leaves lanceolate or some of the lower ovate, the upper about 3 mm long, the lower shorter, acute, the margins entire, revolute, strongly costate nearly to the apex; basal leaf-cells quadrate to elongate-rectangular, smooth, hyaline, above becoming rounded-hexagonal, sub-opaque, densely papillose, smaller and quite regularly hexagonal at the apex; seta very short, 0.5 mm, about one-half enclosed in the involucre; calyptra narrowly campanulate, plicate, hirsute with erect hairs; lid mamillate, rounded but flattened; capsule oblong-cylindric and rather suddenly tapering to the seta, about 1.3 mm high and 0.5 mm in thickness, when moist globose-oblong and 8-striate, when dry deeply 8 furrowed and sometimes contracted below the mouth; capsule always about the same length as the upper leaves, or sometimes slightly exserted when dry; peristome single, the teeth 8, short, equidistant but leaning towards each other in pairs, triangular-lanceolate, papillose, articulate, the divisural usually complete and often split, teeth when dry erect or incurved; spores mature in spring, .014-.017 mm.

On rocks, usually granite or trap; from New England to Ontario south to Missouri and Pennsylvania, and in the Rocky Mountains to British Columbia.

Rare in our region. WESTMORELAND CO.: On sandstone rocks at mouth of Bear's Cave, on slope of Chestnut Ridge above Hillside, September 16, 1910. O.E.J. and G.K.J. (figured).

3. ORTHOTRICHUM STELLATUM Bridel
(O. Braunii Bryologia Europaea; O. strangulatum Sullivant)
Plate XIX

Sparsely cespitose to scattered, less than 5 mm high, dark green: stems sometimes creeping at base, erect-spreading, simple or branched; leaves spreading when moist, the upper somewhat clasping, when dry appressed, not crisped, concave, ovate to lance-ovate, the margins more or less revolute, apex sub-acute to obtuse, sometimes erose-denticulate and sometimes hyaline; costa strong, sub-percurrent basal leaf-cells hyaline, smooth, at margin quadrate, about .016 mm in diameter, toward the costa rectangular and reaching about .090 x .016 mm, median cells papillose, opaque, rounded, about .020 mm in diameter, the apical smaller, rounded and less papillose; capsule oblong-oval, about 1.2 mm long tapering abruptly into a seta about two-thirds as long, 8-costate, when dry much constricted below the mouth and very deeply 8-plicate, somewhat sinistrorse, reddish-brown; peristome-teeth lighter in color, granulose, with distinct divisurals, when dry closely reflexed, when moist erect, segments linear, shorter than teeth; calyptra narrowly conic-mitrate, non-hirsute and plicate; spores globose, somewhat papillose, incrassate, about .017 mm in diameter.

On bark of living trees (often on apple and butternut trees.—Strout); Europe, Asia, northern Africa, and from Nova Scotia to Georgia and Iowa.

Scarce in our region. ALLEGHENY CO.: On base of *Quercus imbricaria* in mixed pine and oak woods at Dutil Church, near Douthett, December 29, 1908. O.E.J. (figured). McKEAN CO.: Bradford. D. A. Burnett. (Porter's Catalogue).

4.   ORTHOTRICHUM OHIOENSE Sullivant
(*O. canadense* Sullivant, not Bryologia Europaea)
Plate XIX

Densely cespitose, yellowish green above, dark or brownish below: stems freely branching, about 6-10 mm high; leaves lanceolate from an oblong base, about 1.5-3 mm long, spreading to ascending, bluntly acute to rounded-obtuse, papillose with entire and revolute margins; costa strong, ending at a little below the apex; median leaf-cells quadrate to rectangular, moderately incrassate, towards the margins and upwards becoming smaller, more incrassate, quadrate, sub-papillose, the upper small, rounded, densely papillose, incrassate: seta shorter than the urn; capsule more or less completely immersed, ovate-oblong when moist to somewhat narrower and pyriform-campanulate when dry, symmetric, when dry 8-striate, pale yellow, tapering at base, slightly constricted below the mouth; exothecial cells at mouth in one to three rows, small, quadrate, below abruptly rounded and strongly incrassate, on the main body of the urn rectangular and much smaller; stomata immersed, the outer peristome of 8 double teeth, yellowish-pellucid, densely puncticulate, triangular-lanceolate, 5-7-articulate; segments of inner peristome of 8 short, linear-subulate segments of two rows of cells; calyptra conic-campanulate, yellowish, plicate, densely erect-hairy; operculum low-convex, apiculate-rostrate; spores yellowish-brown, pellucid, densely papillose, .018-.020 mm, mature in spring.— about April: autoicous, antheridial clusters axillary.

On bark of trees, New Brunswick to Ontario and south to Georgia.

Probably rather common in our region. Ashtabula, Ohio, and as follows: ERIE CO.: On bark of *Populus deltoides*, Presque Isle, September 20-22, 1906. O.E.J. McKEAN CO.: Langmade, Bradford, May 8, 1898. D.A.B. (figured). WASHINGTON CO.: On bark of fallen willow, Hackney Station, A. Linn and J. S. Simonton, April 27, 1894.

4a.   ORTHOTRICHUM OHIOENSE var. CITRINUM (Austin)
Lesquereux and James
(*O. citrinum* Austin)

Leaves dark green, narrowly lanceolate; capsule thin, yellow.
On bark of trees and with about the same range as the species.

Occurs in our region at Painesville, Ohio, and as follows: WESTMORELAND CO.: T. P. James. (Porter's Catalogue).

5. ORTHOTRICHUM PUMILUM Dickson

Densely cespitose, dark green, tufts less than 1 cm high; stems only a few mm high; leaves erect-spreading, lance-oblong, when dry imbricated and straight, obtuse to short-acuminate, margin recurved; upper leaf-cells rounded-hexagonal, rather thin-walled for the genus, relatively rather large, minutely papillose, the basal cells larger, rectangular and smooth; costa strong, ending a little below the apex: seta very short, capsule immersed, small, when moist oval-oblong with a distinct neck, when dry narrower, constricted below the mouth, 8-plicate, yellowish to orange; stomata immersed; exothecial cells quadrate to rectangular-hexagonal, becoming at the mouth much smaller, rounded, and rather obscure; peristome-teeth 8, bigeminate, yellowish-pellucid, triangular-lanceolate, papillose, when dry reflexed, the segments almost as long, lance-subulate, 8 in number; calyptra smooth, short, inflated, lustrous, with few or no hairs, light yellow; spores .012-.015 mm, mature in spring: autoicous.

On trunks of trees; Europe, Asia, Algeria, and, in North America, from southeastern Canada to Tennessee and westward to Idaho and Utah.

Rare in our region. WASHINGTON CO.: Linn and Simonton. (Porter's Catalogue).

6. ORTHOTRICHUM OBTUSIFOLIUM (Schrader) Bridel
Plate LXIII

Small yellowish-green tufts up to about 8-10 mm high; leaves appressed when dry, spreading when moist, about 1.5-2.5 mm long, oblong-ovate to lingulate, entire, decurrent, trough-shaped with plane margins, obtuse to broadly acute; costa strong but ending below apex; thick-walled brood-bodies abundant on apical upper surface of some leaves; upper leaf-cells thick-walled, rounded, basal marginal short-rectangular, basal median somewhat larger and elongate-rectangular, middle and upper cells with low blunt papillae.

On deciduous tree bark, from southern Canada and New England to Maryland and from Alaska to our Southwest.

WASHINGTON CO.: "On fallen ash tree," near Washington, Linn and Simonton, Feb. 10 and Mar. 16, 1894 (figured).

4. ULOTA Mohr

Autoicous, rarely dioicous: mostly forming cushions on living trees: stems often creeping with erect or ascending branches, radiculose; leaves mostly (except *U. americana*) crisped or contorted when dry, mostly spreading to squarrose, from a broadly concave base lance-linear, carinate, with margins mostly revolute below; costa percurrent or nearly so; basal cells narrowly linear, yellowish but with a margin of one to several rows of hyaline, thin-walled, rectangular to quadrate cells: capsule erect, exserted, with long, tapering neck, symmetric, 8-plicate when dry, stomata superficial; annulus persisting; peristome mostly double, segments usually 8, rarely 16 or none; lid convex or conic, rostrate; calyptra mitrate, with 10-16 obtuse folds, incised-lobed at base, hirsute with shining golden-yellow hairs or rarely almost glabrous.

A world-wide genus of about 50 species, most numerous in America; in North America about 15 species; in our region three species.

KEY TO THE SPECIES

A. Rupestral; leaves not crispate when dry ....1. *U. americana*
A. Arboreal: leaves more or less crispate when dry ....B
  B. Capsule smooth, slightly plicate below the distinctly narrowed mouth and at the
    neck ....2. *U. Ludwigii*
  B. Capsule wide-mouthed, distinctly plicate C
    C. Capsule constricted below the mouth, gradually narrowed at base to the long neck:
      teeth confluent ....3. *U. crispa*
    C. Capsule not distinctly constricted below the mouth, abruptly narrowed to the shorter
      neck; teeth separated at apex ....3a. *U. crispa* var.*minus*

1. ULOTA AMERICANA [Beauvois] Limpricht, not Mitten
(*U. Hutchinsiae* Hammar)
Plate XIX

Rather loosely cespitose, blackish with greenish tips, about 1 cm high, or
less: stems creeping, sparingly branched with erect branches, when dry the
leaves appressed and straight; leaves often with hair-like paraphyllia at base,
lance-ovate or linear-lanceolate from an ovate base, carinate, concave at least
below, margins usually revolute in lower half, costa and base of lamina pellucid-
castaneous, apex sub-acute; costa strong, sometimes percurrent; apical and
median leaf-cells incrassate, papillose, rounded-quadrate, rather opaque, the
basal marginal rounded-quadrate to rounded-rectangular, hyaline, towards the
costa becoming linear, more or less vermicular and occasionally anastomosing,
much incrassate and markedly pellucid-castaneous: seta about 2 mm long,
smooth, with a distinct smooth volva at base; capsule yellowish, cylindric-
oblong, basally tapering, when dry 8-costate and with more or less distinct
intermediate costae at mouth, the neck and seta decidedly dextrorse; stomata
immersed; peristome-teeth 16, more or less paired, articulate, granular, when
dry strongly reflexed, segments 8, about one-half as high, bi-seriate below;
calyptra yellowish, mitrate, plicate, incised-lobate at base, densely clothed with
erect to spreading slender hairs; lid conic-rostrate; spores globose, papillose,
incrassate, about .016-.018 mm, mature in spring.

On non-calcareous rocks, mainly in hilly or mountainous regions; Europe,
Asia, and from New Brunswick to Georgia and west to the Rocky Mountains.

Common in our region. CAMBRIA Co.: Cresson. T. P. James. (Porter's Catalogue).
CENTRE Co.: Dry rocks at top of Bald Eagle Mt., near Matternville, July 14, 1909.
O.E.J. FAYETTE Co.: On rocks in bed of Youghiogheny River at Ohio Pyle, September 1-3, 1906. O.E.J. and G.K.J. HUNTINGDON Co.: T. C. Porter. (Porter Catalogue). McKEAN Co.: On rocks, Rutherford, May 13, 1898. D.A.B. SOMERSET
Co.: On dry, crumbling shale, Ursina, May 12, 1905. O.E.J. (figured).

2. ULOTA LUDWIGII (Bridel) Bridel
(*Weissia coarctata* Lindberg)
Plate XIX

Loosely cespitose, yellowish green: stems more or less creeping with erect
shoots often 1 cm high, usually shorter, somewhat branched below; leaves
erect-spreading but slightly twisted when dry, lance-ovate to lanceolate, concave
at base, often carinate-concave in upper third, acuminate above but the extreme

apex rather obtuse, the margin entire and often recurved; costa strong, reddish, sub-percurrent; basal leaf-cells at margin quadrate, hyaline, towards the costa rectangular to linear-vermicular, reddish-pellucid, the median cells rounded-quadrate, incrassate, slightly papillose, the apical cells similar; capsule pyriform, tapering into a slender dextrorse seta, seta and capsule together about 3.5 mm long, capsule strongly costate but with a very small mouth and, even when dry, smooth and plicate only immediately below the mouth, pale yellowish-brown, stomata superficial at the base of the urn; calyptra narrowly conic-mitrate, hairy; lid rostellate; peristome single, or rarely with rudimentary segments, teeth somewhat paired but split apart above, when dry erect, narrowly triangular, granulose, distinctly articulate, with a distinct divisural; spores papillose, globose, about .020-.022 mm in diameter, mature in summer.

On tree-trunks in woods, usually in mountainous or hilly country; Europe, and in North America from the Gulf of St. Lawrence to Ontario and south to North Carolina.

Rather uncommon in our region. CENTRE CO.: Bear Meadows. T. C. Porter. (Porter's Catalogue). MCKEAN CO.: Rutherford, March 6, 1893. D.A.B. (figured). SOMERSET CO.: Bark of Butternut tree, Fall Run, near Barronville, John F. Lewis, May 17, 1930. WASHINGTON CO.: Linn and Simonton. (Porter's Catalogue).

3. ULOTA CRISPA [Linnaeus] Bridel
(*Ulota ulophylla* Brotherus; *Orthotrichum crispum* Hedwig)

Plate XX

Densely cespitose, yellowish-green above, darker below, the tufts about 8 mm high: stems sparingly branched, growing perpendicular to the bark on which it is found, sometimes decumbent at base; leaves straight and erect-spreading when moist, when dry much crisped, narrowly lance-ovate to sharply acute to acuminate at the apex, concave and more or less carinate, often marginally revolute; marginal basal leaf-cells hyaline, the inner basal pellucid, linear, often somewhat vermicular, the median cells incrassate, rounded, bluntly papillose, the apical cells smaller and less papillose; costa strong, sub-percurrent; seta and capsule together about 4 mm long, capsule ovate-globose when wet, about 1 mm long, tapering rather gradually into the neck and seta, when dry somewhat constricted below the mouth, with the neck and seta dextrorse, the costa brownish-pellucid; annulus brown, pellucid, of about 3 series of small, close-set, rounded, cells; teeth triangular-lanceolate, united into 8 pairs, when dry reflexed, each pair confluent and cribrorse at apex, often split along the divisural below; segments 8, consisting of two rows of cells nearly up to the apex, a little shorter than the teeth; spores globose, about .023-.026 mm, mature in summer.

On trees in woods; Europe, Asia, Tasmania, Alaska, and from Newfoundland to Georgia and west to Minnesota.

Fairly common in our region, especially on black oak trunks. Now known from Allegheny, Butler, Cameron, Centre, Crawford, Fayette, McKean, Potter, Washington, and Westmoreland counties. Specimen figured: on black oak truunk, Bald Eagle Mt., near Matternville, Center Co., Sept. 22, 1909. O.E.J.

3a. ULOTA CRISPA var. MINUS (Schwaegrichen) Jennings
(*U. crispula* Bruch)

With shorter stems and leaves than in the species and a capsule which rather abruptly narrows into a long neck, and with a sub-globose to oval urn, which, when dry and empty, is more or less open-mouthed and turbinate, with little or no constriction below the mouth.

This variety is reported with a general range similar to that of the species but we have as yet seen no typical specimens of it from our region. Grout (Moss Flora) does not regard *minus* as sufficiently distinct from *crispa*. Porter's Catalogue lists it from several counties in Eastern Pennsylvania and from McKean County, D. A. Burnett; but a specimen in the Herbarium of the Carnegie Museum collected by Burnett, at Langmade, May 29, 1898, McKean County, is evidently purely *U. ulophylla.*

Family 9. SPLACHNACEAE

Autoicous or dioicous, rarely pseudautoicous: annual or perennial cespitose bog or alpine mosses, usually living on decaying animal or vegetable matter, the tufts green to yellow-green, inside more or less red-radiculose, sometimes blackish: stem delicate with a large central strand; leaves mostly distant, flaccid, more or less broad; costa mostly not quite percurrent, usually with two basal guides; leaf-cells loose, parenchymatous, 4-6-sided, elongate towards the base, sparingly chlorophyllose, often inflated at the margin of the leaf: seta erect, sometimes very long; capsule erect, symmetric, with a long collum or with a large colored hypophysis: usually brownish or red when mature, operculate, and with a peristome of 32 divisions joined together to form 16 teeth (except *Tayloria splachnoides*) and often grouped in twos or fours, and usually consisting of three layers. There is a pre-peristome present in a few species. The peristome teeth more or less hygroscopic, vertically striate, trabeculate, punctate, mostly golden-brown. Annulus usually none; spore-sack surrounded by a cavity; columella strong; spores small to large; operculum convex to umbonate or long-conic, rarely none; calyptra small, either cucullate and united into a tube below or conic and almost entire to lobed.

There are 5 genera and more than 60 species of these peculiar plants, widely distributed in mostly cold northern and alpine regions.

KEY TO THE GENERA

Hypophysis much wider than the capsule ....1. *Splachnum*
Hypophysis not much if any wider than the capsule ....2. *Tetraplodon*

1. SPLACHNUM Linnaeus

A genus of 7 or 8 species of mostly cold northern bogs and on decaying cattle dung. Only the following species known from our region.

1. SPLACHNUM AMPULLACEUM Linnaeus
Plate LII

Loosely caespitose, up to about 1 cm high, in low tufts matted together below by reddish-brown filaments; monoecious, the perigonial branches arising from within the matted material. Leaves of the fertile stem few, about 1 mm long, tufted, thin, obovate to broadly lanceolate, abruptly acuminate, costate into the apex, usually with a few sharp teeth towards the apex; leaf-cells large, lax, irregularly rhomboid-hexagonal but longer towards the margin and base and smaller above; perigonial branches up to about 1 cm high much exceeding the perichaetial, sparsely leafy with lanceolate slenderly pointed, above sharply serrate blades; antheridial flowers capitulate to discoid, surrounded by squarrose very slenderly acuminate squarrose perigonial leaves up to 3 mm long: seta erect, somewhat twisted when dry, reddish; hypophysis much wrinkled when dry, when wet about 3 mm long by 2 mm thick, pyriform, more slenderly tapering below, when ripe red-purple above, somewhat lilac below, composed of loose tissue and with stomata surrounded by a ring of stellately radiating cells; capsule oval-oblong, about 1 mm high; operculum convex, obtusely mamillate; peristome yellowish, consisting of 32 divisions united to form 16 three-layered teeth forming 8 triangular groups, very hygroscopic, inflexed when wet and abruptly strongly reflexed when dry, the areolation of the middle layer of cells strongly predominating when viewed under the microscope and being quite irregular in pattern; pre-peristome consisting of 16 very thin, oblong-lingulate teeth about one-fifth the height of the main peristome; annulus none; areolation of the capsule walls of rounded, small, strongly incrassate cells; columella much exserted from dry capsule dilated at the apex; spores smooth, 6-7 μ in diameter.

Mostly on cow dung, New Jersey, Pennsylvania, and Ohio to Wisconsin, and north to Newfoundland, Quebec, and Ontario.

These specimens are smaller in practically all parts than stated in most descriptions.

ELK Co.: Midmont Swamp. C.M.B. July 1, 1948. Elev. 1940 ft. SOMERSET Co.: Open sphagnum bog, near Mt. Davis. Elev. 2400 ft. C.M.B. & O.E.J. July 15, 1949 (figured).

2.   TETRAPLODON Bruch & Schimper

A genus of at least 9 species, mostly on decaying animal excreta of cold northern and alpine regions and resembling Splachnum excepting for the narrower leaves, hypophysis little if any wider than the capsule, and teeth first in fours then in pairs, and consisting of two layers of cells.

1.   TETRAPLODON ANGUSTATUS (Hedwig) Bryologia Europaea
(*Splachnum angustatum* [Linnaeus f.] Hedwig)
Plate LXXII

In dense tufts; stems erect, about 8-12 mm tall, pale translucent-yellowish, with dense reddish tomentum below; leaves few, rather distant except for about four to seven in a comal tuft, these being about 3-5 mm long by 0.5-0.8 mm wide, narrowly lance-oblong, tapering into a very long slender acumination, usually with a few, scattered, sharply spreading, one-celled teeth; costa loosely cellular, at base about one-fourth to one-third the width of the leaf, tapering gradually into the long, somewhat reddish, flexuous, excurrent point; leaf-cells lax, thin walled, rather irregular rectangular, two to six times as long as wide, narrower along the margin: seta pale yellowish, somewhat translucent, about 4-8 mm long in our specimens and exceeding the leaves, abruptly tapering above into a pale yellowish hypophysis with a dark brownish center; hypophysis when moist about 0.7-0.9 mm long, smooth, pyriform-oval, when dry shrunken and deeply wrinkled and corrugated; capsule when moist about as long as the hypophysis, narrowly cylindric-oval, about twice as high as thick, when dry much constricted in the middle, reddish purple towards the rim; peristome teeth 16 (32 divisions), adhering in 8 groups which, when mature and dry are abruptly reflexed and occasionally split apart into 16 teeth, each of the eight groups triangular, blunt, about twice as high as wide at the base; operculum low-hemisperic, distinctly bluntly apiculate; calyptra narrowly conical; spores smooth, thin-walled, globose to ellipsoid, about .007-.009 mm in diameter.

Usually occurring on animal droppings and heretofore reported as ranging from the Catskills to Minnesota and the Rockies, north to Newfoundland, Athabasca, and British Columbia.

SOMERSET CO.: Open sphagnum bog, near Mt. Davis, at an altitude of 2400 ft., O. E. Jennings, Aug. 21, 1936; and July 15, 1949, Charles M. Boardman (figured). In one case the plants were intermingled in the same tuft with *Splachnum ampullaceum.*

This station marks an extension of more than 250 miles south of the previously known range but the plants were here in company with other northern bog plants such as Menyanthes which is here also at its southernmost frontier. The leaves are somewhat less serrulate than is generally described for *T. angustatus,* the spores slightly smaller, and the fallen capsules which were shaken out of the tufts scarcely appeared to be capable of entirely covering the capsule. Otherwise the specimens seem typical.

Family 10. DISCELIACEAE

Dioicous; gregarious, annual, with persistent protonema: stem very short with gemmiform foliation; inner leaves largest, ovate to lance-oblong, obtuse to acute, with plane margins, entire or irregularly crenulate at apex, faintly costate towards apex; cells irregularly loosely rhomboid-hexagonal, thin-walled, somewhat pellucid, elongated below, smooth, very sparsely chlorophyllose: seta elongate, 2-3 cm, stiff, slender, pellucid, red or castaneous, sinistrorsely twisted; capsule minute, cernuous or horizontal, globose-ovate, smooth, with a very short collum; annulus of one (or two) series of cells, falling away in pieces; peristome inserted below the mouth, simple; teeth lanceolate, acute, red, the lower half usually perforate or split, the exterior usually vertically striate but with no median line, not papillose, the interior with papillae and projecting trabeculae: spores medium size; operculum reddish or orange, large, convex, umbonate; calyptra split down on one side and usually remaining attached to the seta by the constricted base.

A peculiar family consisting of but one genus with only the following species. Occurring on bare soil in northern Europe, Asia, and, in North America, in Illinois, Ohio, eastern Pennsylvania, and New Jersey.

1. DISCELIUM Bridel

1. DISCELIUM NUDUM (Dickson) Bridel

(*Discelium incarnatum* (Schwaegrichen) Jennings; *D. nudum* Bridel;
Weisia incarnata Schwaegrichen)

Plate LXIII

Characters as for the family.

The Ohio station for this species is near Ashtabula, only a few miles from the northwestern corner of Pennsylvania.

ALLEGHENY CO.: Four miles east of Monongahela City, C. M. Hepner, April 8 and April 16 (figured), 1934; roadside ditch 1 mile north of Indianola, C. M. Boardman, Nov. 24, 1935, and May 10, 1936.

Family 11. EPHEMERACEAE

Autoicous or dioicous, rarely polyoicous or synoicous; minute, about 1-2 mm high, singly disposed or gregarious, mostly stemless; protonema persistent; leaves minute, rosette-like, spreading or erect-spreading; leaf-cells mostly lax, more or less elongate below, rectangular to rhomboid-hexagonal, above shorter, usually smooth; costa none to excurrent, usually present: seta none or short; capsule immersed, sub-globose, cleistocarpous (or with dehiscence line in *Nanomitrium*); operculum sometimes differentiated but rarely deciduous of itself; spores mostly large and papillose; calyptra mostly small, delicate, mitrate-campanulate.

Minute plants growing on soil.

1. EPHEMERUM Hampe*

Dioicous, rarely polyoicous: minute plants with abundant and persistent green protonema: upper leaves elongate-lanceolate to linear; costa none or variously developed; leaf-cells lax, mostly thin-walled, rhomboidal: seta rudimentary or none; capsule mostly globose and apiculate, cleistocarpous, walls (exothecium) of two layers of cells with stomata; spores large, up to .08 mm in diameter, warty; calyptra campanulate, delicate, torn at the base or sometimes only on one side.

A cosmopolitan genus of about 30 species; most abundant in North America, perhaps several of these occurring in our region, but on account of their minute size not yet collected.

KEY TO THE SPECIES

A. Costa none ....B
A. Costa more or less complete, or vanishing towards the base C
  B. Leaves lanceolate, erect-patent, spores .060-.080 mm ....
....1. *E. serratum* [Schreber] Hampe

---

* *Nanomitrium* Lindberg (*Micromitrium* Austin) differs from *Ephemerum* in having a rudimentary but not deciduous operculum and the capsule without stomata and with a wall but one cell thick; leaves ecostate and calyptra minute.

Leaves entire ....*N. synoicum* (James) Lindberg
Leaves serrulate ....*N. Austinii* (Sullivant) Lindberg

B. Leaves linear-lanceolate, often secund; spores smaller ....
....(E. serratum var. angustatum Bryologia Europaea)
C. Costa percurrent or vanishing near the apex ....D
C. Costa excurrent and quite strong ....G
   D. Upper leaves broadly lanceolate to elongate-lanceolate ....E
   D. Upper leaves linear to linear-lanceolate, long-acuminate ....F
   E. Capsule short, obtuse; costa effaced at base, upwards towards the apex continuous
....2. E. cohaerans
   E. Capsule acutely beaked; costa loosely areolate, scarcely distinct except towards the
      short, entire, pointed apex ....(E. pallidum Schimper)
      F. Calyptra smooth ....G
      F. Calyptra papillose ....(E. crassinervium var. papillosum (Austin) R. & C.)
G. Leaves linear-lanceolate; costa excurrent, weak at base, serrate at apex ....
....3. E. crassinervium
G. Leaves linear; costa usually strong and wide at base, decidedly excurrent and strongly
   spinulose ....(E. spinulosum Schimper)

1. Ephemerum serratum (Hedwig) Hampe
(Phascum serratum Schreber)
Plate LXIV

Protonema abundant, branched, persistent, alga-like, growing on wet soil. Plants minute, under the hand-lens looking like little buds. Leaves up to 1 or 1.5 mm long, ecostate, ovate to ovate-lanceolate, sharply serrate down to the middle or beyond; leaf-cells irregularly rhomboid-hexagonal to rectangular and up to 6:1. Antheridia usually 3 or 4, narrowly obovoid, about half the length of the longest leaves. (Capsule not seen but described as "shining globular to kidney-shaped, warty, maturing winter to spring."—Grout).

On open, wet soil. Rare. New York to Ohio and North Carolina; California.

Erie Co.: Around margins of Old Fog Horn Pond, Presque Isle. July 27, 1933. Nelle Ammons (figured).

2. Ephemerum cohaerans (Hedwig) Hampe
(Phascum cohaerans Hedwig)

Plants minute, 1-1.5 mm high, densely gregarious or somewhat cespitose: protonema persistent, green or yellowish with age; leaves lance-ovate to lance-oblong, erect-spreading, acute, serrate above; costa thin, stronger above, ending in the apex or just below; leaf-cells lax, oblong-hexagonal, rather thin-walled: capsule sub-sessile, castaneous, sub-globose, obtusely apiculate, bearing stomata all over; calyptra more or less lobed or torn at base; spores large, .060-.080 mm, coarsely tuberculate, mature in late autumn: dioicous.

On moist sandy or clayey soil, Europe and, in eastern North America, south to Louisiana. Not yet collected in our region but occurring in eastern Pennsylvania and in Ohio.

3. Ephemerum crassinervium (Schwaegrichen) C. Mueller, not Hampe
(Phascum crassinervium Schwaegrichen)

Plants minute, not over 1 mm high, gregarious: green protonema persistent; leaves erect-spreading, flexuous, linear-lanceolate, slenderly long-acuminate, rather coarsely serrate above, marginally plane; costa flat, faint below, stronger above, excurrent, denticulate dorsally above; leaf-cells more or less rectangular to oblong-hexagonal, thin-walled: capsule with a very short seta, immersed, globose, apiculate; the capsule about half-covered by the cleft-lobate, mitrate-conic calyptra; spores large, papillose, mature in late fall to early spring.

On moist earth, often in swamps, eastern North America from Connecticut to Florida and Illinois. It occurs in central Ohio and eastern Pennsylvania and is, probably, the plant collected by James in Indiana County as reported in Porter's Catalogue, but specimen not seen.

Family 12. FUNARIACEAE

Autoicous or paroicous, rarely dioicous or synoicous: annual or rarely biennial, low, mostly light green, gregarious or loosely cespitose: stem mostly with a central strand, radiculose only at the base; leaves soft, wide, the upper larger and forming a rosette, concave, margin plane to involute, entire or denticulate upwards, sometimes bordered; costa delicate, rarely excurrent, with two large basal guides, rarely lacking; leaf-cells large, parenchymatous, thin-walled, never papillose, but slightly chlorophyllose, oblong-rectangular below, rhombic-hexagonal above: seta mostly erect and red, twisted; capsule either erect, symmetric and globose to pyriform, or cernuous and arcuate-pyriform; collum mostly distinct; annulus rarely present; peristome inserted back of the periphery to the distance of the thickness of several cells, simple or double, rudimentary or none; teeth, if present, 16, obliquely dextrorse, strongly trabeculate; segments, if present, 16, opposite the teeth, with no basal membrane; columella mostly thick; spores mostly medium-sized; operculum mostly weakly convex, sometimes umbonate or none; calyptra various, often inflated, usually rostrate and cucullate.

KEY TO THE GENERA

```
A. Capsule immersed ..........................................................................................................B
A. Capsule exserted ..........................................................................................................C
    B. Capsule more or less regularly dehiscing at about the equator .........1. Aphanorhegma
    B. Capsule with distinct operculum, smaller than urn .................2. Physcomitrium
    C. Capsules unsymmetric, peristomate, usually with a double peristome; seta much
        longer than stem ...............................................................................................3. Funaria
```

1. APHANORHEGMA Sullivant

Paroicous, rarely synoicous: low, gregarious to almost cespitose, pale green; stem radiculose at base, loosely foliate below, densely foliate above; leaves spreading or the upper almost erect, obovate to oblong or spatulate-lanceolate, acute, serrate in the upper half; costa ending below the apex; leaf-cells lax, the basal rectangular, the upper oblong-hexagonal, the marginal forming a narrow uniseriate border: seta rudimentary; capsule spherical, without a collum, laxly areolate; annulus none; peristome none; spores large, densely spinulose; operculum half-spherical, of same size as urn, obtusely apiculate; calyptra conic-mitrate, lobed, glabrous.

A genus of three species, on damp soil.   One in Cuba and the following two in temperate North America:

KEY TO THE SPECIES

A. With strongly collenchymatous exothecial cells; capsule rather regularly dehiscing
....1. *A. serratum*
A. Exothecial cells not collenchymatous, thin-walled; capsule not regularly dehiscing
....2. *A. patens*

1. APHANORHEGMA SERRATUM (Hooker, f. and Wilson) Sullivant
Plate XX

Gregarious, light green: stems erect, simple or forking, 1-5 mm high, radiculose at base; leaves small and lance-oblong below, rapidly becoming larger up to 3-5 mm long, narrowly lance-obovate above, the lower widely spreading and flexuous, the inner erect-spreading, thin, slightly serrate above the middle, apex acute to acuminate: costa medium, ending in or just below the apex; the median basal cells thin-walled and more or less inflated, rectangular, the marginal narrower, a few quadrate at the base, becoming linear-rectangular above the base, in the upper part of the leaf their tips extending as low serrations, the median rhomboid to short rectangular with walls medium, the apical longer and narrower: seta very short and stout; capsule brown when ripe, globose to depressed-globose, about 0.75 mm in diameter, smooth to apically papillose, splitting in the middle along a line of one or two rows of small more or less orange-pellucid cells, the upper half of the capsule (operculum) apiculate-rostrate; exothecial cells of capsule quadrate, conspicuously collenchymatous; calyptra hyaline, conic-mitriform, 4-6-lobed, covering the upper half of the operculum; spores globose, about .030 mm in diameter, orange-pellucid or even darker, mature in autumn.

On damp clayey soil in the northern and middle United States, in our region usually along streams where submerged during periods of high water.

Now known from Allegheny, Butler, Clarion, Fayette, Greene, Potter, Washington, and Westmoreland counties. Specimen figured: Cheat Haven, Fayette Co., Sept. 6, 1910. O.E.J. and G.K.J.

2. APHANORHEGMA PATENS (Hedwig) Lindberg

(*Physcomitrella patens* [Hedw.] Bryologia Europaea; *Phascum patens* Hedwig)

Gregarious, pale green: stem distinct but very short, about 2 mm; leaves lance-ovate to oblong or oval, usually shortly and bluntly acuminate, the upper often obovate-acuminate and larger, forming a rosette, all serrate above; costa narrow, ending below the apex; leaf-cells lax, widely rectangular to hexagonal: seta short, capsule globose, thin-walled, usually splitting equatorially, brownish, immersed to slightly emergent, obtusely apiculate; spores papillose, .025-.030 mm, mature in autumn: paroicous; antheridia sessile in upper leaf-axils.

On wet clayey or sandy soil in fields, along sides of pools, river banks, etc. Europe, Asia, and, in North America, from Quebec to the northern part of eastern United States. Not uncommon in Ohio and also reported from Lancaster County, Pennsylvania. Not yet reported from our region.

2. PHYSCOMITRIUM (Bridel) Fuernrohr

Autoicous: mostly minute, densely gregarious to cespitose, green, mud-inhabiting mosses: stem erect, simple, radiculose below, loosely foliate; leaves flaccid, mostly appressed when dry, spreading when moist, concave, obovate to oblanceolate or spatulate, mostly not margined, more or less serrate, obtuse to acuminate; costa mostly strong, incomplete to excurrent; areolations lax: seta mostly long; capsule erect, symmetric, globose to short-pyriform, with lax areolation; collum short and thick; annulus small-celled and persistent or large-celled and disappearing in pieces; gymnostomous; spores large, papillose; operculum broad, conic-onvex, umbonate or apiculate; calyptra long and erect-rostrate, mitrate, lobed to the base of the beak, covering one-half or less of the capsule.

A cosmopolitan genus of about 75 species; about 20 species in North America, at least 2 species in our range.

KEY TO THE SPECIES

A. Seta very short; capsule immersed, wide-mouthed; calyptra small ....1. *P. immersum*
A. Seta longer; capsule exserted, not wide-mouthed; calyptra larger ....2. *P. turbinatum*

1. PHYSCOMITRIUM IMMERSUM Sullivant
(*Gymnostomum immersum* Sullivant)
Plate XX

Plants small, erect, gregarious, light green, simple or branching, 3-8 mm high; leaves 1.5-3.5 mm long, obovate to oblanceolate, serrate above the middle, spreading to ascending; costa strong, ending a little below the apex; leaf-cells parenchymatous, rather large and thin-walled, the basal rectangular, about 2-5:1, the upper irregularly oblong, the marginal narrower and in the alar region a few much shorter: capsule immersed, globose to pyriform-globose, 0.6-0.9 mm in diameter, apiculate-rostrate, about the upper two-fifths constituting the operculum, yellow-brown when ripe; seta considerably shorter than capsule and stout; exothecial cells irregularly quadrate to hexagonal, somewhat incrassate, the annulus consisting of one to three rows of much smaller, orange-pellucid, to brown-pellucid cells, the cells of the wall usually laterally elongated for one or two rows above and below the annulus; calyptra mitrate, the basal margin 4-5-lobed, covering about one-half of the operculum; spores densely papillose, orange to brownish-pellucid, globose, in our specimens about .035 mm in diameter, mature in autumn.

Usually on clayey or sandy flood-plains where submerged in time of freshets. Quebec to Colorado, Missouri, and the Carolinas, but not commonly collected, probably on account of its small size and special habitat.

ALLEGHENY CO.: Bare clay bank of creek, Darlington Hollow, Aspinwall. Oct. 25, 1908. O.E.J.; Mud cracks in dry pond basin, Glenshaw. Oct. 30, 1932. J. L. Cartledge. BEAVER CO.: Clay bank of Little Beaver Creek, New Galilee, Sept. 10, 1906. O.E.J.; Bank of Ohio River, Smith's Ferry, Oct. 1, 1910. O.E.J. (figured). BUTLER CO.: On ground in cornfield, Millinger School, Dec. 2, 1934. Sidney K. Eastwood. McKEAN CO.: East Branch, Bradford, June 15, 1895. D.A.B.

2. PHYSCOMITRIUM TURBINATUM (Michaux) Bridel

(*Phascum strangulatum* Kindberg; *P. Hookeri* Macoun)

TURK'S-CAP MOSS; URN MOSS

Plate XX

Gregarious, often densely so, light green; stems 3-5 mm high, erect, usua'ly simple; leaves 3-5 mm long, lance-oblong to obovate-lanceolate, slightly serrulate above the middle, flat and spreading when moist, somewhat crisped and incurved when dry; capsule erect, 1.5-2 mm high, globose to pyriform, when dry becoming turbinate and constricted below the mouth and at the base, finally becoming brown and urn-shaped; exothecial cells slightly incrassate, rhomboid to hexagonal, the mouth bordered by about 9-12 rows of laterally somewhat elongated cells and a narrow fringe of orange-pellucid and much smaller cells in 1-3 rows; operculum convex, bluntly mamillate to sub-rostrate; calyptra somewhat oblique, rostrate, unequally split at base into 3-5 lobes; spores decidedly papillose, orange-pellucid, in our specimens measuring about .016-.040 mm, mature in May and June, occasionally later: autoicous.

Common on bare earth in fields, along roadsides, etc., from Quebec to Florida and west to the Rocky Mountains, and also in California.

Known from Allegheny, Armstrong, Beaver, Butler, Crawford, Fayette, Lawrence, McKean, Somerset, Venango, Washington, and Westmoreland counties. Specimen figured: Douthett, Allegheny County, June 5, 1909. O.E.J.

3. FUNARIA Schreber, Hedwig

Autoicous: the antheridial inflorescences discoid, terminal, the archegoni il on innovations: gregarious to cespitose: stem usually simple, radiculose at base; lower leaves distant, small, the upper becoming much larger, those at the apex more or less upright and tufted or gemmiform, entire or serrate, more or less acute; costa incomplete to excurrent; areolation lax, elongate-rectangular to rhombic, at the margin sometimes longer and narrower, forming a border: seta elongated, erect or cygneous at fruiting time, later erect and twisted; capsule with a thick collum or elongate-pyriform, symmetric to oblique, arcuate, with a narrow mouth, smooth to plicate, erect to cernuous; annulus large-celled, revolute or none; peristome deeply inserted, double in our species; teeth lance-subulate, reddish to brownish-red, obliquely ascnding to the right; segments as long or shorter, yellow, papillose, opposite the teeth; spores medium; operculum flat or convex; calyptra long-persistent, inflated-cucullate, long-rostrate, smooth, entire.

A large cosmopolitan genus of about 200 species (including *Entosthodon*), on soil; about 25 species in North America, 3 in our range.

KEY TO THE SPECIES

A. Body of capsule neither striate nor plicate; no annulus ....1. *F. americana*
A. Capsule striate and more or less plicate; annulus curling off ....B
   B. Leaves long acuminate; costa very often excurrent; segments less than 1/2 length of
      teeth ....2. *F. flavicans*
   B. Leaves short acuminate; costa mostly percurrent; segments more than 1/2 the length
      of teeth ....3. *F. hygrometrica*

1. FUNARIA AMERICANA Lindberg

(*F. Muhlenbergii* Hedwig, — mainly plate, not description, — Lindberg)

Small, gregarious to loosely cespitose: stems very short; leaves erect-spreading, ovate-oblong, long-acuminate, somewhat concave, plane-margined, entire; costa strong, excurrent into a hair-point, leaf-cells lax, moderately thin-walled, the basal quadrate-hexagonal to rectangular, the upper elongate rectangular: seta slender, rather short, up to 1.5 cm long, when dry dextrorse below, sinistrorse above; capsule erect, sub-cernuous, pyriform-oblong, the mouth tilted to one side, when dry the long tapering neck rugulose, the urn smoothish and constricted below mouth; no annulus; peristome-teeth lance-linear, dextrorsely tilted, castaneous-pellucid, papillose, articulate, with divisural, strongly trabeculate; segments about as long and opposite teeth, pale pellucid and papillose; lid conic, obtuse, calyptra inflated, long-rostrate, cucullate; spores papillose, mature in May: autoicous.

On bare ground, or among grass, eastern Pennsylvania to Ohio and Minnesota, south to Georgia, and in California, but not often collected, — perhaps to be expected in our region.

2. FUNARIA FLAVICANS Richardson, Michaux

Loosely cespitose: stems erect, smaller than *F. hygrometrica;* lower leaves small, the upper leaves larger and tufted, oblong-spatulate to obovate, concave, plane-margined, entire, at apex long-acuminate; costa percurrent or excurrent; leaf-cells large, lax; seta long, erect, capsule oval-pyriform to globose-pyriform, more or less horizontal or downward curved, dark reddish when mature, with mouth less oblique and smaller than in *F. hygrometrica,* gradually attenuate below into the seta, not much furrowed when old; lid low-convex, not apiculate; spores about .025 mm in diameter, mature in May or June: autoicous.

. On bare moist earth, usually clay, in eastern United States from Connecticut and New York south and west.

LAWRENCE CO.: T. P. James. (Porter's Catalogue).

3. FUNARIA HYGROMETRICA [L.—Sibthorp] Hedwig
THE CORD MOSS
Plate XXI

Loosely cespitose, rather light green: stems about 3-10 mm high, erect, radiculose at base, simple or basally divided; leaves erect to appressed, concave, forming a bulbiform tuft, oblong-ovate, acute or shortly acuminate, entire or slightly crenate, larger leaves 2-4 mm long by three-fifths as wide, strongly costate to the apex or percurrently costate; cells rectangular to hexagonal, narrower towards margin, above more or less quadrate-hexagonal, the lower more or less inflated, above becoming more or less incrassate: seta about 2-5 cm high, erect, sinistrorse, flexuous, lustrous, chestnut-brown, paler above; capsule unsymmetric, arched and turgid on upper side, 2-3 mm long, strongly incurved at mouth, deeply sulcate when dry, pyriform, yellowish to brown when old, usually more or less horizontal but the upper part of seta often variously bent and curved and strongly hygroscopic; mouth about 0.6-0.8 mm wide, annulus revoluble, deep castaneous; operculum low-convex; peristome-teeth castaneous-pellucid, papillose, strongly trabeculate, spirally twisted, united at apex; segments about three-fourths as long, papillose; spores smooth, round, about .014-.017 mm; mature in May or June; calyptra cucullate, long-rostrate, early deciduous: autoicous.

Widely distributed over the earth; throughout North America. Common in our region on earth, burnt-over spots, etc. (Quite variable in size and leaf-characters but we have not been able to recognize any of the several described varieties in our region.)

Known from the following counties: Allegheny, Beaver, Butler, Cambria, Crawford, Erie, Fayette, Greene, Huntingdon, Lawrence, McKean, Mercer, Somerset, Union, Venango, Washington, and Westmoreland. It probably occurs in every county. Specimen figured: Ligonier to Donegal, Westmoreland Co., June 23, 1904. O.E.J.

Family 13.   SCHISTOSTEGACEAE

This family consists of only the genus *Schistostega* whose characters are those of the family.

1.   SCHISTOSTEGA Mohr

Dioicous: inflorescences gemmiform, terminal, paraphyses none: minute and slender mosses in holes in earth, in caves, etc.: annual, gregarious, on an abundant persistent protonema, which is more or less luminous by reflected light; sterile stems from the middle upwards with distichous, basally confluent leaves; fertile stems with a terminal 5-seriate tuft of leaves; leaves entire, unistratose, ecostate; cells prosenchymatous, lax-rhombic, sparsely chlorophyllose: seta thin, erect, almost hyaline; capsule minute, 0.5 mm long, erect, symmetric, globose, without stomata, annulus, or peristome; operculum small, convex and with a red border; calyptra very small and fugacious, mitrate, covering only the operculum, smooth and naked; propagation often by brood-bodies on the protonema.

One species only, in crevices and caves in non-calcareous districts, in Europe, and, in North America, from Ontario, New England, New York and Ohio to British Columbia.

1.   SCHISTOSTEGA PENNATA [Hedwig] Hooker and Taylor
(*Gymnostomum pennatum* Hedwig, *Schistostega osmundacea* Mohr)
THE LUMINOUS MOSS
With characters as given for the genus. Not yet known in our region.

Family 14.   BRYACEAE

Dioicous, autoicous, paroicous, or synoicous, sometimes heteroicous; antheridial inflorescences with paraphyses; cespitose, persistent, mostly on soil or rocks, sometimes on trees or rotting wood; stem usually rounded-pentagonal, with central strand, radiculose at least at base; leaves in several series, below mostly small and remote, above larger and often tufted, often bordered: costa mostly with 2-5 median guides, often excurrent; cells never papillose, upper prosenchymatous, mostly rhomboidal or rhombic-hexagonal, rarely linear or vermicular, basal rectangular to quadrate: seta elongate, erect, smooth, more or less curved; capsule cernuous to pendulous, sometimes erect, mostly symmetric, rarely arcuate, neither striate nor plicate, ovate or pyriform, rarely almost globose; collum evident, usually wrinkling when dry; annulus usually present, large-celled, spirally deciduous; peristome rarely none, or simple, mostly double, the 16 teeth often bordered, hygroscopic, papillose on the exterior, especially towards the apex, divisural line evident, trabeculae prominent; segments alternating with teeth, delicate, yellowish or hyaline, often with cilia, often united below into a basal membrane; spores small to medium; operculum conic to convex, umbonate to apiculate or rarely short-rostrate; calyptra cucullate, small, fugacious.

A large and cosmopolitan family of about 15 genera and possibly 1,000 species.

KEY TO THE GENERA

A. Leaf-cells narrow, upwards narrowly rhombic to linear ....B
A. Leaf-cells lax, upwards rhombic to hexagonal, never linear C
  B. Leaves long-subulate; cilia prominently appendiculate ....1. *Leptobryum*
  B. Leaves linear-lanceolate; cilia non-appendiculate, often rudimentary or none ... .
  ....2. *Pohlia*
  C. Annulus mostly none; leaves decurrent, non-bordered; costa ending below apex ....
  ....3. *Mniobryum*
  C. Annulus usually present; leaves often bordered; costa usually percurrent or slightly
  excurrent ....D
  D. Sporogonia single; stem without rhizome-like stolons ....4. *Bryum*
  D. Sporogonia often several together; stems erect from rhizome-like stolons ....
  ....5. *Rhodobryum*

1. LEPTOBRYUM (Schimper) Wilson

Synoicous or dioicous; paraphyses of the antheridial inflorescence with an acuminate end-cell; no paraphyses in the archegonial inflorescence: weak, cespitose in low, soft, lax, yellowish-green tufts; stem erect, thin, brown-radiculose at base; lower leaves remote, small, lanceolate, uppermost leaves much larger, tufted, erect to spreading, elongate-subulate from a lanceolate base, canaliculate and often distinctly toothed towards the apex; costa broad, flat, incomplete or percurrently filling the apex; cells very narrow and long, in the subulation linear, the basal rectangular-elongate: seta short to long, very thin, tortuous, twisted when dry; capsule cernuous to almost pendent, with a thin, long, somewhat arcuate, pyriform collum, lustrous, narrow-mouthed; annulus narrow, deciduous; peristome-teeth pale yellow, the upper part subulate and bordered; segments about as long, fenestrate, the lower third forming a basal membrane, the cilia mostly long-appendiculate; spores of medium size; operculum small, convex, and mostly umbonate.

A genus of four species; one in Tasmania, two in South America, and the following, almost a cosmopolitan:

1. Leptobryum pyriforme [Linnaeus] Schimper
(*Webera piriformis* Hedwig)
Plate XXI

Densely cespitose in light yellowish-green, soft, lustrous tufts: stems .5-1.5 cm high, slender, erect, reddish, brown-radiculose at base; leaves mostly erect-spreading, flexuous, the upper forming a comal tuft, linear-setaceous, up to 4-5 mm, long, the basal portion lanceolate, the upper portion flexuous, with plane margin, denticulate above; costa strong but rather wide and indistinct, occupying most of the upper portion of the leaf and somewhat excurrent; leaf-cells narrow and linear-prosenchymatous, or below elongate and parenchymatous, at base rectangular and larger, all thin-walled; perichaetial bracts linear from a wider base: seta slender, flexuous, orange to brown, about 1-1.5 cm long; capsule inclined to pendulous, pyriform with a long narrow neck, altogether about 2.5 mm long, the neck much wrinkled when old, and at least as long as the globose-oval part of the capsule, which is a lustrous orange- to dark chestnut-brown, the mouth rather wide; annulus wide; peristome-teeth yellowish, linear-lanceolate, the upper third suddenly narrower and sub-hyaline and papillose, trabeculate, lamellae and divisural evident; segments about as long, carinately split and sometimes gaping; cilia 3, strongly appendicuate, about as long as segments, basal membrane one-third to almost one-half the height of the teeth; operculum convex-apiculate: spores smoothish, about .012-.015 mm: usually synoicous: mature in June or July.

On moist shaded soil, old walls, shaded cliffs and rocks near trickling water, etc. Cosmopolitan.

Now known from Allegheny, Butler, Erie, McKean, Tioga, Washington, and Westmoreland counties. Specimen figured: On stone wall, Perrysville Ave., North Side, Pittsburgh. May 26, 1909.

2. Pohlia Hedwig
(*Webera* Hedwig)

Mostly paroicous or dioicous: paraphyses mostly present and filiform: robust to weak, gregarious, or cespitose: stem mostly red; leaves more or less tufted on the fertile shoots, linear-lanceolate to lanceolate, non-bordered, towards apex more or less toothed; costa mostly incomplete; cells narrowly rhomboid-hexagonal to linear, the basal slightly more lax: seta long, slender, tortuous and twisted, at apex hooked or curved; capsule cernuous or pendulous, rarely erect, with short collum, obovate to oblanceolate or long-clavate; annulus mostly biseriate; peristome inserted near the mouth; teeth yellowish, papillose, with border narrow or none; segments mostly about as long, rarely rudimentary, often with a low basal membrane, often narrow, usually split but not fenestrate, cilia non-appendiculate, often rudimentary or lacking; spores mostly small; operculum convex-conic, umbonate or apiculate.

A world-wide genus of about 120 species, inhabiting soil, rocks, and decaying wood. About 40 species in North America; at least 5 species in our range.

KEY TO THE SPECIES*

A. Upper leaf-cells very narrow: inner peristome with a low basal membrane, usually
    complete narrow segments, and cilia various, often rudimentary or none ....B
A. Leaf-cells linear to moderately narrow: basal membrane comprising one-third to one-
    half the height of the inner peristome; segments split, cilia well developed C
  B. Paroicous; capsule long and slender with a long slender collum ....1. *P. elongata*
  B. Polyoicous; capsule oblong to pyriform with a rather short collum ....2. *P. cruda*
  C. Paroicous; not bearing gemmae: costa hardly reaching the serrate apex ....D
  C. Dioicous; often bearing gemmae: costa incomplete or percurrent ....E
    D. Cilia two, not sub-appendiculate, articulate ....3. *P. nutans*
    D. Cilia three, distinctly sub-appendiculate ....3a. *P. nutans* var. *triciliata*
  E. Costa not reaching apex except in uppermost leaves; capsule small and very short:
    stem not reddish ....4. *P. pulchella*
  E. Costa percurrent: capsule larger and elongate-pyriform; stem reddish below ....
    ....5. *P. annotina*

1. POHLIA ELONGATA Hedwig
(*Webera elongata* Schwaegrichen)

Gregarious to cespitose, bright pale green: stems erect, up to 2 cm high,
branching towards base; leaves crowded and larger in the comal tufts, lanceolate, erect-spreading, thin, the margin recurved below, the apex gradually
narrowed, serrate; costa brownish, vanishing below or at the apex; leaf-cells
narrow, linear-rhomboidal and vermicular above, hexagonal-rectangular below:
seta long, slender, 2-4.5 cm high; capsule sub-erect to horizontal, narrowly
elliptic, pale, 2-5.5 mm long, the neck slender and longer than the rest of the
capsule, when dry and empty the capsule constricted below the mouth; operculum conic-acuminate or acutely rostellate; outer peristome yellowish, the
inner with a basal membrane about one-third as high as the teeth; cilia two,
more or less well-developed but always short and never appendiculate; paroicous; antheridia in pairs in axils of upper leaves: mature in August.

On earth and among rocks, in crevices, etc., where moist, usually in the
mountains. Europe, northern Africa, Asia, North America from Greenland
to the northern United States and southwards, in the mountains, west to
British Columbia. Rare in our range.

We have seen no specimens from Pennsylvania, but it is reported as follows: Mc-
KEAN CO.: Bradford. (Porter's Catalogue).

2. POHLIA CRUDA [Linnaeus] Lindberg
(*Webera cruda* Bruch)

Robust, up to 6 or 7 cm high, glaucous green and shining above, brownish
below: stems red, simple, cespitose; the leaves below ovate, becoming linear-
lanceolate in the comal tuft, erect-spreading, serrate towards the moderately
acute apex, margin plane, rather rigid; costa reddish at base, not reaching apex;
leaf-cells linear-prosenchymatous above, larger and rectangular at base, where

---

* *Pohlia carnea* (L.) Lindberg has now been found in New York, Ohio, Illinois, and
Iowa. It has widely hexagonal-rhomboid, thin-walled cells up to .018-.025 x .100 mm,
narrowed towards edge; no annulus; capsule dark red, very short (1.5 mm), oval; seta
thickened at top. The leaves are small and narrowly lanceolate.

often reddish: seta long; capsule oblong, with inconspicuous neck, often unsymmetric, mostly horizontal, castaneous or red-brown, when dry and empty ventricose at base and constricted at the mouth; operculum conic-apiculate; peristome yellowish, basal membrane not more than one-third as high as teeth, cilia two or three, well-developed; usually autoicous, sometimes synoicous or dioicous: spores mature in summer.

On shaded earth, clefts in rocks, etc., usually in mountainous regions. Cosmopolitan but local in its distribution. In North America it etxends from North Carolina and Tennessee to the far North. In our region rare, being unknown from western Pennsylvania, but reported from the eastern part of Pennsylvania and from Painesville, northeastern Ohio.

3. POHLIA NUTANS [Schreber] Lindberg
(*Webera nutans* Hedwig)
Plate XXI

More or less densely cespitose, usually dark green: stems about 1-2 cm high, branching by lateral innovations, or from the base, erect, matted with a castaneous tomentum below, reddish; leaves ovate below to much longer and linear-lanceolate in the comal tuft, hardly decurrent, the comal long-acuminate, the margin often somewhat recurved below, denticulate towards apex, leaves somewhat shrunken, twisted and lustrous when dry; costa strong, reddish, ending in or a little below apex; leaf-cells long-rhomboid and more or less pointed and prosenchymatous above, rectangular below, slightly narrower towards the margin: seta slender, flexuous, usually 2-3 cm long, lustrous, castaneous below, often yellowish above; capsule horizontal to sub-pendulous, oblong to obovate, usually about 3-4 mm in length, with a distinct but short neck, often gibbous when dry and then contracted below the wide mouth, yellowish to brown in age; operculum convex-mammillate; peristome-teeth orange-yellow below, paler and papillose in the rather abruptly narrowed upper half, strongly trabeculate, lamellate, divisural zigzag and distinct; segments about as long, carinately split and gaping below but remaining unsplit at apex; cilia nearly as long, two in number, filiform, articulate, basal membrane half as high as teeth; annulus wide, revoluble; spores smoothish, yellowish-pellucid, about .014-.016 mm, mature in early summer: autoicous; antheridia in axils of upper leaves.

On various habitats in moist places or swampy fields and woods. Common and nearly cosmopolitan.

This species is now known from the following counties: Allegheny, Armstrong, Beaver, Cambria, Centre, Crawford, Erie, Fayette, Indiana, Lawrence, Mercer, Montour, McKean, Somerset, Washington, and Westmoreland counties. Specimen figured: Presque Isle, Erie County, May 8-9, 1906. O.E.J.

3a. **Pohlia nutans var. triciliata** NEW COMBINATION
(*W. nutans* var. *triciliata* Jennings)
Plate XXII

Plants laxly to densely cespitose, shining, dark green to yellowish: stem simple or sparsely branched, erect, castaneous, at the base reddish-radiculose, about 6-15 mm high; lower leaves short, about 0.5-1.0 mm long, costate almost to the apex, ovate, above the leaves becoming relatively longer and ovate-lanceolate, denticulate towards the apex; upper leaves clustered, erect-spreading, 2.5-4.0 mm long, lanceolate, sub-decurrent, denticulate at apex, acuminate, non-margined, strongly percurrently to excurrently costate; peri-chaetial leaves elongate-lanceolate to linear, long-acuminate, denticulate at apex, excurrently costate; cells of the lower and median leaves incrassate, above the middle oblong-hexagonal to rhomboidal, about .010-.015 x .035-.065 mm elongate-rectangular at base where about .008-.020 x .040-.100 mm; cells of the comal and perichaetial leaves incrassate, elongate to linear-prosenchyma-tous, about .008-.011 x .040-.065 mm, towards the margin gradually narrower and there reaching .003-.006 x .080-.100 mm, at the base elongate-rectangular: inflorescence paroicous, terminal; antheridia in the axils of the comal leaves: pedicel solitary, slender, lustrous, castaneous, erect, flexuous, about 4-6 cm high; capsule horizontal to sub-pendulous, smooth, castaneous to yellowish-brown, ovate-oblong, often very slightly curved, 2.5-3.5 mm long, when dry and empty contracted under the mouth, the basal third narrowed into a collum; exothecial cells incrassate, yellowish-pellucid, irregularly sub-quadrate to oblong-hexagonal or elongate-rectangular, about .025-.035 x .035-.505 mm, in three to five rows under the mouth abruptly smaller, sub-quadrate, somewhat opaque, and about .006-.010 x .012-.018 mm; annulus broad, revoluble; operculum rather wide, conic-mamillate; teeth of peristome linear-lanceolate, yellowish, articulate, strongly trabeculate, narrowly margined above, sub-hyaline and papillose at apex; segments of inner peristome nearly as long as teeth, hyaline, granular, carinately split and gaping, cilia three, as long as segments, filiform, strongly articulate and often sub-appendiculate, hyaline, granular; basal mem-brane reaching to middle of teeth; spores minutely roughened, yellowish-pellucid, .012-.015 mm in diameter, mature in June.

On earth with more or less humus. Thus far known only as follows:

BUTLER Co.: On earth under pines on rocky hillside, West Winfield, May 26, 1906. O.E.J. CRAWFORD Co.: On hummocks of earth with Polytrichum, near Hartstown, July 26, 1908. O.E.J. *Type Specimen* (figured).

4. POHLIA PULCHELLA (Hedwig) Lindberg

(*Bryum Lescurianum* Sullivant; *Webera pulchella* Schimper)

Plate XXII

Gregarious to loosely cespitose, pale green: stems not red, ascending, usu-ally simple, usually 1-1.5 cm long; leaves small and remote below, gradually increasing in size and number above, the upper lanceolate, the comal linear-lanceolate, up to 2.5 mm long, long-acuminate at the serrulate apex, the mar-gins more or less recurved, the base non-decurrent; costa strong, reddish, ending below apex; leaf-cells elongate-rhomboid-hexagonal, prosenchymatous, rather thick-walled, and basal often reddish and tending to rectangular, the marginal slightly narrower: seta erect, 1-1.5 cm long, yellowish-brown, lus-trous, slender flexuous; capsule horizontal to abruptly pendent, short, 1.5-2 cm long, yellowish-brown, the short tapering neck darker brown, capsule pyriform in general shape, when dry and empty widely flaring at the mouth; operculum

and mostly complete as in *Bryum;* spores mostly large; operculum convex to obliquely rostrate; calyptra cucullate, narrow, mostly fugacious, smooth.

Distributed over the whole earth, most abundant in damp woods and swamps, on earth, bark of trees, or rocks, in the temperate zones. Five genera, of which but one occurs in our region.

1.   MNIUM Linnaeus, Hedwig

Synoicous or dioicous, rarely autoicous: mostly robust, cespitose in bright green to dark green or later brownish tufts; stem erect, often stoloniferous, often bearing creeping flagelliform branches; leaves bract-like and remote below, increasing upwards to the terminal rosette, broadly ovate, obovate, or oblong, to spatulate from a narrow decurrent base, when dry contorted to crispate, when wet erect-spreading to recurved, mostly with a border of 1-3 layers of elongate prosenchymatous colored cells, each layer of the border usually sharply serrate; costa stout; cells rounded to hexagonal, often collenchymatous and punctate, uniform or smaller towards the margin: seta single or clustered, long; capsule cernuous to pendent, rarely erect, mostly oblong-ovoid, rarely arcuate; exothecial cells rounded, annulus revoluble; teeth 16, strong, separate at base, greenish-yellow to reddish-brown, more or less papillose, the zigzag divisural line distinct, the dorsal plates low, the trabeculae numerous, often united by sporadic cross-walls; inner peristome mostly yellowish-red, the basal membrane half-way to the apex and sometimes perforate; segments usually as long as the teeth, lanceolate, mostly abruptly subulate, usually fenestrate and finally gaping; cilia usually in 3's complete, mostly articulate; operculum convex to conic and rostrate; calyptra narrowly cucullate.

About 80 species, cosmopolitan, on various sub-strata, usually in moist or shaded situations; about 30 species occurring in North America, about 11 species in our range.

KEY TO THE SPECIES

A. Leaves not distinctly bordered ....B
A. Leaves distinctly bordered C
  B. Margin with a single series of low irregular teeth in the upper half; cells incrassate ....10. *M. stellare*
  B. Margin not distinctly toothed; cells thin-walled ....12. *M. cinclidioides*
C. Leaves with entire or almost entire margin ....D
C. Leaves with serrate margin ....G
  D. Border indistinct and of one series of cells only ....12. *M. cinclidioides*
  D. Border of 1-4 series of cells in 1-4 layers ....E
E. Lid acutely rostrate; leaves obovate ....F
E. Lid conic-apiculate; oblong to oval or sub-orbicular ....9b. *M. affine* var. *rugicum*
  F. On stones; leaves usually minutely apiculate and percurrently costate ....11. *M. punctatum*
  F. In swamps; leaves not usually apiculate and costa not usually reaching apex; often very large ....11. *M. punct.* var. *elatum*
G. Leaves serrate with a single row of teeth ....H
G. Leaves serrate with a double row of teeth ....K
  H. Leaves serrate only in upper two-thirds ....O
  H. Leaves serrate to the base or very nearly so I
I. Teeth slender and usually of 2-4 cells ....9a. *M. affine* var. *ciliare*
I. Teeth usually of but one cell and not so slender ....J

J. Leaf broadly obovate, apex bluntly rounded, abruptly apiculate or cuspidate; teeth
   blunt ....6. *M. rostratum*
J. Leaf apex more or less acute and cuspidate; teeth sharp ....8. *M. medium*
K. Leaves lanceolate to elliptic-ovate; costa incomplete, dorsally toothed ....1. *M. hornum*
K. Leaves oblong-ovate or wider than lanceolate; costa usually complete in upper leaves
   at least L
   L. Costa toothed dorsally ....:................M
   L. Costa not toothed dorsally ....N
M. Cells not collenchymatous, about .014-.020 mm ....2. *M. orthorrhynchum*
M. Cells collenchyamtous, about .020-.030 mm in diameter ....*M. lycopodioides**
N. Cells rounded and strongly collenchymatous ....3. *M. serratum*
N. Cells angled and not collenchymatous ....4. *M. spinulosum*
O. Cells thin-walled, hexagonal, not collenchymatous ....5. *M. Drummondii*
O. Cells somewhat incrassate, round-hexagonal, collenchymatous ....7. *M. cuspidatum*

1. MNIUM HORNUM Linnaeus, Hedwig
(*Astrophyllum hornum* Lindberg)
Plate LXV

A robust species in dense tufts, up to 6 or 8 mm high with erect unbranched stems and terminal rosettes of leaves which reach a length of 3-5 mm
but are narrowly elliptic-lanceolate to elliptic-ovate, acute, sharply apiculate,
all leaves with a reddish, thickened border, sharply doubly spinosely serrate in
the upper half; the costa ending below the apex and spinose dorsally above;
leaf-cells angular, not very regularly seriate, rather small: seta solitary, 2-3 cm
long; capsule subpendulous, finally horizontal, ovate-elliptic and tapering to a
distinct neck, when old pale yellowish with a red mouth; operculum conic-
apiculate: dioicous, the antheridial flowers being disc-like. The leaves are
proportionally narrower than the other species of the genus and the calyptra
often remains for a time clasping the seta just below the capsule, mature in
late spring or summer.

On shaded soil and rocks and banks of streams: Europe, Algeria, Japan,
North America from Newfoundland to Georgia and west to Ohio and Tennessee. (Lesquereux and James in their manual say: "More generally on
quartz or schistose rocks.") but in our region usually among rocks on sand
where often subject to flooding.

Fairly common in the mountains of Pennsylvania, especially in the Ohio Pyle region
of Fayette County, on sandy soil along the river. Now known from Bedford, Cambria
(Porter), Clarion, Clearfield, Elk, Fayette, Forest, Somerset, Venango, Warren, and
Westmoreland counties. Specimen figured: One mile up Meadow Run, Ohio Pyle. June
23, 1940. Chas. M. Boardman.

2. MNIUM ORTHORRHYNCHUM Bridel
(*Astrophyllum orthorrhynchum* Lindberg)

Quite similar to *M. serratum* but the leaf-cells only about .015-.020 mm;
densely tufted; leaves close, oblong-ovate, doubly spinose-serrate from below
the middle; costa usually ending in the apiculation, toothed dorsally above; leaf-

---

* *Mnium lycopodioides* (Hooker) Schwaegrichen, as reported from Blair and Elk
counties in our region (Porter's Catalogue), has the stem winged with decurrent leaf-
bases; strong reddish, dorsally toothed costa; cells hexagonal and definitely collenchymatous. Eurasia, and rather rare in the northernmost United States.

cells angular, hexagonal to quadrate, non-collenchymatous: seta solitary, red; capsule elliptic-oblong, abruptly contracted into the neck, straight and more or less horizontal, brownish; operculum shortly rostrate: dioicous, antheridial flower discoid. Mature in late summer.

On moist rocks, usually calcareous, along cool shaded ravines and streams: Europe, Asia, North America from Greenland to British Columbia and south through the northern part of the United States to North Carolina.

One report in our region. BLAIR CO.: Porter. (Porter's Catalogue).

3. MNIUM SERRATUM Schrader, Schwaegrichen
(*M. marginatum* Beauvois; *Astrophyllum marginatum* Lindberg)
Plate XXV

Loosely cespitose in soft tufts, rather dark green: stems and lower leaves often deep reddish tinged, stems slender, rather short, usually 1.5-3 cm in our spcimens, simple or branched below with erect branches; leaves rather remote, strongly decurrent, the lower ovate-lanceolate, the upper oblong spatulate-lanceolate, all acuminate, the strong red border sharply doubly serrate, the leaves when dry more or less twisted but hardly crispate; costa in upper leaves confluent with the border in the apiculus but in the middle and lower leaves and often even the upper leaves of sterile shoots the costa ends below the apex, not spinose; leaf-cells from .020-.035 mm in diameter, irregularly rounded, somewhat incrassate, strongly collenchymatous, the basal elongate: seta mostly single; capsule horizontal, yellowish to brown, oval-oblong, tapering at neck; peristome yellow or sometimes brown, inserted, the teeth lance-linear, pellucid yellowish-brown, papillose above, strongly trabeculate, divisural faint; segments a little shorter than teeth, papillose above, slender, cilia 3 (2), the basal membrane reaching somewhat above the middle; spores rounded, about .025-.030 mm; operculum stoutly short-rostrate; synoicous; mature in spring.

Usually near streams on shaded banks or rocks, or in crevices of rocks where moist, in Europe, northern Asia, and, in North America, from Anticosti to Alaska and south to Tennessee, Missouri, and the Southwest.

Now known from the following counties: Allegheny, Armstrong, Butler, Elk, Fayette, McKean, Somerset, Washington, and Westmoreland. Specimen figured: Hawkins and Quintuple, McKean Co. D.A.B. Aug. 2, 1895.

4. MNIUM SPINULOSUM Bryologia Europaea
Plate LXV

Tufted, erect, 1-1.5 cm tall, drying a bright emerald green; stems reddish and radiculose below; similar in many respects to *Mnium serratum,*, the lower leaves small and scale-like, the middle and upper abruptly larger, elliptic to obovate or spatulate at the apex of the stem, decurrent, acute, sharply doubly serrate on the thickened reddish border in the upper two-thirds, not crisped when dry; costa strong, sometimes reddish, percurrent, not dorsally toothed, often ending below the apex in the lower and middle leaves; leaf-cells about .020-.030 mm, angled hexagonal, or below rectangular, incrassate, non-collenchymatous: synoicous: sporophytes single (or clustered), seta erect, usually reddish yellow, 1.5 to 2 cm high, abruptly hooked at the top and abruptly enlarging into the short neck of the cylindric-elliptic capsule; operculum with an upturned slender beak about as long as half the diameter of the capsule; capsule light yellow, 2-3 mm long with red rim at mouth; peristome teeth reddish, lanceolate, minutely papillose, strongly and closely trabeculate below, inner peristome orange; basal membrane nearly one-half height of teeth; segments broad reaching to about three-quarters height of teeth, irregularly and shortly carinate; cilia 3 (2) almost equalling teeth, nodose; spores variable, rather thick-walled, smoothish, elliptic to spherical, .015-.024 mm, ripening in late spring or early summer.

On the ground in evergreen woods, usually in mountainous or hilly regions. Europe and northern North America, from Nova Scotia to Alaska and south to the northernmost United States. It is reported from eastern Pennsylvania and Maryland, and Ohio, but only once from our region.

CLEARFIELD CO.: One mile north of Clearfield, Lawrence Twp., on humus soil in hemlock woods. Sidney K. Eastwood, July 4, 1936 (figured). Capsules deoperculate but still full of spores.

5. MNIUM DRUMMONDII Bruch and Schimper

Bright green, loosely tufted, about 2 cm high, brownish radiculose below; sterile stems more or less stoloniform; leaves slightly crisped when dry, decurrent, broadly obovate-spatulate, acute to short-acuminate, bordered by 1-4 rows of cells, serrate only above, the teeth single and sharp; costa percurrent; leaf-cells thin-walled, non-collenchymatous, hexagonal, about .035-.040 mm; seta slender, reddish; capsules 1-3 (or 4) from flower, pendulous, oblong, yellowish; operculum convex-apiculate; outer peristome yellow, papillose; segments about as long; cilia 2 or 3, somewhat appendiculate; spores roughened, yellowish, ripening in late spring or early summer.

Shaded moist rocks or soil; northern Eurasia, and from southern Canada south to Maryland and Pennsylvania. Not yet reported from our part of the State.

6. MNIUM ROSTRATUM Schrader, Schwaegrichen
(Astrophyllum rostratum Lindberg)

Large, loosely cespitose, stoloniferous: stems erect, short, the sterile shoots creeping or arched; leaves broadly oblong or obovate, rounded at both ends, tapering but little at base, at the apex very broadly rounded or almost truncate, short apiculate, the border strong, brownish, serrate in at least the upper half with a single row of short obtuse or almost obsolete teeth; the comal leaves large, up to 5 mm long, those of the sterile shoots complanate-two-ranked; costa excurrent in the short apiculus; leaf-cells incrassate, collenchymatous, about .025-.030 mm, rounded-hexagonal, not radiating in rows from the costa as in affine var. rugicum, which in the sterile condition it closely resembles: capsules usually 1-3, clustered, sub-pendulous to horizontal, yellowish, operculum long-rostrate; peristome-teeth papillose, yellowish, the inner peristome orange; synoicous: mature in spring to early summer.

On wet rocks and earth in woods: almost cosmopolitan in the temperate zones, in North America from central and southern Canada south to Virginia, Pennsylvania, Ohio, Montana and Oregon, but apparently rather rare.

All Pennsylvania specimens in the Carnegie Museum Herbarium which were labeled *M. rostratum* are non-collenchymatous and the leaf-cells are definitely arranged in series radiating from the costa.

The species is reported from our region as follows: CAMBRIA Co.: James. (Porter's Catalogue). LYCOMING Co.: McMinn. (Porter's Catalogue).

7. MNIUM CUSPIDATUM Linnaeus, Hedwig

(*Mnium sylvaticum* Lindberg)

Plate XXV

Loosely cespitose in large light to dark patches: stems branching with sterile shoots prostrate or sub-erect, in our specimens usually about 1.5-3 cm high, reddish, radiculose below; leaves decurrent, oblong-oval, acute, the upper tending to obovate, those on the branches more rounded or oval, all shortly cuspidate and serrate in the upper half or two-thirds with a single row of short one-celled teeth, occasionally some teeth two-celled, the border of 3-5 rows of incrassate, linear, yellowish-pellucid cells; costa confluent with the border in the apiculate apex or ending a little below the apex; leaf-cells about .020-.025 mm, incrassate, collenchymatous, hexagonal to somewhat rounded, the basal tending to rectangular: seta solitary, pale yellowish or brownish, erect; capsule pale yellowish or brownish, sub-pendulous, oblong-oval, rather abruptly narrowing to the seta, the base and mouth brown; operculum conic-obtuse; teeth yellow, lance-linear, papillose above, divisural indistinct; inner peristome a little shorter, the basal membrane extending to the middle or a little above, the basal part of the segments more or less irregularly fenestrate with rounded holes, the upper part of the segments finally gaping or breaking apart; cilia three, linear, somewhat appendiculate, the inner peristome brownish-pellucid, the tips of the segments and the cilia being paler and papillose; spores rounded, faintly papillose, yellowish, about .025 mm in diameter: synoicous, mature in May.

In moist woods on earth, stones, rotten logs, etc. Common and widely distributed over the temperate parts of Europe, Asia, and of North America.

Common and now known from seventeen counties in western Pennsylvania and probably occurs in all. Specimens figured: Ohio Pyle, Fayette Co., May 30, 1908. O.E.J.

8. MNIUM MEDIUM Bryologia Europaea

(*Astrophyllum medium* Lindberg)

Plate XXV

Widely and rather loosely cespitose, large, light to dark green: stems erect, up to 5 cm in our specimens, branching at the base, densely covered with a brown felted tomentum, sterile shoots long and prostrate or ascending; leaves distant, shriveled when dry, ovate to oblong, somewhat narrowed and slightly decurrent at base, rather obtuse at apex, cuspidate, narrowly margined all around, sharply serrate from near the base with mainly one-celled teeth, the comal leaves rosulate, and up to 5 x 15 mm; costa reddish, strong, percurrent cuspidate; leaf-cells large, rounded above to elliptic-hexagonal towards base, the margin consisting of about two rows of linear, much incrassate, more or less colored cells, the laminal cells all incrassate and collenchymatous and increasing in size towards the costa: synoicous: capsules clustered, occasionally single, on erect stout setae, pendent, oblong; operculum convex, rostrate-apiculate: mature in May.

Mostly on wet rocks and shaded damp earth and logs; cooler Europe and Asia, and, in North America, from Greenland to Alaska and south to New Jersey, Pennsylvania, Minnesota, Idaho to California.

ARMSTRONG CO.: Ravine, west bank of Allegheny River, 1 mi. north of Foxburg. June 10, 1934. Chas. M. Boardman. BEAVER CO.: South branch, Brady Run, 3 mi. west of Fallston. Jan. 28, 1934. Charles M. Boardman. BUTLER CO.: On wet rocks, Sawmill Run, Butler Twp. Nov. 4, 1934. Sidney K. Eastwood. McKEAN CO.: On leaf-mold, etc., at headwaters of Marilla Brook in wet, springy places, September 24, 1894 (figured), West Branch Swamp, May 26, 1895, Bradford, November 2, 1898. All D.A.B.

9. MNIUM AFFINE Blandow, Schwaegrichen
(*Astrophyllum cuspidatum* Lindberg)

As Grout points out in his "Mosses with Hand-lens and Microscope," the true *Mnium affine* Blandow is rare in eastern United States. Andrews, in Grout's *Moss Flora*, regards *M. affine* as so variable as to make it impossible to distinguish the various published varieties. It has the capsules usually clustered, 2-4 together, and the teeth of the leaves shorter than in the variety *ciliare*. Its general range is Europe, Asia, and North America south to New Jersey, West Virginia, and Washington.

Now known from Erie, Forest, and Washington counties. Specimens figured: In ravine, Snake Woods near Washington, May 6, 1893, and Nov. 11, 1893. A. Linn and J. S. Simonton.

9a. MNIUM AFFINE var. CILIARE (Greville) C. Mueller
(*Astrophyllum ciliare* Lindberg; *Bryum ciliare* Greville)

Plate XXVI

Moderately large, loosely cespitose, pale to dark green with age: stems erect, usually about 3 cm high, reddish-brown, rather stout, radiculose below, with long, slender sterile shoots which are prostrate or arched; stem-leaves ovate, varying to oblong-elliptic or at the apex rosulate and obovate to narrow spatulate, somewhat acute, apiculate, up to 6-10 mm long, decurrent, margined, serrate down to the narrowed base with long slender teeth of 2-4 cells; costa excurrent-apiculate, strong; leaf-cells large, .020-.040 (-.070) mm in diameter, angled, somewhat incrassate, hexagonal to irregularly somewhat elongate rectangular, especially towards the base, hardly collenchymatous, marginal cells prosenchymatous-linear and cartilaginous pellucid, often yellowish to reddish: seta single, erect flexuous, strong, reddish, about 2.5 cm long; capsule pendent, elliptic-oblong, about 4 mm long, narrowed to a short darker colored neck, yellowish-brown; lid conic-apiculate; peristome-teeth pale pellucid, strongly trabeculate, the divisural rather faint, finely papillose above; inner peristome brownish pellucid, the basal membrane reaching about half-way, non-fenestrate, the segments and usually three cilia finely papillose above and often exceeding the teeth; spores round, yellowish-pellucid, finely papillose, about .028-.030 mm; dioicous; antheridial flower terminal-discoid; mature in May.

On rocks and soil in swamps and moist woods, Asia, Europe, and in North America through southern Canada south to Georgia, Louisiana, Missouri, Montana, and California.

Known from the following counties: Butler, Cameron, Clarion, Crawford, Erie, Fayette, McKean, Somerset, Venango, Warren, Washington, and Westmoreland. Specimen figured: Ohio Pyle, Fayette Co., September 1-3, 1906. O.E.J. and G.K.J.

9b.   MNIUM AFFINE var. RUGICUM (Laurer) Bryologia Europaea
(*Astrophyllum rugicum* Lindberg)
Plate XXVI

Darker green than true *affine*, almost blackish: stems short, usually simple; leaves oblong to broadly oval or sub-orbicular, the apex blunt and rounded with an apiculation or almost entire, the margin little or not at all serrate: capsule much as in *affine* var. *ciliare* but usually smaller. The leaves often very closely resemble those of *M. rostratum* but Grout says the leaf-cells have thinner walls in *rugicum* and also radiate in more or less definite series from the costa, while in *rostratum* the thick-walled cells are irregularly arranged, or at least not in radiating series.

In cool, shaded ravines and swamps; Europe, and, in North America, from Greenland to Alaska and locally south to Louisiana and Colorado.

In our region not known to range more than fifty miles east of the western State line. ALLEGHENY CO.: Power's Run, April 18, 1906, and June 17, 1909, O.E.J.; Wildwood Hollow, March 29, 1908, and Coraopolis, September 14, 1905. O.E.J. and G.E.K. All sterile. BEAVER CO.s Beaver Falls, May 11, 1907. O.E.J. Sterile. BUTLER CO.: On wet log, 5 mi. north of Zelienople, March, 1927. L. K. Henry. ERIE CO.: Damp woods near Erie. Agnes E. Hartman. July 30, 1927. FAYETTE CO.: Cheat Haven, September 3-6, 1910. O.E.J. and G.K.J. (figured). Ohio Pyle, September 1-3, 1907. O.E.J. and G.K.J. (Both sterile). WASHINGTON CO.: In ravine, Snake Woods near Washington, June 8, 1895, and under waterfalls below Taylorstown, Nov. 16, 1895. A. Linn and J. S. Simonton.

10.   MNIUM STELLARE [Reichenbach] Hedwig
Plate XXVI

Densely cespitose, soft, deep or bluish-green: stems erect, usually 1-3 cm high, branching at base; leaves gradually larger above, elliptic-oblong, to sub-orbicular below, slightly decurrent, rounded and acute at apex to obtuse-apiculate, non-bordered, the upper part of the leaf obtusely irregularly short serrate; costa thin, ending considerably below the apex, smooth on back; leaf-cells incrassate, angular, irregular to hexagonal or subquadrate, fairly uniform in size, about .020-.030 mm; seta solitary; capsule horizontal to inclined, oblong; lid conic-convex; peristome yellowish; dioicous; antheridial flower discoid: mature in late spring or early summer.

At the base of trees or on rocks in swampy woods or on humus, in temperate Europe, Asia, and North America, through lower Canada and northeastern United States. This species rarely fruits and all specimens from Pennsylvania thus far have been sterile.

ALLEGHENY CO.: Under side of rocks in crevices, Fern Hollow, Pittsburgh, March 9, 1908. O.E.J. McKEAN CO.: Rutherford Run, March 12, 1894, and Quintuple, Sep-

tember 9, 1894, and November 13, 1896. D.A.B. WASHINGTON Co.: North Branch of Maple Creek, above Charleroi, April 24, 1908. O.E.J. (figured).
Now known also from Erie and Westmoreland counties.

11. MNIUM PUNCTATUM [Linnaeus] Hedwig
Plate XXVII

Rather large, dark green, erect, loosely tufted, 1-3 inches high: stems rigid, dark, densely tomentose nearly to the apex; dioicous; leaves remote, forming at the apex a rosette and largest there, spreading, the lower smaller, rounded-ovate, the terminal about 4-5 x 6-9 mm, broadly obovate, all narrowed to a few cells at the base, entire, apex usually apiculate, often somewhat emarginate-apiculate, bordered by a cartilaginous-thickened purplish-brown-pellucid rim of about 2-5 rows of elongate incrassate cells; costa strong, usually terminating or percurrent in the apiculus, or sometimes ceasing just below the apex; median cells rounded- to elongate-hexagonal, about .030-.040 x .050-.085 mm, incrassate, often in obliquely ascending series from costa to border, the basal rather larger, rectangular, slightly inflated, the apical smaller, irregularly angular: seta 2-3 cm long, erect, flexuous, purplish-brown, rather lustrous; capsule subpendulous, oval-oblong, yellowish to brown when old, finally when dry somewhat sulcate; operculum conic, acutely rostrate; peristome-teeth yellowish-brown, pellucid, papillose, trabeculate; segments nearly as high, yellow-pellucid, finely papillose, the basal membrane reaching to one-third the height, cilia usually three, slightly shorter than segments; spores smoothish, round, about .030-.040 mm; fruiting in spring rather early (April), and sometimes with two or three capsules to a plant; usually dioicous.

On soil and rocks in damp woods, ravines, swamps, etc. Rather common. Europe, Asia, and North America down to middle United States.

Known from the following counties: Allegheny, Armstrong, Butler, Cameron, Clearfield, Clinton, Crawford, Elk (Porter), Fayette, Forest, Huntingdon (Porter), Lawrence, McKean, Mercer, Somerset, Tioga, Venango, Warren, Washington, and Westmoreland. and probably occurs in all. Specimen figured: Shades, above Blackburn, Westmoreland Co., March 25, 1910. O.E.J.

11a. MNIUM PUNCTATUM var. ELATUM Schimper
Plate XXVII

This variety differs typically from true *punctatum* in that it grows in muddy shaded places and swamps, is much larger,—in our specimens reaching a height of 7 or 8 cm and with leaves up to 10 or 11 mm long, the leaves are rounded and usually non-apiculate at apex, the border consisting of usually but one layer of cells, and the costa ending below the apex.

In swamps and muddy shaded places: Europe, Asia, and, in North America, from the Arctic regions south to Virginia, Michigan, and Idaho. In Pennsylvania most of the specimens of *punctatum* show some of the characters of the variety but we have found no specimen which clearly possesses all the characters attributed to the variety. The following specimens more or less closely approach the variety:

Known from the following counties: Allegheny, Clarion, Crawford, Fayette, Lawrence,

McKean, Mercer, and Westmoreland. Specimen figured: Houston Junction, Mercer Co., July 12, 1902. J.A.S.

12.   MNIUM CINCLIDIOIDES (Blytt) Huebener

Plate XXVII

Large, loosely cespitose, bright green, becoming dark when old: stems rigid, under exceptional conditions reaching 15 or 20 cm or more, our specimens sterile and about 4-8 cm high, stems dark brownish; leaves remote, thin, large, the lower ones ovate to oblong and not at all decurrent, the upper rosulate from a narrow base, widely oblong-lingulate or obovate, rounded and obtuse with a minute apiculus, more or less undulate, up to 7 or 8 mm long and 4 mm wide in our specimens, margin non-bordered, entire with the exception of occasionally projecting marginal cells; costa ending considerably below the apex; leaf-cells rhomboid-hexagonal, arranged in series radiating from the costa, the marginal gradually becoming linear and parallel to the margin, all rather thin-walled, chlorophyllose, the largest up to about .030 x .100 or .110 mm: seta long, rather slender; capsule abruptly pendent, shortly oval; lid conic-apiculate; peristome brownish: dioicous: mature in late spring or early summer.

In bogs, pools, and swamps in the cooler parts of Europe, Asia, and North America down in glaciated regions to New Jersey and Pennsylvania and south-ward along the upland plateaus and mountains; generally sterile.

BUTLER Co.: Wet bank of brook, north of Dougherty's Mills. July 28, 1935. Sidney K. Eastwood. CRAWFORD Co.: In Pymatuning Swamp, Linesville, June 12, 1905. O.E.J. (figured). Sterile. ELK Co.: Wet wood in swamp. Sept. 2, 1935. Sidney K. Eastwood. McKEAN Co.: Sphagnum Swamp, West Branch, July 5, 1896, and July 22, 1894. D.A.B. Sterile. SOMERSET Co.: Cranberry Glade Run, Laurel Hill mt. Swampy woods. Elev. 2300 ft. C.M.B. June 28, 1942. VENANGO Co.: Tarkiln Run, near Van. John Wurdack. Aug. 29, 1936.

Family 16.   AULACOMNIACEAE

Dioicous, rarely autoicous: robust to slender, more or less high-cespitose: stem mostly with a central strand, with one to three innovations below the apex, also with slender sterile shoots from the older portions; leaves 8-seriate, gradually larger above, carinate or concave, ovate or oblong to lanceolate or lance-linear, acute to obtuse, non-bordered, mostly toothed above; costa mostly incomplete, with median guides; areolation small, rounded, incrassate, mostly papillose: sporogonia solitary; seta usually long, erect; capsule cernuous, rarely erect, oblong to cylindric, with a short collum, more or less 8-striate, plicate when dry; annulus present; exothecial cells elongate to rectangular, the longitudinal walls thickened; phanerophore, stomata in the collum only; peristomes free and essentially as in *Byrum;* spores .008-.014 mm; operculum conic to rostrate; calyptra narrowly cucullate, long-rostrate, split on one side, fugacious.

Inhabiting the colder and temperate parts of the world, in moist habitats on soil, rocks, trees, etc. The genus *Leptotheca* with species in the south temperate zone and the following:

1.   AULACOMNIUM Schwaegrichen

With characters as for the family, the stem sometimes bearing flagelliform pseudopodia, which are leafless or nearly so and bear a cluster of gemmae at the tips; leaves crowded, decurrent, erect-ascending, the margins more or less revolute; costa ending below apex; cells each with a central papilla; capsule somewhat arcuate; annulus 2-4-seriate, revoluble; teeth lance-linear and sub-ulate-acuminate, yellow to rusty, the divisural zigzag, finely papillose, with numerous articulations; inner peristome delicate, hyaline; basal membrane one-half height of teeth, segments lance-subulate, gaping; cilia well developed, delicate, mostly only weakly articulate.

Nine species widely distributed; five in North America, two in our range.

KEY TO THE SPECIES

A. Autoicous; leaves strongly serrate from the middle upwards ....1. *A. heterostichum*
A. Dioicous; leaves merely serrulate near the apex ....2. *A. palustre*

1. AULACOMNIUM HETEROSTICHUM (Hedwig) Bryologia Europaea
(*Arrhenopterum heterostichum* Hedwig)
Plate XXVIII

Rather loosely cespitose, pale to yellowish-green: stems branching by ter-minal, annual innovations, the annual growth in our specimens being usually about 8-10 mm, stems brown-radiculose below; leaves usually about 8-10 mm, stems brown-radiculose below; leaves obovate below to oblong or elongate-ovate above, often somewhat unsymmetrically inclined, the leaf plane above, coarsely repand denticulate in the upper half, mostly apiculate; costa strong, yellowish-brown, ending just below apex; leaf-cells incrassate, median and apical rounded-quadrate, about .008-.015 mm in diameter, basal similar, quad-rate to rectangular and 3:1: seta about 6-15 mm long, erect, flexuous, reddish-brown, smooth, little or not at all twisted; capsule about 2.5 mm long, oblong-cylindric, arcuate, inclined, reddish-brown, striate, when dry 8-plicate, tapering below into a short collum; annulate; doubly peristomate; teeth inserted on the capsule-rim, lanceolate, about 25-30 articulate, distinct to the base, yellowish-pellucid, rather indistinctly finely horizontally striate-papillate below, seg-ments of same length or a little shorter, hyaline, more or less completely carinate-cleft in median portion, united in the lower third with the cilia into a basal membrane: cilia 3 (2), somewhat shorter, somewhat articulate; spores pellucid-yellowish, not distinctly papillose, about .010-.014 mm; mature in May to June; operculum convex, obtusely short-rostrate; calyptra long-rostrate, cucullate.

On shaded, moist, earthy banks, bases of trees, etc., Japan and in North America from Ontario to Minnesota, and Texas to Florida.

Known from the following counties: Beaver, Bedford, Butler, Cameron, Clarion, Clear-field, Erie, Fayette, Green, McKean, Somerset, and Washington. Specimen figured: Ohio Pyle, Fayette Co., J.A.S. June 15, 1902.

2. AULACOMNIUM PALUSTRE (Weber and Mohr) Schwaegrichen
(*Hypnum palustre* Weber and Mohr)
Plate XXVIII

Robust, densely cespitose mosses of bogs and moist places on soil or rotten wood; tufts often 2-3 inches deep, light yellowish-green above, below darker

gether; always inserted back from the exothecium by the width of several cells, peristome-teeth dagger-shape, golden brown to reddish-yellow, mostly non-bordered, inner peristome mostly shorter, carinate, the basal membrane one-fourth to one-half the height of the inner peristome; segments at first carinately gaping, then divergently parted, cilia 1-3, rarely well-developed, sometimes none, non-articulate; spore-sac very small; lid small, short-conic, rarely rostrate; calyptra small, cucullate, smooth, fugacious; spores large, round to oval or reniform, papillose.

A large family of nine genera; three genera in our region.

KEY TO THE GENERA

A. Cilia usually well-developed: stem with a whorl of sub-floral shoots ....3. *Philonotis*
A. Cilia poorly developed or none ....B
  B. Leaf-cells mamillate or papillose; leaves 5-seriate or pluriseriate ....2. *Bartramia*
  B. Leaf-cells smooth; stem triangular and leaves 3-seriate ....1. *Plagiopus*

1. PLAGIOPUS Bridel

Synoicous: quite slender, laxly to densely cespitose, dull green, becoming brownish: stem triangular, erect or ascending, the outer layer of cells lax, hyaline, inflated, the central strand poorly defined, branching above the base, the shoots of about equal height; leaves spreading to recurved, somewhat twisted but not crispate when dry, from a non-sheathing base narrowly lanceolate, acuminate, sharply carinate above, the margin usually revolute, doubly serrate above; costa strong, percurrent, or shortly excurrent, dorsally projecting and simply serrate upwards; leaf-cells incrassate, smooth, the upper minute, shortly rectangular and quadrate, basally more elongate and pellucid, the alar slightly more lax and quadrate: seta 1-1.5 cm long, erect, castaneous, not twisted when dry; capsule erect, somewhat inclined when dry, globose, slightly arcuate, brown, finely striate, when dry somewhat shortened at the base and mouth, slightly curved and strongly plicate; peristome double, the teeth smooth, narrowly dagger-like, reddish-brown in the upper half, with inter-lamellar thickenings, the inner peristome shorter and pale yellow, cilia none; lid small, short-conic; spores mostly uniform, warty.

A genus of three species: one in New Zealand, one in Java, and the following:

1. PLAGIOPUS OEDERI [Gunnerus] Limpricht

(*Bryum Oederi* Gunnerus; *Bartramia Oederi* Schwaegrichen; *Bartramia grandiflora* Schwaegrichen)

With characters essentially as given above for the genus. The spores mature in spring.

On moist soil and rocks in shady woods, mainly in non-calcareous and hilly or mountainous districts; Europe, Asia, and, in North America, from Canada to eastern Pennsylvania, Illinois, and west to the Rocky Mountains. It may eventually be found in our region.

2. BARTRAMIA Hedwig

Synoicous, paroicous, autoicous, or dioicous: slender to robust, laxly to densely cespitose, the tufts often blue-green above, brownish-yellow inside:

stem with central strand usually distinct, erect, monopodial or dichotomous, branches not whorled; leaves mostly 8-striate, from a mostly half-sheathing base gradually or abruptly subulate-linear, serrate upwards and often on the back of the costa; lamina upwards, sometimes only at the margin, two-layered; costa strong, projecting dorsally, incomplete to excurrent; leaf-cells small, incrassate, rectangular, mamillate on both sides, the basal elongate rectangular to linear, smooth, pellucid to hyaline: seta mostly 1-2 cm long, rarely very short, mostly straight; capsule mostly inclined, somewhat arcuate, with mouth oblique, globose, no collum, when dry mostly sulcate, more or less shrunken in the middle and flattened on the ends; peristome double or single, rarely none, teeth not united at the apex, neither with inter-lamellar thickenings; cilia mostly none; lid small, inflated to short-conic.

A cosmopolitan genus of more than 100 species, on earth or rocks in dry or moderately moist habitats; at least 15 species in North America; two species in our range.

KEY TO THE SPECIES

A. Leaf-base neither sheathing nor conspicuously scarious, margin revolute ....1. *B. pomiformis*
A. Leaf-base scarious and sheathing, margin plane ....2. *B. ithyphylla*

1. BARTRAMIA POMIFORMIS Linnaeus, p.p., Hedwig
APPLE MOSS
Plate XXVIII

Rather densely cespitose, soft, yellowish-green: stems about 1.5-3 cm long, erect, densely reddish-brown-felted below; leaves about 4-6 mm long, the lance-subulate part spreading rather abruptly from a more or less erect and concave but scarcely sheathing lance-ovate base, more or less crisped when dry, the margin revolute in the basal half at least, serrate above, the costa rather narrow and distinct, excurrent in a spinulose-serrate subulation; basal leaf-cells smooth, hyaline, often reddish-brown and pellucid at insertion, elongate-rectangular, the marginal shorter in a few rows, median cells rounded-quadrate, incrassate, papillose: seta about 5-10 mm long, erect or curved-ascending, smooth, reddish-brown; capsule globose, about 1.5 mm in diameter, striate, unsymmetric, reddish-brown when ripe, globose to oblong or narrowly oblong, when dry deeply sulcate, cernuous, occasionally strumose, often somewhat arcuate; peristome double, teeth reddish-brown, narrowly triangular-lanceolate, faintly papillose, prominently articulate, sub-trabeculate, divisural faint, zigzag; segments two-thirds as long as teeth, carinately split, the cilia two or three and rudimentary, or none; lid convex, bluntly umbonate; calyptra narrowly cucullate, about 2 mm long; spores reddish-brown, pellucid, coarsely papillose, mature in May or June.

Cosmopolitan on rocks or swampy soil in moist and shady woods; in North America from the Arctic regions to Florida and Colorado.

This is an easily recognized moss. The leaves look like tufts of green wool and are surmounted by slender stemmed fruits like miniature apples.

Common in our region—known from 15 counties in western Pennsylvania and probably occurs in all. Speimen figured: On clay roadside bank, Hartstown, Crawford Co., May 29-31, 1909. O.E.J. & G.K.J.

1a. BARTRAMIA POMIFORMIS var. CRISPA (Swartz) Bryologia Europaea

This variety is taller and looser than the species: leaves longer, more distant, when dry more crispate; the innovations are long, often longer than the seta.

In moister or more shaded situations but with much the same general distribution as the species.

McKEAN Co.: D.A.B. (Porter's Catalogue).

2. BARTRAMIA ITHYPHYLLA [Haller] Hedwig

Densely cespitose, silky, glaucous-green or yellowish: leaves closely, rigidly divergent from a white, scarious, erect-appressed glossy base, when dry quite straight and more or less erect, the spreading lamina linear-subulate, abruptly contracted from the obovate base, margin plane, sharply denticulate above; costa strong but not very distinct above, excurrent into the denticulate subulation; basal leaf-cells linear, 4-10:1, hyaline, the median and upper papillose, obscure, about 3-6:1: seta long; capsule similar to that of *B. pomiformis,* globose-oblong, when dry curved and deeply furrowed; peristome-teeth reddish-brown, apically bifid or irregularly perforate; segments yellowish, cleft, much shorter than the teeth: synoicous: spores large, mature in summer.

On moist earth or in moist fissures of rocks, mainly in alpine regions, in Europe, Asia, and in Arctic and temperate North America.

Rare in our region. FAYETTE Co.: Layton's, Rev. S. W. Knipe. (Porter's Catalogue), and Knight. (Lesquereux and James).

3. PHILONOTIS Bridel

Dioiccus, rarely autoicous: very slender to robust, cespitose, bright green to yellowish-green or bluish-green: stem with a distinct central strand, erect, more or less elongate, usually with whorled sub-floral shoots; leaves erect-spreading to secund, uniform or dimorphic, lance-ovate, mostly acute, dentate or serrate, mostly with lamina one-layered; costa percurrent to excurrent, rarely incomplete, cells of the apex elongate to shortly rectangular, sometimes rhomboidal, rarely parenchymatous and 5-6-sided, mostly ventrally or on both sides mamillate, rarely so only dorsally, or rarely smooth, basal cells more lax: sporogonia solitary, seta erect, long; capsule inclined to horizontal, globose, unsymmetric, with mostly short collum, striate, when dry sulcate and mostly constricted in the middle, rarely drying erect and smooth; peristome mostly double, the inner one rarely lacking; teeth 16, generally with interlamellar thickenings; basal membrane high; cilia distinct, except in *P. Muhlenbergii;* lid mostly low-convex to short conic.

A large and cosmopolitan genus of about 175 species, on earth and rock in swamps and springy places and on dripping ledges; probably about 30 species in North America; five species in our general region.

KEY TO THE SPECIES

A. Perigonial bracts mostly obtuse, widely spreading from an erect base; median leaf-cells about .006-.010 mm wide; leaves dimorphic: cilia well-developed ....4. *P. fontana*
A. Perigonial bracts acute ot acuminate ....B
   B. Perigonia gemmiform, often apparently lateral; autoicous; costa percurrent to

rather long-excurrent ....1. *P. longiseta*
B. Perigonia terminal and discoid or rosette-like C
C. Leaves neither plicate nor with either or both margins revolute ....D
C. Leaves plicate and more or less revolute ....5. *P. calcarea* var. *occidentalis*
   D. Costa weak but more or less spinulose-excurrent; leaf-cells linear; cilia well devel-
      oped ....2. *P. marchica*
   D. Costa only percurrent to shortly excurrent; leaf-cells linear-oblong to oblong; cilia
      short and rudimentary ....3. *P. Muhlenbergii*

1. PHILONOTIS LONGISETA (Richard) E. G. Britton
(*Bartramia longiseta* Richard; *Bartramia radicalis* Beauvois)

Stems rather slender, yellowish to green, up to 2 cm high; leaves ascending to spreading, lanceolate to somewhat triangular-lanceolate, about 1-1.5 mm long, margins bluntly serrate and revolute; costa weak but percurrent to distinctly excurrent; leaf-cells papillose, rectangular to linear above, larger below; autoicous, perigonia often lateral, gemmiform, perigonial bracts lanceolate from an ovate to oblong clasping base; perichaetial bracts slenderly lanceolate acuminate from an ovate or oblong base, with costa excurrent; seta up to about 2 cm long, castaneous; capsule tilted or slightly drooping, about 1.5-2 mm long, mouth somewhat oblique; lid low-conic; teeth reddish, lance-acuminate, papillose, strongly trabeculate; segments shorter, the cilia usually adherent; spores about .025 mm, papillose, and said to be oblong or reniform.

From Pennsylvania and Ohio south to the Gulf States. Was collected by Wolle at the Nockamixon Cliffs, Bucks County, and in Lehigh County, but not yet reported from our region.

2. PHILONOTIS MARCHICA (Willdenow) Bridel
(*Leskea marchica* Willdenow)

Tufted, bright green, the older parts tomentose, up to 7 or 8 cm high; leaves ascending to patent, lance-ovate to triangular lanceolate, serrate, sometimes revolute; costa slender but percurrent to spinulose-excurrent; cells oblong-linear above, wider below, mostly with sharp papillae at the upper end: dioicous; perigonia large, terminal, their bracts lance-acuminate and squarrose from a broad sheathing base, serrate; perichaetial bracts lance-ovate, tapering from an oblong base; seta up to 3 or 4 mm long; capsule tending to subglobose, tilted to drooping, with small oblique mouth; lid rounded-convex; teeth reddish, strongly trabeculate, papillose; segments somewhat shorter, yellowish, papillose in lines; cilia various, rarely well developed and separate above; spores oblong-reniform, rough, reddish.

Europe; in America from eastern Canada to Minnesota, Georgia, and Texas.

Collected along Slippery Rock Creek by Lesquereux. (Porter's Catalogue).

3. PHILONOTIS MUHLENBERGII (Schwaegrichen) Bridel
(*P. marchica* Sullivant)
Plate XXVIII

Rather densely cespitose, light yellowish to bluish-green: branches reddish, whorled from below the archegonal clusters, erect to ascending, reddish-tomentose below, about 1-3 cm high, slender; leaves of fertile stems 1-2 mm long, rather distant, lance-ovate, acute, ascending to appressed, when dry somewhat crispate, carinate, with revolute margins but not plicate, more or less spreading, serrulate in apical half, scarcely decurrent; costa strong, brownish, percurrent to somewhat excurrent; leaf-cells mostly parenchymatous, rectangular to hexagonal to oblong above, incrassate, median cells strongly papillose on upper end, about .003-.006 x .015-.030 mm, elongate-rectangular, apical cells narrower and tending to vermicular-hexagonal, basal cells looser, more or less rectangular, up to .012 x .040-.060 mm, smooth; inner perichaetial leaves ovate-triangular at base with the costa excurrent into a subulate apex, the margin entire, the cells rather lax; perigonial leaves erect-spreading, long-acuminate, serrate; seta about 2.5-3 cm long, erect, smooth, shining, reddish-brown, when dry flexuous; capsule globose to ovoid-globose, faintly striate, about 2-2.5 mm long, brownish, when dry sulcate and variously wrinkled, arcuate, cernuous, the neck sunken in, about 4-6 rows of cells at the mouth of the capsule laterally elongate; peristome double, the teeth 16, narrowly triangular-lanceolate, prominently articulate, pellucid, orange to reddish-brown, divisural zigzag, distinct below; segments narrow, about four-fifths as high as the teeth, mostly split apart; cilia three, very short and rudimentary, the basal membrane comprising more than half the height of the inner peristome, the segments and the upper part of the membrane orange-pellucid, papillose-striate; spores globose, papillose, pellucid, orange to reddish-brown, .018-.025 mm, mature in June.

On dripping rocks along streams, wet places, etc., from Virginia to Maine.

Uncommon in our region. ALLEGHENY CO.: In crevices of rocky bed of stream, ravine of Power's Run, May 14, 1908. O.E.J. (figured). LAWRENCE CO.: Wet rocks in deep ravine near Rock Point, June 26, 1909. O.E.J.

4. PHILONOTIS FONTANA [Linnaeus] Bridel
(Mnium fontanum Linnaeus; *Bartramia fontana* Swartz)

Plate XXIX

Cespitose, yellowish-green, sometimes quite glaucous, loose above but interwoven below with a reddish-brown felt-like tomentum: stems erect, reddish, slender, usually 2-6 cm high, densely fulvous-radiculose below, the innovations usually whorled and giving the plants the appearance of being pleurocarpous; leaves about 1.5-2 mm long, lance-ovate, acuminate, appressed when dry, usually quite plicate on each side of the costa near the base, serrate above, usually more or less revolute towards the base; costa strong, often percurrent or even excurrent, usually reddish; basal cells elongate-rectangular to elongate-hexagonal, loose, pale pellucid, about .008-.012 (-.015) mm wide, the end-walls often papillose, the cells in the acumen linear-vermicular, incrassate and more or less papillose at both ends; perigonial leaves spreading, broadly triangular-ovate, the inner often obtuse and rounded at the apex, the costa not reaching the apex: seta dark red, 2-4.5 cm long; capsule ovate-globose, large, brownish, thick-walled, striate, oblong, when dry and empty arcuate and irregularly ribbed; operculum conic-convex, acute; peristome-teeth reddish-brown, pellucid, lanceolate; peristome-segments nearly as long as teeth, narrow, carinately gaping, cilia three (two) about as long as segments; spores very slightly papillose, incrassate, yellowish-brown, about .019-.025 mm, usually mature in June.

Water-loving mosses usually avoiding calcareous habitats, on dripping rocks or in swamps and wet places. Cosmopolitan and occurring in North America throughout, from Canada to Florida, more abundant in the cooler and more mountainous regions.

Common but only occasionally fruiting in our region. Known from Allegheny, Armstrong, Centre, Clinton, Fayette, Huntingdon, Indiana, Lawrence, Lycoming, McKean, Washington, and Westmoreland counties. Thus far this moss has not been found in western Pennsylvania north of the terminal glacial moraine. Specimen figured: Floodplain of Brush Creek, Douthett, Allegheny Co., April 26, 1908. O.E.J. and G.K.J.

4a. PHILONOTIS FONTANA var. FALCATA Bridel

Leaves falcate-secund; branches hooked towards the apex.

CENTRE Co.: Matternville Gap, Bald Eagle Mt., July 15, 1909. O.E.J.

5. PHILONOTIS CALCAREA (Bryologia Europaea) Schimper, f. OCCIDENTALIS Flowers

Plate XXIX

Densely and softly cespitose, bright green, more or less glaucous above, brownish below: stems long, up to 10-12 cm, slender, erect in the dense tufts, red-brown and densely felted-tomentose below; branches in whorls; leaves dimorphic, stem-leaves ovate-lanceolate, acuminate, about 2-3 mm long, deeply concave, plicate, towards the apex sharply serrulate, towards the base the basal papillae of the cells forming rounded projections, especially on the revolute margins, the margins revolute narrowly towards the clasping and sub-decurrent base, the leaves erect-spreading to secund when moist, shrunken and sub-crispate when dry; branch-leaves when moist usually more or less falcate-secund, ovate-lanceolate and narrowly acuminate, about 1-1.5 mm long, by 0.5 mm wide, when dry somewhat shrunken and twisted; costa in both forms of leaves strong, excurrent, dorsally papillose, basal leaf-cells rather thin-walled, rectangular, up to .060-.080 x .015-.018 mm, pale, pellucid, towards the margins and upwards becoming shorter, more incrassate, papillose at the ends, the median and upper leaf-cells becoming quadrate to 2-4 times as wide as long, strongly papillose at their upper ends, incrassate, pellucid: capsule not seen but said to be large and similar to that of P. fontana: perigonial leaves oblong-lanceolate: spores mature in summer, but the capsules rather rarely produced. In vegetative characters this species is difficult to differentiate from forms of P. fontana. Flowers, in Grout (Moss Flora), doubts the occurrence of typical P. calcarea in North America and establishes forma occidentalis to cover our American specimens which seem more or less intermediate between calcarea and fontana. Our specimens seem to belong to the form.

Uncommon in our region. CLINTON Co.: In roadside ditch, north of Renovo, July 15, 1908. O.E.J. (figured). HUNTINGDON Co.: Warrior's Ridge, T. C. Porter. (Porter's Catalogue).

Family 12. TIMMIACEAE

Dioicous or autoicous; robust, in more or less high, lax, dull-green to yellowish-green tufts, brownish inside, with a brown tomentum below: stem erect or procumbent, with central strand, densely-leaved, simple or dichotomous; leaves 8-seriate, of uniform length, from a half-sheathing, non decurrent base spreading to recurved, elongate lance-linear, carinate; lamina unistratose, channeled to concave, non-bordered, serrate; costa strong, percurrent, often dorsally toothed above, with several median guides; leaf-cells green, small, rounded to 4-6-sided, ventrally mamillate; cells of the sheathing part without chlorophyll, sometimes dorsally papillose, elongate-rectangular to linear, narrow towards the margin: sporogonia solitary; seta long, erect; capsule cernuous to almost pendent, from a short collum oblong-oval, brown, not or but slightly striate, when dry ribbed; annulus revoluble; peristome inserted back from the edge of the mouth, always double, the inner as long as the outer, when dry the parts sharply bulged outwards in the middle; teeth 16, confluent at the base, broadly lance-linear, rarely split, plane, below yellowish and transversely striate-punctate, above whitish and vertically papillose-striate, divisural zigzag, dorsal plates low, sometimes cut by cross-walls; inner peristome free, yellow, basal membrane high, carinate, transversely striate, dividing into 64 filiform, papillose cilia, united apically into groups of fours, generally appendiculate on the inner side; spores .012-.023 mm, yellow, almost smooth; operculum hemispheric, often apiculate; calyptra cucullate, long and narrow, often remaining on the seta.

One genus with characters as for the family; 8 species; 4 in North America, one in our range.

1. TIMMIA Hedwig

1. TIMMIA CUCULLATA Richard*

(*T. megapolitana* American authors, in part; *T. megapolitana*
var. *cucullata* (Richard) Sayre

Plate XXIX

Loosely cespitose, bright green above, brownish below: stems erect, sparingly branched, radiculose below; leaves lanceolate to lance linear, spreading from a concave appressed and more or less sheathing base, acute to subacute, the margins serrate almost to the sheathing base, the spreading portion of the leaf about as wide as the sheath, concave, smooth on back or more or less involute; costa rather narrow, strong, ending in the apex; basal leaf-cells elongate-rectangular, rather thin-walled, hyaline, hardly inflated, in upper part of sheathing base becoming shorter to quadrate, and incrassate, the outer walls bulging so as to appear slightly papillose, about .010 mm in diameter: seta

---

* *Timmia megapolitana* Hedwig ranges south to New Jersey, New York, and Missouri, and might occur in our region. Its leaves are narrowed gradually to the apex instead of suddenly as in *T. cucullata*; the mouth of the capsule when dry not wider than rest of the capsule in *megapolitana*, but flaring in *cucullata.*—See Sayre in Grout's *Moss Flora.*

about 2 cm long, erect; capsule inclined to cernuous, oblong, when dry and empty unsymmetric, strongly curved, and somewhat wrinkled and tapering gradually from the wide mouth to the seta; lid rounded and apiculate; annulus revoluble, pluriseriate; peristome double, the teeth 16, lance-linear, yellowish-pellucid, trabeculate on inner side, articulate and with a divisural on outer surface, inner peristome with high basal membrane and 64 filiform cilia united into groups of four each, opposite to and about as long as teeth; calyptra cucullate; spores smoothish, mature usually in May.

In shade on moist banks, or bases of trees, mostly in calcareous districts; Europe, and, in North America, from Newfoundland to Virginia, Kentucky, and Missouri.

McKEAN CO.: Riverside swamp, ten miles north of Bradford, on base of old elm, August 19, 1896. D.A.B. Sterile (figured). WASHINGTON CO.: Bank of Buffalo Creek, Taylorstown, May 18, 1895. Linn & Simonton.

Family 20. BUXBAUMIACEAE

Autoicous or dioicous: perennial, low, gregarious to laxly cespitose, dark green, finally brownish: protonema more or less persistent; stem without central strand, mostly very short, erect, thickly foliate to almost leafless: seta ranging from almost none up to 5-20 cm long, erect; capsule proportionally large, sub-erect to inclined, often finally more or less horizontal, dorsiventrally unsymmetric, flattened above, ovate to oblong or ovate-conic, narrowed to a very small mouth; annulate; peristome double or, apparently, single, the inner consisting of a membraneous plaited cone with an apical opening, the teeth originating from one to four concentric rows of cells, faintly barred; operculum conic, glabrous, smooth; spores very small.

A very small and rather primitive family of mosses, growing on earth or decayed wood. *Theriota*, in Korea, and the following two genera:

KEY TO THE GENERA

A. Seta almost none; capsule immersed in the fringing bristles of the perichaetial leaves
....1. *Diphyscium*
A. Seta 5-20 cm long, thick, red or reddish-brown; leaves none at the time of ripening
.... 2. *Buxbaumia*

1. DIPHYSCIUM [Ehrhart] Mohr
(*Webera* Ehrhart, not Hedwig)

Dioicous: perennial, mostly low and densely gregarious; protonema long-persisting; stem without central strand, short, erect, radiculose, thickly-leaved, simple, rarely longer and branched; leaves twisted or crispate when dry, spreading when moist, the lower lingulate or elongate-spatulate, obtuse or acuminate, entire; costa strong, without guides in distal part, ending below apex; lamina 2- (3-) stratose; leaf-cells on both sides mamillate to smooth, rounded to 4-6 sided, incrassate, often widened transversely, in the basal portion uni-stratose, pellucid to hyaline, lax, elongate 4-6-sided with the transverse walls incrassate, smooth; perichaetial leaves much larger, erect, whitish, membranaceous, elongate, lanceolate to linear, the apex usually fringed and the costa long-aristate-excurrent: seta very short, without central strand; capsule immersed, obliquely ovate-conic, gibbous, without collum, mouth very small; annulus present; outer peristome rudimentary or none, when present consisting of 16 triangular teeth; inner peristome pale, membranaceous, 16-plaited, papillose, short-conic; operculum small, acute-conic, falling away attached to the upper part of the fleshy columella; calyptra very small, conic, glabrous.

A genus of about 15 species, only one in North America.

1. DIPHYSCIUM FOLIOSUM (Hedwig) Mohr
(*Buxbaumia foliosa* Hedwig; *Webera sessilis* Lindberg)

Plate XXIX

Small, widely cespitose, very short-stemmed (1-2 mm), the general appearance being that of a grain of wheat sitting in a tuft of bristles: stem-leaves minute, the largest being about 3 mm long, linear-oblong, obtuse, somewhat concave, crisped when dry; costa broad, nearly reaching apex; perichaetial leaves 4-7 mm long, lance-linear, the costa one-third the width of the leaf at base, brownish-yellow, excurrent as a spinulose arista which often reaches one-half the whole length of the leaf, the apex of the lamina acute and entire or lacerate-ciliate; cells at base of the stem-leaves and of nearly the whole lamina of the perichaetial leaves hyaline, thin-walled, irregularly elongate-rectangular to hexagonal, the costa in the lamina of the perichaetial leaves being bordered on either side by several rows of smaller, chlorophyllose, quadrate, and somewhat opaque cells, the lamina of the stem-leaves also being opaque with very small round-hexagonal cells: capsule 4-6 mm high, ventricose, ovate-conic, yellowish-green; operculum acute-conic; calyptra small but covering the operculum; annulus and outer peristome more or less rudimentary; inner peristome conic, whitish, membranaceous, papillose, 16-carinate; spores moderately thick-walled, .007-.010, papillose, mature from mid-summer to early fall.

Widely distributed in the Northern Hemisphere. In North America it occurs from Alabama to Nova Scotia and Ontario, on moist shaded banks and clayey hillsides, and, in our region, especially along rather bare banks along paths in black oak—scarlet oak woods in the mountains. Usually associated with white flecks of Cladonia lichen thalli.

BUTLER CO.: Roadside bank, McKelvy School, Brady Twp., April 26, 1936. Sidney K. Eastwood. CAMERON CO.: Canoe Run, Lumber Twp., Sept. 1, 1935. A. M. Barker. CENTRE CO.: Tussey Mt., Shingletown, July 15, 1909. O.E.J. FAYETTE CO.: Wooded roadside bank, Sugar Loaf Mt., Sept. 1-3, 1906 (figured), and near Lover's Leap, Ohio Pyle, Sept. 4, 1906. O.E.J. & G.K.J. SOMERSET CO.: Moist bank, Laurel Ridge, 2 mi. s. of Miller School, Oct. 6, 1935. C.M.B. WESTMORELAND CO.: Roadside bank, "Rachelwood," New Florence, Sept. 9, 1907. O.E.J. Alt. 2,100 ft.

2. BUXBAUMIA Haller, Hedwig

Dioicous; antheridial plants microscopic on the green protonema; archegonial plants with a short stem, a few small leaves, and one or two archegonia but no paraphyses: isolated or gregarious, annual: stem barely 1 mm high, simple, with hyaline rhizoids; leaves ovate to lance-ovate, the basal portion green and its cells growing out into long brown filaments during the development of the sporogonia, finally covering the stem and vaginule with a thick tomentum; leaf-cells lax, long-hexagonal; perichaetial and upper leaves soon disappearing: seta 5-20 mm long, thick, red-brown, warty, the central strand being surrounded by an air-space; capsule obliquely ascending, the upper surface flattened, the urn brownish and with a short erect collum and narrowed above to a very small mouth; a low pseud-annulus present consisting of a number of layers of cells; outer peristome of one to several rows of short and irregular teeth; inner peristome a pale, plaited, membranous truncated cone, as in *Diphyscium*, 32-carinate; spore-sac small, surrounded by a large air-space; spores small; operculum small, conic-obtuse, erect, falling tardily with the upper part of the columella attached; calyptra small, covering only the operculum, glabrous, fugacious.

A rather widely distributed genus of 5 species, 3 or which occur in North America, one in our region.

1. BUXBAUMIA APHYLLA Linnaeus, Hedwig
"BUG-ON-A-STICK MOSS"

Plate XXX

Plants minute on a thick, brownish, felted protonema and after the development of the sporophyte usually completely obscured by a dense growth of protonemal filaments: seta erect, stout, rough, about 1 cm high, castaneous; capsule when ripe, lustrous, castaneous, ovate-acuminate in outline, flattened obliquely in the upper two-thirds, with angular edges, smoothish, about 5-7 mm long, resembles a shriveled grain of wheat; operculum about 1.5 mm high, oblong-conic, disproportionately small; calyptra falling early, conic, covering only about one-half of operculum; peristome consisting of an outer series of papillose short, slender teeth, and a longer, papillose, conical, plaited cone; spores smooth, spherical, about .007 mm in diameter, mature in late fall and early spring.

On clayey banks in woods or, particularly, along neglected roadsides, often with thalli of Cladonia. Rarely on decayed wood. Europe, Asia, and, in North America, from Canada to Virginia and Washington State. Found commonly in Butler and adjacent counties, but to find it requires a proper recognition of its habitat and a trained eye. It is usually on clay roadside banks mixed with white flecks of some Cladonia lichen.

Collected by Sidney K. Eastwood from more than thirty localities in Butler County (Eastwood, S. K. Bryologist 39: 127-129. 1936). Now known from the following counties: Allegheny, Beaver, Butler, Cameron (Porter's Catalogue), Clarion, Clearfield, Fayette, Huntingdon (Porter's Catalogue), Indiana, Lawrence, Lycoming, and Westmoreland. Specimen figured: On clay bank with decayed wood, 3 mi. n. of Wurtemberg. G.K.J. Oct. 16, 1910.

Family 21. TETRAPHIDACEAE
(Georgiaceae)

Autoicous: slender to very small, dull, gregarious to cespitose, bright to brownish-green; stem erect, leaves 3-5 seriate, unistratose, costa obscure to well-developed and ending just below the apex; cells parenchymatous, thick-

walled, smooth; perichaetial leaves longer: seta long, erect, straight or geniculate in the middle; sinistrorse below, dextrorse above; capsule erect, symmetric,
smooth, oval or cylindric; annulus none; peristome inserted below the mouth,
consisting of the entire mass of tissue enclosed within the epidermal operculum,
this splitting by two planes vertically into four solid, three-angled, elongate-
pyramidal teeth; columella reaching only to the level of the mouth; spores
.008-.015 mm, smooth; operculum conic, unistratose, cleft on one side; calyptra
conic, glabrous, plicate, the margin lobed.

A very small family of 5 species, occurring on rocks, rotten wood, soil, etc.,
in Europe, Asia, and North America. Two genera; *Tetradontium* and the
following:

1. TETRAPHIS Hedwig
(*Georgia* Ehrhart)

Slender plants, more or less densely cespitose in wide soft tufts, bright
green to brownish, radiculose-tomentose below: stems to 3 cm long, with
central strand, three-angled, branched, with distant, scale-like, ecostate leaves
below; upper stem-leaves abruptly larger, approximate, ovate-lanceolate, acute,
margins plane and entire, with costa ending below, or in the apex, 4-5-stratose
at base, cells incrassate, uniform; leaf-cells incrassate, round-hexagonal, wider
transversely, elongate in the leaf-apex, rectangular at the leaf-base: seta 1-1.5
cm long, often two together; capsule erect, symmetric, greenish, when empty
brownish and weakly dextrorse, without stomata; calyptra enclosing the upper
one-third of the urn, its apex carinate-toothed; gemmae lenticular, borne in a
cup formed of four or five broadly cordate bracts at the apex of the more
slender and flexuous gemmiferous stems.

Four species, all occurring in North America, only the following one in
our range:

1. TETRAPHIS PELLUCIDA [Linnaeus] Hedwig
(*Georgia pellucida* Rabenhorst)
Plate XXX

Loosely cespitose in wide yellowish-green tufts: stems erect, about 1 cm.
high, densely felted-radiculose at the base, reddish blow; basal-leaves minute,
upper leaves larger, tufted, ovate-lanceolate, margin entire; certain stems
bearing at the apex gemmae-cups about 1 mm in diameter, the surrounding
leaves being broadly obovate to reniform, truncate or apiculate at the apex;
perichaetial leaves linear-lanceolate, up to 4.5 mm long; costa of stem leaves
wide, ending below apex, in perichaetial leaves often percurrent; aerolation
dense, rounded, the cells of the perichaetial laves irregularly elongate at base;
the cups enclosing small, many-celled, lenticular gemmae: seta yellowish to
reddish, erect, dextrorse above, about 1-1.5 cm long; capsule cylindric-lanceolate,
erect to ascending, reddish, about 2-2.5 mm long; annulus none; peristome
consisting of 4 linear-triangular thick teeth, reddish to brownish, comprising
about one-fifth of the length of the capsule; operculum lustrous, conic, acute;
calyptra whitish and lacerate below, plicate, enclosing the whole capsule, at
apex solid, acute, rough; spores about .010 mm, thin-walled, slightly papillose,
mature in summer or early fall; capsules persistent.

Widely distributed, on peaty soil, decayed logs, etc., Europe, Asia, and, in North America, in Canada and northern United States.

Common in our region and very often found on the cut end of a partially decayed stump or log. Now known from 16 counties in western Pennsylvania and probably occurs in all. Specimen figured: "Rachelwood," New Florence, Westmoreland Co., Sept. 8-11, 1907. O.E.J.

Family 22. POLYTRICHACEAE

Dioicous, rarely paroicous or synoicous; antheridial flower terminal, large, discoid, generally bearing a shoot in its middle; archegonial flowers terminal, bud-like: perennial, mostly very large, mostly cespitose, with a long horizontal, subterranean, triangular, blackish, branched, radiculose rhizome: stem erect with lower leaves none or remote, leaves weakly costate, three-seriate, without lamellae, red to hyaline, small and scale-like; upper part of stem five-or-more-angled, with specialized central strand; stem structure complex; upper leaves larger, the sheathing base usually yellowish to hyaline, lamina more or less spreading or recurved, when dry mostly erect, sometimes convolute to crispate, mostly lanceolate to lance-subulate, sometimes lingulate, mostly sharply toothed, mostly plane with erect edges, uni-stratose or with two-stratose zone next the costa, rarely two-stratose to the margin, with narrow, vertical, green, longitudinal, mostly uni-stratose lamellae on the ventral surface of the costa and of the bi-stratose lamina; costa narrow to wide, incomplete to aristate-excurrent, dorsally often toothed and rarely lamellate, complex in structure; leaf-cells parenchymatous, small, the basal rectangular to linear and narrower towards the margin: seta elongate, mostly solitary, often flattened and weakly sinistrorse; capsule first erect, later inclined to horizontal or pendent, cylindric to prismatically 4-6-sided or cubic, collum various; annulus none or uniseriate with three or four transitional bordering cells; peristome rarely lacking, mostly simple with 32 to 64, rarely 16, lingulate, short, unbarred teeth, triangular in cross-section, rising from a basal membrane, the teeth hyaline, often with a colored median line, incurved to meet the disk-like apex (epiphragm) of the columella; spores mostly small, .008-.012 or .014-.021 mm, mostly smooth; operculum apiculate to rostrate from a conic to convex base; calyptra cucullate, rarely glabrous, mostly spinulose to long, villous and felted.

A cosmopolitan family, mostly on siliceous or other non-calcareous soils; in colder regions often forming large masses or sods.

KEY TO THE GENERA

A. Capsules cylindric ....B
A. Capsules four-angled or six-angled ....3. *Polytrichum*
   B. Leaves not crisped when dry; calyptra hairy; protonema persistent ....2. *Pogonatum*
   B. Leaves crisped when dry; calyptra not hairy ....1. *Atrichum*

1. ATRICHUM Beauvois

(*Catharinaea* Ehrhart)

Stems of moderate height, in loose tufts or gregarious, dark green to bronze when old, central strand generally well developed; rhizome creeping, branched, bearing loosely- to thickly-leaved erect shoots, densely radiculose at the base;

leaves lingulate to ovate-oblong, not sheathing nor narrowed above the base but slightly embracing the stem, margined, serrate; crisped when dry, costa narrow, on the upper side with 1-12 narrow lamellae, ending below or in the apex, towards the apex often spinose-serrate; cells chlorophyllose, the upper rounded-hexagonal, smooth, the basal mostly rectangular: seta long, erect; capsule smooth, cylindric to oval, rarely obovate, often more or less curved; operculum long-rostrate; peristome of 32 teeth with pale borders and a median orange to reddish-brown line, the basal membrane narrow and reddish-brown or orange; calyptra smooth, except at the apex, where it is sometimes spinulose: mostly dioicous.

A cosmopolitan genus comprising about 40 species, growing on earth, mostly in the temperate zones; about 20 species have been reported for North America; four species in our region.

KEY TO THE SPECIES

A. Upper leaf-cells .015 to .025 mm, in diameter; costa and lamellae not exceeding one-fifth of the width of the median part of leaf ....B

A. Upper leaf-cells .007 to .015 mm in diameter; costa and lamellae extending over one-fifth to two-thirds of the width of median part of leaf C

   B. Lamellae 3-6 in number and 3-6 cells in height, covering about 1/8 to 1/11 of the median lef-width ....2. A. undulatum

   B. Lamellae 5-7 in number and 4-7 cells in height, covering about 1/7 to 1/3 of the median leaf-width ....2a and 2b. A. undulatum var. minus

   B. Lamellae 0-4 in number, 1-3 cells high; leaves crispate when dry ....1. A. crispum

   B. Lamellae 4-6 in number, 6-13 cells in height ....(A. undulatum var. Selwyni)

   C. Lamellae 4-7, 6-9 cells high, covering 1/3 to 1/4 of median leaf-width ....3. A. angustatum

   C. Lamellae 6-8, 8-14 cells high, covering about 1/5 to 1/3 of median leaf-width; upper cells papillose ....4. A. papillosum

   C. Lamellae 7-12, 8-14 cells high, covering about 1/2 to 2/3 of median leaf-width ....5. A. angustatum var. plurilamellatum

1. ATRICHUM CRISPUM (James) Sullivant
(Catharinaea crispa James)

Plate LXIV

Gregarious, yellowish-green, becoming brownish, especially below; branches simple, erect from a branched underground stem; leaves crisped when dry, when wet ascending, lance oblong to oblanceolate, or obovate, up to 8 mm long by 1.2 wide, flat, or but faintly undulate, acute, marginally spinulose-serrate in upper half, bordered from near base to tip with colored, incrassate, narrowly linear cells, 2 or 3 cells wide and usually 2 cells thick; costa strong, percurrent (or excurrent), about 1/10 the width of the leaf, with rarely one or two teeth dorsally near the apex, frequently with from one to three lamella on upper side of costa in upper part of leaf, the lamellae smooth and usually 2-3 cells high; leaf-cells smooth, the basal thin-walled and semi-inflated, rounded-oblong to rectangular, 1-4:1, the marginal much narrower, above base the cells become incrassate, rounded to quadrate-hexagonal. Not seen in fruit in our region, but has seta 15-20 mm tall; capsule terete, more or less erect, with urn 2-3.5 mm long, about 3-4:1, lid with beak half as long as urn.

Stream banks or other moist situations; N.E. to Ontario and Tennessee; also in the Northwest.

BUTLER Co.: On ground in wet ditch, Semiconon Run, 2½ mi. north of Conoquenessing. Sidney K. Eastwood, Sept. 22, 1935. FAYETTE Co.: Partly buried in sand around banks of river, around "Peninsula," Ohio Pyle. Charles M. Boardman. Four collections. Oct. 12, 1935, figured). SOMERSET Co.: Beck Spring, Mill Creek, Laurel Hill Mt. C.M.B. July 26, 1947. WESTMORELAND Co.: On wet clay in roadside ditch, Laurel Hill Mt., 9 mi. s.e. of Rector. H. N. Mozingo. Oct. 7, 1945.

2. ATRICHUM UNDULATUM [Linnaeus] Beauvois
(*Bryum undulatum* L.)

Plate XXX

Loosely cespitose, dull, dark green: stems erect, ranging from 1.5-6 cm long, usually about 3-4 cm, mostly simple, more or less gray-radiculose below, arising from a rhizone-like base; lower leaves minute, increasing in size upwards, the upper leaves lanceolate-lingulate, much crisped when dry, transversely undulate when moist, sub-acute to obtuse, about 6 8 mm long, 1 mm wide, serrulate to the middle or slightly below, the uppermost teeth double, strong, being inserted in a border of 1-3 rows of brownish, pellucid to hyaline, incrassate, narrow cells; the crests of the undulations on the back of the leaf also often spinose in upper part of the leaf; leaf-cells elongate-rectangular at base, reaching about .017 x .033 mm, becoming quadrate towards leaf-middle, towards apex hexagonal and somewhat longer transversely and about .017-.024 mm; costa strong, ending just below apex, sharply dorsally toothed, ventrally with 3-6 longitudinal lamellae which each consist of 3-6 rows of cells similar to those of the leaf-blade, the costa and its lamellae covering rarely more than one-fourth of the total leaf-width (in our region sometimes even narrower; "1/11-1/7 of median width"—Frye: seta erect, flexuose, somewhat sinistrorse, smooth, lustrous castaneous, 2-5 cm long; capsule lustrous, becoming dull with age, castaneous, cylindrical, arcuate to almost straight, inclined, smooth, about 4-5 x 1-1.3 mm; peristome single, the 32 teeth linear-lanceolate, obtuse, about 0.3 mm high, orange-pellucid along the median line, united in the lower third into a reddish-orange basal membrane, the teeth covered (especially along the margins) with a hyaline, densely but minutely papillose layer which, during the winter, becomes deciduous, thus leaving the teeth perfectly smooth; spores smooth, orange, spherical, about .016-.019 mm in diameter; mature in late fall, operculum conic, curved linear-rostrate, about 2.5-3 mm long; calyptra pale, roughened towards apex, covering about one-half to one-third of urn.

Widely distributed throughout the North Temperate Zone on earth, particularly partly shaded clay banks; in North America extending as far south as South Carolina and California.

Common in our region—known from Allegheny, Beaver, Bedford, Butler, Clinton, Crawford, Elk, Erie, Fayette, McKean, Somerset, Washington, and Westmoreland counties. Specimen figured: Hyner Creek, above Hyner, Clinton Co., July 15, 1908. O.E.J.

2a. ATRICHUM UNDULATUM var. MINUS (Lamarck and DeCandolle) Weber and Mohr

Plate XXXI

Differs from the species in having the stem, leaves and sub-erect capsule shorter; lamella covering 1/7-1/5 of median part of leaf.

ERIE Co.: Presque Isle, May 8-9, 1906. O.E.J. (figured). FAYETTE Co.: Ohio Pyle, May 30-31, 1908. O.E.J.

2b. Atrichum undulatum var. allegheniense (Jennings)
NEW COMBINATION*

Plate XXX

Similar to the species in general habit and appearance but usually somewhat smaller and more slender: the lamellae 5-7 in number, usually 6, ranging from 4-7, usually 6, cells in height, the costa and lamellae together occupying from one-sixth to one-third of the width of the upper part of the leaf; the upper leaf-cells about .016-.018 mm in diameter.

This variety is much more abundant in the Pittsburgh district than is the species, evidently preferring habitats with shales and sandstones such as those of the Carboniferous.

Now known from the following counties, thus far apparently avoiding the High Plateau: Allegheny, Armstrong, Beaver, Butler, Crawford, Erie, Fayette, Lycoming, Somerset, Washington, and Westmoreland. Type specimen: Power's Run, across from Verona, Allegheny County. O.E.J. April 18, 1906 (figured).

3. ATRICHUM ANGUSTATUM (Bridel) Bryologia Europaea
(*Polytrichum angustatum* Schwaegrichen; *Catharinaea angustata* Bridel)

Plate XXXI

Loosely cespitose: stems erect, about 1-3 cm high, or more; lower leaves minute, the size of leaves increasing upwards, dull green, much crisped when dry, lance-linear, doubly serrate from about the middle upwards along the margin and dorsally towards the apex; costa with about 5-8 ventral lamellae above, the costa and lamellae together occupying about one-fourth to one-half of the width of the leaf; lamellae 6-8 cells high, cells equal in size; basal leaf-cells elongate-rectangular, rather incrassate, about .010-.025 mm in diameter, above becoming quadrate, towards the apex slightly smaller more or less hexagonal with the longer diameter transverse, about .010-.015 mm: seta erect, about 1.5-3.5 cm long, smooth, lustrous, castaneous, somewhat sinistrorse; capsule lustrous, castaneous, linear-cylindric, usually slightly curved, about 5-8 x 1 mm; peristome-teeth obtuse, about 2.5 mm long; calyptra cucullate, slenderly rostrate, about 4-7 mm long; operculum hemispheric, slenderly rostrate, about 2.5 mm long and more or less abruptly divaricately bent; spores about .012-.018 mm, pale, orange-pellucid, smooth to minutely roughened, somewhat incrassate, mature in late fall and winter.

---

* Frye, in Grout's *Moss Flora*, regards this as synonymous with the preceding *A. undulatum* var. *minus*.

Occurring on wooded shaly or clayey banks; Europe, Asia, and, in North America, from Newfoundland and Ontario to the Gulf States. In our region not very common, seemingly preferring steep slopes of ravines, and there often under hemlocks. Quite variable and often approaching closely the two species next following.

Now known from the following counties: Allegheny, Armstrong, Beaver, Butler, Crawford, Erie, Greene, Lawrence, McKean, Washington, and Westmoreland. Specimen figured: Hartstown, Crawford County, May 29-31, 1909. O.E.J.

4. ATRICHUM PAPILLOSUM (Jennings) Frye*
(Catharinaea papillosa Jennings)
Plate XXXI

Plants loosely cespitose, dark green, dioicous: stems simple or at the base sparsely branched, towards the base radiculose, erect, about 2 cm high, chestnut-brown to purple; lower leaves dark green, short, oblong, above gradually longer, erect-spreading, the upper leaves tufted, erect-spreading to erect, oblong-linear, 3-5 mm long, 0.7-1.0 mm wide, margined, above chlorophyll-bearing, obtuse to somewhat acute, towards the apex dorsally serrate-spinulose, in the margin above the middle more or less doubly serrate-spinulose, when moistened slightly undulate, when dry crisped and circinate, lamellate ventrally along the percurrent costa; lamellae 4-8, mostly 6-14 cells high, smooth or minutely and sparsely papillose above the middle, extending over 1/5 to 1/3 the median width of the leaf; leaf-cells on both sides usually slightly minutely papillose, the lower cells hyaline, hexagonal-rectangular, about 10-15 by .030-.045 mm, the median more or less quadrate, the upper cells quadrate-orbicular, chlorophyll-bearing, about .008-.015 mm, the lower border cells linear, incrassate, in two to three series, more or less two-layered, towards the apex gradually becoming rectangular, in the teeth triangular and sometimes .125-.140 mm long; perichaetial leaves similar to the stem-leaves; the perigonial leaves of the antheridial plants from an ovate-orbicular concave base abruptly linear-acuminate, about 2 mm wide and 3 mm long, towards the apex canaliculte, lamellate marginally and dorsally serrate-spinulose and usually sparsely papillose; lamellae usually papillose, 4-6, only 3-7 cells high, disappearing quickly below the base of the acumen: flowers dioicous or rarely arising from the center of the masculine flower of the preceding year: seta solitary, erect, flexuous, slightly sinistrorse, about 2 cm long, smooth, sub-lustrous, chestnut-brown; capsule linear-cylindric, 3.5-6 mm long, 0.5-0.7 mm in diameter, erect-arcuate, tapering abruptly at the base, smooth, chestnut-brown; cells of the capsule rectangular, their lateral walls much incrassate, in a series of 5 or 6 cells under the mouth smaller, quadrate, dark-incrassate; peristome teeth 32, linear-oblong, about 0.3 mm high, in the median line reddish-orange, towards the sides hyaline, in the margins a little dark and densely although minutely papillose, forming a basal membrane in the lower third; spores smooth, incrassate, orange-pellucid, globose, about .008-.011 mm; calyptra about 5 mm long, narrowly cucullate,

---

* Grout (Moss Flora 1: 251. 1939) regards this as synonymous with *A. Macmillani* (Holz) Frye, of eastern United States, common in the southeast.

much shorter than the capsule, towards the apex spinulose-hairy; operculum hemispheric-conic, shining, dark chestnut-brown, terminating in an oblique linear-subulate rostrum 1.8 mm long. Known from the following ocalities:

In western Pennsylvania this moss is thus far known only from the extreme south-western counties, as follows: ALLEGHENY Co.: Along a shaly roadside bank at the west end of Fern Hollow Bridge, Pittsburgh. O. E. Jennings, March 8, 1903. *Type* (figured). Two pockets of specimens deposited in the Pennsylvania Herbarium of the Carnegie Museum). Same locality March 26, 1910. O.E.J.; Stoops Ferry, October 7, 1905. O.E.J. and G.E.K.; Library P.O., April 29, 1906. O.E.J. BEAVER Co.: Beaver Falls, May 11, 1907. O.E.J. BEDFORD Co.: Wills Mt., near Hyndman, October 9, 1904. O.E.J. BUT-LER Co.: Valencia, September 27, 1905. O.E.J. FAYETTE Co.: Ohio Pyle, May 30-31, 1908. O.E.J. GREENE Co.: 2 mi. e. of Waynesburg. C.M.B. Apr. 23, 1938. LAW-RENCE Co.: Ravine below Graceland Cemetery, New Castle. 1906. Susan Gageby. WASHINGTON Co.: Hanlin, May 23, 1908, and Charleroi, June 24, 1908. O.E.J. WESTMORELAND Co.: "Shades," east of Blackburn, March 25, 1910. O.E.J. and G.K.J.

5. ATRICHUM ANGUSTATUM var. PLURILAMELLATUM (Jennings) Frye
(*Catharinaea plurilamellata* Jennings)
Plate XXXI

Loosely cespitose, dark green, dioicous: stems simple or sparsely branched below, slightly radiculose towards the base, about 1.5 cm tall, erect, flexuous, reddish-brown; lower leaves dark green to purplish, short, becoming abruptly longer above; upper leaves clustered, erect-spreading to erect, linear-lanceolate 4-7 mm long, .9-1.3 mm broad, margined, above with chlorophyll, obtuse to sub-acute, toothed on the back towards apex, more or less doubly serrate in the apical third, not very strongly undulate when damp, crisped and circinate when dry; lamellae 7-12 in number, 8-14 (usually about 11) cells high, smooth or sometimes sparsely minutely papillose, usually occupying from 1/2 to 2/3 of the width of the median part of the leaf; lower cells rectangular, about .010-.016 x .025-.035 mm, the upper rounded-quadrate, about .007-.013 mm, the lower marginal cells linear, incrassate, 2- to 3-seriate and more or less bi-stratose, towards the apex becoming rectangular, with triangular teeth about .025-.040 mm long; perichaetial leaves similar: seta solitary, erect, flexuous, somewhat sinistrorse, about 1.5-2 cm long, smooth, shining, reddish-brown; capsule oblong-cylindric, 4-5 mm long, 0.6-0.9 mm in diameter, erect, arcuate, abruptly tapering at the base, reddish-brown, smooth, shining when fresh; peristome teeth 32, linear-oblong, about .25 mm high, reddish-orange along median portion, hyaline towards margins, when young with densely minutely papillose margins, the lower one-fourth portion united into a basal membrane; spores smooth, incrassate, orange-pellucid, globose, about .008-.011 mm; calyptra about 5-6 mm long, narrowly cucullate, extending to about the middle of capsule, spinulose-hairy on apex; operculum hemispheric-conic, shining reddish-brown, terminating in a linear-subulate oblique beak about 2 mm long.

Known only as follows: ALLEGHENY Co.: Powers Run, September 21, 1905, May 30-31, 1908. O.E.J. FAYETTE Co.: On shaded woodland bank, Ohio Pyle. O.E.J. and G.E.K., September 10, 1905 (figured). *Type*. (Deposited in Pennsylvania Herbarium of the Carnegie Museum). WESTMORELAND Co.: Miss K. R. Holmes, 1902.

2. POGONATUM Beauvois

Dioicous: gregarious to weakly cespitose: fertile stems arising from a creeping underground stem or from a radiculose protonema, erect, stiff, short and simple or some longer and branched; leaves gradually longer upwards, erect-spreading to recurved, more or less clasping at base, stiffened by mostly numerous lamellae, especially towards the apex, the margins more or less distinctly spinulose, leaf-blade smooth dorsally, usually for the most part bistratose; the lower part of costa narrow and plane, dorsally towards the apex toothed; cells of the leaf-blade small, incrassate, in the unistratose border mostly quadrate or transversely elongate, basal cells elongate to linear, yellowish to hyaline, thinner walled: seta solitary, sometimes more, castaneous; capsule erect, straight or curved, cylindrical, without stomata; peristome-teeth 32, pale to yellowish-brown with a darker axis; operculum convex and more or less long-rostrate; calyptra mitrate, densely hirsute, more or less shaggy.

A large genus of about 160 species, growing on earth, widely distributed; about 45 species reported for North America; only one species yet found in our region.

KEY TO THE SPECIES

A. Leaf-margins entire; lamellae 25-35 ....(P. brachyphyllum [Richard] Schwaegrichen)*
A. Leaf-margins more or less serrate; lamellae 10-15 ....pensilvanicum

1. POGONATUM PENSILVANICUM (Hedwig) Paris

(Polytrichum pensilvanicum Hedwig; Pogonatum brevicaule
Beauvois; P. tenue E. G. Britton)

Plate XXXII

Plants scattered on a green felt-like persistent protonema which covers the moist, bare clay: stems very short, usually about 1-2 mm long; leaves lanceolate-subulate, the lower shorter and more ovate, narrowing abruptly to an acuminate apex, margins serrulate in the upper half; upper leaves lanceolate with a long-acuminate, serrulate apex, appressed or somewhat spreading; lamellae 10 to 15, 5 or 6 cells high, terminal cell orbicular to ovoid in cross-section, smooth: seta slender, smooth, yellowish to reddish; calyptra light yellow, very hairy and more or less shaggy, completely covering the capsule; capsule erect, symmetric, long cylindric, minutely papillose, slightly or not at all constricted below the lid, yellowish to reddish, about 4 mm x 0.8 mm; lid obtuse to truncate, abruptly tipped with a beak about 0.4 mm long; spores maturing in our region about November.

A common moss on bare clay banks, especially if somewhat moist and shaded, from Nova Scotia to Missouri and south to Alabama.

Usually found on clay roadside banks where the soil is covered with the dense felt of protonema above which are borne the sporophytes with their light gray shaggy calyptra.

Now known from 14 counties in western Pennsylvania and probably occurs in all. Specimen figured: Darlington Hollow, Allegheny Co., Oct. 12, 1908. O.E.J. & G.K.J.

---

* On clay banks, from the Gulf States extending north to New Jersey and Pennsylvania.

3.   POLYTRICHUM Dillenius, Hedwig
HAIR-CAP MOSS

Dioicous; antheridial flowers cup-shaped, sprouting from the middle: robust, stiff, in green to bluish-green, mostly high tufts; stem with a complete central strand, rising from a subterranean rhizome, often whitish tomentose, mostly simple; leaves dense, erect spreading to recurved, drying stiffly erect, from a sheathing scarious base elongate-lanceolate to linear-subulate, non-bordered, with margin plane to involute, sharply serrate, the sheathing base unistratose and hyaline, at least at the angles; lamina bi-stratose except at the margin; costa narrow and flat below, above stronger, dorsally toothed towards apex, mostly excurrent as a colored, toothed awn; lamellae erect, high, numerous, covering the costa and the bi-stratose lamina ventrally; cells in the sheathing base elongate-rectangular to linear, narrower marginward; laminal cells small, incrassate, quadrate-hexgonal: sporogonia solitary; seta long, stiff yellowish-red to purplish, often drying flat and sinistrorse; capsule first erect, finally inclined or horizontal, mostly prismatic, 4-6-angled, oblong to cubic, collum hemispheric or disk-like, with stomata; spore-sac free; teeth 64, with a colored axis, basal membrane colored; operculum large, conic to convex, rostrate; calyptra cucullate and with the long, shaggy hairs completely enclosing the capsule.

About 100 species, mainly on soil in the cooler parts of the globe; about 20 species in North America; at least 5 species in our range.

KEY TO THE SPECIES

A. Exothecial cells of the capsule not pitted ....B
B. Exothecial cells of the capsule pitted C
    B. Marginal cells of the lamellae like the others in size and cell-walls ....1. *P. gracile*
    B. Marginal cells of the lamellae thicker walled and in cross-section obversely pyriform ....2. *P. ohioense*
    C. Leaf-margin entire, broad and inflexed; marginal cells of lamellae not emarginate in cross section ....D
    C. Leaf-margin sharply serrulate, not inflexed; marginal cells of lamellae emarginate in cross-section ....6. *P. commune*
        D. Excurrent costa long, hyaline; plants low (about 1.5-2 cm tall), simple ....3. *P. piliferum*
        D. Excurrent costa red, short; plants larger ....E
        E. Stems not or but slightly tomentose; capsules oblong-tetragonal ....4. *P. juniperinum*
        E. Stems whitish-tomentose below; capsules more or less cubical ....5. *P. alpestre*

1.   POLYTRICHUM GRACILE Dickson
Plate LXXII

Tufted, dark green, erect; stems 3-10 cm tall, matted together below with brownish tomentum; leaves erect-spreading when moist, somewhat curled and twisted when dry, the upper ones longer, 7-10 mm long, the lower one-fourth to one-third portion of the leaf oblong, about 1.5 mm wide, abruptly tapering upwards into a long, very slenderly acuminate, serrulate-spinose tip, the basal sheathing portion of the leaf with thin rectangular cells .035-.070 mm long, one-half to one-third as wide, with narrower cells in a few marginal rows, the cells in the lamina at the middle of the leaf in 4-9 rows, thick-walled, rounded-quadrate, .009-.014 mm in diameter, the lamina above the sheathing base increasingly serrulate with one-celled somewhat spreading teeth; costa at base about one-fourth the width of the leaf, narrowing slenderly above into a sharply serrulate, red, awl-like point about .007-.010 mm long; lamellae numerous, 4-6 cells high, the cells equal in size, smooth, rounded, about .014-.015 mm in diameter, the terminal one slightly obtusely pointed: seta erect, slender, 4-6 cm long, pale yellowish-red; capsule more or less horizontal, ovoid-cylindric, 4-5 mm long and half as thick, rather irregularly obtusely 4-6-angled, considerably shrunken and wrinkled when dry, the apophysis about half as wide as the capsule and only moderately developed; calyptra reddish-brown, about covering the capsule; operculum low-hemispheric, long-rostrate; peristome teeth 64, pale yellowish-red, with a median darker line and several indistinct, longitudinally parallel atriae: capsule wall of thick, irregularly rectangular or rounded-hexagonal cells .035-.040 mm in diameter; spores greenish-yellow, thin-walled, faintly warty, .018-.020 mm in diameter, mature in early summer.

Widely distributed in bogs, heaths, and boggy woods, northern Eurasia and North America; New Zealand.

Our only collection made by Charles M. Boardman, July 15, 1949, in Mt. Davis bog, Somerset Co., Pa., altitude 2400 feet (figured).

2.   POYYTRICHUM OHIOENSE Renaud and Cardot

OHIO HAIR-CAP MOSS

Plate XXXII

Erect, loosely cespitose, about 2.5-7 cm high (gametophyte), olive-green: stems wiry, slightly or not at all tomentose below, chestnut-brown; leaves widely spreading when moist, erect-appressed when dry, or with the tips flexuous-spreading, lower leaves small and linear, the upper about 8-12 mm long, the linear-lanceolate limb spreading from an oblong sheathing base about 2-3 mm long, the limb serrate and ending in a spinulose, stiff, pellucid acumen, very strongly costate, the costa with about 40-50 lamellae; lamellae 4-6 cells high, the terminal cell wider but not longer and not bi-cuspidate or retuse; cells in alar portion of sheathing base of leaf elongate-rectangular, about .010-.015 x .100-.130 mm, prosenchymatous or parenchymatous, in middle of sheathing base narrower and proportionally longer, somewhat incrassate, in limb rounded, incrassate and pellucid-opaque; perichaetial bracts similar but with a longer more hyaline sheathing base and a narrower limb: seta 4-8 cm long, wiry, flexuous, lustrous, chestnut-brown shading to golden above, erect; capsule erect soon becoming more or less horizontal, acutely 4- (5) angled, narrowed towards the base, about 2-3 by 4-6 mm, yellowish-brown, hypophysis small but distinct; peristome-teeth pale yellow with a darker median portion, about 0.2-02.5 mm long; spores round, smooth, .015-.017 mm, mature in midsummer; cells of exothecium about .007-.010 by .010-.015 mm, quadrate to hexagonal, incrassate, non-porose; operculum with a rostrum about equal in length to the diameter of the capsule; calyptra yellowish, exceeding the capsule.

On earth in moist woods, Alaska to Labrador, south to Missouri and Alabama, also in northern Europe.

Common in old fields, open woods, etc., especially on peaty soil and clay hummocks in the northern and upland counties, where it forms dark patches. Now known from 26 counties in western Pennsylvania and probably occurs in all. Specimen figured: Ohio Pyle, Fayette Co., Sept. 1-3, 1907. O.E.J. and G.K.J.

3. POLYTRICHUM PILIFERUM Schreber, Hedwig

Plates XXXII, LXIV

Rather loosely cespitose, light green, rather glaucous: stems simple, erect, 1-4 cm high, purplish-brown, radiculose slightly at the base, leafy only in the upper 1 cm or thereabouts; leaves when moist ascending, when dry imbricate-appressed, base hyaline, rounded-oblong, about 1.5 mm long, the limb narrowly lanceolate, about 3 mm long with wide margins inflexed and in the upper part meeting or overlapping, the apex abruptly terminating in a hyaline, linear, dentate arista about 1 mm long; costa wide, with about 25-35 lamellae ventrally, dorsally more or less papillose or dentate; lamellae usually of 4-7 cells, the terminal one slightly wider and apically abruptly elongate; leaf-cells in alar region of sheathing base quadrate to rectangular or hexagonal, hyaline, slightly incrassate, in middle of sheathing part larger, rectangular, about .015-.018 x .030-.040 mm, somewhat brownish pellucid, incrassate, at base of limb abruptly passing into rather opaque or brown-pellucid, much incrassate, rounded cells, about .010-.015 mm in diameter, in reflexed margin of limb larger and irregularly obliquely rhombic: seta about 2-3.5 cm long, erect, flexuous, lustrous, light chestnut-brown to paler above; capsule small, about 2-2.5 mm long, tetragonal-oblong to almost cubic, sharply angled, erect to pendulous, usually horizontal in age; operculum shortly rostrate; calyptra covering whole capsule; cells of exothecium hexagonal with a large oblong pore one-half the diameter of the cell; peristome-teeth rather hyaline, about 0.2 mm high; spores round, smooth, about .010-.012 mm, mature in mid-summer.

In dry, sandy soil, heaths, etc., in cooler regions over almost the whole earth. In North America ranging from the Arctic regions south to California.

ERIE CO.: On sand-plain, Presque Isle, Sept. 20-22, 1906. O.E.J. FAYETTE CO.: Upper Cucumber Run, Ohio Pyle, June 23, 1935. C.M.B. (Plate LXIV) McKEAN Co.: Bradford, Dec. 23, 1896. D.A.B. (Plate XXXII) WASHINGTON CO.: Near Washington. Linn & Simonton. (Porter's Catalogue).

4. POLYTRICHUM JUNIPERINUM Willdenow, Hedwig
JUNIPER HAIR-CAP MOSS

Plate XXXIII

Rather loosely cespitose, erect, light green and somewhat glaucous: stems slightly tomentose at base, in our specimens about 5-9 cm high, brown; leaves rather crowded, when moist spreading, when dry erect-appressed, or in the older stems somewhat spreading, the base oblong, sheathing, the limb lance-linear, 5-6 mm long, the margin entire or crenulate and inflexed, the costa strong and excurrent into a reddish dentate arista; cells at base of sheathing portion of leaf linear-rectangular, mainly parenchymatous, moderately incrassate, in middle portion of sheath relatively wider, about .010 x .040-.090 mm, both prosenchymatous, in inflexed margin of limb obliquely quadrate-rectangular-elongate, decidedly incrassate; lamellae about 30-40, usually 6-7 cells high, the terminal cell somewhat broader and with an abruptly narrowed shortly prolonged apex; perichaetial leaves more hyaline with a longer sheathing base and a considerably longer slightly dentate arista: seta erect, flexuous, lustrous, about 4-6 cm high, somewhat sinistrorse; capsule tetragonal-oblong, about 3-5 x 2-2.5 mm, sharply angled, reddish to dark chestnut-brown when old, apophysis short but rather distinct, capsule pendulous to horizontal; spores round, smoothish, about .008-.011 mm, mature in midsummer; cells of exothecium elongate-hexagonal to quadrate-hexagonal, the perforation linear-oblong, about half as long as cell.

Heathlands, dry pastures, thin woods, etc., in hilly or mountainous regions the world over. It occurs from Arctic America south to North Carolina.

Now known from eighteen counties in western Pennsylvania. Specimen figured: On ground in dry pasture, near Kittanning, Armstrong Co., Sept. 24, 1904. O.E.J.

5. POLYTRICHUM ALPESTRE Hoppe, Schwaegrichen*
(*Polytrichum strictum* Banks, Menzies)

Plate XXXIII

Large mosses forming dense tufts up to 20 cm deep, tufts deeply matted with a dirty-white tomentum: stems branching, rather slender, often matted tomentose to within 2-3 cm of the apex; leaves more or less rigidly appressed-imbricate when dry, when moist with the lance-linear limb spreading and 4-5 mm long, from an oblong sheathing base about 1.5 mm long, margin of limb entire, inflexed, the apex rather abruptly narrowed into a linear, reddish-pellucid, slightly serrate acumen, leaves dorsally serrulate nearly to the sheathing base, the costa bearing ventrally about 25-35 lamellae; lamellae 5-8 cells high, the terminal cell broader and abruptly narrowing to an obtuse short acumen, as seen in cross-section; areolation of sheathing base almost hyaline, not so markedly incrassate, the median basal rectangular, 4-8 times as long as broad, towards the margin and upwards in the sheathing portion narrower, longer, either prosenchymatous or parenchymatous, cells of inflexed margin of limb obliquely quadrate or rectangular to linear-oblong in the border, incrassate; perigonial leaves of male plant obovate-orbicular, the costa broad, lamellate on the upper half, percurrent in a broadly acute acumen: seta erect, slender, wiry, sinistrorsly flexuous, 4-8 cm long, lustrous, rich chestnut-brown below and lighter above; capsule more or less cubic, 2-3 mm long, acutely angled, papillose, yellowish to chestnut-brown, apophysis distinct; cells of exothecium more or less hexagonal, the central pore round to oblong, often one-third the diameter of the whole cell; peristome about 0.2 mm high, teeth rather slender; calyptra yellowish-brown, covering the capsule; operculum flattened, the rostrum about 0.5 mm long. Evidently mature in midsummer.

* Frye, T. C., in Grout's *Moss Flora*, reduces this to a variety of *P. juniperinum*, i.e. *P. juniperinum* var. *alpestre* Bryologia Europaea.

From the Arctic regions of North America south to North Carolina; southern South America; northern Europe and Asia. In bogs or boggy woods.

Rare in our region. CRAWFORD CO.: In small *Cassandra* bog near Linesville, May 28, 1908. O.E.J. (figured). WASHINGTON CO.: Hanlin, in tuft of *Leucobryum*. May 21, 1908. O.E.J.

6. POLYTRICHUM COMMUNE Linnaeus, Hedwig

Plate XXXIII

Large, erect, 10-20 cm high, loosely cespitose in large masses, rather dark olive green: stems simple, flexuous, woody, slightly or not tomentose at base, chestnut-brown, rather densely foliate above; lower leaves small, linear, becoming gradually larger above up to about 15 mm long, the limb linear-lanceolate from an oblong sheathing base, when moist spreading or recurved, when dry appressed-erect, serrate to the sheathing base, the apex linear, serrate, pellucid; areolation at base of sheath parenchymatous, rectangular, above becoming linear-prosenchymatous, abruptly grading at base of limb into rounded incrassate cells about .010-.015 mm in diameter, towards apex becoming elliptic with the longest diameter transverse, all pellucid to more or less opaque; lamellae 40-60, 4-9 cells high, the terminal cell broader and retuse to bi-cuspidate at apex, the lamellae extending almost to the base of limb; perichaetial bracts up to 20 mm long, with a longer sheathing portion and few or no lamellae; antheridial flowers conspicuous, cup-shaped, the broadly obovate shortly acuminate bracts which form the cup being about 4 mm long, the costa broad and weak below but stronger and bearing numerous lamellae in the upper half; the successive annual growths of the male plant taking place from the center of the antheridial flower of the preceding season: seta wiry, flexuous, 6-10 cm long, lustrous, chestnut to light golden-brown; capsule erect, but later inclined, and, when old and empty, cernuous, light to deep chestnut-brown, more or less cubial or shortly rectangular, apophysis discoid, distinct; capsule-urn about 3-5 mm long; operculum low-conic, the beak about 1 mm long, straight or curved; peristome-teeth about .25 mm high, more or less reddish-pellucid; exothecial cells hexagonal, the outer face convex and with a rounded to elliptic pore; spores round, smooth, about .008-.010 mm, mature in mid summer—calyptra covering the whole capsule, rather lustrous, yellowish-brown.

Cosmopolitan; in North America almost throughout, in marshy places, pastures, woods, etc.

Now (1942) known from every county in western Pennsylvania except Blair, Clarion, Forest, Fulton, Huntingdon, Indiana, and Venango, but probably occurs in all. Specimen figured: Near Hartstown, Crawford Co., in wet meadow, June 28, 1908. O.E.J. This is the form which some authorities recognize as var. *uliginosum* Huebener, as follows:

6a. POLYTRICHUM COMMUNE var. ULIGINOSUM Huebener

Plate XXXIII

In this variety the stems are less strong and rigid than in the species, and the leaves in the dry specimens are wide-spreading to recurved. It is rather rare in the eastern part of the United States. Perhaps not sufficiently distinct.

CAMBRIA CO.: Cresson, May 18, 1904. O.E.J.; upland plateau near St. Lawrence, July 24, 1908. O.E.J. CRAWFORD CO.: Near Linesville, May 12, 1908; and Hartstown, June 28, 1908. O.E.J. (figured). (Near Linesville this variety forms quite extensive heaths in the low-lying peaty pastures around the Pymatuning Swamp, especially on the low mounds of peaty soil formed by the uprooting and subsequent decay of trees).

6b. POLYTRICHUM COMMUNE var. PERIGONIALE (Michaux)
Bryologia Europaea

Lamellae 6-9 (instead of 4-9 cells high), inner perichaetial bracts much longer than foliage leaves; operculum with straight beak. Arctic America south to North Carolina. Not yet known from our region.

Family 23.   HEDWIGIACEAE

Autoicous; paraphyses long, yellow, filiform: more or less robust, stiff, cespitose; stem without central strand, irregularly to almost pinnately branched, rarely with long, pendent, 2-3-pinnate branches, densely-leaved, radiculose below, sometimes stoloniferous; leaves about 8-seriate, spreading, drying imbricate, broad, thin, ecostate, concave, sometimes plicate, papillose; lamina one-layered, golden-brown at base, cells incrassate, punctate, non-margined, with several rows of small quadrate cells in the alar portion, or margined with the alar portion concave, sharply differentiated by large, colored, 4-6-sided cells; leaves on stolons recurved-squarrose, from a wider base suddenly long piliferous-acuminate; perichaetial leaves erect, longer than the stem-leaves, with ciliate margins at apex; seta various; vaginula ciliate; capsule short, erect, shortly and thickly collumate; annulus none; spores large; operculum low, convex to rostrate; calyptra minute and mitrate to large and cucullate.

A small but widely distributed family of six genera, only one genus in our region.

1.   HEDWIGIA Ehrhart, Hedwig

Autoicous: laxly cespitose, glaucous-green: rarely stoloniferous, erect to ascending, irregularly branched; leaves concave, ovate, tipped with a hyaline, serrate to ciliate acumination, margins revolute, entire, non-bordered; leaf-cells two- to several-papillose, papillae on both sides, the upper cells oblong, the lower elongate, the median basal yellow, linear, becoming quadrate and brownish towards the angles; perichaetial leaves larger, the upper margins furnished with long, sinuose, articulate, sometimes toothed cilia: seta about 5-8 mm long, yellow, thicker upwards; capsule immersed, obovate to globose, smooth, pale brown, the mouth red and wide; spores .028-.032 mm, yellow with vermiform lines; operculum plano-convex, red, sometimes unbonate; calyptra minute, conic-mitrate, fugaceous, covering only the apex of the operculum.

A cosmopolitan genus of one very variable species, occurring on noncalcareus rocks.

1.   HEDWIGIA CILIATA [Ehrhart] Bryologia Europaea
(*H. albicans* Lindberg; *Fontinalis albicans* Weber; *Anictangium ciliatum* Hedwig)
Plate XXXIV

In patches of varying size up to quite large, blackish or brownish below, glaucous-green above, more or less hoary, especially in late summer or in autumn, owing to the colorless tips of the leaves: stems from 2 or 3 up to 8 or 10 cm long, rather slender, irregularly forking and branching, the branches usually rather short; leaves more or less secund on the procumbent stems, when dry imbricated but with recurved apex, when moist spreading, concave, ovate, 1.5-3 mm long, the apex sub-obtuse to long-acuminate, papillose-denticulate to spinulosely denticulate, more or less hyaline; costa none; the median basal leaf-cells yellowish pellucid, not papillose, narrowly linear, incrassate, porose, towards the margin and in upper part of leaf the cells sub-quadrate or rectangular, with more or less sinuose walls, the cells in the angles often brownish and larger, the median and upper cells prominently papillose, longitudinally seriate, varying from quadrate to rounded or hexagonal; perichaetial leaves prominently ciliate towards the apex, not plicate: seta practically none: capsule sub-sessile, immersed, globose-oblong, about 0.6-0.9 mm in diameter, wide-mouthed and truncate when dry and empty, red-rimmed, the urn castaneous; lid convex, sometimes mamillate, about three-fourths as wide as the median diameter of the urn; calyptra small, sub-cucullate and fugacious; annulus none but one or two rows of exothecial cells at the rim of the urn smaller, laterally elongate, and castaneous-pellucid; peristome none; spores mature in spring, minute, shallowly pitted, pale, thin-walled, about .025-.028 mm: autoicous.

On dry rocks, boulders, stone-walls, etc., in non-calcareous habtiats; almost cosmopolitan; in North America occurring from the Arctic regions to Mexico.

Common in our region. Now known from Allegheny, Beaver, Bedford, Fayette, Forest, McKean, Somerset, Washington, and Westmoreland counties. Specimen figured: Ohio Pyle, Fayette Co., May 30-31, and July 4, 1908. O.E.J. Not yet known from the glaciated region of western Pennsylvania.

1a.   HEDWIGIA CILIATA f. LEUCOPHAEA (Bryologia Europaea) Jones
(*H. albicans* var. *leucophaea* Limpricht)

Very hoary; more robust than the species: leaves more falcate, wider, the hyaline base of the piliferous acumination occupying about the whole upper third of the leaf.

With the type and in the same general habitat.

HUNTINGDON Co.: Stone Creek, T. C. Porter. (Porter's Catalogue). WESTMORELAND Co.: T. P. James. (Porter's Catalogue).

PLEUROCARPI

In the following families the flowers, as a general rule are borne in the axils of leaves along the side of the stem. The antheridial flowers are enclosed in an involucre of modified leaves, the perigonial bracts; the archegonial flowers have a similar involucre of perichaetial bracts; and the sporophyte thus is borne laterally on the stem. Most of the pleurocarpous mosses have a creeping habit.

Family 24.   FONTINALACEAE

Dioicous or autoicous: filiform paraphyses few: slender to robust, aquatic, floating, blackish-green or reddish-brown: stem without central strand, 3-5-

angled, or round, much branched but bare below, fastened by a cushion of rhizoids at the base; leaves 3- and 5-seriate, ovate-acute to lance-subulate, carinate to concave or plane, mostly decurrent, rarely winged, entire or dentate at apex; lamina uni-stratose above, bi- to tri-stratose below, with single costa or none; median leaf-cells mostly elongate prosenchymatous, smooth, the basal orange, laxer, rarely loosely rhombic hexagonal: seta rudimentary or normal: capsule erect, non-collumate, without annulus, without stomata; peristome none, single, or double, teeth when present 16, hygroscopic, as long as or shorter than the segments; mostly linear, orange- to brown-pellucid, non-bordered, mostly papillose, ventrally with projecting transverse trabeculae; inner peristome without basal membrane, segments filiform, 16, usually more or less united into a carinate, trellis-like cone, rarely free and appendiculate; lid short-conic to rostrate; calyptra small and conic or cucullate and reaching to below the capsule.

A family of six genera, confined almost exclusively to the temperate and colder parts of the Northern Hemisphere; two of the genera in our range.

KEY TO THE GENERA

A. Leaves ecostate; calyptra short ....1. *Fontinalis*
A. Leaves costate; calyptra enclosing the whole capsule ....2. *Dichelyma*

1. FONTINALIS Linnaeus, Hedwig
WATER MOSSES

Dioicous: floral branches apparently axillary, very leafy; antheridial clusters short and obtusely gemmiform; archegonial branches elongate and acute: slender to very robust: stems sharply 3-angled to round, much branched; leaves of one form, 3-seriate, otherwise as for the family, ecostate; perichaetial leaves larger, almost enclosing capsule, broadly obovate, obtuse, lacerate when old: vaginule and seta rudimentary; capsule oval to ovate, mostly delicate; peristome double, inner and outer of same length, teeth 16, linear-lanceolate, orange to brownish, plane, papillose, mostly apically united in pairs, the divisural zigzag, articulations prominent, the trabeculae projecting both ventrally and laterally; segments 16, filiform, united by lateral processes into a plaited cone, rarely free and appendiculate; spores irregular in size, mostly green, almost smooth; lid conic, calyptra reaching but little below the operculum, the base lacerate when old.

A genus of about 60 species; about 30 reported for North America; at least five occurring in our region.

Most of the specimens of this genus in our collections have been verified by Winona H. Welch.

KEY TO THE SPECIES

A. Older stem-leaves carinate or keeled-conduplicate ....1. *F. antipyretica* var. *gigantea*
A. Older stem-leaves not as above ....B
  B. Leaves essentially one form, not dimorphic ....D
  B. Leaves dimorphic C
    C. Vernal leaves lance-ovate to suborbicular, summer leaves narrowly lanceolate; apical
      cells reminding one of Sphagnum ....2. *F. biformis*
    C Stem-leaves lance-ovate to lanceolate, branch leaves narrowly lanceolate, both acumi-

nate ....3. *F. Sullivanti*
D. Stem-leaves rather firm, more or less distinctly concave ....E
D. Stem-leaves plane or nearly so, mostly distinctly flaccid ....F
E. Leaves narrowly to oblong lanceolate, long-acuminate ....4. *F. dalecarlica*
E. Leaves ovate-lanceolate, apex usually denticulate, broadly obtuse or apiculate ....
....5. *F. novae-angliae*
F. Alar cells enlarged, forming distinct auricles, and leaves clasping the stem ....
....10. *F. Lescurii*
F. Leaves not clasping the stem ....G
G. Majority of leaves 4-8 mm long by 0.5-1.5 mm wide, very long and narrowly acuminate; auricles distinct ....7. *F. flaccida*
G. Majority of leaves 2.4-5.5 mm long ....H
H. Apex of leaf usually acuminate, long and narrow ....6. *F. hypnoides*
H. Apex of leaf usually shorter and broad I
I. Leaf-auricles usually small but distinct ....9. *F. Duriaei*
I. Leaf-auricles none or quite indistinct ....8. *F. nitida*

1. FONTINALIS ANTIPYRETICA Linnaeus, Hedwig

Leaves lance-ovate to lance-oval, 5-8 x 2-4 mm; median leaf-cells about 6-15:1; perichaetial leaves obtuse; peristome teeth papillose.—Apparently mostly represented in eastern United States by var. *gigantea*.

1. FONTINALIS ANTIPYRETICA var. GIGANTEA Sullivant

(*Fontinalis gigantea* Sullivant)

Plate LXIV

Floating, long, dark, brownish-green or golden green: stems denuded below, slender, up to sometimes 6 or 8 dm. long, irregularly divided; the branches turgidly three-cornered and sometimes 2 or 3 dm long; leaves deeply concave, carinate, up to 6-8 mm long, 3-6 mm wide, broadly ovate or lance-ovate to almost orbicular, entire, mostly broadly obtuse at the tip; median leaf-cells about 7-11:1, linear-rhomboid and more or less vermicular, the apical and basal shorter and wider, the alar sub-rectangular and somewhat inflated, forming auricles which are convex upwards (adaxially); perichaetial leaves closely imbricated, the upper sheathing, truncate, rounded, entire, or lacerate at the apex: capsule rather small, sub-sessile, usually only the rostrate calyptra and the conic lid emergent from the sheathing perichaetial leaves when mature, about 2:1, more or less turgid-oblong; lid reddish; peristome usually a bright coral color, smoothish, the inner peristome united at the apex and sometimes well down towards the middle into a lattice-work, the bars incomplete below; spores mature in summer.

In cool streams and in ponds, on stones or on wood; Europe, and from Canada through the northern United States to Alabama. Scarce and confined to the mountains in our region.

BLAIR CO.: T. P. James. (Porter's Catalogue). CAMBRIA CO.: T. P. James. (Porter's Catalogue). CAMERON CO.: Submerged rocks in brook, Tannery School, Lumber Twp., Sept. 1, 1935. S. K. Eastwood. LYCOMING CO.: In spring, Bald Eagle Mt., south of Williamsport, Feb. 15, 1949. Harry Roslund. MCKEAN CO.: D.A.B. (Porter's Catalogue). SOMERSET CO.: Glade Run Swamp, eastern border of county. June 28, 1942. O.E.J. WESTMORELAND CO.: Big Springs, west of Bakersville, Oct. 31, 1933. C. M. Hepner (figured).

2. Fontinalis biformis Sullivant

Yellowish green to dirty green: stems long, much-branching; leaves of two kinds; the vernal large, soft, lance-ovate, concave, blunt to acute, when fresh and moist quite prominently three-ranked, and rather widely spreading, the apical cells somewhat like *Sphagnum* cells; the summer leaves much smaller, narrower, convolute and tubulose above, rigid, covering the younger branches; median leaf-cells of the vernal leaves linear, the apical broadly rhomboidal and sphagniform, the angular quadrate-oblong, much larger, forming small decurrent auricles; costa none; archegonial clusters rare, situated towards the base of the stems; antheridial clusters usually 2 to 4 together and long-stipitate: capsule oblong-oval, enfolded by the suborbicular inner perichaetial leaves; lid conic, rostrate; peristome-teeth lance-linear, about 20-articulate, cilia tessellate and united at the apex, papillose.

In woodland rivulets and streams, Ohio and Indiana.

Rare in our region. Portage County, Ohio, and McKean Co.: (Porter's Catalogue).

3. Fontinalis Sullivanti Lindberg
(*F. Lescurii* var. *gracilescens* Sullivant)

Quite similar to *F. Lescurii* but smaller and more slender: very slender, regularly pinnate with remote and attenuate branches; leaves distant, the stem-leaves lanceolate, soft, narrowly long-acuminate, somewhat concave, acute to somewhat obtuse, entire or sub-denticulate, yellowish, about 5 mm long, the branch-leaves about half as long, more rigid, more concave, acuminate; perichaetial leaves rather short as compared with *F. Lescurii*, not undulate at apex; median leaf-cells linear-flexuous, the apical shorter and broader, the basal shorter and broader, the alar much larger, inflated-oblong forming auricles: capsules sessile, cylindric; lid conic, long-acuminate; peristome teeth papillose, the inner peristome as in *F. Lescurii*; spores minutely roughened.

In stagnant water, swamps, etc., on bushes, tree roots, etc., eastern United States. Not reported from our region.

4. Fontinalis dalecarlica Bryologia Europaea
Plate XXXIV

Stems slender, much-branched, naked below, 1-3 (4) dm long, attenuate, dark-castaneous, sub-lustrous; leaves somewhat close, erect-spreading to somewhat imbricate, more or less glossy, lance-oblong to narrowly lanceolate, acuminate, 2-3 mm long, often slightly toothed at apex, margins usually somewhat involute, concave, sometimes very slightly auricled at base; leaf-cells prosenchymatous, rather incrassate, linear-oblong, about 10-18:1, the marginal slightly narrower, the alar rectangular to irregularly quadrate-hexagonal, considerably larger, usually slightly colored; perichaetial leaves apiculate, the apex finally lacerate: capsule immersed, about 2 mm long; peristome orange to brownish, the teeth slender, granulose, with about 14-22 lamellae, the inner peristome with an imperfect lattice; spores muriculate, about .025-.032 mm, mature in summer.

In rapidly flowing streams, occurring from Greenland to Georgia, Tennessee, and Wisconsin; also in Europe.

CAMERON CO.: On rocks in bottom of creek 3 mi. w. of Truman. June 22, 1935, and Tannery School, Sept. 1, 1935. Sidney K. Eastwood. CENTRE CO.: In swiftly running mountain-stream about three miles south of Boalsburg, Sept. 22, 1909. Sterile. O.E.J. (figured); Bear Meadows. T. C. Porter. (Porter's Catalogue); Stream, Tussey Mt., near Shingletown, O.E.J. July 15, 1909. FAYETTE CO.: Sheepskin Run, one-half mi. e. of Ohio Pyle. C.M.B. Nov. 6, 1943. SOMERSET CO.: Clear Run, Shafer Run, and Blue Hole Creek, all Laurel Ridge, various dates. C.M.B. VENANGO CO.: On submerged rock in creek near St. George. Aug. 4, 1935. Sidney K. Eastwood. WESTMORELAND CO.: On rocks in swift water, Rock Run, Laurel Mts., Aug. 31, 1925. O.E.J. and G.K.J.; Fish Hatchery trough, Rector. W. R. Witz, April 4, 1937; Rock Run, Forbes Forest. C.M.B. Sept. 16, 1934.

5. FONTINALIS NOVAE-ANGLIAE Sullivant

Plate XXXIV

Rather bright green, fairly firm: stems usually 3-4 dm long, wiry, purplish-black, slender, rather freely branching, naked below but quite densely foliate towards the apex; leaves rather close, somewhat appressed, thin, entire, sometimes faintly serrulate at apex, the main branches with leaves about 2-2.5 mm, broad when moist, the branches more or less linear-attenuate; leaves about 3-4.5 mm long, broadly ovate-lanceolate, concave, the margins somewhat revolute, the apex cucullate, rounded-obtuse; median leaf-cells linear-vermicular to somewhat narrowly linear-oblong, prosenchymatous, incrassate, about 6-15:1, the alar cells forming a quite distinct group, quadrate to oblong, moderately enlarged, somewhat incrassate and colored; capsule sub-cylindric to oblong-oval, near base of stem, closely invested by the ovate-sub-orbicular perichaetial leaves, which are lacerate when old; capsules rare; pristome-teeth colored, linear-lanceolate, 18-20 articulate, slightly papillose; cilia tessellate and united at apex only, minutely papillose; spores smooth.

In brooks and swift-running streams from Newfoundland to Ontario and North Carolina.

BUTLER CO.: On rocks in swift stream, 5 mi. north of Zelienople. Oct. 3, 1925 and 4 mi. n.e. of Harmony, May 3, 1930. L. K. Henry; Walley Mill, Parker Twp. July 14, 1935. Sidney K. Eastwood. CLEARFIELD CO.: In rapid stream north of Mahaffey, May 30, 1937. Sidney K. Eastwood. FAYETTE CO.: Cucumber Run, Ohio Pyle. July 18, 1895. C.M.B. FOREST CO.: Buzzard Swamp, June 30, 1948. C.M.B. HUNTINGDON CO.: Spruce Creek, T. C. Porter. (Porter's Catalogue). VENANGO CO.: Submerged rocks in stream near St. George. Aug. 4, 1935. Sidney K. Eastwood. WESTMORELAND CO.: Creek below Hillside Station, September 17, 1909. O.E.J. and G.K.J. (figured).

6. FONTINALIS HYPNOIDES Hartman*

Rather delicate, soft, slender, pinnately divided plants; leaves distant, flaccid, narrowly lanceolate to lance-ovate, gradually acuminate, 3-6 mm long, usually entire; median leaf-cells linear attenuate to linear-rhomboidal, the alar more or less enlarged but indistinct, not forming distinct auricles; capsule about

---

* The descriptions of F. hypnoides, nitida, and flaccida have been largely compiled from Welch's treatment in Grout's Moss Flora.

half emersed, oval; peristome teeth linear, papillose; trellis of inner peristome perfect with appendiculate cross-pieces; spores more or less muricate, about .012-.015 mm in diameter.

Various kinds of water habitats, United States and Canada. Not yet reported from our region.

7.   FONTINALIS FLACCIDA Renauld and Cardot*

Soft, delicate, yellowish green, slender, pinnately divided plants up to 35 or 40 cm long; leaves distant (1.5 mm apart), flaccid, concave at base, less so above, narrowly lanceolate to lanceolate, 4-8 mm long, very slenderly acuminate, the apex itself often obtuse to truncate, often denticulate; alar cells much enlarged, hyaline to yellowish-brown, forming quite evident auricles: capsule immersed, subcylindric, 2 mm long; teeth of peristome linear, slightly papillose; trellis of inner peristome imperfect, muricate; spores smoothish.

Reported variously in stagnant or running water in various parts of eastern United States. Not yet reported from our region.

8.   FONTINALIS NITIDA Lindberg*

Soft, delicate, slender, pinnately divided plants up to 20-40 cm long; leaves about 1 mm apart, flaccid, usually flat, lance-oblong to lance-ovate, gradually acuminate but usually with a short and broad acumen; alar cells enlarged and fairly distinct and often forming auricles: the oval capsule usually immersed; peristome teeth linear, papillose; trellis complete and perfect, muricate, with cross-bars appendiculate; spores finely muricate.

Asia; and in fresh (non-stagnant) waters, United States and Canada. Not yet reported in our region.

9.   FONTINALIS DURIAEI Schimper

Plants soft and weak, green to olive- or yellow-green; stems slender, 10-30 cm long, pinnately but bushily branched, often denuded below; leaves about 0.5-1.5 mm   apart, spreading to erect-spreading excepting at ends of branches where imbricate, plane to sub-concave, lance-oblong to broadly lance-ovate, rather abruptly and broadly acuminate, 3-5 (-7) mm long by 1-2.5 (-4) mm wide; apex acute to sub-obtuse, denticulate to entire; median leaf-cells linear-attenuate to linear-rhombic, .0085-.017 mm wide; 6-18:1 alar cells more or less enlarged, hyaline to yellowish-brown, rectangular to quadrate or sub-hexagonal, auricles none or indistinct: upper perichaetial leaves oval-suborbicular, broadly rounded at apex to apiculate, lacerate when old: capsules immersed, oval to short-oblong, about 2 mm long with conical operculum; peristome brownish orange, the teeth linear, papillose, 0.75-0.9 mm long, frequently united in pairs at apex, with 15-35 lamellae; trellis perfect, muricate, with transverse strands complete; spores minutely muricate or smooth, .015-.020 mm in diameter, mature in summer.

---

* The descriptions of F. hypnoides, nitida, and flaccida have been largely compiled from Welch's treatment in Grout's Moss Flora.

In streams and falls, occasionally in swamps.   Europe, Africa, Canada and the United States.

Known in our region only from a creek west of Linesville, Crawford County, Pa., Aug. 4, 1909. O.E.J. (Det. by Winona H. Welch).

10.   FONTINALIS LESCURII Sullivant

Loose, soft, green to glossy golden-green: stems long, reaching sometimes 3 or 4 dm. naked and blackish below, dividing and branching irregularly except sometimes at the apex, where the branches may be arranged pinnately; leaves erect-spreading, soft, obscurely three-ranked, concave, clasping at the base, lance-ovate to lance-oblong and rather acuminate to a somewhat obtuse apex, slightly denticulate at the apex, usually about 4-6 mm long; median leaf-cells about 12-15:1, elongate-linear, flexuous, the apical and basal shorter and broader, the alar enlarged oblong, inflated, forming quite distinct auricles; perichaetia numerous towards the base of the stems, perichaetial leaves sheathing, the inner rounded-obtuse, broadly oval, reaching nearly to the apex of the mature capsule: capsule short, sub-cylindric, enclosed by the closely folding perichaetial leaves until almost mature, about 2.5:1; lid long-conic; peristome-teeth red-orange, papillose, about 20-25-articulate, the inner peristome more or less compeltely united into a lattice-work at the apex but free and merely appendiculate below; spores mature in summer.

On stones in streams from Nova Scotia to Georgia and west to Tennessee and Oklahoma.

Rare in our region. HUNTINGDON CO.: T. C. Porter. (Porter's Catalogue). MC-KEAN CO.: Bradford. D.A.B. (Porter's Catalogue).

2.   DICHELYMA Myrin

Dioicous; antheridial shoots small, gemmiform; archegonial shoots long; slender to robust, shining, green to golden-brown, blackish below; branching various, the branches recurved at the apex; leaves 3-seriate, falcate-secund to circinate, lance-subulate from a slightly decurrent base, carinate-plicate, weakly serrate; costa complete to long-excurrent; median leaf-cells linear, narrow, the alar not wider; inner perichaetial leaves long, tubular, sinistrorsely wound around the seta: seta long; capsule ovate, soft, brownish; peristome-teeth 16, lance-linear, obtuse, papillose, spreading either when damp or when dry, often more or less cleft or divided along the median line, trabeculae low and distant; inner peristome longer and sometimes falling away with the operculum, segments filiform, more or less united; lid about as long as urn, conic, mostly oblique and curved; calyptra enclosing the whole capsule, split along one side, sinistrorse; spores small and uniform in size.

A rather widely distributed genus of 5 or 6 species; 4 species occurring in North America; 2 species in our region.

KEY TO THE SPECIES

A. Leaves subulate; costa long-excurrent ....1. *D. capillaceum*
A. Leaves acute; costa complete or almost so, subpercurrent to slightly excurrent ....
....2. *D. pallescens*

1. DICHELYMA CAPILLACEUM [Dillenius] Bryologia Europaea

(*D. pallescens* Sullivant and Lesquereux; *Fontinalis capillacea* Hedwig)

Yellowish above, brownish to blackish below; stems slender, often 10-15 cm long, with a few distichous, divaricate, or one-sided branches; leaves erect-spreading, secund to falcate-secund, long-linear from a lance-oval base, about 5-7 mm long, serrulate towards the apex; costa long-excurrent; perichaetial leaves linear, thin, ecostate, pale and twisted and reaching above capsule; leaf-cells narrow, linear-rhomboid: seta short, slender; capsule small, pale yellowish, thin-walled, ovate, the urn truncate and about 1.5-2:1, finally laterally emerging from the perichaetium; lid high-conic; peristome double, the teeth shorter than the inner peristome, narrowly linear, densely papillose, segments longer than teeth, constricted at the articulations, pale yellow, papillose, forming a connected lattice-work only above; spores mature in late summer.

On sticks and the bases of bushes in and around the edges of slow streams, ponds, and swamps; Europe and from New Brunswick and Ontario southward to North Carolina and Tennessee. Yot yet recorded in our region.

2. DICHELYMA PALLESCENS Bryologia Europaea

(*Fontinalis capillacea* Hooker)

Plate XXXV

Slender, light yellowish-green, sometimes glossy: stems usually about 5-10 cm long, the branching sub-distichous; leaves secund, more or less falcate, the ends of the branches and stems appearing hooked, leaves oblong-lanceolate, about 3-5 mm long, gradually long-acuminate, complicate-carinate, nearly entire; or denticulate above, plane-margined, acute to obtuse; costa percurrent or nearly so; median leaf-cells rhomboid-linear, prosenchymatous, about 8-15:1, rather incrassate, the basal colored and somewhat shorter, a few alar indistinctly wider and oblong, incrassate, the apical shorter; perichaetial leaves about as long or usually longer than the seta and capsule together: seta about 4 mm long, slender, enclosed in the perichaetium; capsule small, thin, ovate, yellowish, about 1 mm long, truncate by the falling away of the lid, emerging laterally from the perichaetum; lid high-conic; peristome-teeth linear, rather rudimentary, pale, castaneous-pellucid, with distinct divisural and lamellae, and about 10-12 castaneous-pellucid, low ventral trabeculae; segments filiform, longer than teeth, united only at the summit or entirely free, sometimes remaining on the ripe capsule only as short, filiform, cilia-like structures between the teeth; exothecial cells rounded, castaneous-pellucid, incrassate-collenchymatous, the upper laterally oblong and smaller; spores mature in summer, castaneous-pellucid, incrassate, minutely papillose, varying from about .016-.025 mm.

More or less inundated on sticks and the bases of bushes along creeks and around ponds; New Brunswick to Minnesota and Pennsylvania.

Not yet found in our region, excepting along the northern border. McKEAN Co.: Bradford. D.A.B. (Porter's Catalogue); Riverside, New York, a few miles north of Bradford. D.A.B. October 18, 1897 (figured).

Family 25.   CLIMACEAE

Dioicous; flowers on secondary stems and at base of branches; gregarious, large and stately, growing in swamps: stems rhizome-like, subterranean, radiculose, with smooth, branched, reddish-brown rhizoids, secondary shoots 3- to several-angled, erect, with more or less tree-like branching, with central strand; branches leafy, cylindric, simple, pinnate or bi-pinnate; paraphyllia numerous; leaves dimorphous, the rhizome and lower part of stem having scale-like and appressed colored leaves, the upper stem and branches having green leaves; leaves plicate; costa simple, homogeneous, ending below the apex, at the base widened by two or three layers of laminal cells; leaf-cells smooth, upwardly narrow-rhombic, downwards linear, the basal orange, the alar hyaline, lax, thin-walled and forming a distinct group; perichaetial leaves numerous, long and slender; sporogonia often aggregated: seta long, erect, stiff, sinistrorse; capsule erect and symmetric in *Climacium;* exannulate; peristome double with the parts of equal length; teeth confluent at base, reddish-brown, articulate, papillose, ours not transversely striate, the lamellae numerous; inner peristome yellow, papillose, with more or less of a basal membrane, the segments carinate, more or less gaping along the keel, cilia none; spores medium size; operculum rostrate from a convex base; calyptra cucullate.

Two genera: *Pleuroziopsis,* with one species, in our regions bordering the North Pacific, and the following:

1.   CLIMACIUM Weber and Mohr

Mostly as characterized in the description of the family: branches simple, or sometimes almost pinnate, unequal, attenuate; branch-leaves lance-ligulate from a decurrent, auricled base, bluntly to sharply acute, sharply serrate above; inner perichaetial leaves abruptly acuminate, entire, short-costate; costa of the leaves strong, ending below the apex, dorsally toothed above: seta 15-45 mm long, stiff, castaneous; capsule erect, symmetric, almost cylindric, castaneous; teeth lance-linear, acuminate, with a dark red border, with low papillose dorsal plates, and with closely placed trabeculae; inner peristome orange, vertically striate-papillose, segments linear, carinately gaping, finally divided; spores .015-.020 mm, rusty, warty; calyptra long, narrow, enclosing whole capsule, cleft on one side to apex, sometimes twisted.

A widely distributed genus of about 5 species: 3 occurring in North America and extending into our region.

KEY TO THE SPECIES

A. Plants of dendroid habit ....B
A. Plants not distinctly dendroid, median leaf-cells about 2-3 : 1 ....3. *C. Kindbergii*
    B. Auricles not prominent; median leaf-cells 8-10 : 1 ....1. *C. dendroides*
    B. Auricles broad, median leaf-cells about 5-7 : 1 ....2. *C. americanum*

1.   CLIMACIUM DENDROIDES [Linnaeus] Weber and Mohr
(*Hypnum dendroides* Linnaeus; *Leskea dendroides* Hedwig)

Dendroidal, robust, bright or yellowish-green; the primary stems underground, creeping, divided; the secondary stems rising to a height of sometimes

10 cm, leafless below, bearing at the summit numerous erect-spreading, flexuous, usually straight branches; leaves large; stem-leaves broadly amplexicaul, with a more or less rounded and cucullate or apiculate apex; branch-leaves imbricated, giving to the branches a thick and turgid appearance, about 2 x 0.7 mm, lance-oblong to lingulate-oblong, denticulate at base but quite sharply serrate above, plicate, somewhat cordate but little auriculate at the base; costa nearly reaching apex; median leaf-cells about 6-10:1, linear-rhomboidal to linear-hexagonal, shorter and wider towards the apex and towards the base, the alar somewhat lax, wider, hyaline, few, forming small auricles; perichaetial leaves entire, non-plicate, the inner sheathing: seta deep red, about 2.5-3 cm long; capsule erect, castaneous, oblong-cylindric, about 4 mm long, about 3-4:1; lid often remaining attached to the columella, straight, acutely rostrate; calyptra reaching to below the capsule; peristome large, the teeth forming a cone when moist but usually curved in between the segments when dry; spores mature in fall, green in color.

On wet ground in marshes, at borders of streams, margins of swamps and lakes, etc.; Europe, Asia, and from Arctic America south to New Jersey and the Northwest. It may eventually be found to occur in the northern part of our region.

2.   CLIMACIUM AMERICANUM Bridel
AMERICAN TREE MOSS
Plate XXXV

Loosely cespitose, robust, yellowish-green, lustrous: primary stems creeping stolon-like in the leaf-mould, throwing up at intervals dendroidal secondary stems to a height of 5-8 cm; secondary stems with large, scattering to closely imbricate, ovate, scale-like leaves below, above bearing a closely tufted group of branches; branches ascending, 1.5-2.5 cm long, terete, acute to obtuse; branch-leaves 1.7-2.2 mm long, about two-fifths as wide, broadly lanceolate, sharply serrate in upper half, often denticulate below, acute, broadly auriculate, erect-spreading, when dry imbricate, strong bi-sulcate; costa strong, ending just below apex; median leaf-cells oblong-hexagonal with more or less rounded or truncate ends, 5-7:1, rather incrassate, those of the auricles quadrate along the margin to diamond-shaped towards the interior, the apical and the upper marginal larger and rhombic-oblong: seta erect, stout, dextrorse above, sinis-trorse below, castaneous, about 1-1.6 cm long; capsule castaneous, narrowly cylindric, about 5-6 mm long, 5-6:1, erect to slightly curved, slightly con-tracted below the mouth when dry, nearly smooth; annulus none; operculum conic-rostrate, about 1 mm long; peristome-teeth shallowly inserted, orange-castaneous, non-striate but decidedly papillose, strongly and rather densely trabeculate, the lamellae and divisural not very distinct, the teeth slender and often perforate below; segments usually longer than teeth, linear, arising from a very narrow and often somewhat perforate basal membrane which is usually inserted entirely below the rim of the urn, the segments yellowish, granular-papillose, perforate-cleft in a ladder-like manner along the median line; cilia none, or sometimes represented by mere stubs rising from the basal membrane; exothecial cells heavily incrassate, castaneous-pellucid, oblong, the upper rounded-quadrate, those at the rim smaller and transversely oblong, darkly incrassate; spores yellowish, minutely roughened, about .016-.018 mm, the walls moderately incrassate.

In damp, shady woods on rotten logs, stumps, wet soil, rocks, etc., often in swamps. From New Brunswick to the Carolinas and Alabama and west to the Rocky Mountain region.

Not uncommon in our region but rather rarely found in fruit. Known from Allegheny, Armstrong, Bedford, Butler, Cameron, Clarion, Crawford, Elk, Erie, Fayette, Forest, McKean (Porter), Somerset, Tioga, Venango, Warren, Washington, and Westmoreland counties. Specimen figured: Moon Township, Allegheny Co., 1889. J.A.S.

3. CLIMACIUM KINDBERGII (Renauld and Cardot) Grout
(C. americanum var. *Kindbergii* Renauld and Cardot)*

Plate XXXV

Dark yellowish-green to almost black, usually rather densely cespitose: secondary stems about 3-6 cm tall, sometimes indistinctly dendroidal, stout, castaneous, bearing along the stem rather scattered widely ovate leaves about 3-4 mm long, leaves not sulcate, plane-margined, sub-clasping at base, acute and almost entire at apex, strongly costate into the apex; basal cells in a wide area, rather thin-walled, large, rectangular to rhombic-oblong, often somewhat brownish, above quickly passing into linear prosenchymatous cells about 10-15:1, the apical cells shorter and rhombic oblong; branches densely tufted, ascending to widely spreading, 1.5-2.5 cm long; branch-leaves about 1.5-2.5 mm long, broadly lance-ovate, somewhat clasping by the auriculate base with rounded auricles, strongly sulcate, apex obtuse to acute, margin plane, serrate in upper half, strongly costate almost to the apex; median leaf-cells of the branch-leaves oblong-hexagonal, 2-3:1, somewhat incrassate, the basal short rhombic to quadrate-rectangular in the auricles, the median basal longer with rounded ends, incrassate and more or less castaneous-pellucid: sporogonium not seen from our region but described as having the seta more flexuous and considerably longer than in *C. americanum;* capsule 4-6 mm in length; peristome-teeth perforate.

In swamps and pools in woods from New England to Indiana and the Gulf States. According to Grout, less common inland.

BEDFORD Co.: Raystown Branch, 2½ mi. s. of Schellburg. C.M.B. July 19, 1941. BUTLER Co.: Outlet of West Liberty Bog. C.M.B. Nov. 26, 1948. CRAWFORD Co.: Twin Lakes, Pymatuning Swamp. C.M.B. July 5, 1947. ERIE Co.: Among shrubs in swamp, Presque Isle. Nelle Ammons. Aug. 3, 1935. FAYETTE Co.: Along margin of densely shaded mountain stream, Meadow Run Valley, four miles south of Ohio Pyle, September 1-3, 1906. O.E.J. and G.K.J. (figured); Near Falls, Ohio Pyle, Oct. 12, 1935. C. M. Boardman. MERCER Co.: One mile north of North Liberty, on tree root in wet woods. May 30, 1935. C.M.B.; In swamp, North Liberty, April 14, 1935. Sidney K. Eastwood.

Family 26. LEUCODONTACEAE

Dioicous, rarely autoicous: antheridial shoots gemmiform, axillary; archegonial clusters terminal on short perichaetial branches; both kinds on secondary shoots: paraphyses few, filiform: plants more or less stiff and robust, laxly cespitose, mostly shining; stem cylindric, central axis rudimentary or none; main stem creeping, branched, radiculose with brownish radicles; secondary stems numerous, erect or ascending, rarely pendent, thickly-leaved, simple or branched; leaves pluri-seriate, decurrent, often plicate, ovate to lanceolate, abruptly to slenderly acute, non-bordered, one-layered; costa double or simple or none; leaf-cells incrassate, mostly smooth, rhombic above, below elongate along the middle of the leaf, towards the margin rounded-quadrate in many series; capsule erect, symmetric, oval or ovate to oblong-cylindric; annulus present; peristome double, teeth lanceolate to lance-subulate, densely articulate, non-bordered, mostly papillose, mostly without projecting lamellae, rarely with cross-striae on basal plates; basal membrane of inner peristome low, segments rudimentary and narrow or none, as long or shorter than teeth, cilia none; lid conic, obliquely rostrate; calyptra cucullate; spores medium to large.

On rocks and trees, mainly confined to temperate regions; 7 genera; only 2 genera in our region.

KEY TO THE GENERA

A. Costa double or none ....1. *Leucodon*

A. Costa single ....2. *Leptodon*

1. LEUCODON Schwaegrichen

Dioicous: blackish to yellowish or brownish-green, dull or lustrous: primary stems very long and branched; secondary stems usually simple, equally high, sometimes more or less pinnate, thickly leafy; leaves drying appressed, straight or secund, mostly pluri-plicate, when moist spreading, ovate-acuminate to short-acute, entire or apically serrate, ecostate; median leaf-cells smooth, oblong-rhombic, the basal reddish-yellow; inner perichaetial leaves high-sheathing, long-acuminate: seta mostly more or less elongate, reddish; capsule mostly exserted, oblong to oval (or globose), reddish brown to blackish, with a small mouth and short collum, stomata none; annulus present; peristome double with the inner peristome rudimentary or apparently lacking; teeth whitish to yellowish, mostly gaping in the middle or divaricately cleft; lid conic, constricted at the base, sometimes obliquely rostrate; calyptra smooth, cucullate, enveloping the capsule and upper end of seta; spores .025-.035 mm, yellowish-green, finely warty.

A widely distributed genus of about 30 species, occurring on trees and rocks; 8 species reported for North America; 3 species, probably, in our region.

KEY TO THE SPECIES

A. Leaves plicate; secondary stems well developed: seta about 2-3.5 mm long, with capsule emergent but shorter than the perichaetial leaves ....1. *L. brachypus*

A. Secondary stems less developed: capsule long-exserted ....B

  B. Leaves ovate-elliptic, rather abruptly and shortly acuminate, scarcely plicate ....
....2. *L. julaceus*

  B. Leaves lance-ovate, long and slenderly acuminate, much plicate ....3. *L. sciuroides*

1.   LEUCODON BRACHYPUS Bridel

Plate XXXV

Moderately robust, brownish to light green, loosely tufted: stems usually at least 5-6 cm long, with rather numerous secondary simple or branched divisions; leaves about 2 mm long, ovate, bluntly acute to short-acuminate, obscurely more or less secund, usually plicate with two folds, entire to serrulate above; costa none; median leaf-cells linear-fusiform and castaneous pellucid at base, the interior median rhombic, about 5-8.1, grading to oval at the apex, the marginal basal rounded-quadrate to transversely oblong, all cells incrascate; perichaetial leaves loosely appressed-sheathing, non-plicate, the inner surpassing the capsule; seta about 2-4 mm long, wrapped in the perichaetial leaves; capsule oval-oblong, about 1.2-2 mm long, about 2:1 castaneous, small-mouthed, dark-rimmed; lid conic, obliquely short-rostrate; peristome-teeth rather broad, irregular, pale to whitish, papillose, often bifid at apex, the inner peristome very thin, narrow, and without segments or cilia; spores mature in winter or late fall, pale, rather thin-walled, granular.

On trees and rocks in hilly or mountainous regions; from Nova Scotia to Kansas and south to the Gulf States.

CAMBRIA Co.: Cresson. T. C. Porter and T. P. James. (Porter's Catalogue). CRAWFORD Co.: On bark at base of *Fraxinus nigra*, near Linesville, June 11-12, 1907. O.E.J. McKEAN Co.: Quintuple, November 11, 1893, (approaching *L. sciuroides* in acumination of leaf-apex) and Langmade, near Bradford, August 11, 1895. D.A.B. (figured). WASHINGTON Co.: Linn and Simonton. (Porter's Catalogue).

2.   LEUCODON JULACEUS [Linnaeus] Sullivant

(*Hypnum julaceum* Linnaeus; *Pterigynandrum julaceum* Hedwig)

Plate XXXVI

Resembling the preceding in habit but with shorter secondary stems and distinctly terete branches, which are julaceous when dry: leaves crowded, closely appressed-imbricate when dry, scarcely secund, ovate-elliptic, abruptly short-acuminate, entire or slightly serrulate at apex, the margins often recurved, blade concave, scarcely plicate, the base rounded and sub-clasping, mammillose at back of apex; leaf-cells mainly as described for the genus, but the upper much shorter and broader than in the other species, in the median upper third rhombic-oblong, incrassate, about 2-3:1, seriate; the marginal rounded-hexagonal but towards the base usually densely transversely oblong-hexagonal, the basal median linear-vermicular and much incrassate, those above becoming shorter; costa none; perichaetial leaves linear-oblong, filiform-acuminate, reaching well up to the capsule: seta slender, partly exserted; capsule turgid-oval, castaneous, about 0.5-0.7 x 1 mm; annulus none; lid obliquely short-rostrate, about half as long as the urn; peristome closely similar to that of *L. brachypus*, the teeth apically bifid; spores mature in fall.

In woods on tree-trunks, often mixed with other mosses, from New England to Minnesota and south to Florida and Texas.

As yet known only from the southern third of western Pennsylvania. ALLEGHENY Co.: On base of white oak tree, Library, April 29, 1909. O.E.J. (figured). BEDFORD

Co.: Roystown Branch, 2½ mi. s. of Schellsburg. C.M.B. July 19, 1941. Cambria Co.: T. P. James. (Porter's Catalogue). Indiana Co.: T. P. James. (Porter's Catalogue). Washington Co.: On bark of log, May 8, 1891, and on rotten wood, Nov. 5, 1892. Near Washington. Linn & Simonton.

3. Leucodon sciuroides [Linnaeus] Schwaegrichen

(*Hypnum sciuroides* Linnaeus; *Fissidens sciuroides* Hedwig)

Rigidly cespitose, brownish to olive-green: secondary stems terete and jula-ceous, more or less curved-ascending at the ends, usually 3 or 4 cm long; leaves densely crowded, slightly secund, closely imbricate when dry, more or less open-spreading when moist, lance-ovate, long and slenderly acuminate, entire, usually about 5-plicate, somewhat decurrent; costa none; leaf-cells about as for *L. brachypus;* perichaetial leaves pale, non-plicate: seta about 7 or 8 mm long, rather stout; capsule oblong-elliptic, brown, exserted; lid conic, same color as urn; peristome-teeth slender, pale to whitish, remotely articulate, entire or split towards the base; annulus simple, falling away in fragments; calyptra yellowish-brown apically, reaching to the base of capsule; spores mature in spring but capsules very rarely found.

On trunks of trees, or very rarely on rocks, in woods; Europe, and from lower eastern Canada through the northeastern United States to Pennsylvania and Iowa. Not yet found in our region.

2. Leptodon Mohr

(*Forsstroemia* Lindberg)

Autoicous, rarely dioicous; quite robust to slender, green to brownish-green, mostly dull: leaves drying imbricate and non-plicate or indistinctly pli-cate, when moist erect-spreading, ovate to oblong, short acute, also ovate and acuminate, margin more or less revolute, entire or apex serrate; costa rather narrow, ending about the middle; apical and median cells elliptic or oval, the angular rounded-quadrate to transversely oblong; inner perichaetial leaves sheathing, long and narrowly pointed, costate or ecostate: seta short, 2-5 mm, straight, red to yellowish; capsule mostly exserted, ovate to oval, pale or red-dish-brown; annulus narrow or none; peristome-teeth lance-linear, mostly yel-lowish, pellucid, densely articulate, finely papillose above, sometimes broken through on the divisural; inner peristome none or very rudimentary; spores .020-.035 mm, yellowish-green, finely papillose; lid conic, narrowly acuminate to shortly rostrate; calyptra cucullate with erect hairs, rarely smooth.

A widely distributed genus of about 20 species, mostly arboreal in habitat; 4 species in North America; 1 species in our region.

1. Leptodon trichomitrion (Hedwig) Mohr

(*Pterigynandrum trichomitrium* Hedwig; *Forsstroemia trichomitria* (Hedwig) Lindberg)

Plate XXXVI

Broadly cespitose, rather rigid, yellowish-green; primary stems creeping, filiform, the secondary stems numerous and abundantly branched; leaves close, loosely erect-spreading, lance-ovate, shortly acuminate to acute, entire, when dry somewhat plicate, about 1.5-2 mm long, the extreme apex rather blunt, the base concave, the margins reflexed; perichaetial leaves loose in texture, the inner sheathing, reaching to the base of the capsule or a little higher: seta short, slightly longer than the capsule; capsule ovate-cylindric, thin-walled, rather gradually narrowed below, about 3-4:1, about 1.5 mm long; exothecial cells rather incrassate, irregularly polygonal to rectangular-oblong, several rows at the narrowed mouth smaller, rounded-quadrate and dark-castaneous; peristome-teeth whitish, lance-linear, rather remotely articulate, sometimes perforate along the divisural, the inner peristome entire to more or less torn, adhering to the ventral surface of the teeth; lid short-rostrate; spores mature in winter, orange-incrassate, almost smooth, about .023-.025 mm.

In woods on trees, rarely on rocks; Asia, and from New England to Ontario and the Gulf States.

Common in eastern Pennsylvania but rare in our region. BEAVER Co.: About 8 feet up on elm trunk, along Raccoon Creek, one mile south of Traverse Creek. April 1, 1934. Chas. M. Boardman. McKEAN Co.: Near Latshaw, N. Y. north of Bradford, August 25, 1895. D.A.B. (figured).

Family 27.   NECKERACEAE

Dioicous, rarely autoicous or synoicous; sexual clusters only on secondary shoots and their branches, with filiform, often yellowish paraphyses: slender to robust, mostly stiff, laxly cespitose: stem somewhat dorsiventrally flattened, with or without a rudimentary central strand: primary stem more or less creeping, mostly filiform, mostly sparsely fasciculately radiculose; secondary stems more or less elongate and ascending or much elongated and pendent, mostly distantly or symmetrically pinnate, thickly-leaved, julaceous or flattened; leaves nearly always pluri-seriate, uni-stratose, of various forms; costa mostly delicate, homogenous, simple or double or none; median cells mostly prosenchymatous, the apical sometimes parenchymatous, the basal often colored, the alar sometimes differentiated: capsule mostly erect and symmetric, peristome mostly double, teeth yellowish to brownish, lance-linear, dorsally sometimes abnormally thickened, ventrally trabeculate; the inner peristome with mostly low carinate basal membrane, rarely rudimentary or none, segments linear to filiform, often fenestrate, rarely cleft the whole length, cilia mostly none; lid conic, erectly to obliquely rostrate; calyptra mitrate to cucullate, mostly hirsute; spores of varying size.

A large family, occurring mainly on trees in warmer regions, often forming a conspicuous part of the vegetation; about 20 genera, of which but three occur in our region.

KEY TO THE GENERA

A. Secondary stems flattened, ascending or pendent; leaves mostly conspicuously unsymmetric ....B
A. Secondary stems mostly erect and branched in a tree-like manner; leaves not complanately disposed ....3. *Porotrichum*
 B. Exannulate; basal membrane of inner peristome low, cilia none, segments narrowly linear ....1. *Neckera*
 B. Annulus 2-seriate; basal membrane conspicuous, cilia rudimentary and soon disappearing or well-developed, segments about as broad as teeth ....2. *Homalia*

1. NECKERA Hedwig

Autoicous or dioicous, rarely synoicous: mostly more or less robust, cespitose, green to yellowish or brownish, somewhat lustrous: primary stems often stoloniferous, paraphyllia mostly none; leaves on the filiform shoots small, ecostate, symmetric, concave; normal leaves either 1-seriate, the dorsal and ventral alternately turned to the side, the lateral spreading, or 4-seriate, the dorsal and ventral series lacking, leaves often transversely undulate, unsymmetric, rugose, more or less spatulose from a broader and shortly decurrent base, acute to obtuse or truncate; costa various, upper leaf-cells rounded to rhombic, the lower linear, the alar differentiated, small and quadrate; perichaetial leaves high-sheathing, narrow, long-acuminate: capsule oval or elliptic, immersed to exserted; annulus none; peristome double, inserted far back; peristome-teeth lance-linear, often basally striate, low-trabeculate, sometimes split along the divisural; basal segments 16, the basal membrane mostly very low; cilia none; calyptra mostly cucullate and with erect hairs; spores medium, mostly brownish, papillose.

A widely distributed genus of about 130 species; about 20 species reported for North America; two species definitely known for our region.

KEY TO THE SPECIES

A. Leaves rounded and usually apiculate at the apex ....B
A. Leaves strongly undulate, acute to acuminate; perichaetium longer than seta and capsule ....1. *N. pennata*
 B. Leaves undulate ....1. (*N. pennata* var. *oligocarpa*)
 B. Leaves not undulate C
C. Plants rather robust; leaves complanate; seta 7-10 mm long, exceeding the perichaetium ....2. *N. complanata*
C. Plants very slender; leaves not complanate ....3. *N. gracilis*

1. NECKERA PENNATA [Linnaeus] Hedwig
(*Fontinalis pennata* Linnaeus)

Large with primary stems creeping, often stoloniferous, the secondary stems 6 to 8 or 10 cm long, erect, pinnate or nearly simple; leaves lance-ovate, acute to acuminate, more or less undulate above, the margins entire or slightly denticulate; costa short and faint, more or less bi-striate and wrinkled; median leaf-cells linear at base, towards the apex the upper marginal and apical broadly rhomboid; inner perichaetial leaves entire, half-sheathing, elongate-lanceolate, reaching somewhat beyond the capsule; seta very short; capsule immersed, yellowish, oblong-oval, brown when old, about 2.5:1; lid acute-conic or acuminate; calyptra very small and covering only the operculum; peristome double, teeth irregularly divided, subulate-linear from a lance-linear base, sometimes apically coherent, the segments rudimentary and very short; spores in summer.

On trees or on moist rocks in cool, moist woods, usually on the trunks of deciduous trees; widely distributed in temperate regions, in North America extending from lower Canada south to North Carolina. Probably rather common in the eastern part of our region.

CAMBRIA CO.: Cresson. T. C. Porter. (Porter's Catalogue). MCKEAN CO.: D. A. Burnett. (Porter's Catalogue).

2. NECKERA COMPLANATA [Linnaeus] Huebener

(*Hypnum complanatum* Linnaeus; *Homalia complanata* DeNotaris)

Yellowish to pale green, in rather large and dense tufts, soft: stems long, often reaching 8 or 10 cm, branchlets pinnately arranged; complanate, sometimes more or less flagelliform; leaves oblong-lingulate, compressed, complanate, usually rounded at the apex and short-apiculate, sometimes acute or acuminate, those at the tips of the branches often more or less deflected and falcate, the margin usually inflexed at base on one side, serrulate at apex; costa double, very short and faint, or none; median leaf-cells linear-vermicular, the apical shorter and wider, rhomboidal, the angular quadrate-oval and yellowish-pellucid; perichaetia borne along the sides of the stem, the leaves long-sheathing: seta yellow, about 1 cm long; capsule oval to elliptic-oblong, pale, orange-yellow or castaneous, about 2:1, small-mouthed; lid subulate-rostrate, usually oblique; calyptra cucullate, reaching to about the middle of the urn, one-half length of urn; peristome-teeth long, pale, narrow, the segments about half as long, filiform from an enlarged base; spores mature in spring but capsules rarely produced.

On bark of trees, rarely on rocks; Europe, Asia, northern Africa, and from Labrador to Tennessee.

Rare in our region. Reported from "Allegheny Mountains in Pennsylvania" in Lesquereux and James' Manual.

3. NECKERA GRACILIS (James) Kindberg

(*Homalia gracilis* James)

Minute, slender, irregularly branched plants with stems and branches mostly flagelliform at the ends, complanately foliate, and together with the leaves not much more than 1 mm wide; leaves oblong-lingulate, about 0.1 mm long, not undulate, rounded-obtuse or apiculate, somewhat serrulate at the apex; costa very short, often double; upper leaf-cells rhomboidal, about 8-12 μ wide and but little longer, the basal longer in the median and smaller in the marginal portion.

"On rocks, usually in elevated regions, New Jersey, New York and Vermont."—Grout.

2. HOMALIA (Bridel) Bryologia Europaea

Dioicous or autoicous: slender to robust, in wide, more or less lustrous, dark colored, matted tufts: primary stems with stolons; secondary stems mostly irregularly dichotomous, non-flagellate; leaves 4-seriate, complanately spreading, not transversely undulate, unsymmetric, spatulate to lingulate from a slightly decurrent base, rarely rounded, obtuse, non-bordered, with apex entire or serrulate; costa simple, incomplete or none; upper leaf-cells rounded to hexagonal, lower elongate, at least the median so, rarely all linear; inner perichaetial leaves, short-sheathing, lanceolate, acute; seta long, mostly smooth; capsule mostly erect to cernuous, oblong from a narrowed base, when old sometimes arcuate, red-brown, rarely almost pendent and short-oval; annulus

2-seriate; peristome double, inserted at the mouth; teeth linear-subulate from a broader base, yellow to brownish, apically hyaline, mostly transversely striate and with well-developed lamellae; inner peristome yellow, papillose, marked with fine transverse lines on outer surface of basal plates; basal membrane high, carinate, segments longer and almost as broad as the teeth, broken through in places along the keel, cilia mostly rudimentary and fugaceous, sometimes well-developed and appendiculate: lid conic, obliquely rostrate; calyptra cucullate, mostly glabrous; spores small, brownish.

About 20 species on trees, rocks, and stones, mostly in temperate regions; 4 species in North America; one species in our region.

1.   HOMALIA JAMESII Schimper

In straggling tufts, shining yellow-green, repeatedly distichous, stoloniferous: stems slender, interruptedly foliate by the numerous innovations; the branches strongly complanate-foliate; leaves cultriform, sub-falcate, oblong, obtusely apiculate, minutely serrulate above the middle, striolate lengthwise when dry; costa faint, slender, reaching half-way or more; lower median leaf-cells linear-fusiform, the apical and marginal about 1.5-1:1, about as broad as long, rhomboidal: seta about 1.5 cm long, slender; capsule erect to cernuous, oblong-cylindric, about 2.5:1, symmetric, when dry scarcely constricted below the mouth; peristome double, teeth long, yellowish, confluent at base; inner peristome about as long as the teeth, the segments narrow, sub-linear, more or less carinately perforate, cilia rudimentary and solitary or none; annulus present; spores mature in fall but capsules rarely found.

On rocks and in crevices, in mountainous or hilly districts; from Newfoundland and Nova Scotia to Pennsylvania, also in Washington State. Possibly will be found to occur in the eastern part of our region.

3.   POROTRICHUM Bridel

(*Thamnium* Bryologia Europaea)

Dioicous or, rarely, autoicous; mostly robust to very robust, with a long, creeping primary stem: the primary stem has scale-like leaves, and is more or less densely brown-radiculose; the secondary stem erect to ascending, without branches below, stoloniferous, somewhat dendroid in habit; branches spreading, flattened, obtuse; leaves erect-spreading to spreading, plane to concave, smooth to plicate, not rugose, non-decurrent, unsymmetric, mostly oblong to ovate or ovate-lingulate, the apex obtuse to acute, serrate; costa strong, mostly incomplete; median leaf-cells parenchymatous, the basal sometimes linear; inner perichaetial leaves lanceolate-acuminate and spreading from a half-sheathing base: seta various, mostly 10-15 mm long, in certain species not more than 4 mm, in others up to 4 cm long, red, smooth; capsule inclined to horizontal, arcuate, gibbous, rarely erect, symmetric, and oval; annulus revolute; peristome-teeth lanceolate to linear, subulate-acuminate, yellowish, bordered, with a zig-zag divisural; inner peristome pale yellow, basal membrane prominent, segments broad, carinately split and gaping; cilia often appendiculate; spores small; lid conic, rostrate; calyptra cucullate, glabrous.

About 30 species in temperate and warm regions; 7 species reported for North America; one species in our region.

1. POROTRICHUM ALLEGHENIENSE (Mueller) Grout
(*Hypnum allegheniense* C. Mueller; *Thamnium allegheniense* Bryologia Europaea)

Plate XXXVI

Large, dendroidal in habit, bright to pale green, usually rising to a height of 4-7 cm; leaves of the branches and branchlets up to 3 or 3.5 mm long, rather lustrous and sub-plicate when dry, erect-spreading, oblong-elliptic, short-pointed, concave, the base somewhat narrowed but scarcely concave, the apex broadly acute, the plane margin strongly serrate above; costa strong, extending to near the apex; leaf-cells incrassate, the median shortly rounded- or rhomboid-hexagonal, about 2:1, the basal becoming elongate-oblong, varying to elongate-rectangular, the lower marginal and angular, scarcely wider but sub-rectangular to quadrate; perichaetial leaves erect, sheathing, narrowly acuminate: seta lustrous, of a rich castaneous color, usually about 1 cm long, smooth, arcuate; capsule oblong-cylindric, castaneous and rarely somewhat wrinkled when dry, about 2-2.5:1, about 2 to 2.5 mm long, nearly symmetric but by the curving of the pedicel inclined or horizontal, sometimes curved; lid conic, long- and stout-rostrate, the whole lid being about one-half to one-third as long as the urn; peristome normally hypnoid, large; teeth lance-subulate, distinctly but finely cross-striate in at least the lower half, hyaline and papillose above, castaneous-pellucid below, the dorsal lamellae and the divisural distinct, the trabeculae well developed; segments papillose, pale yellowish, about as long as teeth, cleft carinately between the articulations; basal membrane one-third as high as teeth; cilia 2-3, sub-appendiculate, almost as long as segments; annulus narrow, revoluble, simple; spores mature in late fall or early winter, smooth, castaneous-pellucid, medium-walled (about .009 mm Grout).

On dripping rocks and ledges along streams in the hills or mountains from Nova Scotia to Minnesota and south to the Gulf States.

CAMBRIA Co.: Cresson. T. P. James. (Porter's Catalogue). HUNTINGDON Co.: T. C. Porter. (Porter's Catalogue). McKEAN Co.: On stones in or at the edge of streams, Hedge-hog Hollow, March 18, 1894, Bennett Brook, April 9, 1893 (figured), and Limestone Creek, N. Y., all near Bradford.

Family 28. ENTODONTACEAE

Autoicous or dioicous: slender to quite robust, mostly stiff, laxly cespitose, mostly lustrous; central strand none or but few-celled; stem thickly-foliate, julaceous or complanate; leaves pluri-seriate, uni-stratose, often unsymmetric; costa delicate, homogeneous, never complete, or double and very short, or none; leaf-cells mostly prosenchymatous, the alar differentiated, being quadrate or transversely widened: capsule exserted, mostly erect and symmetric, never plicate; peristome mostly double, the inner rarely lacking; teeth yellow to castaneous, with divisural, trabeculate, mostly papillose; segments narrow or lance-subulate, often split carinately, the basal membrane low, carinate, the cilia rudimentary or none; spores mostly small; lid conic, short- to long-rostrate; calyptra cucullate, glabrous.

Mostly in warmer and temperate regions, on trees, sometimes on rocks or on soil: 14 genera, one genus definitely known from our region.

KEY TO THE GENERA

A. Leaf-cells smooth ....1. *Entodon*
A. Leaf-cells more or less strongly papillose ....(*Pterigynandrum*)

1. ENTODON C. Mueller

Autoicous, rarely dioicous: green to golden-brown: stem prostrate to ascending, complanate-leaved, rarely julaceous, thickly pinnately branched, mostly short, simple, ascending or spreading; stem-leaves compressed, slightly decurrent, concave, the dorsal and ventral imbricate, the lateral spreading, oval, from an ovate base obtuse or apiculate or rarely slenderly acuminate, entire or apically serrate; costa double and very short, or none; median leaf-cells narrowly linear, smooth, and basal lax and incrassate, the alar laxly quadrate and sometimes slightly inflated, forming a distinct hyaline group: seta mostly 1-3 cm long, red or yellow, twisted when dry; capsule erect, straight or weakly curved; collum short; annulate or exannulate; teeth inserted below the mouth, lance-linear, acuminate, thin, plane, mostly non-margined, orange to castaneous, articulate, mostly low-trabeculate; inner peristome without prominent basal membrane, segments linear, carinate, yellow, as long as or shorter than the teeth, cilia none; spores .012-.020 mm.

Nearly 150 species, on trees and on calcareous rocks, in temperate and warmer regions; about 33 species occurring in North America; 3 species in our region.

KEY TO THE SPECIES

A. Leaves narrowly gradually acuminate; segments adhering to teeth ....(*E. brevisetus*)
A. Leaves acute, abruptly acuminate-apiculate, or almost obtuse; segments free ....B
 B. Teeth with not less than twenty articulations; leaves acute to almost obtuse; but
  not apiculate, complanate ....1. *E. compressus*
 B. Teeth with less than twenty articulations C
 C. Leaves acuminate-apiculate: teeth 15-20 articulate: capsule less than 4.5:1; leaves
  complanate ....2. *E. cladorhizans*
 C. Leaves abruptly apiculate: teeth less than 10-articulate; capsule about 5:1: leaves
  not complanate ....3. *E. seductrix*

1. ENTODON COMPRESSUS C. Mueller
(*Cylindrothecium compressum* Bryologia Europaea)
Plate LXXI

Widely and flatly cespitose, glossy yellow-green, with compressed stems and branches: considerably more slender than *E. cladorhizans*, but quite similar in general appearance: leaves about 1.0-1.1 x 0.4-0.5 mm, quite concave, broadly oblong-ovate, obtuse to broadly acute, entire at apex; median leaf-cells linear, the alar quadrate and numerous reaching almost across the base of the leaf, a few on the corner often somewhat inflated; costa none or very rudimentary: seta erect, 1-1.4 cm long; capsule erect, ovoid to elliptic, narrow-mouthed, about 2.5 x 0.6 mm; lid rather long and with a slender, curved rostrum; annulus large, rather persistent; peristome-teeth long, lance-linear, closely articulate; the segments somewhat shorter, linear-subulate, free from the teeth, these latter densely papillose; spores mature in fall or early winter.

In shaded situations on soil and decaying logs and on bases and roots of trees in moist situations, often near water-courses: northern Eurasia and from New Jersey to Missouri and northwards to Rhode Island and Nebraska.

Rare in our region. BEAVER CO.: On base of elm tree along Raccoon Creek one mile south of Traverse Creek. April 1, 1934. C.M.B. (figured). WASHINGTON CO.: On root in damp spot. Taylorstown. Linn and Simonton. Apr. 29, 1899.

2. ENTODON CLADORHIZANS Schimper

(*Cylindrothecium cladorhizans* Schimper; *Neckera cladorhizans* Hedwig)

Plate XXXVI

Cespitose in wide tufts, brightly lustrous, yellowish-green: stems compressed, somewhat pinnately branched, rather acuminate and sometimes up-curved at the apex; branches complanate and spreading widely from the stem, more or less acuminate to attenuate at the apex, where sometimes rooting; leaves loosely imbricate, very concave, non-plicate, narrowed at the apex, margin plane or narrowly revolute below, apex sub-acute, faintly serrulate, usually turned slightly backwards; leaves ovate to oblong, about 1-2 mm long by one-half as wide; costa double, short and indistinct, or none; median leaf-cells long-linear, prosenchymatous, smooth, with firm and hyaline walls, the alar hyaline to somewhat reddish, incrassate, quadrate-rectangular in a tri-angular patch of 6-8 rows in depth, bordered by a few intermediate, sub-quad-rate to sub-vermicular cells, the apical cells shorter and rhombic: seta erect, smooth, sinistrorse, rich castaneous in color, lustrous, about 8-12 mm long; capsule about 4.6:1, oblong-cylindric, tapering abruptly to the seta, smooth, not sulcate when dry, castaneous, narrowed somewhat at the mouth, 2.5-3.5 mm long; annulus early deciduous, large, pluri-seriate with incrassate quadrate cells; exothecial cells yellowish with thin walls, rectangular to oblong, towards the rim suddenly much smaller and incrassate, more or less laterally oblong under the annulus; operculum conic-rostrate, about 0.4-0.6 mm, long, often apiculate; peristome double, deeply inserted, teeth light-castaneous, about 16-20-articulate, below lightly papillose-striate in variously divergent or radiating lines, not finely transversely striate as in most hypnaceous peristomes, some-times perforate, (lacunose) above; segments distinct, linear, very narrow, carinate, hyaline, very slightly granulose-roughened, entire, nearly as long as the teeth, arising from a very narrow basal membrane; cilia none; spores papillose, incrassate, castaneous, about .016-.020 mm, mature in late autumn or early winter.

On leaf-mould, rotting logs, bases of trees, etc.; Europe, and, in America, from New Bruswick to Ontario and south to the Gulf States.

Common in our region. Known from Allegheny, Armstrong, Beaver, Bedford, Butler, Crawford, Fayette, Indiana, Lawrence, McKean, Somerset, Washington, and Westmore-land counties, nearly all in the southwestern corner of the State. Specimen figured: Wild-wood Hollow, Allegheny Co., March 29, 1909. O.E.J. & G.K.J.

3. ENTODON SEDUCTRIX (Hedwig) C. Mueller

(*Neckera seductrix* Hedwig; *Cylindrothecium seductrix* Sullivant)

Plate XXXVII

Robust, widely cespitose in glossy yellowish-green mats: branches sub-pinnately arranged, slender, julaceous, up to 2 or 2.5 cm long; leaves about 0.8-1.4 mm long, broadly oblong-elliptic to ovate, imbricate, deeply concave, short-apiculate with the apiculation often reflexed, margin plane, entire, or sometimes slightly serrulate, at base often slightly reflexed, base of leaf slightly narrowed; costa short and double; median leaf-cells linear-to oblong-prosen-chymatous, alar cells quadrate, slightly incrassate, forming a distinct group sometimes extending along the margin for one-fourth the length of the leaf; perichaetial leaves with a slender acumen, narrower and reaching a length of about 3 mm: seta glossy, red-castaneous, erect, sinistrorse, about 1.5 cm long; capsule 2-3 mm long, castaneous, about 5-6:1, cylindric, erect, symmetric or slightly curved; exothecial cells yellowish with medium walls, rectangular to irregularly oblong, towards the rim smaller, quadrate to laterally oblong in-crassate, and forming a rather indefinite annulus of 2 or 3 series; peristome-teeth few articulate above, deeply inserted, lance-linear, rather short, bordered, not transversely striolate but irregularly papillose, dorsal lamellae and divisural strongly marked; segments nearly as long as teeth, narrowly linear-carinate, free from teeth, arising from a very narrow basal membrane, smooth, cilia none; operculum conic-rostrate, usually somewhat oblique, about 0.5-0.8 mm long; calyptra small, enclosing only about half of the capsule; spores yellow-ish-incrassate, about .014-.018 mm in diameter, minutely roughened, mature in late summer. Variable.

On rotten logs, earth, rocks, roots of trees, etc.; from New England to Minnesota and south to the Gulf States.

Common in our region. Known from Allegheny, Armstrong, Beaver, Butler, Craw-ford, Erie, Fayette, Greene, Huntingdon, Indiana (Porter), Lawrence, McKean, Wash-ington, and Westmoreland counties. Specimen/ figured: Charleroi, Washington Co., Oct. 13, 1906. O.E.J. & G.K.J.

3a. ENTODON SEDUCTRIX var. MINOR (Austin) Grout

Differs from the type in size, being only about one-half to two-thirds as large, usually darker in color: capsule about 3-4:1, about 2 mm long; spores usually about .010-.015 mm in diameter.

ALLEGHENY CO.: Bark of decaying log, mixed oak and pine woods, Dutil Church, Douthett, December 29, 1908. O.E.J.

Family 29. LESKEACEAE

Autoicous or dioicous: slender to robust, mostly stiff, cespitose, bright or dark green, when old brownish, dull or rarely sub-lustrous: stem mostly with-out central strand, the primary stems mostly creeping, simple, pinnate, or vari-ously branched, often stoloniform with distant and minute leaves; secondary stems mostly erect simple, pinnate, or variously branched, both main and secondary stems stoloniferous; paraphyllia mostly present; leaves rarely uniform, usually differentiated into basal and foliate leaves, the latter again into stem-leaves and branch-leaves; basal leaves distant, small, delicate, pale, smooth, ecostate; foliate leaves pluriseriate, dense, spreading, rarely secund, drying appressed to imbricate, symmetric, apex sometimes one-sided, mostly acuminate, mostly concave, often with two short folds at base, unistratose, mostly papillose; costa mostly simple and strong, rarely short, double, delicate, or forked; cells richly chlorophyllose, mostly parenchymatous, small, often oblong to linear in the middle of the base, or up to the middle of the leaf; branch-leaves usually shorter and narrower than the stem-leaves; perichaetial leaves delicate, hyaline, much elongate, ecostate or weakly costate: seta plicate; annulus usually present; peristome double, the teeth mostly basally straight and long; capsule erect and symmetric to cernuous and arcuate, nonconfluent, prominently articulate and trabeculate or dorsally uniformly papillose, with weak ventral plates, whitish to red or brownish, often quite red at the insertion; inner peristome carinate, with basal membrane, segments, and, rarely, with cilia; peristome often degenerate in the species with erect capsules; lid conic or convex-conic and rostrate; calyptra cucullate; spores mostly small.

As here treated this is a large family of about 30 genera sometimes, as by Brotherus, separated into three families: Leskeaceae, Theliaceae, and Thuidiaceae.

Mostly in temperate and tropic regions, mainly on trees and rocks. Eleven genera occur in our general region.

KEY TO THE GENERA

A. Archegonial clusters borne on the branches: primary stems stoloniform with minute leaves; costa simple; capsule erect, symmetric; segments filiform or rudimentary; cilia usually none ....B
A. Archegonial flowers on the stem; stem not stoloniform C
  B. Very slender; costa not reaching above the middle of the leaf: peristome-segments none ....3. *Haplohymenium*
  B. More or less robust; costa ending in or just below apex; peristome-segments filiform ....4. *Anomodon*
  C. Costa short, simple, forked, double, or none, never reaching much above middle of leaf ....D
  C. Costa simple (except *Pseudo-Leskeella*), elongate, ending a little below the apex, or excurrent ....E
    D. Stem creeping, densely simply pinnate, costa short, simple or forked; teeth non-bordered, non-trabeculate ....1. *Thelia*
    D. Stem ascending to erect, irregularly bushy-branched; costa indistinct or none; teeth bordered, trabeculate ....2. *Myurella*
    E. Leaves of stem and branches alike; stem creeping with ascending or erect, short, blunt branches ....F
    E. Stem and branch-leaves unlike; stem 1-3-pinnate, often quite fern-like in general form ....H
      F. Teeth without distinct lamellae; segments filiform ....7. *Leskeella*
      F. Teeth distinctly lamellate; segments narrowly linear or none ....G
      G. Teeth with well-developed lamellae; segments narrowly linear ....6. *Leskea*
      G. Teeth with distinct but low lamellae; segments none ....5. *Lindbergia*
        H. Cilia 3, smooth; cells of stem-leaves elongate-hexagonal to almost linear; stem and branch-leaves similar; paraphyllia felted along stem and leaf-base ....11. *Helodium*

H. Cilia 2-4, nodose to appendiculate: cells of stem-leaves rounded-angular to long-
hexagonal; I

I. Operculum merely sharply acute: costa of stem-leaves percurrent to excurrent; leaf-
margins indistinctly serrate above; apical cell of branch-leaf with a single terminal
papilla ....9. *Haplocladium*

I. Operculum distinctly rostrate: costa incomplete to excurrent; stem- and branch-
leaves dissimilar; paraphyllia not so felted nor attached to leaf-base ....J

J. Margin of stem-leaves entire, base not decurrent; cells uniform, rounded-angular,
the median with 2-6 papillae on each side ....8. *Rauia*

J. Margin of stem-leaves entire or toothed above, the base somewhat decurrent; cells
mostly uniform, rounded- to oval- or oblong-hexagonal, the median ranging
from dorsally unipapillose to both sides pluri-papillose ....10. *Thuidium*

1. THELIA Sullivant

Dioicous: more or less slender, densely cespitose, yellowish to blue-green,
dull; stem elongate, creeping, more or less brown-radiculose, densely-leaved,
thickly pinnately branched; branches short, julaceous, obtuse, erect to ascending; paraphyllia various; leaves densely imbricate, either dry or moist, more
or less decurrent, spoon-like, broadly ovate, abruptly subulate-acuminate, the
margins plane, mostly ciliate-serrate to laciniate; costa short, simple (or
forked); cells rhombic, each dorsally with a high and one- to several-pointed
papilla; median basal leaf-cells elongate, the alar in several series almost
quadrate; inner perichaetial leaves larger, delicate, erect, oblong and subulate-
acuminate, with long marginal cilia, costa ending in mid-leaf, areolation
elongate, the upper cells uni-papillose above: seta 5-15 mm long, thin, drying
twisted, smooth and red; capsule symmetric, erect, oblong to cylindric, golden-
brown; annulus none; peristome-teeth basally confluent, narrowly linear-lanceolate, pale, non-bordered, finely papillose, distantly articulate, non-trabeculate;
inner peristome pale, papillose; basal membrane low, segments very short or
rudimentary, cilia none; lid conic, short-rostrate; calyptra cucullate, smooth;
spores small.

A North American genus of but four species; three species in our region,
more common southwards.

KEY TO THE SPECIES

A. Papillae on dorsal surface of leaf long, curved, with one point ....1. *T. hirtella*

A. Papillae on dorsal leaf-surface lower, each with two or more points ....B

B. Papillae usually two-pointed; leaves ciliate; mostly on trees ....2. *T. asprella*

B. Papillae usually 3 or 4 pointed; leaves non-ciliate; mostly on rocks or sand ....
....3. *T. Lescurii*

1. THELIA HIRTELLA (Hedwig) Sullivant

(*Pterigynandrum hirtellum* Hedwig; *Hypnum hirtellum* C. Mueller)

Plate XXXVIII

Light green to glaucous-green, small, forming thin and loosely adherent
mats: primary stems creeping, felted with a reddish-brown tomentum, pinnate
with numerous short, crowded, julaceous secondary stems and branches; leaves
sub-orbicular, deeply concave, abruptly and narrowly acuminate, decurrent at
base, dorsally papillose, the margins plane, spinulose-dentate above, at least
in the upper half, fimbriate-ciliate below with usually upturned cilia; costa

slender, reaching about to the leaf-middle; median leaf-cells pellucid, rhomboid-elliptic, with long, slender, simple dorsal papillae; apical leaf-cells linear, the basal larger and looser, the alar quadrate to rectangular, almost smooth, rather incrassate; perichaetial leaves numerous, the inner lance-oblong, narrowly acuminate, ciliate-fimbriate in the upper part: seta about 1 cm long; capsule narrowly oblong-cylindric, about 2.5 x 0.5 mm, erect, symmetric, thin-walled; peristome-teeth linear, distinctly lamellate, the inner basal membrane truncate and about one-third as high as the teeth, peristome whitish; spores pale yellow, mature in fall, thin-walled, about .012-.015 mm, smooth.

On trunks and roots of trees and on stumps, in woods; from New England and Ontario to Kansas and the Gulf States.

Not often collected in our region. ERIE CO.: In oak woods, Presque Isle. May 8-9, 1906. O.E.J. McKEAN CO.: On trees, near the ground, Gates Hollow, Bradford, April 18, 1897. D.A.B. (figured). WASHINGTON CO.: On wood, near Washington, 1892. A. Linn & J. S. Simonton. WESTMORELAND CO.: T. P. James. (Porter's Catalogue).

2. THELIA ASPRELLA Sullivant
(*Leskea asprella* Bryologia Europaea
Plate XXXVIII

In most respects quite similar to *T. hirtella*, but more glaucous-green: densely interwoven into mats up to 1.5 mm thick; leaves bordered nearly all around by somewhat longer cilia, and the papillae on the dorsal surface of the leaf more or less branched or stellate: peristome-teeth longer with nodose articulations; spores mature in early fall.

In the same habitat as the last species and often mixed with it; ranging from New England to Ontario and Minnesota and south to the Gulf States.

Known from Bedford, Butler, Cameron, Centre, Clarion, Clearfield, Erie, Fayette, McKean (Porter), Somerset, Washington, and Westmoreland counties. Specimen figured: In oak woods, Presque Isle, Erie Co., May 8-9, 1906. O.E.J.

3. THELIA LESCURII Sullivant

Closely resembling *T. asprella* but with the stouter stems fasciculately branched, whitish or light glaucous-green in color: leaves deltoid-ovate with a shorter acumen than in *T. asprella*, not so distinctly ciliate-fimbriate; the papillae usually stellately 3- or 4-lobed; the capsule relatively more slender and longer and on a longer seta; the teeth shorter and only sub-nodosely articulate, the inner membrane longer and with short segments; spores mature in fall.

On flat rocks, ledges, or on dry, sandy soil; from New England to Missouri and the Gulf States. In eastern Pennsylvania and may occur in our region.

2. MYURELLA Bryologia Europaea

Dioicous: slender, forming cushions or loose tufts, soft (stiff when dry), light to bluish-green, dull to sub-lustrous: in thick tufts the stems are upright, in loose tufts ascending, irregularly bushy-branched with small-leaved stolons, basally bushy-radiculose; branches obtuse, sometimes apically flagelliform; paraphyllia none; leaves 5-seriate, more or less appressed-imbricate, round-ovate, obtuse to abruptly apiculate to acuminate, spoon-shaped, marginally plane to involute, serrate to dentate; costa mostly very short and delicate, simple or forked; sometimes costa none; median leaf-cells small, incrassate, elliptic, some rhomboid, at base short-rectangular to quadrate, smooth or papillose by the thickening of the cell-angles, rarely dorsally mamillate; inner perichaetial leaves red-brown, elongate-lanceolate, long-acuminate, plane-margined, serrate, ecostate, with linear cells: seta 10-20 mm long, thin, drying twisted, red, smooth; capsule erect, somewhat inclined when empty, symmetric, oblong-oval, short-necked, yellow-brown, finally constricted below the mouth; annulus present; peristome-teeth basally confluent, lance subulate, yellow or pale, bordered by the broader dorsal layer, lamellae numerous; inner peristome finely papillose, hyaline to pale yellow, basal membrane yellow, carinate, segments lance-subulate, same length as teeth, cilia mostly shorter, filiform; lid brightly colored, conic, acute to obtuse; calyptra fugaceous, small; spores small.

A genus of six species occurring in Europe, Asia, and in North America; one species in our region.

1. MYURELLA CAREYANA Sullivant

(*M. gracilis* (Weinmann) Lindberg)

Pale glaucous-green, loosely cespitose, interwoven with long radicles below: stems slender, creeping to ascending, stoloniferous, fasciculately branching; the branches julaceous; leaves loosely imbricate, open-erect, wide-ovate, narrowly long-acuminate, spinulose-dentate all around, very shortly costate or ecostate; leaf-cells large, pellucid, elliptic-rhomboid, dorsally with large papillae as in *Thelia asprella;* perichaetial leaves sheathing, lanceolate, filiform-acuminate, dentate: capsules sub-erect, small, inflated, oval-oblong to obovate-oblong; seta up to 1 cm long; peristome normally hypnoid, with articulate, yellowish, transversely-striate teeth, entire segments and cilia two, somewhat shorter than the teeth.

Mainly in crevices and hollows in moist, shaded limestone rocks in hilly or mountainous regions; Europe, Asia, and from Nova Scotia to northwestern Canada, south to North Carolina and Tennessee.

Rare in our region. HUNTINGDON CO.: Alexandria. T. C. Porter. (Porter's Catalogue).

3. HAPLOHYMENIUM Dozy and Molkenboer

Dioicous: slender, stiff, forming mats, dull, dark green to yellowish- or brownish-green: stems filiform, creeping, widely radiculose, here and there in fascicles, more or less pinnately branched, branches spreading, short, obtuse; paraphyllia none; lower leaves smaller, somewhat secund, abruptly lance-subulate and recurved-circinate from a broadly ovate base; costa very short or none; upper leaves spreading to squarrose-spreading, imbricate when dry, from a concave ovate base more or less abruptly lingulate, obtuse to short-acute, nonplicate, margin plane and entire; costa delicate and reaching to mid-leaf, or stronger but not reaching apex; median leaf-cells turgid, thin-walled, rounded-hexagonal, with mostly several papillae over the lumen, the marginal smaller, transversely broader, in many rows towards the basal margin transversely rectangular or hexagonal, only in middle of base oblong and pellucid: seta 2-4 mm, thin, drying twisted, reddish or yellowish, smooth; capsule erect, oval, smooth, brownish, broadly annulate; peristome-teeth basally confluent, lance-linear, yellowish, distantly articulate, split apart above, the ventral layer broader, hyaline, non-trabeculate, but with papillae-like irregular processes; inner peristome smooth, the basal membrane very low, with no segments nor cilia; lid conic, obliquely short-rostrate; calyptra inflated-cucullate, furnished with a few long, erect hairs; spores .020-.025 mm, papillose.

About 20 species, mostly living on tree-trunks, rarely on rocks; one species occurring in North America and reaching our region.

1. HAPLOHYMENIUM TRISTE (Cesati) Kindberg*

(*Leskea tristis* Cesati; *Anomodon tristis* Sullivant)

Plate XXXVIII

Small, very slender, dull dirty-green, loosely, thinly, and intricately ces-pitose: stems prostrate, sometimes pendent, branching with irregularly or pin-nately arranged branches; branchlets erect or curved-ascending; leaves about 0.5-0.8 mm long, appressed when dry, more or less squarrose-spreading when moist, mainly lanceolate from an ovate-base, concave, sub-clasping, crenulate on the plane margins by the large and protuberant cells, apically acute to short-apiculate or obtuse, the apex of the leaf very often broken off in the dried specimens; costa slender, ending in the middle of the leaf; median leaf-cells oblong-rectangular, about .011-.014 mm in diameter, thin-walled, pellucid, the upper more or less rounded-hexagonal, the lower marginal transversely oblong-hexagonal, the lower median often radiating from the basal part of the costa in a characteristic manner: capsule unknown: leaf-cells turgid and bearing several large papillae on each surface.

On bases of trees and on steep, sunny rocks; Europe, Asia, and, in the eastern United States. In the Lesquereux and James *Manual* the habitat is stated as particularly on the Hornbeam.

Rare in our region. CLEARFIELD CO.: T. P. James. (Porter's Catalogue). McKEAN Co.: Gates Hollow, Bradford, July 8, 1895. D.A.B. (figured).

4. ANOMODON Hooker and Taylor

Dioicous: more or less robust, stiff, loosely cespitose, bright to blue-green, dull, later yellowish to brownish, the mats mostly ochraceous inside: stem far-creeping, stoloniform, small-leaved, radiculose, bearing ascending to erect, often basally-stoloniferous secondary stems; all leafy shoots having rather uni-form leaves, the branches sometimes flagelliform; foriage-leaves 5-seriate, dense, rarely secund, when dry mostly imbricated, little different when moist, lingulate from a broadly ovate or oblong and little or not at all decurrent base, or the upper part lanceolate to subulate, margins plane and entire; costa strong, smooth, mostly ending below the apex; median leaf-cells rounded-hexagonal, on both sides densely papillose with one- and two-pointed papillae, rarely unipapillose over the lumen, only the median basal elongate, smooth,

---

* Perhaps better included in the genus *Anomodon*.

rarely rhombic; inner perichaetial leaves elongate, sheathing, above similar to the foliage-leaves, or pale, spreading, lance-subulate, with elongate cells: seta more or less elongate, drying twisted, smooth, straight; capsule erect, symmetric, oblong-cylindric, rarely curved, not narrowed below the mouth; peristome-teeth lance-linear, either pale, papillose, distantly articulate, non-trabeculate, or yellowish, striate and weakly trabeculate; inner peristome finely papillose, with basal membrane low, carinate segments filiform, entire, often attached apically to the columella, cilia rudimentary or, mostly, none; lid conic, obtuse, acute, or rostrate; calyptra cucullate, smooth; spores small.

About 20 species confined to the northern Hemisphere; 10 reported for North America; 5 species in our region.

KEY TO THE SPECIES

A. Slender and flagelliform branches present: annulus rudimentary or none, teeth striate
....4. A. attenuatus
A. Slender and flagelliform branches none: annulus present or absent ....B
  B. Teeth striate: leaves with a hyaline, piliferous-subulate acumination ....5. A. rostratus
  B. Teeth papillose, non-striate: leaf-acumination not piliferous-acuminate C
C. Leaves with rounded, fimbriate-papillose basal auricles, apex apiculate ......1. A. Rugelii
C. Leaves not auricled ....D
  D. Leaves not secund, the upper half of leaf oblong-lingulate: peristome segments
     short or none ....2. A. minor
  D. Leaves more or less secund, lance-lingulate: peristome segments at least ½ the
     length of teeth ....3. A. viticulosus

1. ANOMODON RUGELII (C. Mueller) Keissler

(A. apiculatus Bryologia Europaea; Leskea apiculata W. P. Schimper;
Hypnum Rugelii C. Mueller)

Plate XXXVIII

Cespitose in tangled mats, glaucous-green, reddish or brownish when old: stems creeping, divided, the secondary stems and branches straight or ascending; leaves 1.5-1.8 mm long, more or less obscurely two-ranked, abruptly oblong-lingulate from an ovate or oblong-ovate and broader base, the base non-decurrent but with very large and broadly rounded fimbriate-papillose auricles, the apex often apiculate, the upper margin broadly incurved, the leaves when dry crispate; costa pellucid, ending considerably below the apex; leaf-cells opaque, chlorophyllose, minute, rounded, papillose on both faces, the median basal elongate, smooth, the alar somewhat larger, rounded-quadrate; inner perichaetial leaves long-sheathing: seta erect, about 5-7 mm long, dextrorse above, sinistrorse below; capsule erect or somewhat inclined, symmetric, ovate-cylindric, about 2-2.5 x 0.5 mm thick-walled, castaneous, longitudinally many-plicate when dry; annulus none; lid conic-acuminate, small; peristome double, the teeth lance-linear, nodose-articulate, faintly papillose, the dorsal lamellae and divisural usually very faint or invisible, the segments rudimentary, or very short, from a low basal membrane; spores mature in autumn, medium-walled, brownish, papillose, about .009-.012 mm.

On shaded rocks and bases of trees or on decayed logs, in woods, mainly in mountainous districts; Europe, Asia, and from New England to Ontario and Georgia. Rare in our region.

McKEAN Co.: Bennett Brook, Bradford, November 7, 1897, and Limestone Creek, Bradford, October to December, 1896. D.A.B. (figured). The latter mixed with Grout's No. 134, North American Musci Pleurocarpi.

2. ANOMODON MINOR (Hedwig) Lindberg

(*Neckera viticulosa* var. *minor* Hedwig; *A. obtusifolius* Bryologia Europaea)

Plate XXXVIII

Loosely widely cespitose, glaucous-green, brownish when old; primary stems creeping, flagellate, robust, with numerous, more or less erect, secondary stems and branches usually up to height of 2-4 cm; leaves somewhat complanate, broadly lingulate-obtuse from a broadly ovate base, thick, opaquely chlorophyllose, entire, very densely papillose on both sides; costa pellucid, rather strong, vanishing below apex; leaf-cells minute, about .009-.012 mm, rounded-hexagonal, the median basal elongate and non-papillose, the alar scarcely different from the upper; perichaetial leaves sheathing: seta erect, about 1 cm high, sinistrorse; capsule erect, castaneous, symmetric, oblong-cylindric, about 3:1, the mouth small; lid conic-acuminate, about two-fifths as long as urn; annulus present, large; peristome-teeth narrowly lance-linear, hyaline, faintly papillose, about 8-10-nodose-articulate, the divisural and dorsal lamellae very faint or not visible; segments very short or rudimentary, or none, from a very low basal membrane; exothecial cells rather thin-walled, irregularly quadrate to oblong-rectangular; spores maturing in late fall or in winter, medium to thin-walled, brownish, papillose, .009-.012 mm in diameter.

On rocks and trees, in woods, usually at the base of trees; Asia and from New Brunswick to Dakota and south to the Gulf States.

Rather common in our region. ALLEGHENY Co.: Near Montrose, September 21, 1905. O.E.J. BEAVER Co.: On log along Raccoon Creek, 3 mi. s. of Traverse Cr., April 1, 1894. C.M.B. BUTLER Co.: On base of oak tree 1 mi. s. of Evans City. Jan. 13, 1935. Sidney K. Eastwood. CAMBRIA Co.: T. P. James. (Porter's Catalogue). CLEARFIELD Co.: Phillipsburg. T. P. James.' (Porter's Catalogue). FAYETTE Co.: Laurel Run, 2 mi. e. of Wymps Gap, on tree. C.M.B. Aug. 24, 1940. McKEAN Co.: Lewiston Creek, November 21, 1897. D.A.B. (figured). WASHINGTON Co.: Linn and Simonton No. 43. Bark of tree near Washington, March 24, 1893.

3. ANOMODON VITICULOSUS [Linnaeus] Hooker and Taylor

Large, widely tufted, dark green above, yellowish within: stems creeping, long, sending up secondary stems and branches, the secondary stems 4-10 cm long, sometimes becoming more or less geniculate by repeated innovations: leaves more or less crisped when dry, sub-falcate, secund, lance-lingulate from an ovate base, frequently serrulate at the apex, apex bluntly acute; costa strong, pellucid, ending a little below the apex; median, upper, and lower marginal leaf-cells opaque, minute, rounded-quadrate, the median basal somewhat elongated, cells minutely papillose; perichaetial leaves long, linear-acuminate from an ovate base: seta twisted when dry, erect; capsule oblong-cylindric, symmetric or slightly curved, about 3:1; lid narrowly conic; peristome-teeth lance-linear, more or less irregular, yellowish, the inner peristome consisting of a very low basal membrane and irregular segments up to 1/2 or 2/3 the length of the teeth; annulus double; spores mature in winter or early spring.

Mostly on shaded rocks, sometimes on trees; Europe, Algeria, Asia, and in lower Canada and eastern United States south to Virginia. Occurs in Pennsylvania at least as far west as Franklin County, and is to be looked for in our region, particularly on calcareous habitats.

4. ANOMODON ATTENUATUS [Schreber] Huebener
(*Leskea attenuata* Hedwig; *Hypnum attenuatum* Schreber)

Plate XXXVIII

Slender, loosely and widely tufted, with the secondary stems fasciculately branched and with numerous slender flagelliform branches; leaves spreading to secund, concave, usually more or less distinctly homomallous when dry, about 0.8-1.2 mm long, broadly lanceolate from an ovate base which is plainly narrowed to the insertion, the insertion somewhat excavate and decurrent, the apex acute and minutely apiculate and often with a very few teeth near the apiculation, the leaf-margins plane below, and usually minutely crenulate by reason of the projecting papillae; costa strong, ending a little below the apex; areolation densely papillose on both sides, irregularly hexagonal to quadrate, opaque, rather thin-walled, a few of the median basal elongate-rectangular to oblong, pellucid; perichaetial leaves lance-acuminate from an ovate base: seta about 2 cm long, twisted; capsule long, cylindric, straight or slightly curved, lustrous; castaneous lid long-rostrate; teeth of peristome narrowly lanceolate; segments filiform, irregular, fragile, nearly as long as the teeth; annulus narrow; spores mature in fall.

On bases of trees, stumps, and rocks, in woods; Europe, Asia, and from Newfoundland to British Columbia and south to Florida and Cuba.

Common in our region but usually sterile. Known from 16 counties and probably occurs in all. Specimen figured: Wildwood Hollow, Nov. 19, 1908. O.E.J. & G.K.J.

5. ANOMODON ROSTRATUS (Hedwig) Schimper
(*Leskea rostrata* Hedwig)

Plate XXXVIII

Densely cespitose, tufts bright green above, yellowish inside: primary stems slender, creeping, fasciculately branched with short, slender julaceous secondary stems and branches; leaves densely-imbricate, ovate and concave at base, narrowly lanceolate above with a long and hyaline piliferous acumination, more or less indistinctly two-ranked, the margin crenulate-papillose, often recurved towards the middle; leaf-cells minute, chlorophyllose, opaque, rounded-quadrate to oblong-hexagonal, pluri-papillose on both faces, the median marginal rounded-quadrate, about .008-.010 mm, the median interior about as wide but more oblong, about 2:1, the median basal longer, hyaline and non-papillose or but slightly so, the apical long and linear, smooth; costa strong and ending a little below the apex; perichaetial leaves long, pale, ecostate, the inner with a filiform and often reflexed point about as long as the main portion of the leaf: seta short, about 7-10 mm long, erect, sinistrorse, richly castaneous; capsule about 2 mm long, oval-oblong, about 2.5:1, erect, symmetric castaneous; lid conic, obliquely rostrate, about one-half to three-fifths as long as the urn; teeth small, lance-linear, the divisural and dorsal lamellae indistinct, the teeth with about 15 to 18 nodose articulations, pale, papillose; segments about as long as the teeth, linear, rising from a basal membrane about one-third as high as the teeth, the cilia solitary and rudimentary or none; exothecial cells medium-walled, oblong-rectangular to oblong-hexagonal, becoming quadrate above, about two rows at the rim much smaller and heavily castaneus-incrassate; spores mature in fall, thin-walled, nearly smooth, slightly brownish, about .010 mm in diameter.

In moist places, on rocks or more usually on the bases of trees; Europe, Asia, and from Canada to the Gulf States and to the West.

Very common in our region, especially on the bases of white oak trees. Known from collections in the following counties: Allegheny, Beaver, Bedford, Butler, Cameron, Centre, Clarion, Crawford, Erie, Fayette, Greene, Huntingdon, McKean, Somerset, Washington, and Westmoreland. Figured from specimens collected four miles up the valley of Meadow Run, Ohio Pyle, Fayette Co., May 30-31, 1908, and Sept. 1-3, 1906. O.E.J.

5. LINDBERGIA Kindberg
(*Fabroleskea* Grout)

Autoicous: rather softly and loosely cespitose, bright to brownish-green, dull: stem elongate, creeping, radiculose, densely-leaved, branched with elongate mostly irregularly pinnate branches; branchlets short or unequal in length, obtuse; dry leaves imbricate, when moist spreading to almost squarrose-spreading, somewhat concave, more or less decurrent, ovate to lance-ovate, abruptly subulate-acuminate, non-plicate, margins entire or rarely indistinctly apically serrulate; costa strong, incomplete; median leaf-cells lax, round-oval or rhombic hexagonal, smooth, or unipapillose, the marginal smaller and quadrate or transversely broader, the basal marginal in many rows quadrate to transversely broader; inner perichaetial larger, thin, erect, from a sheathing base subulate-acuminate, entire or serrulate; costa shorter: seta 5-10 mm long, straight, thin, red, smooth; capsule erect, symmetric, oval-oblong, rarely slightly curved, brown, small-mouthed and short-necked; annulus present or none; peristome deeply inserted, teeth lanceolate, obtuse, basally confluent, pale to yellow, non-striate, more or less papillose, divisural zigzag, low-trabeculate; inner peristome papillose with a very low basal membrane, no segments, no cilia; lid conic-obtuse; calyptra cucullate; spores .025-.030 mm.

As here limited the genus consists of 13 species, occurring on tree-trunks in the Northern Hemisphere; three species in North America; one species in our region.

1. LINDBERGIA AUSTINI (Sullivant) Brotherus
(*Fabroleskea Austini* Grout; *Leskea Austini* Sullivant; *Lindbergia brachyptera* var. *Austini* (Sullivant) Grout)

Medium size, intricately matted; stems irregularly divided, the branches usually quite unequal; leaves spreading to more or less squarrose when moist-

ened, imbricate when dry, ovate, long and slenderly acuminate, strongly papillose, entire; costa ending above the middle; leaf-cells unipapillate, elliptic-
rhomboid above, the basal marginal thick, rounded-quadrate; perichaetial
leaves longer, lance-acuminate: seta short, erect; capsule erect, oval-cylindric
with a small mouth; teeth broadly lanceolate, deeply inserted, opaque, papillose on both surfaces, the inner peristome consisting merely of a low basal
membrane scarcely exceeding the rim of the urn; annulus none; lid short-
conic; spores mature in summer.

On tree-trunks and on rocks or stone-walls; southern Canada to South
Carolina and Arizona. In Porter's Catalogue the habitat is given as *Juniperus
virginianus*. Not yet collected in our region.

6. LESKEA Hedwig

Autoicous: rather slender, usually weak, loosely cespitose, dull, dark to
sooty-green: stems creeping, sparsely radiculose, rather thickly-leaved, more or
less pinnately branched, with short, erect or ascending branches; leaves when
dry imbricate, when moist erect-spreading to spreading, sometimes sub-secund,
from a somewhat decurrent, cordate-ovate base narrowed to an acute or obtuse
apex, sometimes apiculate, shortly two-plicate, revolute on one or both lower
margins, rarely indistinctly serrate at apex; costa strong, incomplete; median
leaf-cells either thin-walled, rounded-hexagonal, one- to several-papillose, at the
base almost quadrate, in the middle rhomboidal, or more or less thickened,
with oval to oblong acumen; branch-leaves smaller; inner perichaetial leaves
pale, sheathing, abruptly to slenderly acuminate, entire or serrulate, at the
apex, delicately and incompletely costate: seta long, thin, red, smooth; capsule
erect, oblong-cylindric, sometimes slightly curved and weakly inclined, yellowish, finally light brown and plicate; annulus revoluble; teeth drying strongly
incurved, linear, acuminate, entirely separate, non-bordered, pale yellow, at the
base transversely dorsally striate, thickly trabeculate, papillose above; inner
peristome papillose, basal membrane low, segments linear, carinate, as long or
shorter than the teeth, cilia rudimentary or none; lid acute-conic; calyptra
cucullate, glabrous; spores small.

A widely distributed genus of about 15 species; 5 species reported for
North America; 2 (or 3) in our region.

KEY TO THE SPECIES

A. Branch-leaves more or less secund, lanceolate; capsule sometimes slightly curved,
usually straight ....1. *L. polycarpa**
A. Branch-leaves not secund, ovate, acute to obtuse; capsule erect, straight ....B
  B. Branch-leaves two-plicate, symmetric, the margin often revolute ....2. *L. gracilescens*
  B. Branch-leaves non-plicate, often unsymmetric, plane-margined ....3. *L. obscura*

---

* *Leskea arenicola* Best has pinnately branched stems with distinct, small, central
strand; stem-leaves lance-ovate to ovate and secund; branch-leaves smaller, but scarcely
secund; costa ending in the rather blunt acumination; capsule curved; segments as long as
teeth; basal membrane low: lid long-conical.

Bases of trees, rotten wood, etc. New England to Virginia and west to the Mississippi.
Differ from *polycarpa* in more curved capsules and long conic operculum.

1. Leskea polycarpa Ehrhart, Hedwig
(*L. polycarpa* Ehrhart; *Hypnum medium* Dickson)

Slender, thinly tufted: stems prostrate, pinnately to bi-pinnately branched, 2-4 cm long, with short curved or erect branches, intricately matted into close but thin patches; central strand distinct; leaves erect-spreading to secund, loosely appressed-imbricate when dry, about 0.4 x 1.0 mm, lanceolate and gradually acute from a slightly decurrent, sub-cordate, more or less ovate base, entire, usually two-plicate, acute to acuminate; costa ending a little below the apex; median leaf-cells thin-walled, pellucid, more or less dorsally papillose, hexagonal, about .007-.008 mm wide, with one or two papillae on each surface; branch-leaves smaller and more obtusely pointed: seta about 1 cm. long, reddish; capsule cylindric, narrow, basally tapering, straight or almost so, reddish-brown, constricted below the mouth when dry; lid short-conic, acute; peristome-teeth long, whitish, narrowly linear, connivent when dry; segments about as long, from a low basal membrane narrowly linear, scarcely carinately split: cilia rudimentary or none; spores mature in early summer.

On roots, bases of trees, stones, or decaying wood in wet situations; Asia, and from Newfoundland to British Columbia and southward. Not yet found in our region.

2. Leskea gracilescens Hedwig
(*L. obscura* Lesquereux and James, p. p.; *Hypnum gracilescens* Beauvois)

Intricately cespitose in thin mats: stems prostrate, pinnately branched with numerous simple, erect, somewhat julaceous branchlets; central strand indistinct or none; paraphyllia usually few, lanceolate; stem-leaves erect-spreading when moist, appressed-imbricate when dry, about 0.4-0.5 x 0.7-0.9 mm, ovate, acute or somewhat acuminate, entire, margins more or less revolute, sometimes more quickly tapering to a blunt point, somewhat bi-plicate; costa sub-percurrent; branch-leaves hardly different but scarcely plicate; median leaf-cells usually uni-papillose on dorsal surface, smooth on ventral, quadrate-hexagonal, about .008-.010 mm, the apical more rounded, the basal somewhat quadrate; capsule erect, basally tapering, oblong-cylindric; peristome-teeth whitish, lance-linear, lamellate, about 0.4 mm long; the linear segments shorter, carinate, sometimes more or less rudimentary; basal membrane ¼ as high as teeth; cilia none; lid conic, acute to obtuse; spores mature in summer.

On the base of trees, roots, and on rotten logs, etc.; from eastern lower Canada to the Gulf States and westward to the Rocky Mountains. Commonest in northeastern United States. Reported from Middle Wheeling Creek, W. Va., A. J. Sharp and Miss Gail Holliday, June 11, 1935; and:

Washington Co.: Linn and Simonton. (Porter's Catalogue).

3. Leskea obscura Hedwig
(*L. nervosa* Sullivant; *L. microcarpa* Schimper)
Plates XXXIX, LXVII

Small, loosely and intricately cespitose, dark green: stems prostrate, rather irregularly divided, sparingly branched, the branches short, plump, erect; central strand small but distinct; leaves incurved-appressed when dry, spreading when moist, about 0.8-1.2 mm long, from an ovate base narrowed above to a rather blunt apex, concave, margins plane or incurved, entire or serrulate; costa ending a little below the apex; median leaf-cells quadrate-hexagonal, about .008-.010 mm wide, with several small papillae on the lower surface, on the upper surface less papillose or almost smooth, apical and basal cells somewhat wider and shorter, the alar oblong-quadrate, longer towards the costa; branch-leaves similar; perichaetial leaves long-sheathing, rather laxly-celled, costate; seta about 1.5-2 cm long; capsule erect, straight, short-cylindric, sometimes slightly curved, more or less wrinkled and contracted below the mouth when dry; lid conic, rather obtuse; peristome-teeth yellowish, papillose; segments linear, slender, partly carinately cleft between the articulations, shorter than the teeth, arising from a basal membrane about one-fifth the length of the teeth; spores mature in early summer; annulus 2-seriate.

On stones, roots of trees, logs, etc., often where sometimes overflowed; Japan, and from New Brunswick to Ontario and southwards through the eastern and central part of the United States. Probably fairly common in our region, but sometimes difficult to distinguish from L. polycarpa or L. gracilescens.

ALLEGHENY Co.: On bark of white oak at three feet from ground, Fern Hollow, Pittsburgh, March 8, 1908, and at base of trees in swampy woods near Douthett, December 29, 1908. O.E.J. (figured Plate XXXIX). BEAVER Co.: On decaying bark, 3 mi. east of Legionville, along Sewickley Creek. May 5, 1918. O.E.J. BLAIR Co.: Tyrone. T. P. James. (Porter's Catalogue). CRAWFORD Co.: On bark, Ulmus americana. Conneaut Outlet. C.M.B. Sept. 23, 1949. McKEAN Co.: Tuna Creek, Bradford. Dec. 21, 1895. D.A.B. TIOGA Co.: On large Elm tree, Goodrich Settlement, Tioga. June 24, 1935. Sidney K. Eastwood. WASHINGTON Co.: On tree, subject to inundation, near Washington. May 28, 1892; near Arden, July 20, 1891; and at Hackberry Sta., June 16, 1894. All by Linn & Simonton. WESTMORELAND Co.: Chestnut Ridge, s.e. of Torrance. C.M.B. June 13, 1943.

7.   LESKEELLA (Limpricht) Loeske

Dioicous: slender, in flattened, wide-spreading mats, dark green to brownish, dull; stem widely creeping, fasciculately yellowish-red-radiculose, densely-leaved, numerously-branched, with erect and short branches; leaves drying imbricate, when moist erect-spreading to secund, more or less abruptly long-acuminate from a decurrent, doubly-plicate, cordate base, margins narrowly revolute below but plane in the acumen, entire; costa strong, yellow-brown, ending in the acumen; cells rounded-hexagonal, in leaf-middle oval and oblong, in middle of base rectangular, the alar quadrate; branch-leaves smaller with plane margins and delicate and shorter costa; perichaetial leaves pale, from the erect and half-sheathing base abruptly long-acuminate, delicately costate to the acumen: seta elongate, stiff, dark chestnut-color, smooth; capsule erect, symmetric, cylindric or oblong, rarely weakly curved, finally rust-colored to brown; annulus rather persistent, deciduous in sections; peristome-teeth erect when dry, confluent at base, subulate, bordered, yellowish, cross- and obliquely-striate, smooth or papillose above, not distinctly trabeculate; inner peristome finely papillose, basal membrane moderately prominent, segments irregular, in nodose projections, filiform, etc., sometimes carinate, cilia mostly none; lid convex, obliquely thick-rostrate; calyptra glabrous, cucullate and reaching to base of capsule: spores small.

A small genus of 4 species; only the following in North America:

1.   LESKEELLA NERVOSA [Bridel] Loeske
(*Leskea nervosa* Myrin; *Lescuraea rigidula* Kindberg; *Hypnum nervosum* C. Mueller)

Plate XXXIX

Slender, in thin and appressed tufts, dark green to brownish, the older parts almost black: stems with central strand distinct, creeping, up to 5 or 6 cm long, pinnately divided and again branched into numerous, crowded, short and erect or longer and creeping branches, often with numerous gemmiform branches towards the apex: stem-leaves close, broadly ovate, sub-cordate, open-spreading when moist, imbricate when dry, slightly decurrent, about 0.4-0.5 x 1-1.2 mm, suddenly long-acuminate, the acumen recurved, the margins plane, sub-sinuate, the blade concave and deeply plicate; costa almost percurrent, slender; branch-leaves considerably narrower, lanceolate, more rigidly erect-spreading, smaller, up to about 0.6-0.7 mm long; leaf-cells oblong to oval-hexagonal, ranging from 1 to 3:1, the alar quadrate to transversely oval-hexagonal in about 4-6 rows extending well up the margins and becoming rounded; cells smooth to lightly papillose, incrassate; inner perichaetial leaves long-sheathing, long-acuminate: seta 10-12 mm long; capsule erect, sub-cylindric, symmetric, small, castaneous; lid narrowly conic to short-rostrate; peristome short, the teeth whitish, lance-linear; segments shorter, irregular, subulate, basal membrane 1/4 the length of teeth; cilia none; annulus narrow; spores mature in summer, rough.

Mostly on bases of trees, especially maples, in our region: Europe, and in the northeastern United States south to Pennsylvania.

Not common in our region. CRAWFORD CO.: Bark of Black Ash. Conneaut Outlet. C.M.B. Sept. 23, 1949. FAYETTE CO.: Cheat Haven, September 3-6, 1910. O.E.J. and G.K.J. McKEAN CO.: Bennett Brook, Bradford, July 12, 1896 (figured), and Bolivar Run, 1896. D.A.B.

8.   RAUIA Austin

Autoicous: quite slender, dull, bluish-green to brownish-green: stems thickly-leaved, simple or divided, more or less regularly pinnately branched; branchlets short, ascending, julaceous, obtuse; leaves dimorphic, drying imbricate, when moist erect-spreading; stem-leaves plicate, triangular to cordate-ovate, tapering to a lanceolate or lance-subulate acumination, the margins entire; costa strong, incomplete; median leaf-cells rounded-angular, with low and usually numerous papillae on both sides; branch-leaves lance-ovate, short-pointed, the costa dorsally somewhat rough; inner perichaetial leaves appressed, pale, lance-oblong, slenderly acuminate, entire, incompletely costate, and with elongate, smooth cells: seta slender, 10-15 mm long, reddish, smooth; capsule from nearly upright to horizontal, oblong-cylindric, mostly weakly curved, light brown, drying more or less constricted below the mouth; annulus revoluble; peristome-teeth lance-subulate, bordered, transversely striate, numerously trabeculate; inner peristome yellow, finely papillose, basal membrane prominent, carinate, the segments about as long as the teeth, carinately split, the cilia 2 or 3, more or less complete, nodose; lid conic, short-rostrate; calyptra cucullate; spores .009-.011 mm.

A genus of about 14 species, widely distributed in both hemispheres; 4 species in North America; 1 species in our region.

1. RAUIA SCITA (Beauvois) Austin
(*Thuidium scitum* Austin; *Hypnum scitum* Beauvois)
Plate XXXIX

In appressed, green or yellowish-brown mats, medium-sized: stem prostrate, castaneous, 2-3-times divided; densely pinnately branched; branchlets short and slender, usually about 2-3 mm long, smooth, paraphylla present; stem-leaves broadly cordate-deltoid, acuminate, about 0.5-0.6 mm long, margins plane, finely papillose-denticulate; branch-leaves ovate-cordate, smaller, shorter acuminate, both kinds of leaves concave, erect-spreading; costa pellucid, broad, about three-fifths to four-fifths as long as the leaf; median leaf-cells rounded-hexagonal, minute, .006 mm diameter, with 2-5 small bead-like papillae on each surface, incrassate, rather obscure, the basal median oblong, paraphyllia numerous, linear to ovate, more or less branched, occurring on both stem and branches; inner perichaetial leaves elongate-lanceolate, filiform-acuminate, somewhat longitudinally plicate: capsule sub-erect, about 1.3-1.5 mm long, rather thin-walled, when old and empty more or less wrinkled, urn cylindric, straight or slightly curved, more or less twisted when old, the seta about 1.5 cm long; lid conic-rostrate, curved upward; annulus large; exothecial cells rather thin-walled, mainly quadrate to rectangular; peristome-teeth lance-subulate, shallowly inserted, castaneous and transversely striolate below, hyaline and papillose above; lamellate and trabeculate; segments nearly as long as teeth, carinately partially split, the basal membrane about two-fifths as high, the cilia usually three, nodose; spores medium-walled, castaneous-pellucid, papillose, about .010-.013 mm, mature in fall and winter; autoicious.

On the bases of trees and on stones in woods; from Ontario to Missouri, eastward to the Atlantic Ocean and southward to North Carolina.

Rare in our region. ALLEGHENY CO.: Moon Twp., April, 1902. J. A. Shafer. Mc-KEAN CO.: On base of trees, Rutherford, August 4, 1897, Bradford, October, 1897; Gates Hollow, July 28, 1895, and Limestone Creek, Bradford, October to December, 1896. D.A.B. (figured). The last named specimen issued with Grout's No. 134, in part, North American Musci Pleurocarpi.

9. HAPLOCLADIUM (C. Mueller) C. Mueller

Autoicous: slender, forming mats, yellowish-green to brownish-yellow, dull: stems creeping, elongate, with brownish rhizoids, variously pinnate with branches mostly ascending, julaceous, short, obtuse and simple, or somewhat longer, acute and pinnate with scattering short branchlets; leaves more or less uniform, drying appressed, sometimes weakly secund, when moist erect-spreading; stem-leaves more or less doubly plicate, from a more or less broadly ovate base, lanceolate to lance-subulate, the margin revolute at base, the upper margin indistinctly serrulate to entire; costa strong, sometimes percurrent, sometimes excurrent, mostly smooth; cells more or less pellucid, oval to oblong-hexagonal, with one papilla over the lumen, the alar quadrate; branch-leaves narrower at the base, shorter-pointed, plane-margined, more or less distinctly serrate, with a single terminal papilla on the apical cell; costa shorter, cells mostly opaque; inner perichaetial leaves erect, pale, plicate, from a lanceolate or linear base long-acuminate, incompletely costate: seta 1.5-2.5 cm long, red-castaneous, smooth; capsule inclined, oblong-cylindric, drying more or less horizontal and arcuate, when old and empty contracted below the mouth; annulus present; peristome-teeth lance-subulate, yellow, bordered, transversely-striate, dorsally lamellate; inner peristome yellowish, the basal membrane wide and carinate, the segments lance-subulate, of same length as teeth, carinate, entire or narrowly split, cilia complete, 2 or 3, slender, nodose or appendiculate; lid convex-conic; acute; calyptra cucullate; spores .008-.012 mm.

A genus of nearly 50 species, mostly occurring in eastern Asia and in South America; only the following in our region.

KEY TO THE SPECIES

A. Stem-leaves rounded-ovate, short-acuminate; margins erose-serrate ....1. *H. virginianum*
A. Stem-leaves ovate, more or less long-acuminate; entire to crenulate serrate ....
....2. *H. microphyllum*

1. HAPLOCLADIUM VIRGINIANUM (Bridel) Brotherus

(*Thuidium virginianum* Lindberg; *T. gracile* var. *lancastriense* Cardot; *Hypnum gracile* var. *lancastriense* Sullivant and Lesquereux)

Plate XXXIX

Small to medium-sized, appressed-cespitose, dark to dirty green: stems diffusely divided, the branches short and erect or ascending pinnately; leaves of the stems rounded-ovate, concave, narrowed to the base but scarcely decurrent, about 0.6-0.8 mm long, abruptly acuminate, costate into the acumen, serrulate above, erose-dentate below, appressed when dry, loose when moist; costa ending in the apex; median leaf-cells quadrate-hexagonal, uni-papillate, rather incrassate, the lower marginal more or less transversely oblong-quadrate or hexagonal; branch-leaves about 0.4-0.6 mm long, broadly and shortly acuminate with a serrulate margin above; perichaetial leaves long, pale, up to 2.5 mm long: seta slender, about 2-2.5 cm long, rather richly castaneous, dextrorse; capsule oblong-cylindric, castaneous, curved, more or less horizontal, often when old more or less pendent by the curving of the upper part of the seta, annulate, the urn about 2.5:1, about 2 mm long, constricted below the mouth when dry and empty; lid obtusely short-beaked, about one-third as long as the urn; peristome normally hypnoid, yellowish, the 16 teeth lance-linear, dorsally cross-striate, with zigzag divisural line, distinct dorsal lamellae, and about 35-40 closely placed trabeculae; segments about as long as teeth, carinate; cilia (1-) 2-3, nodose-articulate, the basal membrane about two-fifths the height of the peristome; exothecial cells incrassate, quadrate to oblong-hexagonal, about three series in the rim much smaller and rounded; spores incrassate, yellowish, faintly papillose, about .011-.014 mm, mature in spring.

On the ground or on roots of trees in rather open woods; from New England to Minnesota and Mexico, also in Europe.

Rather common in our region. Now known from Beaver, Blair, Cambria (Porter), Centre, Fayette, Huntingdon, and Westmoreland counties, all in the southern half of our region. Specimen figured: Warrior's Ridge above Huntingdon, July 20 1908. O.E.J.

2. HAPLOCLADIUM MICROPHYLLUM (Swartz; Hedwig) Brotherus

(*Hypnum gracile* Bruch and Schimper; *Thuidium microphyllum* Best)

Plate XXXIX

Medium size, pale green to yellowish, appressed-matted: stems diffusely divided, densely pinnately branched; stem-leaves broadly ovate to lance-ovate, up to 1.2 mm long, concave, long and narrowly acuminate, the margins entire or sinuately denticulate; costa almost percurrent; leaf-cells quadrate-hexagonal, somewhat incrassate, the apical and a very few of the basal elongate, all strongly uni-papillate; branch-leaves narrower and smaller, up to 1 mm long; paraphyllia numerous and branched on the stem but simple and few or none on the smaller branches; inner perichaetial leaves high-sheathing, long-acuminate, costate, up to 2.5 mm long: seta up to 2 or 2.5 cm long, castaneous, twisted, somewhat arcuate above; capsule turgid-oblong, about 2-2.5:1, about 2 mm long, dorsally somewhat turgid, when mature somewhat inclined or pendent by the curving of the upper part of the seta; lid short-conic, mamillate; peristome normally hypnoid, the teeth yellowish, densely trabeculate, dorsally with rather indistinct lamellae and divisural, finely cross-striate, narrowly hyaline-margined; segments carinate, about as long as teeth; cilia 2 to 3, a little shorter than the teeth, strongly nodose to shortly appendiculate, the basal membrane about one-third as high as teeth; annulus simple; spores mature in summer, somewhat incrassate, pale brownish-pellucid, very slightly roughened.

On earth, rotten wood, etc., often on bases of trees; Europe, Asia, and from southern Canada to the West Indies.

Rather rare in our region. BEDFORD CO.: Raystown Branch, Juniata River, 2½ mi. s. of Schellsburg. July 19, 1941. C.M.B. BUTLER CO.: On roadside bank. Ribold. C.M.B. June 2, 1945. ERIE CO.: On dead log, Presque Isle. Nelle Ammons. July 13, 1935. MCKEAN CO.: On hillside at mouth of Langmade Hollow, Bradford, November, 1895 (figured) and Limestone Creek, N. Y., near the Pennsylvania State line north of Bradford, October 16, 1896. D.A.B. WASHINGTON CO.: On rotten log, Snake Woods, near Washington. Aug. 13, 1892. Linn & Simonton.

10.   THUIDIUM Bryologia Europaea

FERN MOSSES

Autoicous or dioicous: slender to robust, mostly stiff, dull, forming greenish to yellowish or brownish mats or cushions: stem with a few-celled central strand, spreading to ascending or rarely erect, radiculose here and there in fascicles, not much divided, once to thrice pinnately branched, flattened like the frond of a fern; leaves dimorphic, when dry incurved or appressed, when moist erect-spreading or open-erect but never secund; stem-leaves plicate, from a narrowed and decurrent base, mostly with revolute margin, entire or apically toothed; costa strong, mostly incomplete, rarely excurrent, sometimes dorsally rough, leaf-cells rather uniform, rounded to oval- or oblong-hexagonal, both sides numerously papillose or uni-papillose dorsally or on both sides; branch-leaves of first order often similar to stem-leaves, those of the second or third order smaller, mostly lance-ovate, with the costa weaker and shorter; inner perichaetial leaves pale, appressed, mostly lanceolate and plicate, often with a prolonged and filiform apex, sometimes with ciliate margins, costa incomplete, cells elongate, smooth: seta elongate, castaneous or red, smooth or rough; capsule inclined to horizontal, oval-oblong to cylindric, more or less arcuate, brown to yellow, drying constricted below the mouth; annulus sometimes persistent; peristome-teeth basally confluent, lance-subulate, bordered, cross-striate, numerously trabeculate; inner peristome yellow to orange, smooth or finely papillose, with prominent carinate basal membrane, segments as long as teeth, carinately split at least in part; cilia 2-4, nodose to appendiculate, or sometimes rudimentary, or none; lid convex-conic, obliquely rostrate; calyptra cucullate, mostly smooth; spores .007-.010 mm or .012-.016 mm.

A widely distributed genus of about 160 species, on tree-trunks, rocks, or earth; about 25 species reported for North America; at least 4, probably more, in our region.

KEY TO THE SPECIES

A. Delicate, small, not over 5 cm; 1-2 pinnate ....B
A. Larger, up to 10 cm; 1-3 pinnate C
  B. Branchlets papillate; leaf-cells about .006 mm: seta 1-1.5 cm long ....2. *T. pygmaeum*
  B. Branchlets smooth; cells about .009 mm: seta 2-3 cm long ....1. *T. minutulum*
C. Stems simply pinnate; plants ascending in tufts ....3. *T. abietinum*
C. Stems 2-3 pinnate, forming flat mats ....D
  D. Leaf-margin revolute; costa not filling entire apex of leaf ....E
  D. Leaf-margin plane; costa of stem-leaves filling the entire apex; perichaetial leaves
      not ciliate ....4. *T. recognitum*
  E. Stem-leaves lance-acuminate, from a triangular-ovate base; perichaetial leaves ciliate
      ....7. *T. delicatulum*
  E. Stem-leaves long-lance subulate; perichaetial leaves not ciliate........................
      ....6. *T. Philiberti*
  E. Stem-leaves shortly and broadly acuminate; perichaetial leaves not ciliate........5. *T. Alleni*

1. THUIDIUM MINUTULUM [Hedwig] Bryologia Europaea
(*Hypnum minutulum* Hedwig)

Plate XXXIX

Small, slender, simply pinnate; stems irregularly divided, not over 3 or 4 cm long, both stems and branches smooth, bearing rather few linear-oblong simple paraphyllia only about 2 to 5 cells high, notched at apex; stem-leaves distant, deltoid, acuminate or apiculate, somewhat revolute on the borders, rather opaque, about 0.6-0.8 mm long; costa strong, ending near the apex; median leaf-cells irregularly polygonal to quadrate-hexagonal, the marginal somewhat larger and sometimes transversely elongate, all leaf-cells incrassate, pluri-papillose, the apical cell with 2 to 5 marginal papillae; branch-leaves ovate-acuminate, about 0.2-0.3 mm long, concave and with a shorter costa; perichaetial leaves erect, slenderly lance-acuminate, the acumen more or less reflexed: seta about 2-2.5 cm long, slender, dark yellow or brown and sinistrorse when old; capsule yellowish, oval-oblong, cernuous to horizontal, the urn about 2 mm long, when dry somewhat constricted below the rim; lid obliquely subulate-rostrate and about 1 mm long; peristome castaneous, the teeth slender, densely trabeculate, the dorsal lamellae cross-striate and projecting to form a narrow margin, the divisural distinct; segments as long as the teeth, split carinately, arising from a basal membrane about one-third as high, cilia usually 2, articulate, nearly as long; spores about .010-.012 mm, pale brown, medium-walled, slightly roughened, mature in fall.

On rotten logs and stumps and at the base of trees in woods. Europe. In North America from Florida and Mexico north to New Brunswick and Minnesota.

In our region known from Allegheny, Blair, Fayette, Huntingdon, McKean and Washington counties. Specimen figured: On stump, Meadow Run Valley, 4 mi. s. of Ohio Pyle. Sept. 1-3, 1906. O.E.J. & G.K.J.

2.   THUIDIUM PYGMAEUM Bryologia Europaea

Plate LXVI

Minute, rather harsh, in dull, olive or yellowish green, thin, interwoven mats; bi-pinnate, 1-2 cm long; branches capillary; with insignificant simple 2-5-celled paraphyllia; stem-leaves triangular-ovate but acuminately narrowed, the lower margins often more or less reflexed, median cells pluripapillate, incrassate, hexagonal-quadrate, about .006 mm in diameter; primary branch-leaves long, ovate with obtuse or sub-acute apex; seta about 1.5 cm long; capsule inclined to horizontal, unsymmetrical, wide-mouthed; annulus conspicuous; lid conic, obliquely rostrate; peristome complete; spores ripening in fall.

Mostly on stones (or soil) in calcareous districts. So stiff and intricately interlaced that it is difficult to separate out individual plants. First described from specimens collected at Columbus, Ohio. Range now extended to Pennsylvania, New Jersey, and Canada.

WASHINGTON CO.: Linn and Simonton. On stones, in a shaded ravine, McCracken Station, vicinity of Washington. Sept. 24, 1892 (figured).

3.   THUIDIUM ABIETINUM [Linnaeus] Bryologia Europaea
(Hypnum abietinum Bridel)

Large, yellowish-green above, brownish below, in dense tufts or mats; stem 5-12 cm long, regularly pinnate, stiffly ascending-erect, the branches 2-10 mm long, unequal, attenuate, slender, terete when dry; stem-leaves crowded, ovate, acuminate, 0.85 mm wide by 1.3 mm long, deeply bi-plicate with margins papillose-serrulate; costa strong ending well above the middle; median cells oval-rhombic, uni-papillate, about .010 mm in diameter; branch-leaves smaller, with one or two papillae on the apical cell; inner perichaetial leaves plicate, with toothed but not ciliate margin; seta 1.5-3 cm long; capsule cylindric, curved, suberect, tapering at base; annulus distinct; operculum long-conic, acute; spores in spring.

Mostly in dry places, on earth, stones, or rocks, especially in calcareous habitats. Arctic America south to Virginia and Colorado. Collected by Porter on a cliff near Easton, Pa.

4. THUIDIUM RECOGNITUM [Hedwig] Lindberg

(*Hypnum recognitum* Hedwig; *T. delicatulum* Bryologia Europaea)

Plate XL

Yellowish-green, not as bright-colored as some of the other *Thuidiums*, quite similar to the preceding but mostly bipinnate: the primary branches are nearly equal in length, thus making the general outline of the frond more linear-oblong; stem-leaves usually about 0.6 to 0.8 mm long, broadly triangular, auriculate-cordate, abruptly acuminate, recurved-spreading when moist, the apex acute and often very slender, the serrulate margins usually plane, the leaves sulcate when dry; costa sub-percurrent, somewhat broadened at apex; leaf-cells incrassate, and each with a long, slender, upcurved dorsal papilla, the median rhombic-oblong to rounded-quadrate, the apical somewhat narrower; branch-leaves with apical cells with 2-4 papillae; perichaetial leaves up to 4.5 mm long, slenderly long-acuminate, non-ciliate: seta about 2-2.5 cm long, slender, castaneous, lustrous, dextrorse above; capsule oblong-cylindric, arcuate, more or less inclined, the urn castaneous, 2.5-3 mm long, when dry quite sharply bent and constricted at the mouth; peristome as in *T. delicatulum;* annulus large, deciduous, pluri-seriate; lid short-rostrate; spores with yellowish, medium-thick, granular walls, about .012-.014 mm, mature in midsummer.

On the ground on rocks or on rotten wood in moist, shaded woods; Europe, Asia, northern Africa, and from northern Canada southeastward to Florida.

ALLEGHENY CO.: On clay bank under hemlocks, Wildwood Road Hollow, March 29, 1908. O.E.J. and G.K.J.; Guyasuta Hollow, October 25, 1908. O.E.J. ARMSTRONG Co.: Kittanning, September 24, 1904. O.E.J. (figured). CLINTON CO.: Between Renovo and Haneyville, July 15, 1908. O.E.J. ERIE CO.: Moist woods. Presque Isle. Nelle Ammons. July 2, 1935. McKEAN CO.: Langmade Hollow, May 3, 1896, Toad Hollow, June 17, 1896, and Bolivar Run, July 17, 1897, all near Bradford. D.A.B. WASHINGTON CO.: On base of beech tree. Claysville. Linn & Simonton. Dec. 17, 1892.

5. THUIDIUM ALLENI Austin

Forming rather loose and thick, wide mats; stems more or less ascending, somewhat irregularly bipinnate; paraphyllia numerous; stem-leaves ovate, broadly acuminate, with apex acute to obtuse, sometimes more slenderly tapering; margins of leaves crenulate-papillose; costate to well above the middle; on each surface; paraphyllia few or none on branches; branch-leaves acuminate median leaf-cells incrassate, rather oblong, 1-2:1, with one or more low papillae from a concave, broadly ovate base, acute to obtuse; perichaetial leaves not ciliate. According to Grout (*Moss Flora*) abundant in Florida. Reported from other states as far north as Pennsylvania and Connecticut. "Mature sporophytes unknown"—Grout.

6. THUIDIUM PHILIBERTI Limpricht
(*Thuidium intermedium* Philibert, not Mitten)

Grout (*Moss Flora*) regards this as "A poorly delimited subspecies of *T. delicatulum.*" Stems to 12 cm or more, bi- to tri-pinnate; branches up to 1 cm; stem leaves cordate-lanceolate, narrowed into a filiform acumination of a single row of 3-8 linear cells, about 1.5-1.8 mm by 0.6 mm; costa strong ending at or in the long acumination; median cells incrassate, roundish-oval, towards the basal margin much more rectangular; branch-leaves ovate, acuminate, about 0.6 mm long by 0.4 mm wide, margins plane, apical cell with 2 or 3 points; inner perichaetial leaves with the slender acumination about three times the length of the body of the leaf, mostly without cilia; seta 1.5-2.5 cm long; capsule inclined, curved, cylindric, about 3 mm by 0.8 mm, castaneous; lid obliquely-rostrate; spores ripe in fall and winter.

In wet swampy situations on ground or bases of trees. New Jersey, Pennsylvania, and in the West. Not yet known from our region.

7. THUIDIUM DELICATULUM [Linnaeus] Mitten
COMMON FERN MOSS
Plate XL

The "Common Fern Moss."—Bright green above, darker below, large, forming rather large and intricately woven mats, when dry rather stiff and harsh; stems elongate, procumbent or arched and alternately rooting, often reaching a length of 10 or 12 cm; the branching is twice or thrice pinnate, very regular and fern-like; stem-leaves triangular-ovate, somewhat cordate, gradually acuminate, about 1 mm long, erect-spreading, appressed when dry, somewhat serrate and marginally more or less recurved; leaf-cells uni-papillate on both sides, rather incrassate, the median quadrate-oblong to rhombic-oval or rounded-quadrate, about .007 to .008 mm across; costa strong and ending in the acumen; branch-leaves much smaller, broadly ovate, acuminate, the apical cells with 2 (to 4) papillae, usually appearing bifid; inner perichaetial bracts with a very few, filiform, articulate cilia on the margins: seta about 2 to 3 cm long, rather stiff, richly castaneous, somewhat dextrorse; capsule large, the urn about 3.5 to 4 mm long, strongly inclined to horizontal, arcuate, narrowly oblong, yellowish to castaneous; lid slenderly conic-rostrate, about 1.5 mm long; annulus narrow, usually 2-seriate; peristome large, reddish, the teeth strongly and numerously trabeculate, often split at the hyaline and papillose apex, dorsally cross-striate below, the divisural and lamellae distinct; segments about as long as teeth, carinately split, papillose above; the 2 or 3 slender nodose cilia rising from a basal membrane about one-third as high as the peristome; spores rather thin-walled, pale-castaneous, very slightly roughened, about .014-.017 mm, mature in winter.

On the ground, stones, rotten wood, stumps, etc.; in moist woods; Europe, Asia, and from Labrador to the Rocky Mountains and south to the West Indies and South America. Very common in the woods of our region.

Known from 18 counties in western Pennsylvania, and probably occurs in all. Specimen figured: Power's Run, Allegheny Co., Sept. 14, 1905. O.E.J. and G.K.J.

11. HELODIUM (Sullivant) Warnstorf
(*Elodium* (Sullivant) Warnstorf)

Autoicous or rarely dioicous: more or less robust, in deep, soft, slightly lustrous, green to yellowish-green or sometimes brownish tufts: stems elliptic in cross-section, without central strand, mostly simple, thickly-foliate, somewhat distichously pinnate; branchlets filiform; paraphyses small, branched, numerous; leaves all similar, when dry appressed, when moist erect-spreading, or erect, concave, with a dorsally projecting main plication; stem-leaves from a narrowed base suddenly lance-ovate, acuminate, the margin almost wholly revolute, mostly entire, sometimes apically serrate; costa incomplete, mostly weak; cells pellucid, elongate-hexagonal to almost linear, smooth or unipapillate over the lumen or in the cell-angle, the basal cells laxly rectangular; branch-leaves smaller; perichaetial leaves erect, pale, plicate, delicate, narrowly acuminate, incompletely costate: seta 2-5 cm long, smooth; capsule inclined to horizontal, oblong-cylindric, brown, more or less arcuate; annulus revoluble; peristome-teeth broadly lance-subulate, yellow, basally confluent, transversely striate, apically almost smooth, hyaline-bordered, high-trabeculate, the plates numerous, and often forked or with transverse walls; inner peristome yellowish, almost smooth, with high basal membrane, carinate; segments as long as teeth, lance-subulate, entire or very narrowly carinately split, cilia 3, complete, delicate, smooth; lid convex-conic, acute; calyptra cucullate, glabrous; spores about .010-.016 (-.024) mm.

A genus of five species, at least one of these in our region.*

1. HELODIUM PALUDOSUM (Sullivant) Austin
(*Hypnum paludosum* Sullivant; *Thuidium paludosum* Jaeger and Sauerbeck)
Plate XL

Yellowish-green, irregularly pinnate: primary stems creeping, branchlets distichous, unequal: stem leaves somewhat rigid, about 1-1.5 mm long, erect-spreading to somewhat appressed, lance-oblong, acuminate, somewhat cordate at base, concave below, reflexed on the borders, smooth on both faces, at the base bearing 1 to 3 paraphyllose branched filaments, the base decurrent, plicate-striate; costa sub-percurrent; median leaf-cells shortly linear-oblong to linear-rhomboid, usually smooth, sometimes dorsally lightly papillose at the distal end; stems and branches with numerous filamentous and branched paraphyllia; branch-leaves narrower, smaller, usually 0.6-0.8 mm long; inner perichaetial leaves oblong, gradually slenderly acuminate, up to 3 mm long, longitudinally plicate: seta about 1.5-3 cm long, slender, red-castaneous, dextrorse above; capsule oblong-cylindric, curved, strongly inclined to almost horizontal, about 3:1, the urn about 3-3.5 mm long; lid conic, apiculate; peristome normally

---

* *Helodium Blandowii* (Weber & Mohr) Warnstorf, is larger than *paludosum*, having stems up to 10 cm long and very regularly pinnate; the stem-leaves quickly narrow to a somewhat clasping base bearing paraphyllose appendages; leaf-cells distinctly papillose dorsally at the distal end. — On wet marshy ground, Eurasia, and from New Jersey, Ohio, and Colorado northwards.

hypnoid, large, the teeth rather broadly lance-acuminate, densely trabeculate, the lower trabeculae often forked and thus united by obliquely transverse bars, the dorsal lamellae numerous and below densely cross-striate, yellowish; segments as long as teeth, carinate but rarely split, the basal membrane about one-third as high as teeth, the cilia 3, nodose or appendiculate above, nearly as long as segments; spores mature in winter, about .018-.022 mm, medium-walled, yellowish, granular; annulus large.

In wet, grassy fields, swamps, and bogs; Asia, and from New England to Ontario and south to Illinois and probably rather common in the northern part of our region.

ALLEGHENY CO.: Swampy ground near Douthett, about on boundary line of Butler and Allegheny counties, April 26, 1908. O.E.J. BEDFORD CO.: In swamp along Raystown Branch, Juniata River, south of Schellsburg. July 19, 1941. C.M.B. BUTLER CO.: Swampy ground near Crider's Corner's April 26, 1908. O.E.J. CRAWFORD CO.: Pymatuning Swamp, near Linesville, June 12, 1905. O.E.J. (figured). ERIE CO.: On decaying log in swamp, Presque Isle. Nelle Ammons. Aug. 3, 1935.

1a. HELODIUM PALUDOSUM var. HELODIOIDES (Renauld and Cardot) Best
(*Thuidium elodioides* Renauld and Cardot)

Leaves smaller with margins dentate-serrate, the cells more or less strongly and often sub-centrally papillose; darker green; cells shorter, elliptic or oval.

In swampy meadows, swamps, bogs, etc.; from New York to Ohio and Indiana. Apparently rare in our region.

Family 30. HOOKERIACEAE

Soft, often complanately foliate; leaf-cells smooth, thin-walled, mostly parenchymatous, alar not differentiated.

A large family of about 700 species mostly tropical and on trees or decaying wood. Only Hookeria in our region, with one species.

1. HOOKERIA ACUTIFOLIA Hooker
(*Pterygophyllum lucens* Sullivant (1864), not Bridel (1819);
Pterygophyllum acuminatum Paris)

Plate LXVII

In large, soft, light green mats with somewhat complanate foliate branches 5-10 mm wide, in ours about 2-3 cm long. When dry, the leaves are thin, soft, translucent, lustrous, and yellowish. Leaves ovate to oblong-ovate, acute, 4-5 mm long, entire, slightly decurrent, the lateral somewhat unsymmetric, the apex often slightly eroded, sometimes producing protonemal filaments; leaf-cells somewhat irregularly oblong-hexagonal, somewhat shorter at basal angles and at apex and slightly narrower along the margin, the median about 3-5:1. Not found fruiting in our region.

On earth and rocks in cool wet situations. Connecticut to Ohio and the southern Appalachians.

FAYETTE CO.: Ohio Pyle on rock below Cucumber Falls, wet with spray. O.E.J. & G.K.J. and Dr. and Mrs. W. H. Emig, May 12, 1917 (figured); on dripping shaded rocks, Meadow Run ravine, Sullivant Moss Society Foray. John Churchill and C. M. Boardman, June 23, 1940.

Family 31. HYPNACEAE

Autoicous or dioicous, rarely pseudautoicous or polyoicous: antheridial clusters gemmiform, small, archegonial clusters on short mostly rooting perichaetial branches: slender to robust, variously cespitose, rarely floating, dull to lustrous: stem without central strand, mostly woody, often stoloniferous, mostly irregularly pinnate, but the branches often regularly pinnate; leaves pluriseriate, unistratose, erect-spreading to squarrose, rarely densely imbricate, often secund or circinate, of various forms, sometimes unsymmetric; costa homogeneous, mostly thin and rather short, simple, double, forked, or none, rarely strong and complete to excurrent; leaf cells mostly narrowly prosenchymatous, rarely parenchymatous, at the base looser, the alar mostly differentiated into a distinct group, rounded to oval or 4-6 sided, small to inflated, mostly hyaline: seta elongated, mostly smooth; capsule mostly inclined to horizontal, mostly arcuate, rarely pendent, or erect, mostly smooth; collum scant; peristome double, both parts of same length, teeth lance-subulate, mostly strongly hygroscopic, mostly confluent at base, rarely separate, yellow, red-brown to purple, mostly transversely striate with divisural zigzag, with trabeculae numerous and well-developed; basal membrane of inner peristome wide, segments keeled, mostly lance-subulate, cilia mostly complete, filiform, nodose to articulate, rarely rudimentary or none; lid usually conic-convex, in our species obtuse to acute or only very shortly rostrate; spores small.

As here treated, a large and cosmopolitan family, distributed on all kinds of substrata. The limitations of both the family and the genera are treated variously by the authorities.

KEY TO THE GENERA

A. Costa in our species single, usually extending to leaf-middle or beyond; lid never strongly rostrate; plants not complanately foliate; capsules mostly curved-cylindric, or subcylindric ....D. (*Amblystegiae*)

A. Costa short, double or single or none, rarely single in *Homomallium* and *Hygrohypnum;* lid sometimes rostrate ....B

  B. Stem-leaves and branch-leaves usually distinctly dissimilar, at least as to size, symmetric and normally inserted ....O

  B. Stem- and branch-leaves more or less closely similar, although often secund or falcate, or inserted obliquely and unsymmetrically C

    C. Leaves either symmetric and normally inserted or unsymmetric and obliquely inserted; lid sometimes rostrate ....T

    C. Leaves more or less obliquely inserted and apparently two-ranked, mostly unsymmetric; branches mostly complanate; lid conic to short-rostrate, rarely long-rostrate ....U

      D. Leaves bordered ....7. *Sciaromium*

      D. Leaves non-bordered ....E

        E. Leaves mostly large, broad, and obtuse or sometimes apiculate ....9. *Calliergon*

        E. Leaves not as above ....F

          F. Costa strong, sub-percurrent, or sometimes excurrent ....G

          F. Costa not reaching leaf-apex ....K

            G Paraphyllia often present, polymorphic; leaves non-plicate, mostly erect-spreading; more or less aquatic; basal leaf-cells mostly rectangular, incrassate, pellucid ....

....6. *Hygroamblystegium*

G. Not as above; paraphyllia none or scarce ....H

 H. Leaf-cells linear-vermicular to the leaf-base, mostly with blunt ends, alar cells forming a small, distinct, fairly well-defined group of quadrate or rectangular cells ....11. *Hygrohypnum*

 H. Leaf-cells hexagonal and 2-6 times as long as wide or prolonged-linear and becoming wider and shorter basally, alar cells forming a group which is large and often extends to the costa I

I. Ends of shoots usually circinate. Leaves falcate to circinate; alar cells parenchymatous; mostly enlarged and inflated ....8. *Drepanocladus*

I. Alar cells more or less prosenchymatous or rounded ....J

 J. Median leaf-cells prolonged-linear; leaves concave, large, ovate to oblong or circular ....9. *Calliergon*

 J. Median leaf-cells prosenchymatous-hexagonal, 2-6 times as long as wide; aquatic; leaves mostly erect-spreading ....6. *Hygroamblystegium*

K. Leaves cordate to ovate-lanceolate, acuminate; costa weak; reaching the middle of leaf or beyond; leaf-cells rarely linear, mostly parenchymatous and 4-sided or prosenchymatous and 6-sided; small plants; capsules relatively large ....
....1. *Amblystegium*

K. Characters not combined as above L

 L. Leaf-cells narrowly linear; leaves broadly ovate or cordate, with reflexed-squarrose and subulate-acuminate tips ....12. *Campylium*

 L. Leaf-cells and leaves not as above ....M

M. Small plants; leaves ovate to oblong-lanceolate, long-acuminate, 0.7-1.0 mm long; cells narrowly prosenchymatous; plants shining ....3. *Homomallium*

M. Not as above ....N

 N. Slender, dull; leaves spreading, lanceolate to lance-linear; median leaf-cells rhomboidal to oblong-hexagonal, 2-4 or rarely 4-8 times as long as broad; operculum not rostrate ....2. *Amblystegiella*

 N. Median leaf-cells prolonged-linear, mostly very narrow ....O

O. Leaves erect-spreading to imbricated, oblong-ovate to rounded, obtuse or apiculate, often deeply concave and cucullate; costa short and double or none; no paraphyllia ....10. *Calliergonella*

O. Leaves more or less falcate-secund to circinate, from a mostly narrowed and somewhat decurrent base becoming ovate- to triangular- or cordate-lanceolate, more or less slenderly acuminate, costa weak, reaching somewhat above the leaf-middle or even in some cases excurrent; no paraphyllia ....8. *Drepanocladus*

O. Not as above ....P

 P. Paraphyllia numerous; leaves more or less erect, spreading to squarrose-recurved, from abruptly to shortly acuminate, mostly plicate, concave ....16. *Hylocomium*

 P. Characters not combined as above ....Q

Q. Leaves falcate-secund or circinate ....R

Q. Stem-leaves not secund, imbricate, broadly ovate or rounded and with an obtuse apex; apex finely crenulate; annulus none; cilia three ....17. *Hypnum*

 R. Very robust; stem-leaves turgidly imbricate but strongly rugose and falcate-secund, lustrous, narrowly lance-acuminate from a broadly oblong base ....
....15. *Rhytidium*

 R. Not as above ....S

S. Plants distantly and irregularly pinnate; leaves squarrose or spreading and secund; alar cells little or not at all differentiated ....14. *Rhytidiadelphus*

S. Closely pinnate; leaves circinate secund; alar cells quadrate to rectangular and numerous but not inflated ....13. *Ctenidium*

 T. Aquatic or subaquatic on stones and rocks in running water; leaves mostly oblong-ovate, flaccid, obtuse, rounded, often somewhat secund ....11. *Hygrohypnum*

 T. Not as above V

U. Leaf-cells very narrowly prosenchymatous, alar cells mostly not differentiated;

leaves oblong to linear, short-pointed, ovate to linear-lanceolate, acute to long-
acuminate or piliferous, not decurrent ....20. *Isopterygium*
  u. Leaf-cells often wider, alar cells broader proportionally, hyaline and thin-walled;
     leaves broadly lanceolate to oval, more or less long-acuminate, distinctly decur-
     rent ....21. *Plagiothecium*
     v. Terrestrial or sub-aquatic; leaves mostly squarrose or recurved-squarrose, ovate to
        lanceolate, acuminate, decurrent; capsule curved ....12. *Campylium*
     v. Not as above ....w
  w. Capsule erect and symmetric or nearly so x
  w. Capsule more or less cernuous or horizontal, and unsymmetric ....BB
     x. Leaves closely imbricate when dry, concave ....22. *Pterygynandrum*
     x. Leaves erect-spreading or but slightly secund ....Y
     x. Leaves falcate-secund or circinate ....AA
  y. Alar cells quadrate not inflated ....z
  y. Some alar cells inflated and enlarged ....19. *Stereodon*
     z. Median leaf-cells about 2-4:1; leaves lanceolate to lance-subulate ....2. *Amblystegiella*
     z. Median leaf-cells about 6-9:1, leaves ovate to lance-oblong ....5. *Platygyrium*
  AA. Segments attached to a wide basal membrane; cilia rudimentary or none; branches
      short, erect or ascending ....4. *Pylaisia*
  AA. Not as above ....19. *Stereodon*
      BB. Stem-leaves decurrent, plicate, cordate-auriculate at base and abruptly long and
          slender acuminate; quadrate alar cells numerous, none inflated ......13. *Ctenidium*
      BB. Not as above CC
  cc. Robust to slender, simple or pinnate, mostly irregularly pinnate; leaves ovate- to
      cordate-lanceolate, shortly to slenderly acuminate, generally circinate secund in 2
      series; capsule erect to symmetric to cernuous and unsymmetric ....19. *Stereodon*
  cc. Not as above ....DD
      DD. Slender; lustrous; leaves ovate to lance-oblong, 0.7-1.0 mm long ....
          ....3. *Homomallium*
      DD. Robust plants ....EE
  EE. Branching plumosely complanate-pinnate; median leaf-cells about 10-15:1 ....18. *Ptilium*
  EE. Branching irregularly- to bi- or tri-pinnate; stiff; median leaf-cells not more than
      10:1 ....16. *Hylocomium*

1. AMBLYSTEGIUM Bryologia Europaea*

Autoicous: usually more or less slender, in thin and spreading mats:
stem creeping to ascending or even erect, irregularly to pinnately branched, the
branches mostly more or less erect; stem-leaves similar to branch-leaves, erect-
spreading to squarrose, mostly shortly decurrent, cordate- to ovate-lanceolate,
long-acuminate, rather concave, non-plicate, entire to serrate; costa thin, simple,
reaching to the middle of the leaf or beyond, rarely complete; cells parenchymatous; and rectangular to elongate-prosenchymatous and hexagonal, rarely linear, smooth, the alar quadrate to rectangular; the inner perichaetial
leaves erect, broadly lanceolate, mostly costate: seta long, thin, reddish to castaneous, flattened when dry; capsule, from an erect collum, curved to oblong
or cylindric, smooth when dry, constricted below the expanded mouth, annulate; peristome-teeth basally confluent, yellow to orange, lance-subulate, bordered, dorsally cross-striate, above pale and papillose, densely trabeculate

---

* Species with thinner-walled and longer leaf-cells; with costa single and well developed; and leaves spreading to erect-spreading are treated under the genus *Leptodictyum* in
Grout's *Moss Flora*.

below; inner peristome yellowish, basal membrane high; segments carinate, entire, or slightly gaping along the keel; cilia complete, nodose, rarely appendiculate; lid conic, obtuse to acute; spores small.

A genus of about 50 species occurring mainly in temperate regions, on various sub-strata; about 20 species in North America; at least five in our range.

KEY TO THE SPECIES

A. Leaves erect-spreading (widely spreading in *A. Juratzkanum*); median leaf-cells about 2-6:1 ....B

A. Leaves mostly loosely and widely to squarrosely spreading; median leaf-cells mostly 4-8:1, rarely 10-15:1 ....F

B. Cells in middle of leaf about 2-4:1 C

B. Cells in middle of leaf about 4-6(-8):1 ....E

C. Very slender; costa thin, ending near the middle of the leaf ....1. *A. serpens*

C. Less slender; costa stronger, almost reaching apex ....D

    D. Stem-leaves ovate-acuminate, acute, slenderly acuminate; entire or nearly so ....G

    D. Stem-leaves ovate-cordate, abruptly narrowed to a rather blunt acumination ....
....3. *A. orthocladon*

E. Costa reaching to about three-fourths the length of the leaf ....4. *A. Juratzkanum*

E. Costa reaching about to the middle of the leaf ....*Campylium radicale*, p. 251

    F. Slender: median leaf-cells prosenchymatous, hexagonal to linear, 4-8(-10):1 ....
....6. *A. Kochii*

    F. Rather robust: median leaf-cells elongate-prosenchymatous to linear, 5-10(-15):1;
leaves very slenderly acuminate ....7. *A. riparium*

G. Costa reaching apex or almost so; median leaf-cells averaging about 3:1 ....
....2. *A. varium*

G. Costa a little shorter; median leaf-cells averaging about 4:1 ....5. *A. trichopodium*

AMBLYSTEGIUM SERPENS [Linnaeus] Bryologia Europaea
(*Hypnum serpens* Linnaeus)

Plate XLI

Dull, more or less yellowish-green, very small and slender, forming thin, soft, densely interwoven mats: stems prostrate, radiculose, irregularly branching, the branches ascending or spreading or erect; leaves rather crowded, when moist variously spreading, when dry more or less appressed and imbricate; stem-leaves lance-ovate to ovate-acuminate, usually long-acuminate, the largest about 0.8-1.0 x 0.4-0.5 mm, often much smaller, narrowed and decurrent at base, denticulate or entire, somewhat concave, the margins plane; costa usually reaching about to the middle of the leaf or above, often quite faint and indistinct; branch-leaves similar but smaller and narrower, usually more lanceolate; median leaf-cells oblong- to rhomboid-hexagonal, about 2-4:1, the basal broader and more rectangular, the alar quadrate to transversely elongate but not forming a well-defined group, some of the apical considerably longer; perichaetial leaves lanceolate, thin, plicate, up to 1.5 mm long: seta rather slender, 1-3 cm long, reddish, dextrorse; capsule cylindric, the urn below 1.5 mm long, strongly curved, cernuous, constricted below the mouth when dry; lid convex-conic, rather obtusely apiculate; peristome rather large for the capsule, typically hypnaceous, teeth pale castaneous, strongly trabeculate, below dorsally cross-striolate, the dorsal lamellae projecting to form a more or less crenate hyaline margin; segments about as long as teeth, carinately split, rising from a basal membrane about two-fifths as high, the cilia 1 (sometimes 2 or 3), as long as segments, slender, nodose to appendiculate; annulus 2-3-seriate; spores papillose, when mature brownish or yellowish, medium-walled, about .014-.018 mm, mature in spring: autoicous.

On bases and roots of trees, decaying logs, soil, rocks, etc., in moist woods; cosmopolitan; in North America occurring from the Arctic regions to the Gulf of Mexico.

Fairly common in our region. Now known from Allegheny, Beaver, Cambria, Crawford, Erie, Fayette, McKean, and Washington counties. Specimen figured: Meadow Run Valley, four miles south of Ohio Pyle, Fayette Co., Sept. 1-3, 1906. O.E.J. & G.K.J.

2. AMBLYSTEGIUM VARIUM (Hedwig) Lindberg

(*Leskea varia* Hedwig; *Stereodon varius* Mitten; *Hypnum debile* Bridel)

Plate XLI

More or less loosely cespitose, green to light-green above, darker below, the stems and branches similar but larger than *A. serpens;* leaves rather close together, erect- to widely-spreading, the stem-leaves ovate-acuminate, the largest about 1-1.5 mm x 0.5-0.7 mm, usually long-acuminate, somewhat concave, the margins entire or very slightly denticulate, plane, the base very slightly decurrent; branch-leaves similar but smaller and more lance-ovate, usually about 0.6-0.8 x 0.3-0.4 mm; costa strong, more or less colored, usually yellowish or brownish, reaching usually into the acumen; medium leaf-cells rhomboid-hexagonal, usually about 2-4:1, somewhat incrassate, rather regularly arranged, the basal larger and more incrassate, sometimes yellowish, short-rectangular, the basal marginal distinctly quadrate; inner perichaetial leaves slenderly lance-triangular, about 1.6 mm long; seta reddish, slender, dextrorse, varying from 1-2 cm in length; capsule reddish-yellow, about 4-6:1, cylindric, arcuate, the urn about 1.3 mm long, rather smooth, even when dry and empty; annulus 2-3-seriate; peristome typically hypnaceous, similar to that of *A. serpens*, the teeth basally confluent, dorsally cross-striolate below, hyaline-papillose above, strongly and closely trabeculate; the segments about as long, slightly carinately cleft, the basal membrane about two-fifths as high, the cilia 1 or 2, nodose to shortly appendiculate; lid conic-acute; spores about .012-.018 mm, slightly papillose, medium-walled, mature in late spring: autoicous.

On bases of trees, soil, rocks, rotting wood, etc., in moist woods; Europe, and, in North America, from Canada to the Gulf of Mexico. Very common in our region. Quite variable.

Now known from Allegheny, Beaver, Butler, Crawford, Erie, Fayette, Lawrence, McKean, Mercer, Somerset, Washington, and Westmoreland counties. Specimen figured: Slope of Chestnut Ridge above Hillside, Westmoreland Co., September 16-17, 1909. O.E.J. and G.K.J.

2a. AMBLYSTEGIUM VARIUM var. OVATUM Grout

Slender, more or less julaceous; stem-leaves smaller, 1.2-1.5 mm long, concave, round-ovate, abruptly shortly acuminate; leaf-cells 2:1, the quadrate alar cells numerous and extending ½ the way up the margin of the body of the leaf. — St. Louis, Mo., and Bushkill, eastern Penna.

3. AMBLYSTEGIUM ORTHOCLADON (Beauvois) Jaeger

(*Hypnum orthocladon* Beauvois; *A. varium* var. *orthocladon* Husnot)

Plates XLI, LXVI

In deference to Dr. Grout's extensive work on this group of mosses I am following him in placing this species under the genus *Hygroamblystegium*, which *see*, page 233.

4. AMBLYSTEGIUM JURATZKANUM Schimper

Plate XLI

Light yellowish-green, small: stems prostrate, rooting, slender, the branches irregularly disposed, often ascending to erect, and rising to a height of 1-1.5 cm; leaves when dry usually squarrose-spreading and shriveled, ovate-lanceolate, gradually acuminate, about 1 to 1.4 mm long by 0.5 mm wide but quite variable, almost entire to minutely denticulate, plane, the base narrowed, decurrent and slightly concave; costa yellowish, fairly strong, reaching to somewhat above the middle; median leaf-cells prosenchymatous, linear-hexagonal, about 4-8:1, moderately incrassate, hyaline, the apical similar, the basal tending to sub-quadrate or shortly rectangular, the alar forming a rather distinct group, sub-pellucid, 2-3 times as wide as the median cells, decidedly incrassate, and always as long or longer than wide; perichaetial leaves 1.5-2 mm long, acuminate, thin, plicate: seta castaneous, smooth, about 2-2.5 cm high, when dry flattened, flexuous, dextrorse; capsule unsymmetric, cernuous, decidedly arcuate, often describing a half-circle, about 1.5-2.0 mm long, smooth, reddish when dry and empty much contracted below the wide mouth; peristome typically hypnoid; teeth reddish, pellucid, strongly articulate and trabeculate, confluent slightly at base, hyaline-margined, divisural zigzag, dorsal cross-striae evident; segment as long as the teeth, sub-entire, reddish-yellow, carinate, not at all or but slightly split, cilia 1-3, of equal length, or some shorter, nodose, united a little below the middle with the segments to form the basal membrane; spores rather clear, minutely papillose, medium to rather thin-walled, mature in spring, .010-.012 mm in diameter.

On moist soil and stones; Europe, Asia, and, in North America, from Canada to the Gulf of Mexico. Rather common in our region. This species is intermediate between *A. serpens* and *A. Kochii*, but from the former differs in the more squarrose-spreading leaves, longer alar cells, and stronger costa, while from the latter it differs mainly in smaller size and longer-pointed leaves.

ALLEGHENY CO.: Douthett, June 5, 1909, Fern Hollow, Pittsburgh, April 25, 1909, Power's Run, May 7, 1905, Nine-Mile Run, May 17, 1907. O.E.J.; Moon Township, May 18, 1902, and Laschell Hollow, June 15, 1902. J.A.S. CRAWFORD CO.: Linesville, in Pymatuning Swamp, June 11-12, 1907, and May 12, 1908. O.E.J. (figured). ERIE CO.: Presque Isle, June 9-11, 1905. O.E.J. FAYETTE CO.: Ohio Pyle, September 1-3, 1906. O.E.J.

5. Amblystegium trichopodium C. Hartman

(*Amblystegium riparium* var. *trichopodium* Bruch and Schimper;
Leptodictyum trichopodium Warnstorf)

Loosely matted; stems 2-4 cm long; branches often ascending; stem-leaves loosely to widely spreading, ovate to lance-ovate, abruptly long-acuminate, about 1.5 mm long, plane, sometimes sub-serrulate; costa strong almost reaching apex; median leaf-cells elongated hexagonal to rhomboidal, about 4:1, rectangular to oblong at base; branch leaves smaller and more lanceolate: seta about 3 cm long; capsule ovoid to somewhat cylindric, cernuous and curved; peristome complete; spores ripe in spring.

Frequent across northern North America, but not yet reported for our region.

6. Amblystegium Kochii Bryologia Europaea

(*Leptodictyum trichopodium* var. *Kochii* (Bruch and Schimper) Brotherus)

Plate XLII

Stem prostrate with short erect or ascending branches, the branches not usually reaching more than 5 or 6 mm long, the general color of the loose mats being pale green to deep green: stem- and branch-leaves very similar, spreading rather widely or almost squarrose, erect-spreading when dry, cordate-ovate, narrowed but scarcely decurrent at base, the apex long and slenderly acuminate, the leaves sometimes narrower and more lanceolate but always long-acuminate, usually 1-1.5 mm long, entire to faintly serrulate, plane-margined; costa medium strong, yellowish, usually about three-fourths as long as the leaf; median leaf-cells more or less chlorophyllose, thick-walled, rhomboid-hexagonal, the ends blunt or parenchymatous, about 4-6:1 or longer, the basal wider, the alar rectangular to rounded-quadrate, quite densely incrassate, hyaline or colored, but scarcely forming distinct alar patches; perichaetial leaves up to 2 mm long, lance-linear, long-acuminate: seta about 1.5-3 cm long, castaneous, flexuous, dextrorse; capsule hypnoid, similar to that of *A. serpens*, the urn oblong-cylindric, inclined to cernuous, arcuate, about 2-2.5 mm long, contracted below the mouth when dry; peristome-teeth brownish or yellowish, hyaline and papillose above, cross-striolate below, hyaline-margined, strongly and closely trabeculate, the dorsal lamellae and divisural plain; segments about as long as the teeth, slightly carinate, split, the basal membrane about two-fifths as high; cilia usually 3, pale, papillose, some of them as long as the teeth, nodose; annulus rather large, two-seriate; upper exothecial cells small, rounded-hexagonal or quadrate, below becoming elongate-hexagonal or oblong-rectangular; spores in late spring or early summer, somewhat incrassate, castaneous, minutely roughened, about .015-.018 mm.

On moist earth in swampy or marshy places; Europe, Asia, and probably throughout temperate North America. Fairly common in our region but in its smaller sizes difficult to satisfactorily distinguish from *A. Juratzkanum*. Grout (Moss Flora) treats this as a variety of *A. trichopodium*.

Now known from Allegheny, Centre, Crawford, Fayette, Lawrence, McKean, Washington, and Westmoreland counties. Specimen figured: On root of black walnut, tree, Hanlin. May 21, 1908. O.E.J.

7.   AMBLYSTEGIUM RIPARIUM [Linnaeus] Bryologia Europaea
(*Hypnum riparium* Linnaeus; *H. laxifolium* Bridel; *Stereodon riparium* Mitten; *Leptodictyum riparium* Warnstorf)

Plate XLII

Loosely cespitose, yellowish-green, the flat tufts soft: stems creeping, sub-pinnate, the branches usually 2 or 3 cm long, spreading to horizontal, the stems sometimes floating and reaching a length of 8 or 10 cm; stem-leaves 2-4 mm long, rather widely spreading or almost squarrose both wet and dry, often somewhat complanate, at tips of branches more or less secund, widely lance-ovate to oblong-lanceolate, gradually tapering to a fine, flat, non-channeled acumination, shortly decurrent, rounded at base, non-auriculate, somewhat excavate; branch-leaves similar but smaller, all leaves entire and plane-margined; costa fairly strong, reaching from one-half to three-fourths the length of the leaf; median leaf-cells linear-rhomboid, prosenchymatous, usually 8-12(-15):1, thin-walled, chlorophyllose, towards the base lax and sub-rectangular, at the angles often somewhat larger, rectangular, and sub-inflated, but not forming very distinct nor hyaline patches: seta usually 1-2 cm long; capsule rather turgid, oblong-cyilndric, arcuate, inclined; peristome hypnoid but relatively rather large; teeth dark orange, cilia 2 or 3, appendiculate, about as long as the entire or slightly parted segments, the basal membrane reaching to about two-fifths as high as the peristome; annulus 2-3-seriate; exothecial cells very much smaller at rim, below becoming irregular to rectangular, medium-walled; spores minutely roughened, .011-.014 mm, mature in spring: autoicous.

In swamps, springs, brooks, etc., on bases of trees, roots, stones, etc., sometimes floating; almost cosmopolitan; in North America ranging from the Arctic regions to Louisiana and Cuba.

Probably common in our region, in suitable habitats. Now known from Allegheny, Beaver, Butler, Centre, Crawford, Erie, Indiana, and Lawrence counties. Figured from specimen collected at Beaver Falls, Beaver Co., O.E.J., May 14, 1907.

The specimen from Centre Co., in swampy spot in gap of Bald Eagle Mt., near Matternville, O.E.J., Sept. 20, 1909, has slenderly acuminate leaves approaching *longifolium* (Schultz) Bryologia Europaea.

7a.   AMBLYSTEGIUM RIPARIUM var. FLACCIDUM (Lesquereux and James) Renauld and Cardot

Plate XLII

Smaller and of a much more slender habit; leaves more distant and tending to narrowly lanceolate and slenderly acuminate.

MCKEAN CO.: East Branch swamp, near Bradford, June 15, 1895. D.A.B. (figured).

2.   AMBLYSTEGIELLA Loeske

Autoicous or dioicous: very slender, stems filiform, mostly creeping, irregularly branched; leaves rather laxly disposed, erect-spreading or rarely weakly secund, lanceolate to lance-subulate from a sometimes somewhat decurrent base, slightly concave, non-plicate, margin plane and entire; costa none or very short and weak; median leaf-cells rhomboid-hexagonal or oblong-hexagonal, 2-4(-8):1, the basal rather lax, parenchymatous, the alar quadrate; inner perichaetial leaves erect, basally sheathing, lanceolate to lance-oblong, long-acuminate, ecostate, or with the costa ending in or above mid-leaf: seta 5-12 mm long, drying flattened, yellowish-red to castaneous; capsule mostly erect and symmetric, rarely secund and cernuous, obovate to oblong-cylindric, when dry and empty constricted below the wide mouth, smooth; annulus present; peristome-teeth narrowly lance-ovate, basally confluent, yellowish, bordered, dorsally cross-striate, above pale and papillose, densely trabeculate below; inner peristome pale or yellow, basal membrane high, segments entire or but slightly split, cilia rarely 1-3 and complete, mostly solitary and rudimentary or none, non-appendiculate; lid high-convex, obtuse to acute; spores small.

A genus of 9 species, confined to the Northern Hemisphere, occurring on trees and rocks; 5 species in North America; two species occurring in our range.

Key to the Species

A. Leaves not narrowed to insertion; inner perichaetial leaves irregularly toothed ....
....1. *A. minutissima*
A. Leaves narrowed to the insertion ....B
  B. On tree bases; leaves lanceolate to linear-lanceolate; inner perichaetial leaves entire
....3. *A. subtilis*
  B. On rocks; leaves ovate to lance-ovate; inner perichaetial leaves denticulate above
....2. *A. confervoides*

1. Amblystegiella minutissima (Sullivant and Lesquereux) Nichols

(*Hypnum minutissimum* Sullivant and Lesquereux;
Amblystegium minutissimum Jaeger)

Minute, pale green: stems prostrate, short, up to about 1 cm long, with radicles in fascicles, the branches occurring sub pinnately and spreading to erect; leaves loose, narrowly triangular-lanceolate, broadest and not narrowed at base, 0.3-0.4 mm long, more or less serrulate, ecostate or very faintly marked with striae; leaf-cells large, oblong, about 4-8:1, the marginal alar cells about 2:1; capsule minute, about 0.5 mm long, ovoid, symmetric or slightly curved, constricted below the mouth and turbinate when dry and empty, thin-walled, yellowish; seta slender, 4 or 5 mm long; teeth yellowish, hyaline-bordered; cilia as long as segments and 1 or 2 in number; annulus 2-seriate, persistent; lid conic, apiculate-rostrate, about one-half to nearly as long as urn; spores ripe in summer.

On rocks and stones in shaded ravines, said to prefer limestone, from New Jersey and Pennsylvania westward to Illinois, Ontario, the Rocky Mountains and British Columbia. Rare in our region.

Rare in our region. Huntingdon Co.: Alexandria. T. C. Porter. (Porter's Catalogue).

2. AMBLYSTEGIELLA CONFERVOIDES (Bridel) Loeske

(Hypnum confervoides Bridel; *Hypnum conferva* Schwaegrichen;
A. conferva (Schwaegrichen) Jennings)

Dark green, minute; stems irregularly branching, about 0.5-1.0 cm long; leaves very small, about 0.1-0.3 mm. long, rather distant, more or less appressed both wet and dry, entire or almost so, ovate, acuminate, ecostate; leaf-cells irregularly quadrate-rhomboid to oblong-hexagonal, ranging from 1-3:1, some of them wider transversely, the apical shorter than the median, usually not more than twice as long as wide, the alar numerous and quadrate to transversely elongate, extending up to the edge of the leaf: capsule cernuous, reddish-brown, more or less curved, oblong, minute; peristome perfect with double cilia or sometimes 3; spores mature in summer to autumn: autoicous.

Mainly on shaded ledges of limestone; Europe, Asia, and, in North America from New Brunswick to southeastern Pennsylvania and westward to the Rocky Mountains.

Rare in our region. HUNTINGDON Co.: On limestone rocks, one mile south of Pennsylvania Furnace, July 13, 1909. O.E.J.

3. AMBLYSTEGIELLA SUBTILIS (Hedwig) Loeske

(Leskea subtilis Hedwig; *Amblystegium subtile* Bryologia Europaea)

Small, slender mosses in dark green, thin mats; stems about 2-3 cm long, with numerous but irregular branches; leaves lanceolate to lance-linear, narrowed at the base, and with long and slender acumination, usually not much over 0.5 mm long, non-decurrent, entire; costa faint or none; median cells oblong-hexagonal, 2-3:1, the alar quadrate and often wider than long: inner perichaetial leaves entire; seta about 1 mm long; capsule slightly longer, oblong-cylindric, usually erect; annulate; lid convex to conic; cilia rudimentary or none; spores ripe in late summer or early fall.

Bases of hardwood trees in moist, cool woods. Southeastern Canada to Minnesota and south to Illinois, Ohio, Pennsylvania, and New Jersey. Not yet reported from our region.

3. HOMOMALLIUM (Schimper) Loeske

Autoicous: slender, rarely somewhat robust, light to brownish or yellowish-green, more or less shining; stems creeping, divided and irregularly pinnately branched, with the branches short, erect, and more or less curved; leaves erect-spreading or secund above, the lower mostly straight, the upper often curved, concave, non-plicate, lance-ovate to ovate, the base narrowed and but little decurrent, apex elongate-subulate, the margins plane, entire or serrate at apex; costa none or short, thin, and double, or longer and sometimes forked; leaf-cells narrowly prosenchymatous, smooth or with projecting ends, towards the base shorter and a little wider, the alar numerous, small, quadrate, green, passing rapidly into the narrower cells above; inner perichaetial leaves almost sheathing, abruptly acuminate: seta 1-2 cm long, thin, compressed, reddish; capsule inclined to horizontal, oblong, when dry and empty strongly curved and narrowly constricted below the mouth; annulus revoluble; peristome-teeth yellow, basally confluent, dorsally cross-striate, bordered, pale and papillose above, trabeculae numerous and closed below, above strongly projecting; inner peristome yellowish, papillose, and with a high basal membrane, segments keeled, split, cilia 2-3, papillose, nodose; spores small; lid shortly and acutely rostrate.

A genus of about 10 species, occurring on rocks and tree-trunks; 2 species in North America; 1 species in our region.

1. HOMOMALLIUM ADNATUM (Hedwig) Brotherus

(*Hypnum adnatum* Hedwig; *Amblystegiella adnata* Nichols; *Stereodon adnatum* Mitten)

Plate XLIII

Widely cespitose in thin, closely adherent mats, pale green, or yellowish-green, darker below: stems irregularly branching, creeping, the branches close, short; leaves close, erect-spreading, lanceolate to ovate or oblong, shortly and widely acuminate to slenderly acuminate, entire or nearly so, concave, ecostate or slightly bistriate at base, the margins often more or less recurved below, the leaves 0.6-1.0 mm long; median leaf-cells somewhat pellucid, sub-rhomboidal, prosenchymatous, about 4-8:1, the apical often shorter, the alar numerous, smaller, more incrassate and opaque, quadrate and extending along the margin to one-fourth or one-third the length of the leaf; outer perichaetial broadly ovate, narrowly gradually acuminate, spreading, the inner oblong, erect, more abruptly acuminate, dentate, and costate nearly to the middle: seta erect, 1.5-2 cm long, dextrorse; capsule arcuate, oblong, narrowed to a distinct neck, cernuous, reddish or yellowish, when dry constricted below the mouth but not wrinkled; lid paler, acutely conic; annulus present; exothecial cells rounded-hexagonal near the rim, rectangular below; peristome perfect, the teeth prominently and numerously trabeculate, hyaline and papillose apically, hyaline-margined and dorsally cross-striolate below, the segments entire and very slightly split, about as long as the teeth, the cilia 1-2, about as long, hyaline and slightly papillose, the basal membrane about two-fifths as high; spores rather incrassate, pale-castaneous, papillose, .009-.012 mm, mature in summer.

On rocks and on bases of trees in woods; Asia and from lower Canada to West Virginia and Texas.

Fairly common in our region. Now known from Allegheny, Butler, Fayette, Huntingdon, McKean, Washington, and Westmoreland counties. Specimen figured: Limestone rocks, Pennsylvania Furnace, Huntingdon Co., July 13, 1909. O.E.J.

4. PYLAISIA Bryologia Europaea

(*Pylaisiella* Kindberg)

Autoicous; slender to rather robust, lustrous, in flat, thin tufts: stem creeping, long, unsymmetrically pinnate; branches short, ascending to erect, often curved, in cross section appearing appressed: leaves homogeneous, more or less imbricate, when moist erect-spreading, often secund, somewhat decurrent, concave, non-plicate, ovate to lance-oval, more or less long-acuminate, mostly plane and entire; costa double, very short or none; leaf-cells linear-rhombic, smooth, alar numerous, quadrate: seta 1-2 cm long, castaneous, drying twisted, smooth; capsule erect, symmetric, rarely somewhat curved, oval to oblong-cylindric, collum short; annulus small-celled or none; peristome deeply inserted; teeth lance-subulate, at the apex often irregular and sometimes remaining in the lid or attached to the segments, yellowish, hyaline-bordered, striate, densely articulate and trabeculate; basal membrane low, segments narrowly lance-subulate, as long as the teeth or shorter, sometimes two-cleft, the divisions remaining attached to the teeth; cilia mostly rudimentary; spores small to large; lid conic to rostrate.

About 15 species, mainly on trees, in temperate regions; about 7 or 8 species in North America, probably four species in our region.

KEY TO THE SPECIES

A. Segments completely adherent to the teeth ....1. *P. intricata*
A. Segments free, at least in the upper third ....B
  B. Annulus 2-3-seriate, large-celled; spores about .017-.024 mm ....2. *P. Selwynii*
  B. Annulus uni-seriate;; spores .010-.016 mm C
C. Operculum rostrate; cilia none; spores .009-.012 mm ....3. *subdenticulata*
C. Operculum merely conic; cilia single, short or rudimentary; spores .012-.016 mm
  ....4. *P. polyantha*

1. PYLAISIA INTRICATA (Hedwig) Renauld and Cardot

(*P. velutina* Bryologia Europaea; *Pylaisiella velutina* Kindberg;
Pterygynandrum intricatum Hedwig)

Plate XXXVII

Similar in appearance to *P. Selwynii* with which it is often confused and with which it grows, light-green, glossy, in closely entangled mats: branches ascending or erect, when dry usually more or less hooked at the end; leaves lanceolate, long-acuminate, usually falcate-secund, about 0.8-1.2 mm long, about 0.2-0.3 mm wide; leaf-cells similar to those of *P. Selwynii* but with a smaller group of incrassate, quadrate, obscure alar cells; median leaf-cells about 6-10:1, sub-vermicular, about .004-.005 mm wide; costa none: seta straight, smooth, about 4-5 mm long; capsule ovoid-cylindric, about 2 mm long, erect, symmetric, castaneous; lid long-conic, about 0.5 mm long; peristome-teeth closely trabeculate, dorsally distinctly lamellate and with divisural, finely cross-striate; segments very delicate, split and adherent to the teeth throughout their whole length, basal membrane indistinct or none; spores densely incrassate, castaneous-pellucid, finely papillose, in our specimens about .018-.030 mm in diameter, mature in fall.

On bases of trees or on stumps or logs, usually in mountainous or hilly regions; Newfoundland to Ontario and Minnesota, south to North Carolina.

Rare in our region. BUTLER Co.: On log in woods, Millingar School, Oakland Twp., Dec. 2, 1934. Sidney K. Eastwood. McKEAN Co.: Bennett Brook, October 23, 1897, and Limestone Creek, near Bradford, October to December, 1896 (figured). The latter mixed with Grout's No. 134. North American Musci Pleurocarpi. WASHINGTON Co.: On bark of fallen tree, near Washington, Aug. 4, 1892. A. Linn and J. S. Simonton.

2. PYLAISIA SELWYNII Kindberg

(*P. intricata* Bryologia Europaea; *Pylaisiella intricata* Grout;
Pylaisia Schimperi Cardot)

Plate XXXVII

In thin, densely interwoven mats, dark-green, glossy; rather closely and regularly pinnate: branches more or less ascending to erect, usually about 3-4 mm long, when dry decidedly curved or hooked at the end; leaves close, imbricate at the base, prominently falcate-secund, especially so when dry, lance-ovate, about 0.7-1.0 mm long by about one-third as wide, rather long-acuminate, sub-serrate to entire, rounded at the base, concave, the margin plane and non-bordered; costa short and double, or none; median leaf-cells about 6-10:1, usually .003-.004 mm wide, linear-prosenchymatous, the apical shorter and wider, the alar distinct, numerous, quadrate to transversely rectangular, yellowish-incrassate, forming a triangular group extending up along the leaf-margin to one-third the length of the leaf; perichaetial leaves similar but longer, up to 2.5 mm, and more slenderly acuminate: seta about 1.5 cm long, lustrous, red-castaneous, dextrorse above; capsule ovoid-oblong castaneous, about 2 mm long, about 2.5:1, erect, symmetric, small-mouthed; peristome-teeth narrowly triangular lanceolate, closely trabeculate, the dorsal lamellae narrow, numerous, finely cross-striate, pale yellow, bordered up to two-thirds or three-fourths by the linear, adherent, hyaline and somewhat papillose segments, which are usually united at the tip but widely split below; cilia none; basal membrane very narrow or none; annulus 2-3-seriate, narrow; exothecial cells yellowish, somewhat incrassate, irregularly round-hexagonal to oblong-rhomboidal, below the annulus several series being much smaller and transversely rhomboid-oblong; lid about 0.5 mm high, conic-obtuse, often somewhat oblique; spores densely chlorophyllose, densely incrassate, castaneous-pellucid, papillose, about .018-.025 mm, mature in September or October.

On stones and bark of trees; Siberia, and from Canada to Florida.

Common in our region. Known from Allegheny, Butler, Clearfield, Elk, Erie, Fayette, Indiana, Lawrence, McKean, Washington, and Westmoreland counties. Specimen figured: Ohio Pyle, Fayette Co., Sept. 1-3, 1906. O.E.J. and G.K.J.

3. PYLAISIA SUBDENTICULA Bryologia Europaea

(*Pylaisia denticulata* Sullivant)

Intricately cespitose, glossy, yellow-green; stems creeping with erect or ascending branches about 5-6 mm long; branch-leaves subfalcate, secund, erect-spreading to imbricate when dry, lance-ovate, entire below, sub-denticulate above, acuminate, concave, ecostate or faintly costate at base; leaf-cells linear-rhomboidal, 6-8:1, quadrate alar cells numerous, incrassate, extending up the margin: seta short, erect; capsule oblong, about 2.5-3.5 mm long, about 3-4:1, erect; lid shortly rostrate; annulus narrow; peristome-teeth lance-linear, segments free, basal membrane distinct, cilia none; spores about .008-.012 mm in diameter, mature in autumn.

On bases of trees and on rocks, in woods, ranging irregularly from New

York and New Jersey to Illinois and Minnesota, south to North Carolina and New Mexico. Not yet found in our region.

4. PYLAISIA POLYANTHA [Schreber] Bryologia Europaea
(*Leskea polyantha* Hedwig)

Intricately matted, yellowish-green: stems prostrate, rooting on bark, not stoloniform, up to 6 or 8 cm long, with numerous erect or ascending, curved branches about 0.5-1 cm long; branch-leaves erect and secund or pointing upwards, when dry loosely imbricate, small, ovate-lanceolate, rapidly narrowed into a tapering acumination of about same length as the body of the leaf, entire, slightly concave, non-plicate, plane-margined, ecostate or with a very short and faint double or single nerve; median leaf-cells thin-walled, about 6-10:1, the alar few, quadrate, pellucid, rather broad and distinct; stem-leaves somewhat broader and more abruptly acuminate: seta about 1.5 cm high; capsule oblong-cylindric, about 3.5-4:1, about 2.5 mm long; lid conic, acute, short; annulus single, narrow; peristome-teeth lance-linear, closely articulate, somewhat granular above, segments about as long as teeth, lance-linear, granulose, somewhat split when old; cilia single, usually rudimentary; spores mature in fall or winter, about .012-.016 mm.

On tree trunks and in hedges, etc.; Europe, Asia, and in lower Canada and the northern United States.

Apparently rare in our region. McKEAN CO.: Bradford. D. A. Burnett. (Porter's Catalogue).

5. PLATYGYRIUM Bryologia Europaea

Dioicous, medium size, flatly cespitose, green to golden or brownish-green, lustrous: stem elongate, creeping, ventrally densely radiculose, thickly-leaved and unsymmetrically pinnate; branches julaceous, mostly short, simple; leaves imbricate when dry, moist spreading, decurrent, non-plicate, ovate to oblong-lanceolate, sharply acute, smooth, margins revolute; costa short and double or none; apical cells rhomboid, linear below, alar quite large, numerous, quadrate; seta 8-15 mm, sometimes 20 mm, smooth, castaneous; capsule erect, symmetric or slightly arcuate, narrowly oblong to almost cylindric; annulus broad, pluriseriate, revoluble entire or sometimes in pieces; peristome inserted on the mouth, double; teeth lance-linear, yellow, broadly bordered, non-striate, trabeculae thickened; basal membrane not prominent, segments narrowly linear, carinately cleft, cilia none; spores .012-.018 mm, lid conic, shortly and obliquely rostrate. A widely distributed genus of about 4 species; one species in North America.

1. PLATYGYRIUM REPENS [Bridel] Bryologia Europaea
(*Pterogonium repens* Schwaegrichen; *Anomodon repens* Fuernrohr; *Cylindrothecium repens* DeNotaris; *Entodon repens* Grout)

Plate XXXVII

Densely but thinly matted, bright to dark green, pinnately branching: leaves ecostate, crowded, erect-spreading when moist, imbricate when dry, concave, subscarious, lustrous, ovate to long-lanceolate, about 0.7-0.9 mm long, acuminate, the margin entire and recurved below; leaf-cells all medium-walled, at apex rhomboidal, the median linear-rhomboidal prosenchymatous, about 6-9:1, the alar distinct, quadrate and relatively large, extending up the margin; inner perichaetial leaves about twice as long as the branch-leaves, ecostate, more acuminate: seta erect, 10-15 mm long, smooth, lustrous, dark-castaneous, sinistrorse; urn of capsule about 1:0-2.5 mm long, erect, symmetric, oblong-cylindric, castaneous, not narrowed below the mouth when dry; operculum about two-fifths the length of the urn, slenderly and obliquely but bluntly rostrate; annulus persistent, large, 2-3-seriate, and appearing like modified upper exothecial cells; peristome-teeth rather deeply inserted, linear-lanceolate, light yellowish-brown, strongly about 15-18 trabeculate, widely hyaline-bordered, papillose below in irregular and often radiating lines, but not cross-striate below as in most hypnaceous peristomes, lamellae and divisural line rather indistinct; segments about two-thirds as long as teeth, linear, narrow, arising from a very low basal membrane, more or less carinately cleft; cilia none; exothecial cells quadrate to irregular or oblong-hexagonal, yellowish; spores about .014-.018 mm, yellowish, minutely roughened, medium-walled, mature in autumn; gemmae often abundant in the axils of the upper leaves.

On bark at base of trees, on decaying logs, stumps, and in woods; widely distributed in the Northern Hemisphere; in North America from New Brunswick to the Pacific and south to the Gulf of Mexico.

Very common in our region at lower altitudes, rarely found in the mountains or plateau uplands. Known from the following counties: Allegheny (more than 50 collections), Armstrong, Beaver, Butler, Crawford, Erie, Fayette, Greene, Somerset, Washington, and Westmoreland. Specimens figured: On rotten log, oak woods, Keown, Allegheny Co., Nov. 14, 1909. O.E.J.

6. Hygroamblystegium Loeske

Autoicous or dioicous: aquatic or sub-aquatic; slender to quite robust, mostly stiffly cespitose, dark-green to blackish-green, dull: stem more or less elongate, mostly floating, rarely more or less erect, mostly rather regularly pinnate, with forward-directed, rarely erect, mostly simple branches; leaves close, spreading to secund, concave, non-plicate, not at all or but slightly decurrent, rarely long-decurrent, mostly ovate to oblong-lanceolate, long-acuminate, margins plane, entire or remotely indistinctly denticulate; costa strong, short or percurrent, sometimes thickly excurrent; cells green, prosenchymatous, hexagonal, 2-4(-6):1, alar cells more or less plainly differentiated; perichaetial leaves elongate-lanceolate, costa complete or sub-percurrent: seta elongate, castaneous; capsule inclined to horizontal, early symmetric or somewhat dorsally gibbous, oblong-cylindric, later more or less arcuate, when dry and empty constricted below the mouth; peristome-teeth dark-yellow to orange, more or less basally confluent, lance-subulate, broadly bordered, dorsally cross-striate, apically pale and papillose, the margin step-like, the trabeculae strongly projecting; inner peristome yellow, finely papillose, with high basal membrane, segments mostly carinately split, cilia complete, nodose to short-appendiculate; lid high-convex and apiculate or acute; spores small.

A genus of about 10 species, in very damp or frequently submerged places or in water, mostly in temperate or cooler regions; 5 species occur in North America; at least 5 species in our region.

KEY TO THE SPECIES

A. Leaves non-decurrent, entire or indistinctly and remotely serrate ....B
A. Leaves mostly decurrent, mostly with small but distinct teeth C
   B. Stem-leaves lance-oblong to oblong-ovate with rather obtuse point ....1. *H. fluviatile*
   B. Stem-leaves triangular lanceolate to triangular ovate, sub-obtuse to acuminate ....D
  C. Costa sub-percurrent to percurrent; leaves with decurrent auricles of inflated cells
       ....4. *H. filicinum*
  C. Costa excurrent; leaves non-decurrent, non-auriculate, not basally excavate ....
       ....5. *H. noterophilum*
   D. Stem-leaves more or less acuminate ....2. *H. irriguum* (= *tenax*)
   D. Stem-leaves sub-obtuse to acute ....3. *H. orthocladon*

1. HYGROAMBLYSTEGIUM FLUVIATILE [Swartz] Loeske

(*Amblystegium fluviatile* Bryologia Europaea; *Hypnum fluviatile* Swartz)

Plate XLIII

Robust, aquatic, floating in flat and elongated tufts, soft, olive- to dark-green, devoid of leaves below: stems with few branchlets, long, the branchlets more or less parallel and scarcely pinnate; leaves oblong-lanceolate to oblong-ovate, not markedly narrowed below, rather remote, erect-spreading, especially when dry, non-decurrent, gradually tapering to a short, blunt point, entire or very faintly serrulate, very concave, the margins more or less recurved at base; costa thick and strong, yellowish, ending in the apex; median leaf-cells loose, hexagonal-rhomboid, about 3-6:1, the basal cells rectangular, pellucid, sometimes somewhat opaque, strongly incrassate, not forming auricles, sometimes quite orange; perichaetial leaves erect, strongly costate: seta about 1.5 cm long, castaneous, dextrorse; capsules about 2.5 mm long, oblong-cylindric, sub-erect, sub-arcuate, rather thick-walled, yellowish-brown, when dry and empty strongly arcuate and constricted below the mouth; below the 2-3-seriate annulus the exothecial cells small and rounded-quadrate; peristome slightly inserted, teeth strongly confluent at base, dorsally cross-striolate, brownish below, apically hyaline and papillose; segments about as long as teeth, carinately split, the three nodose cilia about as long, the basal membrane about two-fifths to one-half as high as teeth; spores medium-walled, minutely papillose, brownish, about .016-.019 mm, mature in early summer.

On earth and on rocks and stones in running water, usually in non-calcareous districts; Europe, and, in North America, from Newfoundland to New Jersey and westward to the Mississippi. Most of our specimens seem to belong to forma *brevifolium* Boulay, with concave, oblong-ovate leaves, sub-obtuse at apex, and with colored opaque basal cells.

Now known from Allegheny, Beaver, Butler, Cameron, Fayette, McKean, and Westmoreland counties, all in the non-glaciated area. Specimen figured: Shades Ravine, Blackburn, Allegheny Co., June 13, 1908. O.E.J.

2. HYGROAMBLYSTEGIUM IRRIGUUM (Wilson) Loeske

(*Hypnum irriguum* Wilson; *Amblystegium irriguum* Bryologia Europaea; *Hypnum tenax* Hedwig—fid. Cardot; *Hygroamblystegium tenax* Jennings)

Plate XLIII

Dark green, aquatic, cespitose: stems rigid, irregularly pinnate, long, denuded at the base, usually with a few paraphyllia at the nodes; stem-leaves ovate to widely triangular lanceolate to triangular—about 1-1.5 mm long, gradually acuminate, acute or sub-acute, narrowed at the base, sub-decurrent, spreading and sub-secund, or on the longer branches erect-spreading, entire to sub-serrulate, plane-margined; branch-leaves narrower and tending to lance-ovate; costa thick and wide, yellowish-brown, narrowing and becoming indistinct in the acumen but often reaching the apex; median-leaf-cells hexagonal-rhomboid, about 3-6:1, incrassate, often sub-opaque, smaller in the apex, at the base one or two rows usually somewhat enlarged, rectangular, incrassate, often colored, a few rows above these shorter, quadrate, but no distinct auricles being formed: seta about 1.5-2.5 cm long, smooth, castaneous, dextrorse; capsule oblong-cylindric, the urn 2-2.5 mm long, sub-cernuous and sub-arcuate before ripening to strongly arcuate when dry, smooth, constricted below the mouth, brownish; annulus 3-seriate; lid convex-conic, apiculate; peristome-teeth basally confluent, orange-pellucid and dorsally cross-striolate below, bordered, strongly trabeculate; the segments slightly shorter than the teeth, carinately split but scarcely gaping, yellowish-hyaline, the 3 cilia nodose, hyaline-papillose, about as long as the segments, the basal membrane about two-fifths as high; exothecial cells small and rounded, hexagonal to transversely rounded at rim but soon becoming rather elongate oblong-hexagonal or rectangular below; spores mature in late spring or early summer, brownish, medium-walled, papillose, .016-.019 mm.

On stones and earth in very wet situations or in water, usually in non-calcareous districts; Europe, Asia, northern Africa, and, in North America, from Ontario to California, south to Georgia and Arkansas.

Now known from Allegheny, Bedford, Butler, Cambria (Porter), Crawford, Erie, Fayette, Huntingdon (Porter), Washington, and Westmoreland counties, and apparently avoiding the upland plateau region. Specimen figured: Hillside, Westmoreland Co., May 23, 1908. O.E.J.

2a. HYGROAMBLYSTEGIUM IRRIGUUM var. SPINIFOLIUM (Schimper) Grout

(*H. fallax* var. *spinifolium* Warnstorf; *Amblystegium irriguum* var. *spinifolium* Schimper; *A. fallax* var. *spinifolium* Limpricht)

This variety differs from the species in being more robust, with longer stems, longer and narrower leaves, the leaves reaching nearly 2 mm in length and with a strongly excurrent and stout costa: Grout states the upper leaf-cells to be about 6-8:1, and the basal cells more lax.

Usually in and around calcareous springs and probably distributed mainly as is the species. Ohio, Pennsylvania, New Jersey, and Ontario.

BUTLER Co.: On wet cliffs, Winfield Junction. C.M.B. June 8, 1940. CRAWFORD Co.: Pymatuning Swamp, Linesville, May 12, 1908. O.E.J.

3. HYGROAMBLYSTEGIUM ORTHOCLADON (P.B.) Grout

(*Hypnum orthocladon* P. Beauvois; *Amblystegium orthocladon* (P.B.) Jaeger)

Plates XLI, LXVI

This plant is regarded by Grout after extensive study as belonging to Hygroamblystegium, intermediate between *H. irriguum* and the wider and more obtuse-leaved variety brevifolium of *H. fluviatile*. In deference to Dr. Grout's extensive studies in this group I am here placing it under *Hygroamblystegium*.

Rather dark green, sometimes olive-green, rather stiff when dry, commonly tufted; stems irregularly branched, the branches of plants in the denser tufts often erect and sometimes 2 cm tall, but usually less than 1.5 cm long; leaves up to 1 mm long, broadly cordate-ovate, usually rapidly and uniformly narrowed to an acute or sub-obtuse apex, rounded to a narrower base, slightly concave, slightly decurrent, widely spreading both wet and dry, the margins plane and entire; branch-leaves smaller, narrower, and more acute; costa strong, wide at base, yellowish, usually extending up into the apex; leaf-cells sub-incrassate, the median oblong-rhomboidal to elongate-hexagonal, with rounded ends, .010-.020 mm long, about 2-4(-6):1, the apical similar, the median basal oblong-rectangular, the cells of the angles somewhat wider, varying to short-rectangular or quadrate, incrassate, often opaque or colored: seta usually about 1-1.5 cm long but occasionally reaching 3-4 cm; castaneous; capsule castaneous, oblong-cylindric, arcuate, cernuous, constricted below the rim when dry, narrowed at base to a distinct neck, the urn about 1.6-1.9 (to 3) mm long; peristome typically hypnoid; basal membrane high, cilia about equalling segments; operculum short-conic; spores mature in spring, somewhat incrassate, smoothish, about .010-.018 mm.

On stones, rotten wood, bases of trees, etc., along or in brooks or in moist situations in woods; Europe, and probably widely ranging through more elevated parts of eastern United States. Grout (*Moss Flora*) treats it as a subspecies of *Hygroamblystegium irriguum*. The specimen figured from Washington County is unusually large.

Now known from the following counties: Allegheny, Butler, Crawford, Fayette, Greene, McKean, Warren, Washington, and Westmoreland. Specimens figured: Cheat Haven, Fayette Co., Sept. 26, 1910. O.E.J. & G.K.J. (Plate XLI).; On stones in Calcar Spring, Snake woods, near Washington, Washington Co., Dec. 12, 1897, A. Linn and J. S. Simonton (Plate LXVI).

4. HYGROAMBLYSTEGIUM FILICINUM [Linnaeus] Loeske*

(*Amblystegium filicinum* DeNotaris; *Stereodon filicinus* Mitten; *Hypnum compressum* Bridel; *Cratoneuron filicinum* Roth)

Variable, forming loose to dense tufts, rather rigid, bright or golden yellow: stems usually densely brownish tomentose, especially on the prostrate or procumbent forms, rather regularly pinnately branched, with usually numerous oval to lanceolate, laciniate paraphyllia; branches slender, short, stiff, non-radiculose, with few or no paraphyllia, usually hooked at the apex; stem-leaves

---

* Grout (*Moss Flora*) treats this as a species of *Cratoneuron*.

cordate-triangular, finely and gradually acuminate, varying from erect-spreading to sub-secund; branch-leaves rather narrower, more usually strongly falcate-secund; all leaves rigid, altered but little in drying, not plicate, markedly decurrent, the base cordate and narrowed, the margin plane or recurved at the base and closely and finely serrulate from base to apex; costa strong, usually ending in the apex; median leaf-cells elliptic-hexagonal to elongate rectangular, mostly about 3-6:1, usually obtuse at the ends, the alar abruptly inflated, hyaline or colored, forming well-defined auricles of sub-rectangular cells, these cells reaching to the base of the costa or nearly so; perichaetial leaves erect, strongly costate but scarcely plicate, denticulate: seta long, reddish, flexuous, up to 3-5 cm long, flattened and twisted; capsule reddish, sub-cylindric, rather turgid, arcuate, when dry and empty constricted below the mouth and more or less sulcate; lid conic, acute, or apiculate; peristome hypnoid, the segments more or less cleft carinately, cilia 2 or 3, nearly as long as the segments and teeth; annulus simple, narrow; spores mature in spring.

On earth, stones, etc., in or near springs, streams, or swamps, principally in calcareous districts; Europe, Asia, northern Africa, and, in North America, from the Arctic regions south to the southern part of the United States.

Rare in our region. HUNTINGDON CO.: Spruce Creek. T. C. Porter. (Porter's Catalogue).

5. HYGROAMBLYSTEGIUM NOTEROPHILUM (Sullivant) Warnstorf

(Hypnum noterophilum Sullivant; *Amblystegium noterophilum* Holzinger;
Hypnum irriguum spinifolium Lesquereux and James)

Larger than fluviatile, dull dark green in older parts, rather stiff, irregularly branching; stem with strong central strand and thick-walled cortical cells; leaves entire, lance-oblong when aquatic, when emersed ovate and up to 2.5 mm long; basal and costal part of leaf bi-stratose; capsule highly stomatiferous; spores mature in early summer.

In springs and running water in calcareous regions. Ontario and northern United States, the type locality in Franklin County, Pennsylvania.

7. SCIAROMIUM Mitten

Mostly dioicous: more or less robust, stiff, cespitose, dull, dark green to blackish: stem long, floating, sparsely radiculose, with irregularly and sometimes rather fasciculately arranged branches mostly directed forwards and mostly long and simple; leaves close, spreading to secund, concave-carinate, non-plicate, not at all or but slightly decurrent, ovate to lance-oblong, sub-acute to acuminate, plane-margined, mostly entire, broadly and thickly bordered; costa strong, ending apically in the border or excurrent; median leaf-cells chlorophyllose, strongly incrassate, rather opaque, prosenchymatous-hexagonal, 2-4(-6):1, the basal cells more lax, the alar somewhat differentiated, the marginal slender, strongly incrassate, hyaline, in several layers; costa ending in the border at the apex: seta 1-3 cm long, castaneous below, more yellowish above; capsue inclined, unsymmetric, oblong, when dry somewhat constricted below the mouth, annulate; peristome-teeth yellow, bordered, cross-striate, apically pale and papillose, the margin step-like, trabeculae numerous; inner peristome yellowish, with high basal membrane, segments keeled, narrowly carinately split, cilia 1-3, shorter than the segments and nodose; lid high-convex, apiculate; spores small.

A genus mainly confined to South America and embracing about 20 species; only 1 species occurs in North America and this occurs rarely in our region.

1. SCIAROMIUM LESCURII (Sullivant) Brotherus
(*Hypnum Lescurii* Sullivant; *Amblystegium Lescurii* Jaeger)

Plate XLIII

Loosely cespitose, dull, dark green to blackish-green: stems closely and unequally branched, the branches as described for the genus, but often with short branchlets, 1-1.5 cm long, more or less erect, and pinnately disposed; leaves of the stem thick, rather opaque, erect-spreading, entire below to subserrulate all around, broadly ovate-cordate to oblong-ovate, 1-1.3 mm long, abruptly short-acuminate, the branch-leaves similar but more lance-ovate; median leaf-cells prosenchymatous, hexagonal to oblong, about 1-3:1, not much differentiated except for the yellowish or castaneous border which is composed of 4 or 5 rows of linear, prosenchymatous, flexuous, highly incrassate cells, the border cells in the alar region becoming short and rectangular or obliquely quadrilateral; costa very strong, castaneous or yellowish, merging at apex into the border: seta 1-3 cm long, reddish; capsule reddish, short-necked, the urn about 2.5 mm long, oblong, cernuous, somewhat arcuate; the teeth confluent at base, hyaline-papillose above, yellowish below, dorsally lamellate and cross-striate, numerously trabeculate, hyaline-margined; segments yellowish, carinately split and about as long as the teeth, the basal membrane about two-fifths as high; cilia 3 (or 4), pale, papillose, nearly as long as segments; annulus compound; spores mature in late spring or early summer, castaneous, medium-walled, smoothish, about .012-.015 mm; lid conic-apiculate.

On stones and rocks in streams, usually in mountainous or hilly regions; occurring from New England to Ontario, Alabama and Georgia.

Rare in our region. FAYETTE Co.: Ohio Pyle, May 30-31, 1908. O.E.J. (figured).

8. DREPANOCLADUS (C. Mueller) Roth

Dioicous, rarely autoicous: mostly robust, often densely cespitose, green to yellowish or brownish, lustrous: stem procumbent to erect, often floating, variously pinnate, the ends of the shoots usually circinate: leaves usually more or less circinate-secund, rarely erect to squarrose, more or less concave, from a mostly narrowed and decurrent base ovate- to triangular- or cordate-lanceolate, acute to prolonged acuminate, entire or serrulate; costa mostly simple and thin, ending usually above the middle of the leaf, sometimes strong and percurrent or even excurrent; leaf-cells mostly long-linear, smooth, in the more or less excavate angles parenchymatous, thin-walled, hyaline and inflated or thick-walled and colored, usually forming a well-defined group sometimes reaching to the costa; inner perichaetial erect, mostly plicate, elongate-subulate: seta long to very long; capsule inclined to horizontal, cylindric, arcuate, when dry constricted below the mouth, smooth, annulate; lid convex, apiculate.

A difficult genus of over 40 species of water-mosses, quite largely swamp-mosses, — often forming quite large masses of vegetation, — almost exclusively confined to temperate and cold regions; about 22 species occur in North America, perhaps the following 8 to be included in our list. Species not well-defined and extremely variable. See Grout's *Moss Flora* for descriptions of many forms and varieties.

KEY TO THE SPECIES

A. Stem without central strand or inflated cuticular cells; leaves without inflated alar cells ....2. *D. vernicosus*
A. Stems with central strand ....B
   B. Stem in cross-section displaying cortical layer of enlarged, thin-walled, hyaline cells ....E
   B. Stem without enlarged cuticular cells C
C. Leaves usually entire ....F
C. Leaves serrulate, ends of stems and branches hooked ....D
   D. Costa usually less than three-fourths length of leaf; alar group of cells not reaching over to the costa ....7. *D. fluitans*
   D. Costa extending well up to the apex of leaf; alar group of cells large, excavate, and extending over to the costa ....8. *D. exannulatus*
E. Leaves strongly plicate, 3-5 mm long ....1. *D. uncinatus*
E. Leaves not plicate, about 2 mm long ....3. *D. intermedius*
   F. Ends of stems and branches more or less strongly hooked (See also forms of *D. Kneiffii*). ....G
   F. Ends of stems and branches not or but moderately hooked (certain forms strongly hooked); leaves broad-lanceolate to ovate-oblong ....5. *D. Kneiffii*
G. Stem-leaves falcate-secund; enlarged, inflated, thin-walled, auricular cells usually reaching nearly to the costa; costa usually about to middle of leaf ....4. *D. aduncus*
G. Enlarged, medium thick-walled, auricular cells not reaching costa; costa usually extending into the acumen ....6. *D. Sendtneri*

1. DREPANOCLADUS UNCINATUS [Hedwig] Warnstorf
(*Hypnum uncinatum* Hedwig; *Amblystegium aduncum* Lindberg)

Rather slender and loosely interlaced, pale green or golden green: stems distantly and irregularly pinnately branched, 2-10 cm long, in cross-section showing a layer of large hyaline cortical cells and a central strand; leaves 3-5 mm long, rather crowded, regularly falcate to sub-circinate, little altered when dry, spirally flexuous at the points in the younger and softer branches, narrowly elongate-lanceolate, strongly plicate both wet and dry, gradually very long and slenderly acuminate, usually denticulate above, texture very thin; costa narrow, about 0.30-0.35 mm at base, extending well into the acumen; leaf-cells very long, linear-flexuous, thin-walled, pointed, uniform to the base and apex, the alar forming a rather small and indistinct group of slightly enlarged and slightly inflated cells, and extending decurrently below and marginally a short distance above; perichaetial leaves erect, straight, long, plicate, sheathing: seta variable, but usually 2-3 cm high; capsule cylindric, arcuate, orange-red, darker when old, when dry and empty somewhat constricted below the mouth, smooth; annulus broad, 3-seriate; lid high-convex, conic-acuminate; peristome hypnoid, teeth orange-yellow, paler above, segments somewhat carinately split, cilia 2, slender and about as long as segments; spores mature in late spring or early summer.

On earth, decaying wood, stones, etc., bordering streams or in wet situations in the shade, mainly in hilly or mountainous regions almost the world over; in North America from Arctic regions south to the Gulf States. Extremely variable with many named varieties.

Rare in our region. CAMBRIA CO.: T. P. James. (Porter's Catalogue). HUNTINGDON CO.: T. C. Porter. (Porter's Catalogue).

2.   DREPANOCLADUS VERNICOSUS (Lindberg) Warnstorf
(*Hypnum vernicosum* Lindberg)

Deeply tufted, yellowish-green, darker or brownish below; stems slender, more or less regularly pinnate, hooked at the ends; central strand none but outer cuticular cells small and somewhat incrassate; stem-leaves plicate, neither auricled nor decurrent lanceolate to ovate-lanceolate, strongly circinate or falcate-secund, gradually long acuminate and entire; costa usually reaching beyond the middle of leaf; median leaf-cells linear-flexuous, about 10-12:1; about 2 or 3 rows of the basal cells incrassate, reddish or brownish; alar not differentiated: inner perichaetial leaves erect, acuminate, costa long: seta 4-5 cm long, reddish; capsule castaneous, cylindric-ovoid, cernuous, curved, narrowed under mouth when dry; lid conic-apiculate; annulus 3-seriate; spores in May or June. Rarely fruiting.

In usually non-calcareous regions in wet places and swamps. Eurasia, and from Canada south to New Jersey, Pennsylvania, and Ohio.

3.   DREPANOCLADUS INTERMEDIUS (Lindberg) Warnstorf
(*Hypnum intermedium* Lindberg)

Yellowish-green to brownish tufts; stems slender, showing central strand and inflated hyaline cuticular cells, ascending to erect, 8-15 cm long, irregularly pinnate; leaves non-plicate, non-decurrent, from an ovate to oblong base long-acuminate, about 2 mm long, entire; costa thin, disappearing above the middle; leaf cells very narrow, 2-4 in the angles thin-walled and slightly enlarged, forming a faint group; inner perichaetial leaves erect, long and slenderly acuminate, delicately costate; seta 4-5 cm long, reddish; spores ripe in May or June.

In bogs, marshy places, or on wet rocks, often forming masses of vegetation. Possibly to be expected in the northern part of our region.

4.   DREPANOCLADUS ADUNCUS (Hedwig) Warnstorf
(*Hypnum aduncum* Hedwig, not Linnaeus)
Plate LXVII

An extremely variable moss of which many varieties and forms have been named. Yellowish- green mats (or tufts), brownish below; stems 2-3 cm long or in forms up to 30 or 40 cm, bushy branched with erect branches or floating; stem-leaves triangular ovate to lance-ovate and acuminate or lanceolate and very slenderly acuminate when in water, often secund or falcate at ends of branches, non-plicate, entire, the large inflated, thin-walled cells at the excavated auricles decurrent, usually hyaline and reaching well towards the costa; costa disappearing at or above the middle; median; median leaf-cells linear-flexuous (or wider in some varieties); branch-leaves smaller and narrower, and often more falcate or even falcate-secund; seta about 2-4 cm long, rather slender; capsule about 2-2.5 mm long, curved, cernuous; spores in late spring or early summer; lid conic-apiculate; annulate. Not often found in fruit.

Eurasia, northern Africa, New Zealand, and widely distributed in colder and temperate parts of North America.

CRAWFORD Co.: Pymatuning Swamp, Linesville. O.E.J. Aug. 19, 1904 (figured). ERIE Co.: Numerous collections on Presque Isle by Nelle Ammons. Summer of 1935. LAWRENCE Co.: In moist field with *Gentiana crinita*, Frew Mill Road, e. of New Castle. C.M.B. Sept. 18, 1948. WARREN Co.: Iron Spring bog, Columbus. C.M.B. Sept. 1, 1948. WESTMORELAND Co.: On rock in stream, Tannery Hollow, Chestnut Ridge. C.M.B. Apr. 30, 1944. Elev. 1700 ft.

5. DREPANOCLADUS KNEIFFII (Schimper) Warnstorf
(*Hypnum aduncum* var. *Kneiffii* Schimper; *Amblystegium Kneiffii* Bryologia Europaea)

Stems slender, long, flexuous, prostrate or ascending, more or less pinnately branched, the cross-section showing a central strand, but not a distinct cortical layer of enlarged hyaline cells; leaves distant, broadly lanceolate to ovate-oblong, costate to the middle at least, usually not secund nor falcate except sometimes at the end of the branches, the acumen flat and entire, the lower leaves usually shorter and wider; basal leaf-cells much as in *D. aduncus*, the alar large, inflated, and extending about half-way to the costa. Closely related on the whole to *D. aduncus*, and by some bryologists regarded as merely a variety of that species.

Along streams and ditches, about as widely distributed as is *D. aduncus*.

BUTLER Co.: In swamp among grasses, 1 m. west of West Liberty, June 28, 1941. Charles M. Boardman. ERIE Co.: Cranberry Pond, Presque Isle, Erie, July 30, 1935, Nelle Ammons; on base of Alnus, May 8-9, 1906. O.E.J.

6. DREPANOCLADUS SENDTNERI (Schimper) Warnstorf
(*Hypnum Sendtneri* Schimper)

Rather strong plants in yellowish tufts, brownish below; stems 10-15 cm long, erect, sparsely irregularly pinnately divided; leaves close, strongly falcate or circinate, hooked at the ends of stems and branches, lanceolate to lance-ovate, about 10-11 mm long, long-acuminate, entire, non-plicate, short-decurrent; costa strong and wide, extending into the leaf-tip; median leaf-cells narrowly linear to somewhat oblong, about 6-10:1, basal larger, incrassate, the alar forming a well-defined group of colored, incrassate, excavate, inflated cells; dioicous; seta 3-4 cm, reddish, slender; capsule resembling that of *aduncus.* Grout suggests that *Sendtneri* is a calcicolus form of *aduncus,* which it parallels in many of its forms.

In wet limy bogs, swamps, etc. Eurasia, and, in North America extending from Canada south to North Carolina, and in the west to California.

7. DREPANOCLADUS FLUITANS [Linnaeus] Warnstorf
(*Hypnum fluitans* Linnaeus; *Amblystegium fluitans* DeNotaris)
Plate LXIX

Loosely and softly cespitose, yellowish to dark brown, irregularly to regularly pinnately branched: leaves more or less secund or falcate, narrowly lanceolate to oblong-lanceolate, tapering gradually into a very slender flexuose acumination, the branch-leaves somewhat narrower than the stem-leaves but quite similar, all denticulate, excavate at the base, sometimes reaching a length of 4 mm, decurrent; costa not markedly wide, reaching into the apex or at least nearly so; leaf-cells about 20-30:1, long, reaching to .100 mm or more, pointed, narrow, somewhat incrassate, the alar, hyaline or colored and often forming more or less distinct auricles reaching sometimes to the base of the costa, somewhat inflated: seta red, long, up to 5 or 6 cm or sometimes much longer, flexuous, strongly dextrorse; capsule more or less inclined, curved, rather thin-walled, with a distinct collum, about 3-4:1; lid high-convex, bluntly apiculate; peristome-teeth rather short, segments rarely carinately split, cilia usually 1 or 2, usually considerably shorter than the segments; annulus none; spores mature in early summer. Very variable and split up into many forms and varieties by various authors.

In ditches, swamps, bogs, stagnant pools, among willows, cat-tails, etc., often immersed or floating, almost cosmopolitan in temperate and cold regions; in North America, throughout Canada and the northern United States.

CENTRE Co.: Bear Meadows. T. C. Porter. (Porter's Catalogue). ERIE Co.: Entirely submerged in lily pond. Presque Isle. Nelle Ammons. July 13, 1935. MCKEAN Co.: In stagnant water. West Branch Swamp, Bradford. Among willows. D.A.B. May 26, 1895 (figured) and June 9, 1895. SOMERSET Co.: Pleasant Union, Sept. 7, 1942; and Mt. Davis Fire Tower, elev. 3210 ft., Sept. 21, 1947. C.M.B.

8. DREPANOCLADUS EXANNULATUS (Guembel) Warnstorf
(*Hypnum exannulatum* Bryologia Europaea; *Amblystegium exannulatus* DeNotaris)
Plate XLIV

Typically more rigid, compact, and more completely pinnate than *D. fluitans,* the leaves more falcate, usually serrulate, frequently striate, especially when dry: the costa reaching well towards the apex and rather stronger than in *D. fluitans,* biconvex; the alar cells hyaline and much enlarged, forming an excavate and well defined excavate auricle extending across to the costa. In our region the specimens show the following characteristics: yellowish-brown, floating, the stems up to 8 or 10 cm long, the tips of stems and branches hooked; leaves rather remote, reaching 4 mm long, irregularly and widely spreading, not definitely circinate or secund, except at the tips of stems and branches, slenderly acuminate into a sub-channeled acumen, entire, the base rounded to somewhat excavate and decurrent auricles, so that the insertion is more or less of a semi-circle; median leaf-cells linear, rather incrassate, about 10-15:1, reaching 0.3 mm or even longer, towards the base rapidly becoming shorter and quickly passing into large, hyaline, oblong, much-inflated cells, thus forming a distinct patch reaching to the costa and, below, passing abruptly into the narrowly linear epidermal cells of the stem; in cross-section the stem may be seen to have the 3 or 4 outer layers small and very thick-walled.

In bogs and wet places, usually in cool or alpine regions; northern and temperate Europe and Asia and, in North America, from Greenland to Alaska south to the northern United States.

CRAWFORD Co.: In pools, Pymatuning Swamp, Linesville, August 19, 1904. Sterile. O.E.J. (figured). ELK Co.: Midmont Swamp. Elev. 1940. C.M.B. July 1, 1948. ERIE Co.: Among cattails in swamp. Presque Isle, Nelle Ammons. July 22, 1933. McKEAN Co.: Cathrine Swamp. C.M.B. Sept. 2, 1948.

9. CALLIERGON (Sullivant) Kindberg

Mostly dioicous: more or less robust, stiffly and loosely cespitose, greenish to brownish or yellowish, rather lustrous; stem long, in water and in deep swamps not bearing rhizoids but assuming a more or less erect habit, in dry places procumbent and bearing rhizoids, irregularly to regularly pinnately branched; stem-leaves large, erect-spreading to imbricate, concave, rarely somewhat plicate, ovate to oblong or almost circular, the apex broadly rounded to cucullate, the margin plane and entire or rarely somewhat revolute below; costa mostly strong and almost complete, sometimes indistinctly forked at the end; leaf-cells elongate, linear-hexagonal, shorter below, the alar forming a distinct group of large, quadrate, rectangular, and polygonal cells, at first thin and hyaline but later colored and incrassate, the alar portion of the leaf excavate; branch-leaves smaller, narrower, the apex often canaliculate; the inner perichaetial leaves erect, more or less long-acuminate, mostly non-plicate, with a simple costa: seta mostly very long, drying flat, red to castaneous; capsule inclined to horizontal, thickly oblong to oblong-cylindric, more or less dorsally gibbous, drying arcuate, smooth; annulus none to broad; peristome normally hypnoid; lid convex, acute to obtuse-conic.

A genus of about 15 species of aquatic, largely swamp-inhabiting mosses, confined to temperate and cold regions: 8 species occurring in North America; 1 species within our range and others to be expected.

KEY TO THE SPECIES

A. Costa weak; alar cells incrassate ....4. *C. trifarium*
A. Costa strong; alar cells thin-walled and inflated ....B
   B. Costa extending to the middle or a little above ....3. *C. stramineum*
   B. Costa sub-percurrent C
      C. Plants slender, simple or but sparingly branched; alar cells gradually enlarged and
         long-decurrent ....1. *C. cordifolium*
      C. Robust and profusely branched; alar cells abruptly enlarged and inflated ....
        ....2. *C. giganteum*

1. CALLIERGON CORDIFOLIUM [Hedwig] Kindberg

(*Hypnum cordifolium* Hedwig; *Amblystegium cordifolium* DeNotaris)

Plate XLIV

Slender, tall, loosely and softly cespitose, green: stems brownish, 10-20 cm in length; when growing in swamps, more or less erect; when in dryer situations, more procumbent, and furnished with rhizoids; sparsely branched, the branches more or less pinnately branched or simple, cuspidate at the tips; leaves distant, erect-spreading, to spreading, thin, shrinking when dry, large, 2-5 mm long, concave, cordate- to oblong-ovate, entire, the apex rounded and sometimes cucullate, the base decurrent; costa slender, reaching nearly to the apex; median leaf-cells large, about the apical and upper marginal short and wide, the cells towards the base gardually becoming large, wide and more or less hyaline-inflated, rounded-hexagonal to rectangular, forming a wide but not distinctly bounded group or band reaching clear across the base of the leaf and quite strongly decurrent; perichaetial leaves erect, sheathing, from an ovate base long-acuminate, up to 2.5-3 mm long: seta erect, flexuous, usually 4.5-8 cm long, castaneous, when dry flattened and dextrorse; capsule oblong-cylindric, about 3 mm long, rather turgid-arcuate, inclined to horizontal, castaneous, slightly constricted below the mouth when dry, exannulate; peristome-teeth pale yellow, rather thin, rather long, hayline-margined, strongly trabeculate, the dorsal lamellae hyaline and papillose above, the basal portion rather irregularly striate, the teeth confluent at base; the segment entire or but slightly carinately split, about as long as the teeth; cilia 2 or 3, slender, nodose, about as long as the segments; the basal membrane about one-half as high as the teeth; exothecial cells incrassate, rounded-quadrate to rounded-hexagonal; lid conic, acute to apiculate; spores mature in late spring or early summer, about .012-.015 mm, yellowish, smooth, rather thin-walled.

In swamps, margins of pools, marshy places, etc.; Europe, Asia, New Zealand, and in North America from the Arctic region south to New Jersey, Pennsylvania, and Ohio.

Fairly common in our region and now known from the following counties: Allegheny, Butler, Cambria, Crawford, Erie, Fayette, McKean, Somerset, Warren, and Westmoreland.. Specimen figured: Pymatuning Swamp, near Linesville, Crawford Co., May 18, 1905. O.E.J.

2. CALLIERGON GIGANTEUM (Schimper) Kindberg

(*Hypnum giganteum* Schimper)

Usually robust mosses in wet places or even in deep water, up to 10-30 cm long; rather regularly densely pinnate with irregular branches which are often sharp pointed; stem-leaves up to 4 x 2 mm, plicate and lustrous when dry, decurrent, cucullate at apex, entire; costa wide, vanishing in the apex; median cells linear-flexuose, only about .007 mm wide, apical cells wider, alar forming wide abruptly inflated auricles; branch-leaves narrower; seta 5-6 cm long, red; exannulate; ripe in May or June.

In cold swamps, Eurasia, and from Canada south to eastern Pennsylvania and New Jersey.

3. CALLIERGON STRAMINEUM (Dickson; Bridel) Kindberg
(*Hypnum stramineum* Dickson)

Very slender yellowish-green mosses of cold bogs, erect or ascending in soft tufts; stems up to 20 cm long; stem-leaves oblong-lingulate, concave, cucullate at apex, entire, up to 2 x 1 mm; alar cells abruptly enlarged forming decurrent auricles, apical tending to rounded-quadrate; costate to about ¾ length of leaf. Northern Eurasia and from Arctic America south to New Jersey and eastern Pennsylvania (Pocono Mts.). Not reported from our region.

4. CALLIERGON TRIFARIUM (Weber and Mohr) Kindberg
(*Hypnum trifarium* Weber and Mohr)

When dry, in rather stiff and lustrous tufts, yellowish-green above to brown below; stems and branches julaceous both wet and dry; stem-leaves appressed, concave, broadly ovate to almost orbicular, obtuse, entire, scarcely decurrent; costa thin, vanishing at about the middle or little above; median leaf-cells linear-flexuous, shorter but scarcely wider above, the basal and alar thick-walled, shorter and broader, but not much different. Cold bogs, especially if calcareous, Eurasia and from Arctic America, south to Ohio and Connecticut. Not yet found in our region.

10. CALLIERGONELLA Loeske
(*Acrocladium* Mitten, in part)

Autoicous or dioicous: robust, rather stiffly but loosely cespitose, lustrous, green to yellowish or brownish; stems long, densely foliate, the apex of the shoots rigid and acuminate by reason of the convolute apical leaves, the stems erect, not bearing rhizoids, or procumbent, here and there with fascicles of rhizoids, irregularly branched; stem-leaves appressed, smooth, drying somewhat imbricate, when damp erect-spreading, concave, often cucullate, from a narrow and sub-decurrent base broadly oblong-ovate, obtuse, rarely apiculate, entire, the margin apically more or less involute; branch-leaves smaller and proportionally narrower than stem-leaves; costa short and double or none; leaf-cells narrowly vermicular, smooth, wider and porose towards the base, in the exca-vate alar portions lax,, oval-4-6-sided, hyaline, thin-walled, forming a distinct auricular group; inner perichaetial leaves erect, entire: seta 3-7 cm high, twisted, reddish; capsule horizontal from an erect collum, oblong to cylindric, drying arcuate and dorsally gibbous, smooth or plicate, little narrowed below the mouth; peristome normally hypnoid with appendiculate cilia; lid convex-conic.

As here recognized the genus consists of one species.

1. CALLIERGONELLA CUSPIDATA [Linnaeus] Loeske
(*Hypnum cuspidatum* Linnaeus; *H. flexile* Bridel; *Calliergon cuspidatum* Kindberg; *Acrocladium cuspidatum* Lindberg)

Plate XLIV

Tall and moderately robust with characters mainly as outlined for the genus: leaves usually bright, glossy, yellowish-green, or almost pure green; stem-leaves broadly elliptic-oblong, up to 2.5 mm long, concave-cucullate, entire, the apex often apiculate, ecostate or the costa short and double, leaves crowded, usually more or less erect-spreading when moist, towards the tips of the stems and branches imbricate-convolute so as to make the tips cuspidate; branch-leaves smaller and relatively narrower; median leaf-cells linear-vermicular, about 10-15:1, the alar suddenly inflated, thin-walled, hexagonal, hyaline or colored, forming a very distinct group, the apical rather abruptly shorter, rounded, and incrassate: seta 4-6 cm long; capsule reddish-brown; peristome-teeth orange, hyaline-bordered, the margins step-like above; cilia 3, appendiculate, slightly shorter than the narrowly cleft segments; spores mature in summer, the large capsules being but rarely produced; annulus 3-seriate.

In marshy places, swamps, and bogs; Europe, Asia, northern Africa, the Argentine, and, in North America, through Canada and the northern part of the United States south to New Jersey, Pennsylvania, and Iowa. Rather uncommon in our region.

ERIE Co.: Under *Cephalanthus* thicket, border of Cranberry Pond, Presque Isle. C.M.B. Sept. 3, 1934. McKEAN Co.: East Branch, Teina Swamp, north of Bradford, January 18, 1895. D.A.B. SNYDER Co.: In bog between Shamokin Dam and Richfield, July 17, 1908. O.E.J. (figured).

11. HYGROHYPNUM Lindberg

Autoicous or dioicous: slender to robust, in flattish or cushion-like tufts, lustrous, green to yellowish-green or golden-green: stem long, procumbent, with few or no rhizoids, remotely and irregularly branched; branches ascending; leaves spreading to secund or imbricate, concave, smooth to weakly plicate, more or less decurrent, lance-ovate, and acuminate or mostly broadly oval and obtuse to rounded, sometimes almost orbicular, margins plane, entire or serrate; costa mostly unequally forked, short, weak, rarely simple and long; leaf-cells to the base uniformly narrowly linear-vermicular, mostly with obtuse ends, smooth, the apical often shorter and rhombic, the basal yellow to orange, the alar portions little or not excavate but with wider, quadrate to rectangular, hyaline to colored cells forming a small but often well-defined auricular group; inner perichaetial leaves erect, elongate, plicate, costa simple or forked, short: seta long, reddish, drying flattened and twisted; capsule inclined to horizontal, mostly oval to oblong, dorsally gibbous, drying arcuate and mostly constricted below the mouth, annulate; peristome normally hypnoid; lid convex-conic.

A genus of about 25 species in wet or moist places in cool regions; in North America about 12 species have been reported; in our region at least 5 species, probably others to be expected.

KEY TO THE SPECIES

A. Epidermal stem-cells hyaline and enlarged; leaves usually distinctly falcate-secund
....3. *H. ochraceum*
A. Epidermal stem-cells not as above ....B
  B. Leaves widely spreading, broadly ovate to almost orbicular, and harsh when dry
....5. *H. dilatatum*

E. Leaves otherwise C
C. Costa single and reaching midleaf or beyond ....D
C. Costa none or short and double ....E
   D. Leaves less than 1 mm long ....4. *H. Closteri*
   D. Leaves more than 1 mm long ....1. *H. luridum*
E. Leaves entire, concave, often sub-tubulose above ....*H. luridum*
E. Leaves denticulate or serrulate towards apex ....F
   F. Leaves widely spreading; costa single, reaching to midleaf or above ....
   ....4a. *H. Closteri* f. *serrulatum*
   F. Costa none, or short and double or forked ....G
G. Terminal leaves secund; stems and branches rather julaceous; alar cells suddenly in-
   flated forming distinct auricles ....2. *H. eugyrium*
G. Stems and branches attenuate and stoloniferous at ends; alar cells only somewhat
   enlarged, rectangular to quadrate; leaves sub-clasping ....6. *H. novae-caesareae*

1.   HYGROHYPNUM LURIDUM [Hedwig] Jennings

(Hypnum palustre Hudson; *Amblystegium palustre* Lindberg; *Hypnum*
luridum Hedwig; *Calliergon palustre* Kindberg)*

Yellowish-green, or dark-green, irregularly cespitose in low patches: stems denuded below, long, divided irregularly, the branches erect to ascending, often more or less hooked at the tip; leaves close, either imbricated or more or less falcate-secund, always concave, the margins strongly incurved towards the summit, narrowly oval- to broadly ovate-oblong, entire, about 1-1.5 mm long, the apex variable, either obtuse or acute or rounded and apiculate; costa usually single or forked and reaching about half way up the leaf, but variable; leaf-cells rather lax, about 5-10:1, usually linear-rhomboid, rather opaque, somewhat shorter towards the apex and towards the base, the alar few, quadrate, sub-opaque, somewhat inflated, forming small, ill-defined auricles which are somewhat decurrent: seta about 1-2 cm long; capsule oblong or oval-oblong, orange-brown, arcuate, rather short and thick, more or less horizontal, dark when dry, exannulate: lid orange-yellow, conic, obtuse to apiculate; peristome normally hypnoid, teeth yellowish, segments scarcely carinately cleft, a little longer than the 2 or 3 cilia; spores mature in summer.

On wet, cold rocks, where often overflowed, especially in calcareous districts: Europe, Asia, and the northern United States and Canada, south to New Jersey and Pennsylvania.

Rare in our region. HUNTINGDON Co.: T. C. Porter. (Porter's Catalogue). Mc-KEAN Co.: D.A.B. (Porter's Catalogue)

2.   HYGROHYPNUM EUGYRIUM (Bryologia Europaea) Loeske

(Hypnum eugyrium Bryologia Europaea; *Amblystegium eugyrium* Lindberg;
Calliergon eugyrium Kindberg)*

Widely cespitose in low, dense, usually sand-filled tufts, lustrous, green to reddish to brownish: stems prostrate, often leafless below; branches numerous, erect or procumbent, usually from 0.5-1.0 cm long; leaves wide-spreading when moist, distinctly falcate-secund towards ends of branches, when dry imbricate-erect and concave, thus giving the branches a turgid appearance, oval-oblong or lance-oblong, narrowed to the base, slightly denticulate towards the shortly acuminate acute apex, the margins incurved towards the apex; costa short, indistinct and double, or none; median leaf-cells linear, somewhat incrassate, often somewhat obtuse at ends, about 8-10:1, shorter at the apex, the alar abruptly much enlarged and inflated, the marginal thin-walled, the inner ones incrassate, hyaline to yellowish-brown, forming well-defined and somewhat inflated auricles; perichaetial leaves whitish, the outer with flexuous spreading tips, the inner erect, long-acuminate, often erose-denticulate at the apex, plicate: capsule short, oval to oblong, cernuous, turgid, yellowish-brown; peristome-teeth yellowish, slender, strongly trabeculate; segments carinately cleft and about equalled in length by the 2 or 3 granulose and nodose cilia; lid conic-convex; annulus usually 3-seriate; spores mature in spring.

On rocks in streams or along the banks where kept wet, in hilly or mountainous and usually non-calcareous regions; Europe, and from Newfoundland to Alaska and south to Georgia and Colorado.

Some specimens from McKean County show intergradations with the following variety.

FAYETTE Co.: On rock in stream-bed, Cucumber Run, above Falls, Ohiopyle, June 24, 1934; and on rock in stream, Sheepskin Run, Ohiopyle, Nov. 6, 1943. C.M.B. WESTMORELAND Co.: On rock in stream one mi. above Darlington, May 19, 1945. C.M.B.

2a. HYGROHYPNUM EUGYRIUM var. MACKAYI (Schimper) Brotherus

(*Hypnum eugyrium* var. *Mackayi* Schimper; *Hygrohypnum Mackayi* Loeske; *Hypnum Mackayi* Breidler)

Plate XLV

Leaves about 1-1.5 x 0.6-0.7 mm, broadly oblong, distinctly serrulate at apex, sub-clasping and auriculate at base, less strongly falcate than in the species; perichaetial leaves hyaline, plicate, the inner reaching 3 mm in length: seta about 2 cm long, castaneous, smooth, somewhat flexuous, dextrorse above; capsule with urn 2-2.5 mm long; exothecial cells rounded-hexagonal, somewhat incrassate-collenchymatous, rather uniformly seriate; peristome-teeth about as long as the slender carinate segments, the basal membrane about two-fifths as high; spores minutely papillose, rather thin-walled, faintly yellowish, about .024-.027 mm, mature in late spring or early summer

When sterile it is very difficult to distinguish this moss from *Sematophyllum marylandicum*. In the *Sematophyllum* the walls of the outer alar cells are not much thinner than are the walls of the inner alars. *Sematophyllum* also sometimes has a faint double costa.

On stones in streams in hilly or mountainous regions and with about the same general distribution as the species.

Rare in our region. McKEAN Co.: On stones in brook at head of Bennett Brook, Bradford, August 26, 1894, November 2, 1896, and July, 1897 (figured), the latter issued as Grout's North American Musci Pleurocarpi. No. 129. Also Limestone Creek, Bradford, July 7, 1895. All D.A.B. Also Tionesta Tract, Wetmore Twp., C.M.B. Sept. 23, 1939.

3. HYGROHYPNUM OCHRACEUM (Turner) Loeske

(*Hypnum ochraceum* Turner; *Amblystegium ochraceum* Lindberg;
Limnobium ochraceum Bryologia Europaea)

Plate XLV

Yellowish or rusty green, softly cespitose in wide tufts: stems up to 8 or 9 cm long, ascending or horizontally floating, sparsely and irregularly pinnately branched, without rhizoids, the stems and branches somewhat hooked at the apex, the cortical cells of the stem very large and thin-walled; leaves falcate-secund, concave, plicate, widely lance-oblong to ovate-oblong, somewhat rounded at the base, the margins plane, entire excepting for slight serration at the rather widely sub-obtuse apex; costa single or double, often reaching half the length of the leaf; median leaf-cells linear-vermicular, about 8-14:1, fairly thick-walled, usually rounded at the ends, the apical oval-rhomboid and much shorter, the basal larger and towards the angles of the leaf forming distinct decurrent auricles of abruptly enlarged, hyaline, inflated, rectangular cells: perichaetial leaves ecostate, lance-acuminate: seta slender, flexuous, erect; capsules sub-erect to cernuous from a short erect collum, oblong, arcuate; lid convex, mamillate; peristome hypnoid, the teeth yellowish, broadly margined, rather distantly trabeculate, equalled in length by the carinately split segments, the cilia shorter, unequal, nodose, two or three in number; annulus large, usually 3-seriate; spores mature in spring or early summer.

On rocks in streams or on dripping ledges, in the mountains of northern and temperate Europe and Asia, and, in North America, from the Arctic regions south to the latitude of New Jersey and West Virginia.

Although rare in this district, so far as now known, this species may eventually be found to be not uncommon in cool, rocky streams in the more mountainous parts of our region. FAYETTE Co.: On rock in stream, Blue Hole Creek. C.M.B. July 5, 1948. WESTMORELAND Co.: In mountain rivulet, Mellon's estate, Laurel Hill Mt., New Florence, September 8-10, 1907. O.E.J. Sterile (figured).

4. HYGROHYPNUM CLOSTERI (Austin) Grout

(*Hypnum Closteri* Austin)

Slender, in loose tufts, green to yellowish; stems creeping, irregularly branched; leaves rather widely spaced, spreading, not or rarely secund, leaves ovate or oblong-ovate, rarely reaching 1 mm long, flat apex obtuse, margin entire, only very slightly decurrent; costa normally single, reaching to mid-leaf or beyond; median leaf-cells linear, somewhat opaque, about 3-5:1, apical shorter; basal shorter and wider, alar but little enlarged: seta 6-8 mm long, castaneous; capsule, brown, ovoid, cernuous, arcuate, much constricted below mouth when dry and old; annulate; lid low-conic, apiculate; spores ripe in spring.

On stones in cool streams. Vermont to eastern Pennsylvania and Virginia, but not yet found in our region.

4a. HYGROHYPNUM CLOSTERI f. SERRULATUM Grout

Leaf-cells more hyaline; leaves often serrulate above.

MCKEAN Co.: Bolivar Run, Burnett No. 3208 (Type). September 11, 1898.

5. HYGROHYPNUM DILATATUM (Wilson) Loeske

(Hypnum dilatatum Schimper)

Yellowish-green above, blackish below, the tufts stiff and harsh when dry; stems ascending towards tip and with erect, short, blunt branches; leaves widely spreading, somewhat secund, from a narrower, somewhat decurrent base broadly oval-elliptic to almost orbicular, obtuse to apiculate, up to 2 mm long, entire or faintly denticulate at apex; costa usually faint, forked, rarely reaching mid-leaf, occasionally single; leaf-cells incrassate 10-15:1, towards base 20:1, at apex 2-4:1, the alar cells form a weak group of oval-angular to rectangular, yellowish, thick-walled: seta 1-2 cm; capsule oblong from a narrow neck, 2 mm long, castaneous, constricted below the mouth when dry and empty; annulus 2-seriate; lid orange, high convex, with red apiculus; spores ripe in summer.

On non-calcareous stones in swiftly flowing mountain brooks. Eurasia, and in North America from Canada south to West Virginia and the Southwest. To be expected in our mountains also.

6. HYGROHYPNUM NOVAE-CAESAREAE (Austin) Grout

(Hypnum micans Wilson, not Swartz; *Rhynchostegium novae-caesareae* Austin; *Raphidostegium novae-caesareae* Renauld and Cardot)

Plate LIII

Small, yellowish-green, glossy, forming wide, thin mats: stems prostrate, very slender, sparsely branching, often flagelliform, the branches short, simple or sparsely branched, sub-erect; leaves spreading or the upper sometimes sub-secund, sub-orbicular, apiculate to shortly acuminate, 0.6-0.8 mm long, serrulate above, concave, the margins somewhat reflexed below; costa double and very faint; median leaf-cells linear, flexuous, about 6-10:1, the apical rhomboid-oblong, rather incrassate, much smaller than the median, the basal a little shorter and wider than the median, the alar region with about 6 to 10 larger, quadrate to rectangular, rather incrassate cells and with the outermost one to three cells much larger and more or less inflated: the capsules of this species have thus far been found but once, — on damp rocks along Stony Creek, Carbon County, Pennsylvania, by Francis Wolle: capsules small with a shortly rostrate lid, the exothecial cells non-collenchymatous: dioicous.

On damp rocks in cool and moist mountain ravines, Eurasia, and from Vermont to western Pennsylvania and Georgia, in the mountains.

Rare in our region. FAYETTE CO.: Beck Spring, Laurel Ridge, July 26, 1947, and clinging to rock, Blue Hole Creek, Laurel Ridge. July 5, 1948. C.M.B. MCKEAN CO.: Bennet Brook, July 10, 1898. (figured).

12. CAMPYLIUM (Sullivant) Bryhn

Mostly dioicous: slender, rarely robust, mostly stiffly cespitose, green to yellowish or brownish, drying more or less lustrous; stems creeping to ascending or erect, bushy to variously pinnate; leaves from a shortly decurrent base broadly ovate or cordate, gradually or abruptly narrowed into a long, slender, canaliculate acumination which is mostly strongly squarrose-reflexed, margin plane, mostly entire; costa various, mostly short; cells narrowly rectangular-oblong to linear-prosenchymatous, smooth; alar cells forming a distinct group, yellowish, incrassate to inflated, small, quadrate: seta long, drying twisted, reddish to yellowish-red; capsule inclined to horizontal, sub-cylindric, arcuate, annulate; peristome normally hypnoid; lid convex, acute to conic-obtuse; spores small.

About 30 species in both dry and wet habitats, mainly confined to the temperate regions; about 20 species reported for North America; 4 species now known in our region.

KEY TO THE SPECIES

A. Costa simple, thin, ending in about the middle of the leaf, or somewhat above the middle C
A. Costa none or very short ....B
   B. Stem slender, creeping; leaves finely serrulate all around; alar cells small, quadrate ....1. C. hispidulum
   B. Stem usually erect or ascending; leaves entire; alar cells dilated, sub-rectangular ....4. C. stellatum
C. Leaves strongly squarrose; alar cells scarcely enlarged ....2. C. chrysophyllum
C. Leaves spreading-erect; alar cells enlarged ....D
   D. Stem-leaves very slenderly acuminate from a broadly lanceolate blade 3. ..C. polyganum
   D. Stem-leaves abruptly acuminate from a cordate-ovate blade ....5. C. radicale

1. CAMPYLIUM HISPIDULUM (Bridel) Mitten

(*Hypnum hispidulum* Bridel; *Chrysohypnum hispidulum* Roth; *Stereodon hispidulus* Mitten; *Amblystegium hispidulum* Kindberg)

Plate XLV

Slender, interlaced in bright green tufts more or less yellowish below; stems creeping radiculose, abundantly but irregularly branching, the branchlets slender and erect or ascending; leaves widely spreading to distinctly squarrose, about 0.5-0.8 mm long, triangular-cordate, abruptly acuminate, the slender acumen about one-third as long as the main body of the leaf, the leaf slightly concave, decurrent, sub-serrulate all around, excavate at the base; costa double and very short, or none; median leaf-cells about 3-6:1, with .005-.006 mm wide, prosenchymatous, elongate-oblong with blunt ends, the alar numerous, sub-rectangular to quadrate, granulose, up to twice as wide as the median cells: seta pale castaneous to yellow, about 1.5-2 cm long, slender dextrorse; capsule small, oblong, more or less incurved, yellowish-brown, wide-mouthed, the urn about 1.2-1.4 mm long, when dry furrowed and narrowed below the mouth; annulus uni-seriate; lid convex-conic with an upturned apiculation; peristome normally hypnoid, the segments slightly cleft and almost equalled in length by the nodose to sub-appendiculate cilia; spores mature in summer, yellowish, medium-walled, minutely papillose, about .011-.014 mm.

On the bases and roots of trees, on decaying wood, on humus, etc., always near the ground in moist shaded places; in Europe, Asia, and, in North America from Canada to the southern part of the United States.

Rather common in our region. Now known from Allegheny, Cambria (Porter), Centre, Erie, Indiana (Porter), Fayette, McKean, Washington, and Westmoreland counties. Specimen figured: Edge of pond at Scotia, Centre Co., Sept. 20, 1909. O.E.J.

2. CAMPYLIUM CHRYSOPHYLLUM (Bridel) Bryhn

(*Hypnum chrysophyllum* Bridel; *Chrysohypnum chrysophyllum*
Loeske; *Amblystegium chrysophyllum* De Notaris)

Plate XLV

Cespitose in low, lax, or dense, bright golden-green tufts or mats; stems slender, rather long, prostrate, more or less regularly pinnate, the branchlets erect or spreading; leaves close, small, 1-1.5 x 0.4-0.8 mm, squarrose-spreading from the sub-clasping base, sometimes secund, stem-leaves ovate-cordate to triangular-cordate, decurrent, narrowed abruptly to a long somewhat channeled acumination, entire or very slightly denticulate at base; branch-leaves similar but smaller and narrower; costa single, reaching about to the middle or higher; median leaf-cells about 5-10:1, about .005-.010 mm wide, rather incrassate, the alar forming a group of small, incrassate, sub-opaque, sub-quadrate cells: seta castaneous, about 2-2.5 cm long, slender, flexuous; capsule oblong-cylindric, inclined to horizontal, arcuate, castaneous to orange; lid conic-apiculate; annulus large, compound; peristome normally hypnoid, the teeth yellowish, hyaline-margined, strongly trabeculate, dorsally lamellate, cross-striolate below, hyaline and papillose above; the segments not usually carinately split, the cilia stout, nodose, 2 or 3, and about as long as segments, basal membrane one-half as high as segments; spores in early summer, light brown, smooth, .010-.012 mm: dioicous.

On earth, stones, roots of trees, etc., in moist places; Europe, Asia, and, in North America, from Canada to the southern and southwestern United States. Common in our region excepting on the High Plateau.

Now known from Allegheny, Beaver, Butler, Crawford, Erie, Fayette, Indiana, Lawrence, McKean, Washington, and Westmoreland counties. Specimen figured: Pymatuning Swamp, Linesville, May 12, 1908. O.E.J.

3. CAMPYLIUM POLYGAMUM (Schimper) Bryhn

(*Hypnum polygamum* Wilson; *Chrysohypnum polygamum* Loeske)

Plate XLVI

Moderately robust, yellowish-green to golden, low, cespitose: stems erect to ascending, about 3-6 cm long, divided and with rather numerous, irregularly pinnate, rather crowded, and erect or ascending branchlets; stem-leaves lance-ovate, 2-2.5 mm long, moderately close, erect-spreading both wet and dry, with an ovate or oblong base narrowed above into a long, gradually tapering, channeled acumination, entire, the base rounded and clasping, somewhat decurrent; branch-leaves elongate-lanceolate, with the sides tapering in a straight line from the rounded-ovate base, the leaves averaging about 3 mm long; median leaf-cells narrowly linear, about 8-12:1, in the older leaves somewhat incrassate, towards the base often porose, the alar sub-rectangular, somewhat enlarged, distinct, forming often orange-pellucid auricles; costa not very strong but distinct and usually reaching somewhat above the middle of the leaf: seta slender, flexuous, about 3-4 cm long; capsule oblong-cylindric, curved; lid conic-apiculate; peristome normally hypnoid, cilia well developed; annulus present; spores mature in summer.

In moist places in meadows and swamps and said to prefer sandy soils; Europe, Asia, and from Arctic North America south to New Jersey, Virginia, and Pennsylvania.

Rare in our region. ALLECHENY CO.: Schenley Park, Pittsburgh, August 26 1906. O.E.J. (?). CRAWFORD CO.: Near Linesville in the Pymatuning Swamp, May 10-11, 1906. O.E.J. (figured). ERIE CO.: On soil among cattails in swamp, Presque Isle, Nelle Ammons. July 18, 1933. MCKEAN CO.: Wildcat Hollow, Marvin Creek. On twig in stream. C.M.B. Sept. 1, 1935.

4. CAMPYLIUM STELLATUM [Schreber] Lange and C. Jensen

(Hypnum stellatum Schreber; *Chrysohypnum stellatum* Loeske;
Amblystegium stellatum Lindberg)

Plate XLVI

Robust, densely tufted, soft, lustrous, bright to golden green: stems stout, usually ascending, up to 8 or 10 cm long, irregularly divided, the branchlets sub-pinnate and more or less crowded and erect; leaves close, from 1-3 mm long, from a widely squarrose to an erect-spreading and more or less cordate base narrowed, often rather abruptly, to a gradually long-acuminate, acute, ascending or usually squarrosely spreading acumen, the base entire or some-times slightly denticulate, slightly excavate and with rounded and sub-decur-rent auricles, the upper part of the leaf more or less channeled; costa none or very short, either single, forked, or double, but usually appearing only as yel-lowish or brownish striae; median leaf-cells narrowly linear, about 8-15:1, in the older leaves rather incrassate and blunt at the ends, the basal often porose, the alar somewhat enlarged, sub-rectangular, incrassate, sometimes rather opaque usually more or less orange-pellucid, forming distinct, often somewhat decurrent auricles: seta rather long, castaneous, up to 4.5 cm long, stout, dex-trorse above, flexuous; capsule oblong-cylindric, about 3-4.5:1, arcuate, the urn 2-2.5 mm long, inclined to horizontal, sulcate and constricted below the mouth when dry and empty, brownish; lid highly convex-acuminate; annulus 2-3-seriate; peristome normally hypnoid, large, the teeth trabeculate, confluent at base, the lower part orange-colored and dorsally cross-striolate, the lamellae and divisural distinct, the upper part paler and papillose; segments somewhat shorter and slightly carinately split; cilia 2 (or 3), nodose, about as long as the segments; spores mature in spring (?) or summer, minutely papillose, rather thin-walled, pale yellowish, .011-.014 mm.

On wet banks and tufts in cool swamps and bogs. Europe, Asia, and from Arctic America southwards to Pennsylvania and Ohio; and the West.

BUTLER CO.: West Liberty Bog. O.E.J. June 28, 1941. ERIE CO.: Presque Isle. O.E.J. May 8-9, 1906. LAWRENCE CO.: Frew Mill Road, in patch of *Gentiana crinita,* Sept. 18, 1948; and also on wall of old Van Port limestone quarry ½ mi. e. of New Castle, Nov. 26, 1948. C.M.B. The Presque Isle specimen was figured.

5. CAMPYLIUM RADICALE (Beauvois) Grout

(*Hypnum radicale* Beauvois; *H. bergenense* Austin;
Amblystegium radicale Mitten)

Plate XLII

Loose, slender, pale-green, little branched, the branches often erect and up to 2 cm or more long; branch-leaves distant, more or less widely spreading, lanceolate- to ovate-cordate, up to 1.5 x 0.7 mm, concave at base, entire or almost so, decurrent, abruptly slenderly acuminate and somewhat channelled; median leaf-cells about 4-8:1, sometimes longer, medium-walled, the alar sometimes more abruptly enlarged and hyaline; costa well developed, orange, up to two-thirds or three fourths as long as the leaf; perichaetial leaves slenderly acuminate and up to 2.5 mm long, plicate, erect: seta up to 3 cm long, castaneous, strong, dextrorse; capsule yellowish, the urn about 2.7 mm long, arcuate, oblong-cylindric, contracted below the mouth when dry; peristome-teeth strong, castaneous, strongly trabeculate, hyaline-margined, the dorsal lamellae cross-striolate below, papillose and hyaline above; segments entire or nearly so, about as long as teeth, the basal membrane about two-fifths as high as teeth; cilia 2 or 3, usually one, at least, as long as the segments, nodose, hyaline, minutely papillose, medium-walled, about .016-.019 mm, mature in spring.

On rotten logs, roots of trees, wet soil, etc., in wet, shaded places: Europe, Asia, and apparently well distributed throughout temperate North America.

The species occurs in eastern Pennsylvania and has been found twice in our region. BUTLER CO.: West Liberty Bog. C.M.B. Aug. 29, 1931. McKEAN CO.: In springy places near Bradford, May 17, 1895. D.A.B. (figured).

13. CTENIDIUM (Schimper) Mitten

Usually dioicous, mostly slender, soft, cespitose, green to yellowish or golden-brown, lustrous: stem long, here and there with clusters of rhizoids, more or less regularly pinnate, branches short and mostly horizontally spreading; leaves falcate to circinate-secund, decurrent, more or less plicate, mostly abruptly lance-subulate from a broadly cordate base, serrate (*C. procerrimum* is entire); costa double and very short or none; cells narrowly linear, the upper angle usually ending in a forward-projecting papilla, the alar cells distinct, quadrate and rectangular, the angles sometimes weakly excavate; branch-leaves smaller: seta 1-2.5 cm long, red, smooth or nearly so; capsule inclined to nearly horizontal, thickly oval, dorsally gibbous, not constricted below the mouth; annulus broad, revoluble; peristome normally hypnoid; lid long-conic, acute or obtuse; calyptra mostly more or less hairy.

A genus of 30 species occurring mainly on trees and rocks in temperate and warm regions; 4 species in North America, the following species in our range.

1. CTENIDIUM MOLLUSCUM [Hedwig] Mitten

(*Hypnum molluscum* Hedwig; *H. compressum* Roth)

Plate XLVI

Very densely cespitose, soft, lustrous, golden-green, rather robust: stems reaching 10 cm in length, prostrate or ascending, closely regularly pinnate, plumose; leaves densely imbricated, falcate-secund to circinate, stem-leaves 1.8-2.5 mm long, when dry usually plicate, and, especially towards the points, more or less undulate and crisped, from a cordate-acuminate, plane-margined, auriculate base rather abruptly and slenderly long-acuminate, plane-margined, strongly serrate, especially at the base, somewhat decurrent; costa very short and double or none; median leaf-cells about 8-15:1, the corners somewhat projecting dorsally, gradually towards the angles becoming irregularly quadrate-hexagonal, shorter and wider, pellucid, forming poorly defined auricles of about the same color as the rest of the leaf; branch-leaves considerably smaller and narrower, not cordate-auriculate; perichaetial leaves slenderly lance-acuminate; paraphyllia ovate, mostly at the base of the branches: seta brownish, flexuous, slender, about 1.0-2.5 cm long, castaneous; capsule-urn about 2.5 mm long, oblong to oval, slightly curved to almost straight, from the curved apex of the seta mostly horizontal, not constricted below the mouth when dry; lid conic-acuminate; annulus broad; peristome normally hypnoid, teeth yellowish, segments carinately cleft, about as long as teeth, the cilia 2 or 3, stout, about as long as the segments, the basal membrane about one-half the height of the peristome; calyptra somewhat hairy when young; spores mature in summer, smooth, yellowish-incrassate, about .015-.018 mm.

On moist, shaded earth and rocks, or bases of trees, in woods, more particularly in hilly or mountainous districts; Europe, Asia, northern Africa, and from Newfoundland to the Rocky Mountains and south to Georgia and Oklahoma.

ARMSTRONG CO.: Crooked Creek, one mi. s.w. of Tunnelton. C.M.B. Aug. 18, 1935. BEAVER CO.: On ground, Raccoon Creek, 2 mi. w. of Little Traverse Creek. C.M.B. Sept. 15, 1935. BLAIR CO.: A. P. Garber. (Porter's Catalogue). BUTLER CO.: On wet roadside bank, Semiconon Run, 2½ mi. w. of Conoquenessing. Sidney K. Eastwood. March 24, 1935. CAMBRIA CO.: Cresson. T. C. Porter. (Porter's Catalogue). ELK CO.: McMinn. (Porter's Catalogue). McKEAN CO.: On rich, shaded bank of stream, Langmade, April 3, 1897, and April 25, 1897 (figured), and on rocks bordering rivulets, head of Gates' Hollow, Bradford, October 27, 1895. D.A.B. WASHINGTON CO.: Linn and Simonton. (Porter's Catalogue).

14.   RHYTIDIADELPHUS (Lindberg) Warnstorf

Dioicous: more or less robust, stiff, loosely cespitose forming loose, wide, stiff, green to yellowish or grayish, and rather lustrous mats; stem angled, long, without rhizoids, simple to regularly or irregularly pinnate; branches partly short and obtuse, partly long and acuminate, and often curved above; upper half of the leaf spreading-squarrose to reflexed-squarrose, sometimes circinate-secund, mostly plicate, scarcely decurrent, from an ovate or cordate base more or less long-acuminate, plane-margined, rather sharply serrate; costa reaching above mid-leaf, or short, double, or sometimes none; cells narrowly linear, smooth, or the upper angle projecting dorsally as a tooth, the basal wider, shorter, more or less incrassate and porose, colored, the alar mostly not differentiated; seta 2-4 cm long, castaneous; capsule horizontal to pendent, from a very short neck thickly oval, dorsally gibbous, when dry and empty plicate, but not constricted below the mouth, annulate; peristome normally hypnoid; lid convex, conic-acute.

A genus of 6 species of forest and meadow in the temperate and cold regions of the Northern Hemisphere; 4 species in North America; 2 species in our region.

KEY TO THE SPECIES

A. Cells smooth both sides; stem-leaves not plicate, squarrose-recurved, long and slender-ly acuminate ....1. *R. squarrosus*
A. Cells dorsally spinose; stem-leaves strongly plicate, spreading, short-acuminate ....
....2. *R. triquetrus*

1. RHYTIDIADELPHUS SQUARROSUS [Linnaeus, Hedwig] Warnstorf

(*Hypnum squarrosum* Linnaeus; *Hylocomium squarrosum* Bryologia Europaea)

Widely and softly cespitose, bright green, lustrous: stems robust, but slender, up to 10 or even 15 cm long, procumbent or more or less ascending to erect at the ends, the branchlets rather distant, flexuous, unequal, attenuated and more or less sub-flagelliform; stem-leaves crowded, about 3 mm long, abruptly squarrose from a cordate-ovate more or less erect-sheathing base, not secund, imbricated, the squarrose portion long and gradually tapering and channeled, denticulate above, the apical leaves somewhat stellately spreading, branch-leaves smaller but otherwise very similar to stem-leaves; costa short, double, faint; median leaf-cells smooth dorsally, about 8-10:1, narrowly-linear, the alar gradually rectangular-hexagonal, larger, short, opaque to pellucid, numerous, but not forming abruptly differentiated auricles; perichaetial leaves squarrose, the inner linear-acuminate and apically serrate: seta usually 3-4 cm long, flexuous; capsule castaneous, short, ovoid, dorsally gibbous, inclined to horizontal, or even pendent by the curving of the upper part of the seta; lid convex-conic, rather acute; annulus 2-seriate; peristome normally hypnoid, segments carinately split between the articulations, cilia 3; spores mature in winter or early spring.

On soil, rocks, or logs, in cool places in moist or wet meadows and borders of woods in grassy places; Azores, Europe, Asia, and, in North America, from the Arctic regions to the northern United States as far south as Pennsylvania and Tennessee.

Rare in our region. CAMBRIA CO.: Lesquereux, at Cresson. (Porter's Flora). SOMERSET CO.: Beck Spring, Laurel Ridge. C.M.B. July 26, 1947 (figured).

2. RHYTIDIADELPUS TRIQUETRUS [Linnaeus, Hedwig] Warnstorf

(*Hypnum triquetrum* Linnaeus; *Hylocomium triquetrum* Bryologia Europaea)

Plate XLVII

Very robust, stiff, elastic, bright to yellowish-green, bushy-cespitose: stems long, up to 15 or 18 cm, branching unequally and irregularly, sometimes more or less pinnately, reddish, woody, ascending or sometimes erect; stem-leaves large, 4-5 mm long, stiff, scarious, divaricately or horizontally spreading both wet and dry, widely cordate- to deltoid-triangular, widely rounded-auriculate at base, the insertion narrow and decurrent; leaves plicate, denticulate, papillose dorsally, gradually tapering above to a sub-acute apex; branch-leaves narrower and smaller towards the ends of the attenuate branches; costa forked, or of two parallel divisions reaching about three-fourths the length of the leaf; perichaetial leaves non-costate, the acuminations squarrose; median leaf-cells linear, about 8-10:1, at the angles oblong-hexagonal, pellucid, not usually forming distinct auricles, the upper cells dorsally forming spinulose papillae: seta 1.5-3.5 cm long, rather rigid, lustrous, castaneous; capsule turgid-oblong, large, castaneous, about 3 mm long, dorsally gibbous, inclined or more nearly horizontal by a curve in the upper part of the seta, when dry more or less plicate and constricted below the mouth; the exothecial cells rounded-hexagonal, rather small, incrassate, castaneous; lid conic, acute; annulus 2-3-seriate; peristome normally hypnoid, the teeth orange-yellow, strongly trabecu-late, dorsally lamellate, the lamellae papillose but non-striate, projecting to form a distinct border; the segments carinately split, the cilia 2 (or 3) and about as long as the segments, stout, the basal membrane reaching about one-half the height of the peristome; spores medium-walled, smooth, yellowish, .018-.025 mm, ripening in winter or early spring.

On shaded banks, humus, or rotten logs in cool woods with a moderate amount of moisture, or in swamps; Europe, Asia, northern Africa, and, in North America from the Arctic regions south to the northern United States, and along the mountains in North Carolina, in ravines and cool, rocky woods.

CAMBRIA Co.: T. C. Porter. (Porter's Catalogue). ELK Co.: McMinn. (Porter's Catalogue). McKEAN Co.: On decaying leaves under hemlocks, Marilla Brook, Bradford, June 5, 1895 (figured), and September 29, 1894; Bennett Brook, July 15, 1893. D.A.B. WASHINGTON Co.: Linn and Simonton.

15. RHYTIDIUM (Sullivant) Kindberg

Dioicous: very robust, in wide, loose, yellowish or brownish-yellow tufts or mats: when dry stiff and lustrous; stems long, tumid, with hooked tips, prostrate to ascending or erect, with few or no rhizoids, simple to regularly pinnate, or bipinnate, rarely bushy; branches 2-seriate, short and thick, or longer, acuminate and downwardly arcuate; leaves crowded, imbricate, falcate-secund, concave, plicate, rugose, scarcely decurrent, lance-ovate to oblong-ovate, narrowed into a long, canaliculate, lance-subulate, sharply-toothed point, the margin more or less revolute; costa simple, thin, reaching to mid-leaf; median leaf-cells narrowly vermicular, with dorsally (sometimes a few ventrally, also) projecting and forward-pointing teeth-like papillae at the upper end of the cell, towards the costa at base the cells more lax, rectangular, porose, incrassate, the alar region not excavate, the alar cells forming a distinct longi-tudinal band of small, quadrate and polygonal, yellowish, incrassate, numerous cells; inner perichaetial leaves elongate-lanceolate, slenderly acuminate, plicate, serrate, ecostate: seta 2-5 cm long, castaneous, when dry twisted; capsule in-clined to horizontal, elliptic to sub-cylindric, dorsally gibbous, when dry arcu-ate and constricted below the mouth, brownish; annulus 3-seriate, remaining attached to the operculum; lid convex-conic, shortly and obliquely rostrate;

peristome normally hypnoid, teeth rusty-yellow, segments broadly split, cilia 2, as long as the segments; spores in summer but capsules very rarely produced.

One species, as follows, on exposed sunny rocks and ledges, and in dry, grassy places; Europe, Asia, and from Arctic America south through Canada to North Carolina. Usually in hilly or mountainous regions on calcareous substrata. Rare in our region.

1. Rhytidium rugosum [Ehrhart, Hedwig] Kindberg

(Hylocomium rugosum DeNotaris; *Hypnum rugosum* Ehrhart)*

Plate LXVI

Stems reaching 8 or 10 cm or more, the branches tumid and sometimes 4-6 mm in diameter; the leaves 3 mm long or more, sometimes costate above the middle, margins narrowly reflexed.

Beaver Co.: On ground in *Pinus virginiana* forest, along Service Creek, one mile west of Raccoon Creek, C. M. Boardman, Feb. 10, 1935 (figured). Huntingdon Co.: T. C. Porter. (Porter's Catalogue).

16. Hylocomium Bryologia Europaea

Dioicous, more or less robust, stiffly and laxly cespitose in green or yellowish and more or less lustrous tufts: stem mostly very long and procumbent or ascending, more or less arcuate, once to three times pinnate; paraphyllia numerous, much-branched; leaves more or less spreading, concave, mostly plicate, oblong to cordate, long-acuminate, plane-margined, serrate; costa thin, double, sometimes reaching mid-leaf; cells linear, mostly smooth, basally shorter and laxer, colored, incrassate, porose, alar not differentiated; inner perichaetial leaves with reflexed-squarrose acuminations: seta more or less elongate, red; capsule inclined to horizontal, thickly ovate or oblong-oval, somewhat dorsally gibbous, with neck short and narrowed into the seta, drying mostly smooth and scarcely constricted below the mouth, annulate; peristome normally hypnoid; lid convex with a conic-acute point or shortly and obliquely rostrate.

A small, variously delimited genus mainly inhabiting forests in temperate and cold regions; 3 species in our region.

Key to the Species

A. Leaves at base semi-amplexicaul, with very large and rounded auricles; stems erect or arched ....3. *H. brevirostre*
A. Leaves with broad insertion but not with rounded auricles ....B
  B. Stem closely 2-3 pinnate; leaves obscurely bi-costate, rarely reaching midleaf ....
  ....1. *H. splendens*
  B. Stem irregularly or distantly 1-2 pinnate; costa double and reaching to mid-leaf or more ....2. *H. umbratum*

1. Hylocomium splendens (Hedwig) Bryologia Europaea

(Hypnum splendens Hedwig; *Hylocomium proliferum* Lindberg)*

Plate XLVII

Widely cespitose in loose mats, lustrous, yellowish to brownish or olivegreen: stems long, trailing, red, with green, branched paraphyllia, stems sometimes up to 15 or 20 cm long, divided, the fern-like shoot of each year ascending from the side of the upper third of the preceding year's shoot, the divisions usually complanately and loosely bi- to tri-pinnate; stem-leaves crowded, erect-spreading to loosely imbricate, broadly ovate to ovate-oblong, 2-3 mm long, the insertion wide, the upper portion of the leaf abruptly acuminate into a slender, transversely undulate and flexuous point, or sometimes shorter and obtuse, the leaves basally plicate, sub-decurrent, somewhat concave, recurved at margin below, denticulate and dorsally spinulosely papillose above; branch-leaves usually acute, smaller and non-plicate, concave, elliptic-oblong; costa double and reaching to one-fourth or one-third the length of the leaf, but faint; median leaf-cells linear-flexuous, about 8-10:1, the lower more or less porose, the basal orange-pellucid, incrassate and larger, but not forming distinct auricular groups; perichaetial bracts long, the inner erect, narrowly acuminate and sheathing: seta about 1.5-2.0 cm long, red, usually stiff, curved, when dry wrinkled and sometimes sinistrorse; capsule oblong-ovate, orange-brown, somewhat turgid, usually horizontally inclined, the urn about 2-3 mm long; peristome hypnoid, the teeth basally confluent, trabeculate, lamellate, dorsally striolate below, papillose above, brownish; segments about as long, widely carinately gaping, yellowish, the three slender, nodose cilia about as long, the basal membrane about two-fifths as high as the teeth; lid rostrate; exothecial cells brownish, rather thin-walled, rectangular to hexagonal, several rows at the rim much smaller; spores smooth, medium-walled, .010-.014 mm, mature in spring.

On stones and logs in cool, rich, moist mountain woods and ravines; Europe, Asia, northern Africa, and, in North America from the Arctic regions south to North Carolina.

Not common in our region. BEDFORD CO.: On big blocks of "gannister" on the open rock talus slope in gap west of White Sulphur Springs. O.E.J. June 15, 1941. BLAIR Co.: T. C. Porter. (Porter's Catalogue). CLARION CO.: Thoms Run, Cook Forest. S. K. Eastwood. Sept. 15, 1935. ELK CO.: McMinn. (Porter's Catalogue). JEFFERSON Co.: Kate Stoy. McKEAN CO.: On logs and on ground over leaves, Rutherford Run, April 25, 1893, West Branch Swamp, on logs, October 15, 1893, and on rich, shaded banks over leaves, Marilla Brook, June 30, 1895 (figured), all Bradford. D.A.B. TIOGA Co.: On wet cliff near Leetonia. S. K. Eastwood. Sept. 6, 1936. WASHINGTON CO.: Linn and Simonton. (Porter's Catalogue).

2. HYLOCOMIUM UMBRATUM [Ehrhart] Bryologia Europaea

(*Hypnum umbratum* Ehrhart)

Plate XLVIII

Slender, not so large and not complanately branched as in *H. splendens*, more erect and forming loose, green tufts often 12 or 15 cm high, sometimes yellowish, somewhat lustrous: stems rigid, pinnately or bi-pinnately, bushily branched, the branchlets unequal, often drooping, sometimes distinctly flagelliform, the stems reddish, bearing numerous conspicuous and branched paraphyllia; stem-leaves quite broadly triangular-ovate, rather distant, rather spreading, about 2 mm long, acute to long-acuminate, decurrent, strongly plicate, undulately strongly dentate all around, the teeth sometimes recurved, no papillae on back of leaf; branch-leaves more ovate and smaller; costa double and strong, reaching to about mid-leaf; median leaf-cells about 8-10:1, linear, not forming distinct auricles, the extreme basal castaneous-incrassate, rounded; perichaetial leaves broad, apically spreading: seta slender, 3-4 cm long, flexuous; capsule short, about 2:1, turgid-ovate, more or less horizontally inclined, somewhat plicate and constricted below the mouth when dry and empty; peristome normally hypnoid, segments carinately split, the cilia usually 2, about as long as segments; annulus none; lid conic, shortly apiculate; spores mature in winter or early spring.

Over rocks, logs, and woods-humus, in cool mountain woods and ravines; Europe, Asia, and, in North America, from Newfoundland to Alaska south to Ohio, and southwards in the mountains to North Carolina.

Rare in our region. McKEAN Co.: In deep, densely shaded ravines, altitude 1700 feet along Marilla Brook one-half mile above Bradford, April 21, 1879. D.A.B. (figured).

3. HYLOCOMIUM BREVIROSTRE [Ehrhart] Bryologia Europaea
(*Hypnum brevirostre* Ehrhart; *H. interruptum* Bridel)

Plate XLVIII

Robust, rigid, forming large, swollen tufts of a dark but glossy yellow-green: stems much-divided, up to 12-15 cm long, erect to arched-procumbent, irregularly pinnately branched, the branches unequal, attenuate, not complanately arranged, but bushy, paraphyllia rather small, branched, stems reddish-brown; stem-leaves somewhat crowded, spreading to squarrose, about 2-4 mm long, cordate-ovate to triangular-ovate, abruptly narrowed to a rather long channeled acumen, the base notably with large rounded, sub-clasping, and somewhat decurrent auricles, the margins finely and regularly denticulate, the leaves when dry much plicate; branch-leaves smaller, narrower, more ovate, less squarrose; perichaetial leaves sheathing at base, subulate-acuminate, squarrose, apically serrate; costa of stem- and branch-leaves double and reaching to about one-third the length of the leaf; median leaf-cells linear, about 5-8:1, rather incrassate, basal cells shorter and wider, colored, with pitted walls, the alar not differentiated: seta flexuous, about 2 cm long, dextrorse and arcuate above, castaneous; capsule turgidly ovoid-oblong, horizontally inclined, the urn about 2 mm long, castaneous, arcuate and constricted below the mouth when dry; lid conic-acuminate, about 1 mm long; annulus usually 2-seriate, rather wide; peristome hypnoid, teeth orange-yellow, dorsally lamellate, cross-striolate below, papillose above, moderately trabeculate, confluent and inserted at base; segments slender, about as long at teeth, yellowish, carinately gaping, finely spinose-papillose above, the basal membrane about two-fifths as high; cilia usually short, nodose-appendiculate; exothecial cells laterally strongly castaneous-incrassate, rounded-hexagonal to rounded-rectangular; spores about .021-.024 mm, oblong to round, castaneous, moderately incrassate, somewhat papillose, mature in winter or early spring.

In cool, deep, shaded ravines and in swamps on soil, rocks, or at the bases of trees, usually confined to mountainous regions; Europe, Asia, northern Africa, and, in North America, from Nova Scotia to Ontario and south in the mountains to Georgia; Missouri.

It is probable that deforestaion and lumbering activities have largely so modified the environment that this species is becoming rare. Most of the collections recorded were made prior to 1900.

Rather common in our region. Known from Beaver (Porter), Blair (Porter), Cambria (Porter), Clinton, Elk (Porter), Fayette, McKean, Somerset, Warren, and Washington (Porter) counties. Specimen figured: Densely shaded rocks, Marilla Brook, Bradford, McKean Co., April 25, 1895. D.A.B. (This was distributed in Grout's N. Am. Musci Pleurocarpi, No. 44).

17. Hypnum Linnaeus, Hedwig

Dioicous: robust, stiff, deeply and loosely cespitose, dark to pale green or almost straw-colored, more or less lustrous: from a decumbent base ascending to erect, with straight pointed ends and rather regularly pinnate; branches mostly spreading and 2-seriate, usually slenderly attenuate, sometimes thick, julaceous, and obtuse; no paraphyllia; leaves crowded, imbricately appressed, spoon-shaped, more or less distinctly plicate, scarcely decurrent, broadly ovate to ovate-oblong, apex blunt, the margin often narrowly revolute below and broadly involute upwards, at the very apex only weakly crenulate or serrulate; costa indistinct, or very thin, short and double; median leaf-cells narrowly prosenchymatous, smooth, the basal shorter, laxer, porose, incrassate, yellowish to orange-red, the alar abruptly enlarged, quadrate to shortly rectangular, or several-angled, incrassate, colored, the alae more or less excavate; perichaetial leaves sheathing, lance-oblong, rather abruptly acuminate, indistinctly costate: seta 2-4 cm long, sinistrorse, tortuous, yellowish-red to red; capsule cernuous, 2-2.5 mm long, usually horizontal, symmetric, or dorsally somewhat gibbous, drying arcuate, slightly constricted below the mouth, brownish, smooth; annulus none; lid high-convex, acute or conic-obtuse.

The genus is variously delimited by different authors; as here restricted it contains only the following species.

1. Hypnum Schreberi Willdenow, Schwaegrichen

(H. parietinum Linnaeus; H. muticum Swartz; Stereodon Schreberi
Mitten; Hylocomium parietinum Lindberg)

Plate XLVIII

Usually bright yellowish-green: stems up to 12 or 15 cm long, bright red; stem-leaves 1.5-2.5 mm long; median leaf-cells about 10-15:1, the apical shorter: capsules produced rather infrequently; exothecial cells transversely oblong-hexagonal, laterally strongly castaneous-incrassate; peristome-teeth slender, strongly trabeculate, dorsally lamellate, faintly transversely papillose-striolate, margined, yellowish, confluent below; segments broad, nearly as long as the teeth, widely carinately gaping, yellowish and papillose; cilia subappendiculate, about as long as the segments, usually single; the basal membrane about two-fifths as high as teeth; spores about .014-.018 mm, smooth, moderately incrassate, castaneous, ripe in autumn.

Grout, in his *Moss Flora of North America*, places this species, together with *Calliergon cuspidatum*, in Loeske's genus *Calliergonella*.

Mainly over humus, etc., in moist, shaded woods, but occurring in moist pastures, dry open woods, and bogs as well; Europe, Asia, and from Arctic America to the northern United States; as far south as Virginia in the mountains.

Not uncommon in the elevated plateaus and in the mountains of western Pennsylvania. Now known from Bedford, Somerset, Fayette, Huntingdon, Cameron, Elk, Forest, McKean, Warren, Washington, and Westmoreland counties. Specimen figured: On decaying log, West Branch Swamp, Bradford, McKean Co., April 5, 1895. D.A.B.

18. PTILIUM (Sullivant) DeNotaris

Dioicous: robust, stiff, laxly cespitose, plume-like, yellowish-green, in shade bright green, lustrous; stem 5-20 cm long, ascending to erect, simple or 2-3-divided, regularly and densely complanately pinnate with dense complanate branches; branches horizontally spreading, circinate at the apex, of nearly equal length below, rapidly becoming shorter at the apex; leaves crowded, circinate to almost coiled, deeply pluri-plicate, long-lance-subulate from a broadly ovate and scarcely decurrent base, plane-margined, finely serrulate above the middle; costa none, or double and short; median leaf-cells very narrowly linear, vermicular-prosenchymatous, smooth, the basal shorter, wider often and porose, a few alar indistinctly differentiated, quadrate to shortly rectangular: seta 3-5 cm long, tortuous, red, drying dextrorse above; capsule cernuous to horizontal, arcuate, about 2 mm long, castaneous, cylindric, smooth; annulus narrow, 2-seriate; lid dome-like, shortly apiculate.

The genus contains only 1 species, as follows:

1. PTILIUM CRISTA-CASTRENSIS [Linnaeus] DeNotaris
(Hypnum crista-castrensis Linnaeus; *Stereodon crista-castrensis* Mitten)
PLUME MOSS
Plate XLIX

An easily recognized, rigid, robust, plume-like, bright yellowish-green species: stem-leaves about 2-3 mm long; median leaf-cells about 10-20:1, branch-leaves not usually reaching 2 mm in length; exothecial cells strongly castaneous-incrassate, small and rounded in several series at the rim, below becoming oblong-rectangular; peristome-teeth castaneous, large, strongly trabeculate, lamellate, crosswise faintly and finely dorsally papillose-striolate, confluent below; segments as long as teeth, yellowish, papillose; the basal membrane about one-half as high; cilia 2-4, slender, hyaline, about as long as the segments, nodose-appendiculate; spores smoothish, castaneous, medium-walled, about .010-.014 mm, usually mature in early autumn.

On woods-humus, rotten logs, and moist earth, in cool woods, usually in mountainous regions; Europe, Asia, and from Arctic America south to the northern United States and southwards in the mountains to North Carolina.

Not uncommon in the more mountainous portions of our region. Now known from Bedford, Somerset, Fayette, Washington, Blair, Cambria, Clinton, Elk, Clarion, McKean, and Warren counties. Specimen figured: Allegheny Mts., August 17, 1875. B. H. Patterson.

19.   STEREODON Bridel, Mitten

Mainly dioicous: robust to quite slender, green to yellowish-green or golden brown, lustrous: stems elongate, decumbent or ascending, rarely erect, mostly non-stoloniferous, simple or divided, irregularly or rarely regularly pinnate, the shoots mostly with hooked or circinate ends; leaves entire or serrulate, often apparently 2-seriate, in most species falcate-secund, non-decurrent or but slightly so, rather concave, ovate- to cordate-lanceolate, acuminate to more or less subulate-acuminate; costa short and double or none; leaf-cells narrowly prosenchymatous, smooth on both sides (except *S. molluscum*), the basal mostly incrassate and porose, parenchymatous in the mostly somewhat excavate angles; inner perichaetial leaves plicate, lance-subulate: seta long, drying twisted; capsule cernuous to horizontal, rarely erect, oblong to cylindric, arcuate or rarely straight, mostly smooth and annulate; lid convex-conic, umbonate to apiculate, or sometimes short-rostrate.

A large genus mainly confined to the temperate regions. Many authors now include most of the species under *Hypnum* (See Brotherus and Grout).

This genus makes up a large part of the mossy mantle over old logs, roots, bases of trees, roots, and earth in our woods, particularly in the southwestern counties.

KEY TO THE SPECIES

A. Leaves neither distinctly falcate nor secund ....B
A. Leaves more or less distinctly falcate or secund C
   B. Leaves entire ....9. *S. Haldanianus*
   B. Leaves distinctly serrulate, at least towards the apex ....*S. nemorosus**
C. Leaves usually distinctly entire ....D
C. Leaves serrate to serrulate at least towards the apex ....F
   D. Usually distinctly and regularly pinnate ....7. *S. Patientiae*
   D. Not distinctly regularly pinnate ....E
E. Alar cells gradually enlarged, not sharply differentiated; perichaetial leaves plicate;
      capsule, when dry, curved, not plicate ....8. *S. pratensis*
E. Quadrate alar cells numerous, inflated ones few; perichaetial leaves not plicate; capsules unsymmetric ....5. *S. cupressiformis*
F. Alar cells strongly inflated ....M (see also L)
   F. Alar cells not much inflated, or, if so, very few in number; or none ....G
G. Not regularly pinnate; leaves usually entire ....
      ....5. *S. cupressiformis* (See also *S. pratensis*)
G. Rather regularly pinnate; leaves serrate or serrulate, at least above ....H
   H. Capsule symmetric or nearly so; a few alar cells somewhat inflated I
   H. Capsule more or less curved or arcuate ....J

---

* *S. nemorosus* (Koch) Lindberg is a southern Appalachian species extending north to Virginia. It might occur in the mountains of Fayette or Somerset counties. Once reported in eastern Pennsylvania.

I. Capsule 3-4 mm long with apiculate or subrostellate lid ....
....4. *S. imponens* (See also *S. cupressiformis*)
I. Capsule 2 mm long; lid ½ as long as urn ....12. *S. tenuirostris*
   J. Quadrate alar cells very numerous; 6-10 along the margin ....K
   J. Quadrate alar cells few or none L
    K. Leaves little or not serrulate; inflated alar cells few; dioicous ....5. *S. cupressiformis*
    K. Leaves distinctly serrate; no inflated alar cells; monoicous ....S
     L. Monoicous; capsules often not plicate when dry and empty; a few subquadrate
        alar cells and a few inflated angle cells ....3. *S. fertilis*
      L. Dioicous; capsules strongly plicate when dry and empty; alar cells not quadrate
        but broader, incrassate, often colored ....6. *S. curvifolius*
M. More or less regularly and evenly pinnate ....Q
M. Not regularly pinnate ....N
   N. Operculum not rostrate ....O
   N. Operculum distinctly rostrate ....P
    O. Leaves entire or serrulate at apex; decurrent cells inflated; leaf-apex gradually long-
     acuminate ....6. *S. curvifolius*
    O. Leaves entire; a few alar cells abruptly inflated and hyaline; leaf-apex broadly acu-
     minate to acute or blunt ....7. *S. Patientiae*
     P. Lid about ½ as long as the urn ....10. *S. recurvans*
     P. Lid about as long as the urn ....11. *S. delicatulus*
Q. Slender and sparsely branched; lid about ½ as long as the urn; cilia rudimentary
   or none ....12. *S. tenuirostris*
Q. More robust and abundantly branching; lid relatively short; cilia well developed ......R
   R. Leaves entire, broadly acuminate to acute or blunt; a number of alar cells abrupt-
    ly inflated and hyaline ....7. *S. Patientiae*
   R. Leaves entire or serrulate near apex; only a few enlarged or inflated alar cells L
S. Capsule more or less arcuate; quadrate alar cells very numerous and extending up
   along the margin 10 or more cells ....1. *S. reptilis*
S. Capsule erect and symmetric or nearly so; quadrate alar cells few; in the mountains
   at higher altitudes ....2. *S. pallescens*

1.   STEREODON REPTILIS (Richard) Mitten

(*Hypnum reptilis* Richard)

Plate XLIX

Small, dark or yellowish-green, lustrous, widely and loosely cespitose:
stems more or less regularly pinnate, closely interwoven; stem-leaves crowded,
lance-acuminate from an ovate-oblong base, about 1 x 0.4-0.5 mm, falcate-
secund, slightly decurrent, serrate above, serrulate to entire below, the margins
usually revolute; median leaf-cells linear-rhomboidal to linear-flexuous, about
8-12:1, shorter and more or less colored towards the base, the alar cells numerous, quadrate, much incrassate, sub-opaque, none inflated; branch-leaves similar
but proportionally much narrower; paraphylla small and few; costa double,
short, yellowish, or none; inner perichaetial leaves long-acuminate; usually
faintly bi-costate, apically serrate, strongly plicate: seta castaneous, lustrous,
about 1.5 cm long, when dry dextrorse above; capsules about 2.5 mm long,
cylindric, yellowish, mostly abruptly arcuate just below the mouth so that the
lid often points at right angles to the direction assumed by the base of the
capsule, when dry the urn more or less wrinkled and narrowed below the
mouth; lid yellow, rather large, high-convex, narrowly obliquely rostrate; peristome hypnoid, the teeth subulate-acuminate, orange-yellow and dorsally cross-

striolate at base, hyaline and papillose above; segments about as long as teeth, carinately cleft between the articulations; cilia usually 2, articulate, slightly shorter than the segments; annulus large, compound; spores rather strongly incrassate, yellowish-brown, papillose, about .014-.017 mm, mature in mid-summer; usually fruits abundantly.

On bases of trees, roots, logs, etc., in dense woods, especially in spruce woods and mainly confined to hilly or mountainous regions; Europe, Asia, and from Canada south in the mountains to North Carolina and in the West to Arizona.

ERIE Co.: Eight collections on Presque Isle. Nelle Ammons, various dates summers of 1933 and 1935. McKEAN Co.: Several collections of D. A. Burnet, in various localities of northern McKean Co., 1895-1897. SOMERSET Co.: On tree root, hemlock woods, near Buckstown, Oct. 7, 1934, and on logs and tree base, Shafer Run and Clear Run, Sept. 14, 1946, and Oct. 6, 1935. C.M.B.; on base of dead tree, near Bakersville. C. M. Hepner. Oct. 21, 1933. WARREN Co.: Bark of sugar maple, near Big Bend. C.M.B. Sept. 2, 1935. WASHINGTON Co.: On rotten wood, Snake Woods. Linn and Simonton. Nov. 1892.

2. STEREODON PALLESCENS (Hedwig) Lindberg

(*Leskea pallescens* Hedwig; *Rhynchostegium Jamesii* Sullivant; *Hypnum protuberans* Brotherus; *Hypnum pallescens* Bryologia Europaea)

Slender, in thin silky mats, more or less pinnate; stem-leaves weakly falcate, loosely arranged, from an ovate somewhat decurrent base narrowly and long acuminate, about 1 mm long, plane, weakly apically serrulate; costa short and double or none; a few of the alar cells quadrate and at least the marginal hyaline: seta 6-10 mm long, reddish; capsules about 1.5-2 x 0.5 mm, castaneous, nearly symmetric, not shrinking below the mouth when dry and empty; lid reddish yellow, slightly rostrate; spores ripe in mid- to late summer.

Mostly on trunks and roots of coniferous trees, or on rotten wood; Europe, and south in the mountains from Canada to Tennessee. Not yet found in western Pennsylvania, but to be expected.

3. STEREODON FERTILIS (Sendtner) Lindberg

(*Hypnum fertile* Sendtner)

Plate XLIX

Yellowish-green, lustrous, usually darker below, densely interwoven: stems prostrate or ascending, from 3-10 cm long, scarcely branching, castaneous, densely and rather regularly, complanately and somewhat plumosely pinnate with short branchlets; stem-leaves 1.5-2.0 mm long, concave, falcate-secund, scarcely complanate, from an oblong-ovate base slenderly acuminate, the base not decurrent, sub-auriculate, somewhat excavate, the margin plane, entire below, serrulate above; costa usually bi-furcate or double, rarely none; branch-leaves similar to stem-leaves but smaller and narrower, strongly falcate to circinate-secund; inner perichaetial leaves lance-acuminate, plicate, faintly bi-costate, serrulate above; median leaf-cells linear-vermicular, about 1:15-20, rather incrassate, sub-acute, median basal cells strongly incrassate, castaneous-pellucid, porose, the alar portion with several oblong inflated hyaline cells, above which is a patch of about 9-15 smaller, incrassate, quadrate to oblong-hexagonal cells often more or less castaneous-pellucid: seta 1.5-2.0 cm long, dextrorse, castaneous, lustrous; capsule about 1.8 mm long, oblong, inclined to horizontal, arcuate, bright castaneous with a darker and lustrous rim, when dry narrowed below the mouth and sub-costate or smooth; lid short, conic-acute; peristome-teeth lance-subulate, brownish-pellucid, more or less narrowly hyaline-margined, dorsally cross-striolate below, the divisural line and the lamellae fairly distinct, above hyaline and papillose, the trabeculae numerous and strong; segments pale, about as long as the teeth, carinately split between the articulations, the basal membrane about two-fifths as high, the cilia usually 2, hyaline, nodose, somewhat shorter than the segments; exothecial cells rather thin-walled, quadrate-hexagonal to oblong-hexagonal, at the mouth smaller and deeply castaneous; spores medium-walled, somewhat brownish, smooth or very nearly so, about .015-.018 mm, mature in summer.

On decaying logs in moist and cool places, usually in hilly or mountainous regions; Europe, Asia, and, in North America, from New Brunswick to British Columbia and southwards to the northern United States.

Armstrong Co.: West bank Allegheny River, Foxburg. June 10, 1934. C.M.B. Fayette Co.: Laurel Run, 2 mi. e. of Wymp's Gap, elev. 2100 ft. Aug. 24, 1940. C.M.B. McKean Co.: Leer's Run on decaying log, August 5, 1895 (figured), Lang-made Hollow, August 11, 1895, Gates' Hollow, October 27, 1895, and Bennett Brook, August 8, 1897. D.A.B. Somerset Co.: Cranberry Glade Run, Laurel Hill. On log in swampy woods. June 22, 1947. C.M.B.

4. Stereodon imponens (Hedwig) Lindberg

(*Hypnum imponens* Hedwig; *H. cupressiforme* Hooker)

Log Moss

Plate XLIX

Robust in flat, thin, widely interwoven tufts of a yellow-green color: stems rigid, reddish-brown, with numerous paraphyllia, closely, rather regularly and more or less complanately pinnate, prostrate or sub-erect, sometimes reaching more than 10 cm in length; stem-leaves usually somewhat complanate-secund, from a triangular-oblong base gradually long-acuminate, the base not excavate, scarcely decurrent, the acumen strongly falcate-secund, the whole leaf about 2 x 0.5-0.7 mm, serrulate above, the margin often narrowly recurved below; branch-leaves narrower, otherwise similar to the stem-leaves, about as long; costa short and double or none; median leaf-cells linear-vermicular, about 10-15:1, the basal broader and more or less orange-pellucid, the alar cells sub-quadrate, a few somewhat inflated at the extreme angles, forming a small but quite distinct auricular patch of an orange-brown color, all cells rather incrassate; perichaetial leaves plicate, ecostate, spinose-serrulate above: seta about 3 cm long, castaneous, sinistrorse when dry; capsule cylindric, nearly erect, slightly curved, about 3-4 mm long, castaneous, about 4-6:1; lid convex at base with an oblique long-acuminate point; peristome normally hypnoid, the teeth strongly trabeculate, the trabeculae often dividing, the lamellae and divisural distinct, cross-striolate below; the segments about as long, slightly carinately split, the basal membrane reaching about two-fifths as high, the cilia articulate and usually single; annulus compound, adherent; exothecial cells yellowish-pellucid, laterally quite incrassate, oblong-quadrate to long-rectangular; spores yellowish, medium-walled, minutely roughened, about .013-.015 mm, mature in late autumn or early winter.

This is commonly sold in the Pittsburgh markets at Christmas time in sheets and called "Log Moss."

On earth, stones, roots, logs, etc., with us mainly on humus or rotten wood, in moist woods; Europe, Asia, and from Canada southwards to California and Georgia.

Very common in our region. Now known in 15 counties in western Pennsylvania and probably occurring in all. It is particularly abundant in the southwestern counties growing in sheets over decaying logs. Specimen figured: Wildwood Hollow, Allegheny Co., Nov. 19, 1908. O.E.J.

5. STEREODON CUPRESSIFORMIS [Linnaeus] Lindberg

(*Hypnum cupressiforme* Linnaeus; *H. compressum* Schultz)

Widely cespitose in flat, soft tufts, usually yellowish or brownish-green: stems up to 10 cm long, greenish, procumbent, irregularly pinnate, the branches spreading or ascending, usually curved; leaves closely imbricate, concave at the base, not decurrent, falcate-secund, lustrous, oblong- to ovate-lanceolate, narrowed rather abruptly to a long acumination, plane-margined, typically entire, sometimes denticulate towards the apex; costa none or very short and double; median leaf-cells about 10:1, linear-vermicular, rather obtuse, the angular sub-quadrate, numerous, rather opaque, a few at the extreme angles larger, scarcely inflated, somewhat orange-pellucid, or hyaline, rather incrassate, the auricles not well-defined; perichaetial leaves denticulate, not plicate: seta red, about 3-4 cm long; capsule sub-erect, curved, sub-cylindric or oblong, castaneous, somewhat constricted below the mouth when dry; lid convex at base, with an acuminate or sub-rostrate apex; peristome normally hypnoid; cilia usually one or two; spores mature in late autumn or early winter.

On soil, rocks, roots, and bases of trees, in moist woods or ravines; practically cosmopolitan, — in North America occurring from the Arctic regions to the Gulf States. Rare in our region. Quite variable. There are a number of named varieties.

CAMBRIA CO.: T. P. James. (Porter's Catalogue). McKEAN CO.: Three pockets so-labeled in the Carnegie Museum Herbarium are apparently typical *S. fertilis* and the Porter Catalogue record is probably founded upon some of the same Burnett collections.

5a. STEREODON CUPRESSIFORMIS var. FILIFORMIS (Bridel) Jennings

(*Hypnum cupressiforme* var. *filiforme* Bridel)

Plate L

More slender, distantly pinnate, the branches long, very slender and almost filiform; leaves very small, falcate-secund, more or less regularly and neatly imbricated in two rows.

Habitat and range as for the species.

Rare in our region. McKEAN Co.: Rutherford Rocks, on moist and densely shaded fragments of sandstone at base of cliff, May 5, 1895, and Hawkin's Hollow, August 2, 1895. D.A.B. (figured).

6. STEREODON CURVIFOLIUS (Hedwig) Mitten

(*Hypnum curvifolium* Hedwig)

Plate L

Robust, lustrous, yellowish-green in large flat mats: stems prostrate, rather regularly pinnately branched, the branchlets short and unequal, the whole plant complanately secund; leaves crowded, imbricate in two rows, falcate-secund, thus giving to the plants a plaited appearance from the dorsal viewpoint; stem-leaves about 0.7-0.8 x 1.4-1.8 mm, oblong-ovate to elongate and triangular-ovate, long-acuminate, plane-margined, crenulate-serrulate about to the middle, and at the angles, concave, at the base abruptly narrowed and cordate or sub-cordate, somewhat decurrent; costa none or double and faint; branch-leaves similar but proportionally shorter and narrower, about 0.4-0.5-x-1-1.5 mm; median leaf-cells about .005-.007 x .035-.050 mm, linear-vermicular, basal median cells incrassate, porose, more or less vermicular to linear-oblong, a few of the alar cells sub-quadrate, yellowish or brownish and incrassate, about .020-.025 mm in diameter, the decurrent cells enlarged, thin-walled, and hyaline; perichaetial leaves erect, whitish, numerous, the inner sheathing, plicate, reaching 4-5 mm long: seta about 2.5 cm long, dextrorse above, sinistrorse below, castaneous, sub-lustrous; capsule about 2.5 mm long, pale castaneous, constricted below the mouth when dry and empty and then also strongly plicate, the urn oblong, arcuate, cernuous; lid conic, apiculate; peristome normally hypnoid, teeth yellowish pellucid, slender, strongly trabeculate, the lamellae and divisural distinct, the apical portion of the teeth hyaline and papillose, the lower dorsal surface cross-striolate; segments about as long as the teeth, slender, slightly carinately cleft, pale yellowish-pellucid, cilia two or three, about as long as segments, articulate, hyaline, papillose; annulus 3-seriate, revoluble; spores yellowish, medium-walled, granulose, about .019-.023 mm, mature in early spring.

On soil, rocks, or more usually on decaying logs in moist, cool woods; Asia, and from Arctic America south to Georgia, Missouri, and Colorado. Common in our region. The type was from Lancaster, Pennsylvania.

Now known from the following counties: Allegheny, Armstrong, Beaver, Butler, Cambria (Porter), Crawford, Erie, Fayette, McKean, Mercer, Somerset, Washington, and Westmoreland. Specimen figured: Pymatuning Swamp near Linesville, Crawford Co., May 12, 1908.

7. STEREODON PATIENTIAE Lindberg

(*Hypnum arcuatum* Lindberg; *H. Lindbergii* Mitt.; *H. Patientiae* Lindberg; *Stereodon arcuatus* Lindberg)

Plate L

Robust, widely cespitose in yellowish-green mats, usually more or less regularly pinnate, lustrous at least on the younger parts: stems prostrate, usually sparsely branched; stem-leaves about 1.6-2.2 mm long, complanately falcate-secund, lustrous, ovate-oblong, decurrent, the margins plane and entire or sub-denticulate at the apex, the leaves rather shortly and broadly acuminate, the tip flat and widely acute to somewhat obtuse, the decurrent auricles are made up of large, oblong, inflated, thin-walled, and hyaline cells bordered above by about two series of smaller, quadrate, usually brownish-pellucid, thicker-walled cells, these latter grading quickly into linear-vermicular median cells about 12-20:1, the apical cells oblong-rectangular or obliquely more or less rhomboidal; costa very short and double or none; branch-leaves similar; perichaetial leaves sheathing, the inner lanceolate to lance-linear, up to 6 or 7 mm long, plicate, entire, acuminate; seta about 2.5-3 cm long, dextrorse, lustrous, castaneous; capsule about 2-2.5 mm long, about 4-5:1, oblong-cylindric, erect at base but arcuate so that the lid usually points more or less horizontally, when dry plicate but scarcely narrowed below the mouth; annulus large, revoluble; lid conic, apiculate, scarcely longer than wide; peristome hypnoid, the teeth lance-linear, dorsally cross-striolate, yellowish-pellucid below, hyaline and papillose above, the divisural and dorsal lamellae prominent, the trabeculae strong and numerous; segments rising from a basal membrane about two-fifths the height of the teeth, the segments about as long as teeth, narrow, somewhat carinately split; cilia 1-3, shorter, nodose, hyaline-papillose, often joined together above; spores smoothish, yellowish, moderately incrassate, about .014-.018 mm, mature in late spring or early summer.

On the ground in woods and wet, grassy places in swamps, around springs, etc.; Europe, Asia, and from Arctic America to the northern United States and south, in the East, to Florida.

Now known from 13 counties in western Pennsylvania and probably occurs in all. Specimen figured: Kittanning, Armstrong Co., May 28, 1907. O.E.J.

8. Stereodon pratensis (Koch) Warnstorf
(*Hypnum pratense* Koch; *Isopterygium pratense* Lindberg)
Plate LXX

Softly and flatly cespitose, bright green, complanately flattened: stems prostrate to sub-erect, non-radiculose, irregularly sub-pinnate, branchlets rather sparse; leaves sub-secund on the larger branches and on the stems, plane to somewhat concave, entire; costa double and very faint and short or none; median leaf-cells narrowly rhomboid-vermicular, the alar rather gradually enlarged, fewer, less enlarged and less differentiated than in *S. Patientiae*; perichaetial leaves plicate, the inner long-lanceolate and shortly acuminate: pedicel long, twisted in two directions; capsule non-plicate, oblong to turgid-ovate, cernuous, arcuate when dry; lid convex-conic; annulus 3-seriate; peristome normally hypnoid, the cilia 3, about as long as the segments; spores mature in spring. The capsules are rarely produced.

Specimens sometimes show an abruptly enlarged group of alar cells typical of *S. Patientiae* in the larger stem-leaves, while less vigorous leaves are of the *S. pratensis* type, as in the Linn & Simonton specimen, *see* figure, Plate LXX.

In open swamps and marshy meadows, Eurasia, and from Pennsylvania and New Jersey to Arctic America. Varieties of it range farther south.

CAMBRIA CO.: Wiltmore. T. P. James. (Porter's Catalogue). McKEAN CO.: Near Bradford. D.A.B. WASHINGTON CO.: McCracken Sta., W. & W. Ry., Oct. 21, 1893. Linn & Simonton (figured).

9.   STEREODON HALDANIANUS (Greville) Lindberg
(*Hypnum Haldianum* Greville; *Heterophyllon Haldani* Kindberg; *Hypnum pulchrum* Hooker)

Plate L

Widely and loosely cespitose, dark to brownish-green: stems long, creeping, irregularly pinnate, the branchlets unequal and disposed much as in some of the *Brachytheciae;* leaves loosely and more or less evenly imbricate to loosely spreading; stem-leaves usually decurrent, about 0.7-1.5 mm long, oblong-ovate to somewhat lanceolate, rapidly narrowed to a short and acute apex, entire, plane-margined, concave; branch-leaves lance-ovate to lanceolate, about 0.5-1.5 mm long, short-acuminate, otherwise similar to the stem-leaves; median leaf-cells linear-flexuose, about 12-20:1, prosenchymatous, the alar inflated, rather incrassate, large, forming a quite distinct auricle, bordered above by a few considerably smaller and chlorophyllose cells; costa rudimentary or none, or double and short; perichaetial leaves spreading, abruptly filiform-acuminate, the inner non-plicate; paraphyllia large and numerous: seta about 2 cm long, lustrous, castaneous, when dry sinistrorse; capsule long-cylindric, dull-castaneous, curved, sub-erect to more or less inclined, about 4-6:1, urn about 2.5-3 mm long, the lid conic and obliquely short-rostrate; peristome-teeth confluent at base, transversely striolate and yellowish below, strongly trabeculate, the divisural and the dorsal lamellae usually faint; segments slightly carinately cleft, below more or less faintly transversely striolate-papillose, above papillose, about as long as the teeth; cilia usually single and shorter, sometimes two and rudimentary, or sometimes none, articulate; spores granulose, yellowish-brown, somewhat incrassate, about .015-.016 mm, mature in late fall or winter.

On earth, humus, rocks, rotten logs, etc., in woods; Europe, Asia, and, in North America, from Nova Scotia to Montana and southwards to the Gulf States.

Common in our region. Known from numerous collections from the following counties: Allegheny, Armstrong, Beaver, Butler, Cambria (Porter), Crawford, Elk (Porter), Erie, Fayette, McKean, and Somerset. Specimen figured: Wildwood Road Hollow, Allegheny Co., Nov. 19, 1908. O.E.J. and G.K.J.

10.   STEREODON RECURVANS [Richard] Brotherus
(*Hypnum recurvans* Schwaegrichen: *Sematophyllum recurvans* E. G. Britton; *Leskea recurvans* Richard; *Rhapidostegium recurvans* Bryologia Europaea; *Brotherella recurvans* Fleischer)

Plate LI

Very glossy, widely cespitose in flat tufts, usually yellowish-green: stems prostrate, reddish, irregularly pinnate; leaves about 1.2-1.5 mm long, strongly complanately falcate-secund, close, imbricate at base, soft, thin, more or less concave, lance-ovate, slenderly long-acuminate, non-decurrent, more or less sharply serrate at the apex, the margin often narrowly recurved below; costa obsolete, or very short and double; perichaetial leaves gradually long-acuminate, serrate at apex; median leaf-cells linear-flexuose, the basal yellowish or brownish, shorter, wider, the alar consisting of a group of 4 to 8 hyaline or colored, much inflated and enlarged cells forming a group bordered above by a few sub-quadrate and smaller cells: seta about 1.5-2 cm long, lustrous, castaneous, somewhat sinistrorse; capsule oblong-oval, slightly curved, obliquely inclined to almost horizontal, the urn about 3-4:1, about 1.5-2 mm long, light castaneous, the tapering base darker, the urn when old strongly arcuate; annulus present; lid conic and together with the slender beak about one-half the length of the urn; peristome hypnoid, the teeth large, strongly trabeculate, the divisural faint, the thin dorsal lamellae transversely papillose-striolate; segments about as long as teeth but usually not splitting, the basal membrane about two-fifths as long, the cilia usually one, sometimes two, slightly appendiculate, somewhat shorter than the segments; spores .016-.018 mm, medium-walled, granulose, brownish, mature in late fall, the capsules often remaining in good condition until early spring: dioicous.

On soil, humus, bases of trees, logs, etc., in moist woods, mainly in mountainous or hilly regions; from Newfoundland to Manitoba and south in the mountains to Georgia.

Common in our region. Known from eleven counties in western Pennsylvania and probably occurs in all, although most abundantly collected in the southwestern counties. Specimen figured: As to old capsules and peristome, Ohio Pyle, Fayette Co., May 30-31, 1908. O.E.J. As to other figures, Ohio Pyle, Sept. 1-3, 1906. O.E.J. & G.K.J.

11. STEREODON DELICATULUS (James) Brotherus

(*Hypnum laxepatulum* Lesquereux and James; *Rhynchostegium delicatulum* James; *Sematophyllum delicatulum* E. G. Britton; *Rhapidostegium deliculatum* Paris; *Brotherella delicatula* Fleischer)

Small, depressed cespitose, dark green, scarcely lustrous: stems slender, prostrate, subpinnately branching; leaves rather open, mostly falcate-secund, two-ranked, sharply serrulate towards the apex; costa none or very short and double; leaves concave, ovate, narrowed into a long acumination; a few of the extreme alar cells much enlarged and inflated as in *S. recurvans*, colored or hyaline, bordered by a few sub-quadrate and smaller, the median linear-flexuous, prosenchymatous; perichaetial leaves non-plicate, sharply serrate above: seta shorter than in *S. recurvans;* capsule about 1-1.5 mm long, ovoid-oblong, almost erect and only slightly curved, about 2-3:1, urn about equalled in length by the slenderly long-rostrate lid; peristome hypnoid, segments entire, cilia usually one or two; spores mature in late fall.

On rotten wood, or soil, or at the base of trees, mainly in the mountains from New England to Alabama.

Rare in our region. McKEAN Co.: Bradford. D. A. Burnett. (Porter's Catalogue).

12. STEREODON TENUIROSTRIS (Bruch and Schimper) Brotherus

(*Sematophyllum tenuirostre* E. G. Britton; *Hypnum cylindrocarpum*
C. Mueller; *Rhaphidostegium cylindricarpum* Jaeger)

Plate LI

Flatly and broadly cespitose in thin intricate mats, slender: stems prostrate, reddish, or green, pinnately branched, branches few, slender; stem-leaves sub-lustrous, about 1.5 mm long, falacte-secund but not complanate, narrowly lance-oblong, non-decurrent, acuminate, concave, apically serrate, marginally somewhat reflexed to the base of the acumen; median leaf-cells linear-prosen-chymatous, the apical usually a little larger, the alar few in number, inflated, sub-quadrate, bordered above by a few small quadrate, sub-opaque, often transversely elongated cells; branch-leaves similar to the stem-leaves, some-times a little larger; costa very short and double or none; perichaetial leaves erect, the inner plicate and gradually narrowed to a very slender serrate point, with a very short and double costa or none: seta about 5-7 mm long, sinis-trorse above, lustrous, castaneous; capsule cylindric to lance-oblong, the urn about 1-1.5 mm long, erect to somewhat inclined, symmetric; annulus none; exothecial cells somewhat collenchymatous, brownish, oblong-rectangular, the upper 3 or 4 rows rounded-quadrate; peristome-teeth yellowish, lance-subulate, finely cross-striolate, strongly trabeculate, the dorsal lamellae projecting to form a rather conspicuous hyaline border; segments about three-fourths as long, slender, carinately split between the articulations, the basal membrane about one- third as high as the teeth, cilia none or very rudimentary; lid conic and with a slender rostrum about one-half as long as the urn; spores in late fall to early spring, about .014-.018 mm, smoothish, brownish, rather thinly in-crassate.

On rotten logs and bases of trees and on rocks in dark woods, in the moun-tains from North Carolina and Georgia north to New York and Indiana.

ALLEGHENY CO.: Wildwood Road Hollow, side of ravine under dense shade of hemlocks, November 19, 1908. O.E.J. CAMERON CO.: On wet rocks 3 mi. w. of Tru-man. June 22, 1935. Sidney K. Eastwood. FAYETTE CO.: On rock in shaded woods in valley of Meadow Run, four imles four south of Ohio Pyle, September 1-3, 1906. O.E.J. and G.K.J. WESTMORELAND CO.: "Shades," near Blackburn, March 25, 1910. O.E.J. and G.K.J. (figured).

20. ISOPTERYGIUM Mitten

Autoicous or dioicous: mostly slender to very slender, cespitose, soft, mostly bright or yellowish-green and glossy: stem creeping to ascending, up-right only in the thick mats, mostly irregularly branched; leaves uniform, most-ly complanately and obliquely inserted, smooth, usually more or less two-seriate, from a narrow and little or not at all decurrent base oval to oblong and short-pointed or else ovate to lance-oblong and acute to piliferous, margins plane and entire to serrate; costa double, very short, or none; cells prosen-chymatous, smooth or papillose in the upper angle, the basal shorter, the alar not usually differentiated: seta long, smooth, mostly drying twisted; capsule sub-erect to cernuous or horizontal, with a collum, oval to oblong or cylindric, almost symmetric or weakly gibbous, when dry only rarely arcuate and narrowed below the mouth, mostly smooth; annulus present or none; peristome-teeth basally confluent, subulate, yellowish, mostly hyaline-bordered, with divisural zigzag, cross-striate, apically hyaline and papillose, lamellae numerous; cilia 1-2, nodose, rarely 3 and appendiculate; lid conic-convex, sometimes rostrate.

A genus of world-wide distribution and containing about 170 species, mostly occurring on decaying wood; about 25 species reported for North America; about 7 species in our region.

KEY TO THE SPECIES*

A. Leaves entire or only obscurely serrulate at apex ....B
A. Leaves usually distinctly serrate or serrulate at least in upper half ....E
  B. Leaves perfectly entire C
  B. Leaves obscurely serrulate at apex ....D
    C. Cells about .005-.008 x .075-.160 mm, about two rows at the base shorter and sub-oval; cortical stem-cells not enlarged and hyaline ....5. *I. pulchellum*
    C. Cells about .003-.005 x .080-.100 mm, hardly different at base; cortical cells of stem enlarged and hyaline ....1. *I. Muellerianum*
    D. Alar cells few, quadrate, forming a small group ....6. *I. micans*
    D. Alar cells very indistinctly sub-rectangular, not forming a well defined group ....2. *I. elegans*
    D. *See also I. pulchellum var. nitidulum*
  E. Leaves shortly bi-costate; annulus large and compound; leaf-cells papillose by protruding cell angles ....4. *I. geophilum*
  E. Leaves ecostate or obsoletely costate ....F
    F. Leaves serrulate to the base or nearly so ....G
    F. Leaves not serrulate below the middle ....*I. micans*
      G. Operculum conic; leaf-cells not papillose dorsally towards leaf-apex; leaves complanately spreading ....7. *I. turfaceum*
      G. Operculum short-rostrate; leaves closely complanately overlapping ....3. *I. deplanatum*

1. ISOPTERYGIUM MUELLERIANUM (Schimper) Lindberg
(*Plagiothecium Muellerianum* Schimper)

Yellowish-green, laxly cespitose; the branches long, flattened, straggling out into flagella or stolons or forming flattened strands, very slender; the stems and branches thick, often more than .150 mm in diameter, with very large and thin-walled outer cells which are 3 or 4 times as wide as the lower cells of the leaf and usually about .015-.025 mm wide; leaves rigid, not much different when dry, the points directed forwards and upwards so that the dorsal surface of the branch is concave, lance-ovate, long-apiculate, concave, non-decurrent, plane-margined, entire; costa double, very faint and short; median cells linear, narrow, up to .100 mm long, about 20-25:1, the alar and basal scarcely different; perichaetial leaves ovate-oblong, acuminate, entire: seta rather short, castaneous; capsule smooth, small, long-necked, obovoid, erect to inclined, when dry pale brown, wide-mouthed and campanulate; lid conical,

---

* Also *I. subfalcatum* Austin, with sub-cultiform leaves turned backwards, non-decurrent, apically serrate. In cracks and crevices of rocks, Pennsylvania to New England. See Sullivant's *Icones Muscorum*. Supplement, plate 67.

rostellate;. peristome-teeth with rather distant articulations, cilia short and unequal; annulus 1-seriate; spores mature in autumn; dioicous.

On moist earth and rocks in cool ravines, etc., mostly in hilly or mountainous regions; Europe, Asia, and from northeastern Canada to Ohio and Minnesota, and southward in the mountains to North Carolina. Not yet reported from our region but to be expected, — especially in the more mountainous portions.

2. ISOPTERYGIUM ELEGANS [Hooker] Lindberg

(*Hypnum elegans* Hooker; *Isothecium elegans* Bridel;
Plagiothecium elegans Sullivant)

Plate LXVIII

Small, densely cespitose, thin, pale shining green: stems branching irregularly, the branches slender, partly procumbent, partly ascending, numerous, usually pointing one way; usually there are also axillary, gemmiferous branchlets; leaves complanate, sub-distichous, the points usually pointing downwards, lustrous, little changed when dry, about 1-1.5 mm long, lance-oblong to ovate-oblong, rather gradually narrowed from about the middle, then abruptly narrowed to a fine, short acumen, the base rounded, non-decurrent, plane-margined, entire except at the acumen where a little denticulate; costa double and short, faint or sometimes reaching one-third the length of the leaf; median leaf-cells narrowly linear, about 20-30:1, about .004-.007 mm, pointed, hardly differentiated at the angles; perichaetial leaves lance-acuminate: capsule turgid-ovoid, slightly inflated at the curved neck, nearly symmetric but horizontal or sub-pendent by a curve in the upper part of the seta, when dry and empty somewhat wide-mouthed, turbinate, costate; peristome hypnoid, yellow, teeth broadly lanceolate, blunt, segments entire, cilia 3, rather slender, as long as the segments; annulus simple; lid conic, obtusely pointed; spores mature in spring.

On rocks or earth usually in moist, cool crevices of ledges, etc., in hilly or mountainous regions in woods; Europe, Asia, and from Arctic America to northern United States and south in the mountains to North Carolina and Tennessee.

ARMSTRONG CO.: At small waterfall, west bank Allegheny River, 2 mi. n. of Parkers Landing. C.M.B. June 10, 1934. MCKEAN CO.: D. A. Burnett. (Porter's Catalogue). WESTMORELAND CO.: On rock cliff, Meadow Run at Jacobs Creek. C.M.B. Aug. 18, 1945 (figured).

3. ISOPTERYGIUM DEPLANATUM (Sullivant) Mitten

(*Hypnum deplanatum* Sullivant; *Rhynchostegium deplanatum* Schimper);
Plagiothecium deplanatum Grout)

Plate LXIX

Golden-green, lustrous, small, flattened: stems prostrate, irregularly pinnately branching; leaves 2-ranked, imbricate, giving stems and branches a plaited appearance, thin, concave, ovate-lanceolate, gradually long-acuminate, serrulate all around, more sharply so above, plane-margined; median leaf-cells linear, flexuous, prosenchymatous, the basal somewhat larger but very similar, a small group of short-rectangular or quadrate cells at the angles; costa none or but very faint: capsule oval-oblong, cernuous, arcuate, plicate when dry and then constricted below the mouth; peristome hypnoid, segments narrow, cilia 2 or 3, about as long as the segments, unequal; annulus none; spores in autumn, but capsules rarely produced.

Over earth, stones, and rotten wood and humus, in woods; from Nova Scotia to Manitoba and southward to Missouri and Tennessee.

Rare in our region. McKEAN Co.: D. A. Burnett. Porter's Catalogue). WASHING-TON Co.: On rock, near Washington. December 5, 1891 (figured). A. Linn and J. S. Simonton.

4. ISOPTERYGIUM GEOPHILUM (Austin) Jaeger

(Rhynchostegium geophilum Austin; Plagiothecium geophilum Grout;
Hypnum depressum Sullivant and Lesquereux)

Plate LXVIII

Dark green, very glossy, thinly, softly, and loosely matted, leafy branches about 2.5-3 mm wide; stems prostrate, irregularly divided, more or less compressed; leaves long, somewhat concave, distichous, rather distant, widely spreading, ovate to oblong-lanceolate, gradually and symmetrically narrowed to a somewhat blunt apex, serrulate above, rounded at the base, non-decurrent; costa short, double, rather distinct or none; median leaf-cells linear, prosenchymatous, flexuous, about 8-12:1, a few alar sub-rectangular, thick-walled, only a little enlarged and not forming a distinct auricle, upper cells shorter, papillose dorsally by projecting cell-wall angles; many branches of our specimens (July 26, 1947) were tipped with capitate clusters of linear, often forked gemmae: capsule small, ovate, gibbous, thin-walled, unsymmetric, inclined; urn about 1 mm long; peristome normally hypnoid, teeth yellowish, segments narrow, linear, the cilia 2 or 3, some as long as segments; annulus large, 2-seriate; lid conic, obliquely long-rostrate; spores mature in spring or summer.

On moist earth or stones, usually near water in lowlands or in shady ravines; occurring from New York to Wisconsin and south to Maryland and Georgia.

CAMBRIA Co.: Cresson. T. C. Porter. (Porter's Catalogue). SOMERSET Co.: Beck Spring, Laurel Ridge. C.M.B. July 26, 1947 (figured).

5. ISOPTERYGIUM PULCHELLUM (Dickson) Jaeger

(Plagiothecium pulchellum Bryologia Europaea; P. pseudo-latebricola
Kindberg; Leskea pulchella Hedwig)

Slender, in prostrate and straggling tufts, bright glossy metallic green: stems creeping, usually not much more than 1 cm long, the branches numerous and slender, erect or curved-ascending; leaves subdistichous, about 1 mm long, more or less falcate at tips of stems and branches, very glossy, hardly altered when dry, entire, plane-margined, narrowly lance-ovate, from near the base rounded but not decurrent nor excavate; costa usually none; median leaf-cells narrowly linear, about 12-25:1, .005-.008 mm wide, pointed, the basal suboval and wider and shorter but not differentiated otherwise at the angles: monoicous; seta reddish, slender, about 1-1.5 cm long; capsule small, rather variable, ranging from oblong and tapering below into the neck to short and ovoid, and from erect and symmetric to curved and more or less horizontal, when dry usually wide-mouthed and constricted below the rim, ranging from greenish-brown when young to castaneous when old; lid conic, apiculate; peristome-teeth densely barred, cilia 2, a little shorter than the segments; annulus 2-seriate; spores mature in early summer.

On rocks and roots of trees and on rotten wood, in moist woods; Europe, Asia, and from Arctic America to the northern United States as far south as Pennsylvania.

ISOPTERYGIUM PULCHELLUM var. NITIDULUM (Wahlenberg) Brotherus
(Hypnum nitidulum Wahlenberg)

Larger plants in thinner mats, with often stoloniferous stems and more complanate branches; leaves with very slender acuminations, often serrulate above; capsule almost horizontal; annulus 1-seriate often falling still attached to the operculum.   Range about the same as the species.

ELK CO.: Benezette. McMinn. (Porter's Catalogue).

6.   ISOPTERYGIUM MICANS (Swartz) E. G. Britton
(Hypnum albulum C. Mueller: *H. micans* Swartz; *Sematophyllum micans* Braithwaite; *Plagiothecium micans* Paris)

Small, thinly matted, loose, glossy, whitish-green to yellowish-green: stems prostrate, rooting, irregularly branching; leaves loose, erect-spreading to secund and pointing downwards, very small, about 0.8-1.2 mm long, ovate-lanceolate, gradually long-acuminate, serrulate above, thin; costa usually none; perichaetial leaves abruptly acuminate, the inner apically serrate; median leaf-cells linear, prosenchymatous, flexuous, about 15:1, at the base a row considerably enlarged and broad, at the angles a few sub-quadrate: seta long and slender; capsule very small, ovate-oblong, light castaneous, constricted below the mouth when dry and empty, slightly incurved; peristome-segments not split, about as long as teeth, the cilia 1 or 2, short, nodose; annulus none; lid conic, apiculate to short-rostrate; spores mature in mid-winter.

On earth and rotten wood in moist woods; mainly along the eastern United States from New York southwards.

Rare in our region. CENTRE CO.: Bear Meadows. T. C. Porter. (Porter's Catalogue).

7.   ISOPTERYGIUM TURFACEUM (Lindberg) Lindberg
(Hypnum turfaceum Lindberg: *Stereodon turfaceus* Mitten; *Plagiothecium turfaceum* Lindberg)

Plate LI

Small, light green to yellowish-green, loosely matted: stems prostrate, more or less pinnately branching with short branches, rooting at the perichaetia and at the main forks and usually quite difficult to separate from the substratum without breaking in pieces; leaves about 1.5 mm long, complanately arranged, lance-ovate, long-acuminate from an ovate-oblong base, sharply serrate above the middle, margins plane, serrulate, or entire towards the base; costa none or very short and faint; perichaetial leaves ovate, basally concave, abruptly short-pointed, dentate at apex; median leaf-cells fusiform to broadly linear, prosenchymatous, about 8-12:1, the basal a little shorter and wider, the alar either not differentiated or a few sub-quadrate to rectangular and incrassate: seta slender, about 1.5 cm long, castaneous, somewhat twisted; capsule oblong, about 2-3.1, about 2 mm long, slightly curved and somewhat inclined when young, when old and empty arcuate, horizontal, plicate, castaneous, and constricted below the mouth; annulus large, double; lid conic; exothecial cells small and rounded in three or four series at the rim, gradually becoming oblong-rectangular or irregular-oblong below, the upper more or less distinctly castaneous-collenchymatous; peristome small, the teeth lance-subulate, papillose above, dorsally transversely striolate below, strongly trabeculate and lamellate, slightly confluent at base; segments nearly as long, narrow, not split, papillose, yellowish, basal membrane about two-fifths as high; cilia strong, nodose, often about as long as the segments, 1 or 2 in number; spores more or less greenish-yellow, about .008-.011 mm, papillose, rather thin-walled, mature in summer.

On rich woods-humus in moist woods or in peat bogs; Europe, and from Canada to Georgia and Texas.

CAMBRIA Co.: Ebensburg. T. P. James. (Porter's Catalogue). CRAWFORD CO.: In swamp near Hartstown, May 29-31, 1909. O.E.J. and G.K.J. (figured). McKEAN Co.: East Branch Swamp, Bradford, July 1, 1896. D.A.B.

21. PLAGIOTHECIUM Bryologia Europaea*

Autoicous or dioicous, rarely polyoicous: usually more or less robust, mostly softly cespitose, bright to yellowish or whitish-green, lustrous: stems creeping to ascending, or in thick cushions erect, with ascending and small-leaved stolons, mostly irregularly branched; branches often elongate-flagelliform; paraphyllia none; leaves uniform, obliquely inserted, non-plicate, some species complanate-distichous, concave from a narrow and more or less decurrent base, broadly lanceolate to ovate, acuminate, mostly plane-margined and entire, sometimes serrate; costa short, mostly double, sometimes none; median leaf-cells chlorophyllose, elongate-rhomboid to linear, thin-walled, the basal shorter and wider, the alar lax and hyaline: seta long, reddish, drying twisted; capsule erect to cernuous, with collum, oblong to cylindric, symmetric to weakly dorsally gibbous, drying wrinkled or smooth and often arcuate; annulus mostly revoluble; peristome-teeth yellowish, confluent basally, lance-subulate, mostly

---

* *Plagiothecium* and the next following genus (*Isopterygium*) are probably best treated as one genus. Grout (Moss Flora, 1932) unites them under *Plagiothecium*. Brotherus (Die Naturlichen Pflanzenfamilien. 2nd edit. 1925) recognizes *Plagiothecium* and *Isopterygium* as here treated except that he places *deplanatum* and *geophilum* in a third genus *Taxiphyllum*.

hyaline-bordered, the divisural zigzag, the teeth dorsally cross-striate, numerously lamellate; lid convex-conic, acute to rarely rostrate.

A genus of about 70 species, mostly growing on rocks and stones, rare in the tropics; about 17 species in North America; at least 4 species in our region.

KEY TO THE SPECIES

A. Leaves spreading more or less uniformly in all directions ....B

A. Leaves distinctly complanately disposed C

  B. Leaves erect-spreading; alar cells not inflated ....2. *P. Roeseanum*

  B. Leaves squarrose, more or less serrulate; alar cells inflated ....1. *P. striatellum*

C. Costa forked, often reaching to the middle of the leaf; capsule usually striate when dry ....3. *P. sylvaticum*

C. Costa thin, short and double. or none; capsule usually smooth when dry; lid conic to short-rostrate ....4. *P. denticulatum*

1. PLAGIOTHECIUM STRIATELLUM (Bridel) Lindberg
(*Hypnum Muehlenbeckii* Schimper; *Plagiothecium Muehlenbeckii* Bryologia Europaea; *Leskea striatella* Bridel)

Plate LI

Slender, dense, dark green, lustrous: stem prostrate, branches crowded, erect or ascending, straight or slightly curved; leaves about 1-1.3 mm long, crowded, sub-complanate, the branch-leaves squarrose-spreading, ovate-lanceolate or triangular-lanceolate with a long slender and flexuous acumen, plane-margined, serrulate above at least, the base strongly decurrent: costa double and faint; median leaf-cells linear-fusiform, flexuous, rather short, about 6-10:1, the basal somewhat larger, the alar abruptly very much enlarged, inflated, hyaline to colored, and forming the much decurrent and plainly distinct auricles; inner perichaetial leaves half-sheathing, the apex filiform-flexuous and usually recurved: capsules about 2 mm long, slightly curved, oblong-cylindric with a tapering neck, distinctly striate when dry; lid conic, rather obtuse; annulus large, compound; exothecial cells minute and rounded in three to five series at the rim, below rapidly becoming irregularly oblong and more or less incrassate; teeth short, yellowish, papillose above, dorsally cross-striolate below, lamellate, strongly trabeculate, slightly confluent at base; segments about as long, slender, pale, granulose, only slightly carinate cleft; basal membrane only about one-fourth to one-third as high as the teeth; the cilia 1 to 3, a little shorter than the segments; spores mature in late spring or early summer, yellowish, papillose, rather incrassate, .007-.010 mm.

On earth, rocks, and rotten logs, in woods, usually in non-calcareous habitats; Europe, and from Arctic America south to North Carolina.

BUTLER CO.: One mi. e. of Mercer Road Sta. C.M.B. Oct. 4, 1941. CAMBRIA Co.: Ebensburg. T. P. James. (Porter's Catalogue). FAYETTE Co.: Cucumber Falls, Ohiopyle, June 22, 1940, and Laurel Run, Chestnut Ridge, Dunbar Twp., June 16, 1940. C.M.B. LAWRENCE CO.: Slippery Rock Creek, 1906. Miss Susan Gageby. McKEAN Co.: On sandstone rocks, Rutherford Rocks, altitude 2000 feet, July 7, 1894, Divide between Hawkins and Rutherford Hollows, April 25, 1893, and March 12, 1894, and Langmade, May 9, 1896 (figured). All near Bradford. D.A.B.

2. PLAGIOTHECIUM ROESEANUM (Hampe, mss.) Bryologia
(*Hypnum Sullivantiae* Schimper; *H. Roeseanum* Hampe)

Plate LXXI

Compactly cespitose, pale green to yellowish-green, somewhat shining; stems more or less erect, sparsely branched, radiculose at base; leaves about 2 mm long, somewhat crowded, sub-imbricate, ovate-oblong, abruptly and very shortly acuminate, rarely slightly serrulate towards the apex, thin, concave, the leaves hardly complanate, but the branches appearing julaceous; costa various, often bifid, rather strong and long; median leaf-cells narrowly linear, about 10-15:1, towards the base gradually becoming shorter and broader; perichaetial leaves erect, the inner oblong, narrowly acuminate: capsule cylindric-oblong, erect to sub-inclined, smooth and constricted at the neck when dry; lid conic, obliquely short-rostrate; annulus large, simple; peristome hypnoid, the two cilia strong and about as long as the entire segments; spores mature in summer.

This species apparently intergrades with *P. denticulatum*. The stems are quite brittle and it is difficult to separate the leaves from them without breaking them.

On stones and earth in moist or swampy woods; Eurasia, and from Nova Scotia to Alaska and south to Georgia.

ALLEGHENY Co.: Powers Run, O.E.J. & G.K.J. May 25, 1904 (named by F. E. Wynn. 1944). FAYETTE Co.: On face of large rock, Laurel Run, Chestnut Ridge, Dunbar Twp. C.M.B. June 16, 1940 (figured).

3. PLAGIOTHECIUM SYLVATICUM [Hudson, Bridel] Bryologia Europaea
(*Hypnum silvaticum* Bridel; *H. denticulatum* C. Mueller)

Plate LI

Both this and *P. Roeseanum* are perhaps but varieties of *P. denticulatum*, but until better known should probably be kept apart as separate species. Tufts large, dull or but slightly glossy, deep olive-green to yellowish-green; stems prostrate, stoloniferous; leaves rather soft, large, concave about 2-3 mm long, not very regularly complanate, widely sperading, shrinking and somewhat twisted when dry, broadly ovate-lanceolate, narrowed considerably towards the decurrent base, tapering abruptly to the acute, entire or obsoletely denticulate apex, plane-margined; costa rather faint, double, often reaching one-third the length of the leaf: median leaf-cells about 8-10:1, about .016 mm wide, large, hexagonal-rhomboid, the alar cells numerous and quadrate-oblong, sub-inflated, hyaline and decurrent; perichaetial bearing rhizoids at base, about 3 mm high, the leaves sheathing with a flexuous acumen, non-costate; seta castaneous, slender, about 2-4 cm long, dextrorse above when dry; capsule yellowish, about 2 mm long, long-cylindric from a tapering neck, inclined, arcuate, smooth, but when dry and empty somewhat striate; lid conic, acuminate to sub-rostrate, about one-half as long as the urn; peristome-teeth bright orange at base, pale above, lance-subulate, confluent at base, closely trabeculate, the dorsal lamellae finely cross-striolate; segments slender, about as long as the teeth, narrowly carinately gaping, the basal membrane about one-third as high, the cilia very slender, about as long as the segments, nodose, usually 3 in number; exothecial cells moderately incrassate, small and quadrate at rim, larger and oblong-rectangular, to rounded-hexagonal below; annulus large, revoluble, 2-seriate; spores pale yellowish, smooth, rather thin-walled, .006-.010 mm, mature in mid-summer.

On humus, rocks, rotten logs, etc., in woods; Europe, Asia, northern Africa, and from southern Canada to Alabama and from Alaska to Oregon.

Known from Allegheny, Armstrong, Butler, Crawford, Erie, McKean, Washington, and Westmoreland counties. With the exception of the McKean County station these records are all from the western part of our region and seem to indicate that this species is at least not common in the mountains and plateau counties. Specimen figured: Wildwood Hollow, Allegheny County. June 11, 1908.

4. PLAGIOTHECIUM DENTICULATUM [Linnaeus] Bryologia Europaea

(*Hypnum denticulatum* Linnaeus)

Plate LIII

Variable, in flattened tufts of a pale and lustrous green, moderately robust, the more or less ascending and elongate branches complanate; leaves rather close, complanate and sub-distichous, rather spreading, when dry little changed, glossy, 2-3 mm long, sub-concave, oval to lance-oblong, shortly and sometimes almost apiculately acute, usually slightly denticulate at the apex, the lower margins entire and often narrowly recurved, the base narrowed to a rather wide and strongly decurrent insertion; costa thin, variable, usually short and double, sometimes forked and reaching almost to the middle, sometimes none; median leaf-cells rhomboid-hexagonal, rather large, about 10-15:1, about .010-.015 mm wide, thin-walled, chlorophyllose, gradually becoming laxer, pellucid, and more or less rectangular at base, the alar more hyaline, sub-rectangular, sub-inflated, and still somewhat larger but not forming clearly differentiated auricles, strongly decurrent; the apical leaf-cells much smaller, incrassate, rhomboid: seta about 2.5-4 cm long, flexuous, dextrorse above when dry, slender; capsule-urn about 2.5 mm long, sub-erect to horizontal, cylindric and with a distinct neck, arcuate to nearly symmetric, when dry and empty sometimes striate; lid conic, obtusely acuminate to long-acuminate, about one-third as long as the urn; annulus usually 2-seriate, large, revoluble; exothecial cells rounded-quadrate, small at rim, gradually larger and more oblong below, all incrassate; peristome-teeth lance-subulate, hyaline and papillose above, yellowish and dorsally cross-striolate below, strongly lamellate and trabeculate, confluent at base; segments slender, as long as the teeth, basal membrane one-third as high, cilia 2 or 3, usually 3, slender, nodose; spores smooth, medium-walled, yellowish, .008-.011 mm, mature in summer.

On stones, humus, and rotten wood, in moist forests; cosmopolitan in temperate and cooler regions; in North America from the Arctic regions to the northern United States and southwards in the mountains to Georgia.

This is a common and quite variable species now known from numerous localities in 13 counties and probably occurring in all. Specimen figured: Falls Creek, Jefferson Co., July 18, 1904. O.E.J.

Other mosses closely related to *P. denticulatum* are *P. Ruthei* Limpricht, with asymmetric leaves each clasping the base of the leaf above something like *Fissidens*, and occurring in swamps from New England to Georgia and Maryland, and Minnesota. Also *P. laetum* Bryologia Europaea, with slenderly acuminate leaves, scarcely decurrent, and with capsules almost erect and symmetric; no cilia. This species occurs from eastern Pennsylvania to Canada in rock crevices in mountain areas.

22. PTERYGYNANDRUM Hedwig

Dioicous; slender to quite robust, variously cespitose, green to yellowish-green, dull or lustrous, primary stem stolon-like, irregularly radiculose; secondary stems secund, filiform-julaceous, the base stolon-like, radiculose, often flagelliform, densely-leaved, ascending, forked, bushy or pinnately branched; leaves imbricate, sometimes secund, somewhat decurrent, non-plicate, deeply concave, short-acuminate to somewhat obtuse, margins narrowly revolute to the middle or above, entire or serrulate upwards; costa usually very short and thin, forked or double, rarely single and reaching to the middle of the leaf; cells narrow linear-vermicular to rhombic-hexagonal, strongly and sharply dorsally papillose, the median about 3-5:1, basal cells wider and longer, alar quadrate in several series; inner perichaetial leaves thin, broadly lanceolate, sheathing, acute, the margins entire and plane: seta 8-15 mm long, red or yellow-red, drying twisted; capsule erect, mostly symmetric, cylindric, yellow to brown; annulus 2-seriate, narrow; peristome inserted near the mouth; teeth lanceolate, confluent at the base, yellowish, below transversely and obliquely striate, above smooth, distantly articulate, non-trabeculate; inner peristome hyaline, smooth, with quite low basal membrane, the segments very narrow, short, or sometimes almost as long as the teeth; cilia none; spores .010-.018 mm; lid conic, shortly and mostly bluntly rostrate.

Three species; only the following in North America:

1. PTERYGYNANDRUM FILIFORME [Timm] Hedwig
(*Leskea cylindrica* Bridel)

On bases of trees and on rocks, in woods, widely distributed in the Northern Hemisphere, — in North America, extending from Greenland to British Columbia and southwards to the northern United States. Occurs in the Pocono region of eastern Pennsylvania and, possibly, will be found in the northern or northeastern part of our region.

Family 32. FABRONIACEAE

Autoicous or dioicous: slender to very slender, weak, cespitose, mostly bright or light green, mostly lustrous: stem without central strand, weak, creeping, thin, with red, fasciculate radicles; the secondary stems densely-leaved, simple or branched, erect; leaves 5-8-seriate, drying appressed, spreading when moist, rarely secund, more or less concave, unistratose, non-decurrent, ovate to lanceolate, non-bordered, non-plicate; costa simple, delicate and short, rarely ecostate; median leaf-cells mostly prosenchymatous, smooth, mostly thin-walled, towards the basal angles quadrate to rectangular: capsule exserted, erect, symmetric, oval to sub-cylindric, drying often longitudinally wrinkled and constricted below the mouth, the collum short and thick; peristome deeply inserted, single or double; teeth plane, distantly articulate, non-lamellate, in our genera non-bordered, teeth rarely none; inner peristome none or consisting generally of subulate segments; lid broad, mostly conic and rostrate; calyptra cucullate, naked, smooth, small, fugaceous; spores small.

Mostly occurring on tree-trunks in warm regions; only 3 genera within our range.

KEY TO THE GENERA

A. Costa none or very rudimentary; leaves serrulate the whole length ....3. *Schwetschkeopsis*
A. Costa plainly evident ....B
  B. Inner peristome none, teeth short, broad, and blunt; leaves denticulate to ciliate-dentate ....1. *Fabronia*
  B. Peristome double; teeth broadly lanceolate; leaves essentially entire .... 2. *Anacamptodon*

1. FABRONIA Raddi

Autoicous, rarely dioicous: stem creeping, partly stoloniform, rarely erect, irregularly branched; branches often partly stoloniform and partly leafy; leafy branches thickly julaceous, the leaves often drying imbricate, sometimes secund, ovate to ovate-lanceolate, mostly subulate-acuminate or piliferous, entire to serrate or even ciliate-laciniate; costa mostly delicate and short, sometimes indistinct; median leaf-cells elongate-rhomboid to elongate-hexagonal, the alar quadrate in several series, sometimes not differentiated; inner perichaetial leaves sheathing, subulate-acuminate, ecostate: seta mostly 1-7 mm long, thin, pale yellow, smooth, drying twisted; capsule erect, symmetric, ovate to pyriform, with a short neck, drying plicate, the collum shrinking and the capsule becoming cup-shaped to hemispheric, light brown, wide-mouthed; annulus none; peristome simple, rarely none, teeth very hygroscopic, at first united in pairs, later separating, broad, obtuse, often cleft or perforate divisurally, brown, non-bordered, longitudinally striate-papillose, non-trabeculate; lid conic-convex to low convex, mostly short-rostrate.

A genus of about 100 species, widely distributed in warm regions, mostly arboreal in habitat, rarely on rocks; 13 species reported for North America; two species in eastern Pennsylvania and perhaps reaching our region.

KEY TO THE SPECIES

A. Leaves obscurely serrate ....1. *R. Ravenelii*
A. Leaves ciliate-dentate ....2. *F. ciliaris*

1. FABRONIA RAVENELII Sullivant
(*F. caroliniana* Sullivant)

Very small, delicate, loosely cespitose, bright green: stems creeping with more or less erect branches; leaves loose, elongate-lanceolate, subulate-acuminate, concave, costate to the middle, entire or but obscurely serrate; median leaf-cells linear-fusiform, the basal and alar quadrate; inner perichaetial leaves ecostate, oblong, short-acuminate: capsule more or less pyriform; the teeth of the peristome brown, 16, approximate in pairs, orange-pellucid, acuminate-deltoid; lid conic, obtuse; spores about .017 mm in diameter.

On bark of trees, rotten logs, etc., extending from the South up into southeastern Pennsylvania.

2. FABRONIA CILIARIS (Bridel) Bridel

(*F. octoblepharis* Schwaegr.; *F. pusilla* Schwaegr.;
Pterogonium octoblepharis Schleicher)

Small, delicate, thinly cespitose: stems creeping with erect branches; leaves lance-ovate, filiform-acuminate, thin, green, spreading, sometimes 2-ranked, coarsely and irregularly lacerate-dentate on the border the acuminate tip consisting of a single elongated cell, costate to considerably above the middle, non-plicate, plane-margined, closely imbricate when dry; median leaf-cells thin-walled, linear-rhombic to hexagonal, about 3-5:1, the basal clear across the lower one-fourth or one-fifth of the leaf quadrate or sub-quadrate: seta rather long; capsule oval, neck rather distinct, the urn erect, symmetric, more or less contracted below the mouth when dry and empty; peristome single, with the teeth united in pairs, dark brown, recurved when dry, when old more or less bifid; spores mature in spring, about .015 mm in diameter.

On rocks and trees from New Jersey throughout the Central States to Minnesota and southwards. Occurs in southeastern Pennsylvania and may reach the southern part of our region.

2. ANACAMPTODON Bridel

Autoicous: mostly densely cespitose, dark green, when old brownish to yellowish, lustrous: stem long-creeping, densely radiculose; the branches short, densely-leaved, erect to ascending; leaves spreading, often secund, ovate to oval, long-acuminate, entire; costa strong, ending above the middle of the leaf; leaf-cells rich in chlorophyll, elongated rhombic-hexagonal, the basal rectangular; inner perichaetial leaves elongate, not sheathing, generally acuminate, thinly costate; seta 5-8 mm long, quite thick, straight, smooth, red to dark castaneous, drying twisted; capsule erect, symmetric, oval, short and thick-necked, drying strongly constricted below the mouth, smooth; annulus broad, delicate but persistent; peristome double, deeply inserted, the teeth strongly hygroscopic, apically united in pairs, broadly lanceolate, pale brown, divisural line almost straight; teeth articulate below, densely finely papillose; basal membrane of inner peristome none, the segments filiform, somewhat shorter than the teeth, non-carinate, brown, almost smooth; lid conic-convex, straight or obliquely rostrate; spores about .008-.010 mm.

A genus of 7 species of which 5 are confined to Asia. The following occurs in Europe and eastern North Ameria:

1. ANACAMPTODON SPLACHNOIDES [Froelich] Bridel

(*Campylodontium hypnoides* Schwaegrichen; *Neckera splachnoides* Schwaegrichen)

KNOT-HOLE MOSS

Plate XXXVII

Dark-green or bluish-green, small, delicate, thinly tufted: stems creeping, with erect branches; leaves lance-ovate, up to 1.5 mm long, acuminate, entire, plano-concave, chlorophyllose, soft, closely imbricated when dry, non-decurrent, non-plicate; costa rather slender, reaching to above the middle of the leaf; median leaf-cells rhombic-hexagonal, about 3-5:1, with a few quadrate and sub-inflated cells at the base; perichaetial leaves few: seta about 6-8 mm long, sinistrorse when dry; capsule erect and symmetric, about 2:1, oval-oblong, thick-necked, constricted below the mouth when dry; peristome double, teeth approximately in pairs and reflexed when dry; 16 in number, lanceolate, pale, articulate, the divisural zigzag; segments filiform, about one-half to two-thirds as long as teeth; no basal membrane; annulus none; exothecial cells castaneous-incrassate, rectangular or irregularly oblong, above smaller and quadrate, those at the rim minute and rounded; lid short-rostrate from a conic base, more or less oblique, one-half to two-thirds as long as the urn; calyptra whitish, covering only the upper part of the urn; spores about .010 mm, minutely papillose, yellowish-green, medium-walled, mature in June.

In moist cavities in decaying wood, knot-holes in trees, in forks of tree-trunks, etc.; Europe, Asia, and from New England to Illinois and south.

Collected but seldom in our region, and then only in small quantities. FAYETTE Co.: In knot-hole 20 feet up in a beech tree, Tates Hollow. Dec. 1, 1933. John Lewis. INDIANA Co.: T. P. James. (Porter's Catalogue). McKEAN Co.: Bradford, different dates, in cavities in decaying wood. D.A.B. (figured). Issued as No. 148. Grout's North American Musci Pleurocarpi. SOMERSET Co.: Near Trent. Aug. 19, 1933. Chas M. Hepner. WASHINGTON Co.: In knot of a beech log, near Washington, Sept. 15, 1891. Linn & Simonton.

3. SCHWETSCHKEOPSIS Brotherus

Dioicous: slender, soft, forming tufts, green to yellowish: stem long, creeping, radiculose, mostly densely and symmetrically pinnately branched; branches somewhat julaceous to complanately-leaved, obtuse, short to long, ascending, simple or branched; branch-leaves when dry imbricate, when moist erect-spreading, non-decurrent, concave, plicate, lance-ovate, acuminate to subulate-pointed, serrulate, plane-margined; costa none; leaf-cells oblong-oval to oblong-linear, dorsally papillose above, alar quadrate and numerous, chlorophyllose, occupying most of leaf-base: seta up to 7 mm long, slender, tortuous, yellowish-red, smooth, when dry twisted; capsule oblong-ovoid, mostly erect and symmetric, shortly collumate; exannulate, peristome double, teeth lanceolate, yellow, with zigzag divisural, densely transversely striate, closely trabeculate; inner peristome hyaline, basal membrane one-third as high as teeth, smooth, segments about as long as teeth, broad, split along keel, finely papillose, cilia rudimentary or none; spores about .015 mm; lid obliquely rostrate.

Three species, on trees: one in Japan and Korea, one in Nepal, and the following:

1. SCHWETSCHKEOPSIS DENTICULATA (Sullivant) Brotherus

(Leskea denticulata Sullivant)

Plate XXXVI

Light green, soft, silky: stems usually 2-3 cm long, sometimes more, irregularly branched, paraphyllia none; stem-leaves erect-spreading, close, concave, ovate, somewhat decurrent, abruptly and narrowly acuminate, 0.4-0.9 mm long, 0.3-0.4 mm wide, plane-margined, sometimes slightly striate, marginally undulate-denticulate; ecostate; apical leaf-cells dorsally uni-papillate, the median oblong-oval to elongate-rhomboidal, sometimes vermicular, about 4-8:1, about .005-.008 mm wide, the marginal uni-seriate and curvi-linear, the alar forming a large group of quadrate incrassate cells; branch-leaves smaller and less abruptly acuminate, with more oblong and shorter cells: seta yellowish-red, slender, tortuous, erect; capsule erect or nearly so, oblong, about 2-3:1; operculum conic-rostrate, about two-thirds as long as the urn; peristome about the same width as the teeth; no cilia; no annulus; fruit rarely found.

Mostly on bases of trees, rarely on rocks, occurring in Asia and from Connecticut to the Mississippi River and south to the Gulf.

Apparently rare in our region. BUTLER CO.: On base of tree, 2 mi. s.e. of Brownsdale, Aug. 18, 1935. Sidney K. Eastwood. McKEAN CO.: Lewis's Run, Bradford, November 24, 1895, and Limestone Creek, Bradford, December, 1896. D.A.B. (figured). The latter issued as Grout's No. 134, North American Musci Pleurocarpi.

Family 33. SEMATOPHYLLACEAE

Autocoius or dioicous; antheridial clusters gemmiform, small; archegonial clusters on very short, usually rooting, perichaetial branches: slender to robust, cespitose, green to yellowish or brownish, often lustrous: stem without central strand, creeping to ascending, mostly irregularly branched, sometimes more or less regularly pinnate; paraphyllia none; leaves pluriseriate, mostly uniform and symmetric, of various forms; costa double, very short or none; cells mostly prosenchymatous, smooth or papillose, in the leaf-angles one row being oblong, inflated, thin-walled: capsule exserted, mostly cernuous to pendent, mostly oval to oblong, usually unsymmetric, collum weak; exothecial cells collenchymatous; annulus none; peristome-teeth as long as the segments, the latter rarely lacking, the teeth mostly entirely separate, mainly dorsally striate, lamellae mostly well-developed, inner peristome free, basal membrane high, segments mostly carinate and lance-subulate, rarely filiform, cilia usually present; spores mostly small; lid from a convex-conic base slenderly rostrate; calyptra mostly cucullate and glabrous.

A rather large family almost exclusively of tropic and sub-tropic distribution and mostly living on trees; in our region there occurs but one genus, as follows:

I. SEMATOPHYLLUM Mitten

(Rhaphidostegium (Bryologia Europaea) DeNot.)

Usually autoicous: mostly slender, mostly densely and widely cespitose, dark to pale green or yellowish to brownish: stem creeping, more or less elongate, regularly pinnately branched or irregular, with branches horizontally spreading to erect, rather julaceous; leaves uniform, non-plicate, concave, entire, ovate to oblong or oblong-elliptic, obtusely to piliferous-acuminate; usually ecostate, rarely obsoletely bi-costate; cells narrowly prosenchymatous, the apical sometimes rhombic, the basal golden-yellow, narrowly rectangular, incrassate and porose, the alar oblong, inflated, hyaline to yellowish or red-brown and forming a small, non-excavate group bounded above by small quadrate cells: seta long, mostly smooth; capsule sub-erect or horizontally inclined, oval to oblong, smooth; peristome hypnoid, teeth lance-subulate, with divisural zigzag, hyaline-bordered, prominently lamellate, especially so in the upper third; peristome-segments yellowish, carinate, with a high basal membrane, mostly split, cilia 1 or 2, nodose, or sometimes rudimentary; spores small, lid slenderly subulate-rostrate; calyptra glabrous.

A genus of about 100 species of temperate and warmer regions, occurring mainly on trees and rocks; 3 species in our region.

KEY TO THE SPECIES

A. Capsules erect and symmetric or nearly so; branches curved at ends and with apical leaves secund ....3. *S. adnatum*
A. Capsules more or less inclined or horizontal; leaves erect-spreading in all directions, or somewhat secund ....B
　B. Leaves usually more than 1.5 mm long ....2. *S. marylandicum*
　B. Leaves usually less than 1.5 mm long ....1. *S. carolinianum*

1. SEMATOPHYLLUM CAROLINIANUM (Mueller) E. G. Britton

(Hypnum carolinianum C. Mueller; *H. demissum* var. *carolinianum*
Lesquereux and James; *Rhaphidostegium carolinianum* Jaeger)

Plate LIII

Rather dark green, drooping-cespitose, lustrous: stems irregularly branching, often buried in the sand and then more or less leafless and with erect to ascending simple branchlets about 1-1.5 cm long; leaves imbricate, more or less secund or complanate above, non-plicate, concave, lance-ovate or lance-oblong, more or less sub-serrulate at apex, shortly acute, the margin often rather broadly reflexed; costa none, or faintly indicated by striae; median leaf-cells linear-flexuous, small, incrassate, about 8-10:1, towards the base shorter and broader, the alar abruptly much enlarged and inflated to form a group of 2-8 pellucid and hyaline or colored cells; perichaetial leaves rather closely imbricate, lance-oblong, acuminate: seta erect, sinistrorse below, castaneous, about 1 cm long; capsule curved and inclined, constricted below the mouth when dry and empty, the urn about 1.2-1.5 mm long, oblong-pyriform, yellowish; exothecial cells rounded-hexagonal, collenchymatous; peristome orange-yellow, the teeth with distinct divisural and lamellae, dorsally cross-striolate, hyaline-margined, strongly trabeculate; segments about as long, slender, rarely split, the cilia 1 (or 2), about one-half to two-thirds as long as segments, the basal membrane about two-fifths the height of the peristome; lid comparatively large, the beak oblique, subulate, and about two-thirds to three-fourths as long as the urn; spores smooth, yellowish-incrassate, usually chlorophyllose, about .014-.018 mm, mature in summer or early autumn.

On wet non-calcareous rocks, mainly in ravines in hilly or mountainous districts; Asia, and from Newfoundland southwards to Georgia.

Probably not common in our region. ALLEGHENY CO.: Haysville Hollow, September 20, 1908. O.E.J.; on damp rocks under hemlocks, Wildwood Road, November 19, 1908. O.E.J. and G.K.J. FAYETTE CO.: On damp rocks in deep hollows and ravines, Ohio Pyle, September 1-3, 1906, and September 1-3, 1907. O.E.J. and G.K.J. (figured); also May 30-31, June 13, and July 4, 1908. O.E.J.; Ohio Pyle, June 15, 1902. J.A.S. SOMERSET CO.: Near Trent. C. M. Hepner, July, 1932; and Clear Run, Laurel Ridge, C.M.B. Oct. 6, 1935. On wet rock in stream. WESTMORELAND CO.: Four collections in Laurel Hill and Chestnut Ridge Mts. C.M.B. 1934-45.

2. SEMATOPHYLLUM MARYLANDICUM (Mueller) E. G. Britton

(*Rhaphidostegium marylandicum* Jaeg. & Sauerb.; *Hypnum marylandicum* C. Mueller)

Plate LII

Dark green loosely interwoven, matted mosses with often subsecund at stem- and branch-tips, oblong-ovate, shortly acuminate to acute, 1.5-2 mm long, concave, entire, margin not reflexed; median leaf-cells linear, about 8-12:1, shorter, incrassate, and pellucid at base, alar cells inflated in a small group, apical cells about 2-4:1, rhomboid-oblong; spores ripe in spring.

On wet stones and ledges in cool mountainous habitats from New England to Georgia.

This species is very difficult to distinguish from *Hygrohypnum eugyrium* var. *Mackayi*, but the Hygrohypnum has usually a faint double costa, sometimes lacking, and the walls of the outer alar cells are much thinner than are the walls of the inner cells.

McKEAN CO.: Cathrine Swamp. C.M.B. Sept. 2, 1948 (figured). SOMERSET Co.: Bluehole Creek, Laurel Ridge. C.M.B. On rock in stream. July 5, 1948; and H. N. Mozingo, wet rock in stream, near Mt. Davis, Aug. 26, 1945.

3. SEMATOPHYLLUM ADNATUM (Richard, Michaux) Britton

(*Leskea adnata* Richard; *Rh. microcarpum* Jaeger; *Leskea microcarpa* Bridel; *Rhaphidostegium adnatum* Bryologia Europaea)

Small, in tangled, thin, green to golden-green mats: stems prostrate, with short and incurved branches; leaves rather closely imbricate when dry, sub-homomallous, the upper usually distinctly secund, narrowly oblong-lanceolate, the apex rather shortly acuminate, subserrulate to entire, margins quite broadly reflexed; costa double but very short and faint; median leaf-cells linear-fusiform, flexuous, about 8-12:1, shorter and wider at the base, towards the angles a border of sub-rectangular and scarcely inflated cells and at the extreme angle a few distinctly inflated alar cells: seta short and smooth, about 5-8 mm long; calyptra more or less persistent, cucullate, reaching to a little below the mouth of the urn; capsule castaneous, about 1-1.3 mm long, oblong to oblong-cylindric, about 2-2.5:1, erect and symmetric or nearly so, thin-walled but with collenchymatous exothecial cells, slightly constricted below the reddish rim when dry and empty; annulus none; lid obliquely subulate-rostrate from a conical base, about as long as the urn; peristome-teeth with an unusually distinct and heavy divisural, cilia single and usually about half as long as the usually entire segments, basal membrane reaching to about one-third the height of the inner peristome; spores mature in late summer to fall.

On base of usually living trees; in moist woods from southern New England to Ohio and southwards to the Gulf States. Not yet found in our region.

Family 34. BRACHYTHECIACEAE

Autiocous or dioicous; paraphyses filiform; antheridial clusters gemmiform; archegonial clusters on very short, rooting branches: slender to robust: stem with central strand, creeping to ascending, or rarely erect, often interruptedly stoloniferous, fasciculately radiculose, mostly irregularly pinnate; branches mostly acute, often flagelliform and rooting at the ends; leaves unistratose, pluriseriate, erect-spreading or appressed, rarely homomallous, dimorphic in the stoloniferous species; cordate-oblong to lance-ovate or lanceolate, acuminate or rarely obtuse; costa mostly incomplete; median leaf-cells prosenchymatous, elongate-rhomboid to linear-vermicular, smooth or rarely papillose towards the upper end of the cell, the basal cells lax and often porose, the alar usually differentiated, being quadrate, green or hyaline, sometimes inflated: seta elongate, often rough; capsule cernuous to horizontal, mostly short, ovoid or oblong and dorsally gibbous, when dry and empty more or less arcuate, rarely erect and symmetric, oval to oblong-cylindric, never pendent, smooth; collum faint; exothecial cells collenchymatous; peristome hypnoid, imperfect in some species with capsules erect; teeth lance-subulate, mostly strongly hygroscopic, basally confluent, yellow or orange to red-brown, with a zigzag divisural, dorsally cross-striate, lamellae numerous and well-developed; inner peristome mostly free, with a high basal membrane, carinate segments which are lance-subulate, cilia mostly complete, rarely none or rudimentary; lid conic, obtuse to acute, often long-rostrate; calyptra cucullate, early deciduous, mostly glabrous.

A large and cosmopolitan family on various substrata, containing about 20 genera with more than 500 species.

KEY TO THE GENERA

A. Capsule erect to suberect, and somewhat unsymmetric to symmetric; basal membrane mostly low ....H
A. Capsule cernuus to horizontal, unsymmetric; basal membrane mostly high ....B
  B. Leaves mostly with several deep plications ....2. *Camptothecium*
  B. Leaves not deeply plicate c
  c. Lid conic, sometimes acute; alar cells differentiated ....4. *Brachythecium*
  c. Lid long-rostrate, alar cells few or none ....D
    D. Cells narrow, dorsally smooth ....E
    D. Cells oblong-rhomboid to rhomboid-hexagonal, those of the branch-leaves more or

less dorsally rough ....8. *Bryhnia*
E. Leaves complanate (Also see *Oxyrrhynchium*) ....9. *Rhynchostegium*
E. Leaves imbricate or spreading ....F
    F. Leaves deeply concave, spoon-like abruptly piliferous-acuminate ....5. *Cirriphyllum*
    F. Leaves plane or somewhat concave, acute or gradually acuminate, not piliferous ......G
G. Leaves not much concave, non-plicate ....6. *Oxyrhynchium*
G. Leaves mostly distinctly concave and plicate ....7. *Eurhynchium*
    H. Calyptra hairy; segments adhering to the peristome-teeth ....1. *Homalotheciella*
    H. Calyptra smooth; segments not adhering to the peristome-teeth. (See also some
       species of *Brachythecium*) ....3. *Chamberlainia*

1. HOMALOTHECIELLA (Cardot) Brotherus

Autoicous: slender, soft, laxly cespitose, green, lustrous: stem creeping, elongate, beset thickly with obtuse, short, ascending to erect, densely-leaved branches which are often arcuate when dry; paraphyllia none; when dry the leaves imbricate, when moist erect-spreading, non-decurrent, non-plicate, concave, oval to oblong, the apex acuminate to lance-subulate, upper half of leaf serrulate to entire; costa simple, sometimes reaching to mid-leaf; median leaf-cells oblong-elliptic, thin, smooth, the alar green, numerous, quadrate; inner perichaetial leaves abruptly serrate-subulate from a sheathing base; seta about 7 mm long, castaneous, rough; capsule erect to almost horizontal, more or less unsymmetric, oblong, drying somewhat constricted below the mouth and often sub-arcuate; annulus present; inner peristome much shorter than the outer, teeth basally confluent, lance-linear, dorsally cross-striate, apically papillose, lamellae laterally projecting; inner peristome somewhat united with the outer, yellow, smooth, with low basal membrane, segments short, narrow, adherent to the teeth; cilia none; lid long-rostrate; calyptra slightly hairy at base.

A small genus of three (4) North American species, one species occurring in our range.

1. HOMALOTHECIELLA SUBCAPILLATA (Hedwig) Cardot

(*Pterigynandrum subcapillatum* Hedwig; *Homalothecium subcapillatum* Sullivant; *Platygyrium brachycladon* Kindberg)

Forming light green, thin, glossy mats: stems prostrate, irregularly branching; leaves loosely imbricate when dry, elliptic-oblong, abruptly long-acuminate, more or less serrate above, about 0.9-1.2 mm long, concave, non-plicate, not papillose; costa usually reaching about to the middle of the leaf; median leaf-cells, about 8-10:1, fusiform-elliptic, towards the apex somewhat shorter, the alar quadrate, numerous and forming a group which extends upwards along the margin to often one-third the length of the leaf; inner perichaetial leaves sheathing, long-acuminate: seta rough, about 6-9 mm long, slender; capsule about 2-3.5:1, sub-erect, slightly incurved, dorsally somewhat gibbous, slightly constricted below the mouth when dry; operculum conic or convex; annulus 2-seriate; peristome-teth confluent at base, dark red, with a broad pellucid central stripe marked by a delicate medial line, the segments adhering to and lining the teeth inside, forming a hyaline border; spores mature in autumn, about .025 mm.

On bark of trees and on fallen trunks in woods; in the eastern United States from New England to North Carolina.

Rare in our region. Elk Co.: McMinn. (Porter's Catalogue).

2.   Camptothecium Bryologia Europaea

Dioicous and pseudautoicous: slender to robust, widely cespitose, mostly yellowish-green, drying stiff, mostly lustrous: stem elongate, procumbent to ascending to erect, thickly-leaved, sometimes stoloniferous, more or less regularly pinnate; leaves erect-spreading, sometimes weakly secund, non-decurrent, slightly concave, strongly plicate, lance-oval, subulate-acuminate, serrulate all around; costa simple, ending near or in the apex; median leaf-cells prosenchymatous, 10-20:1, vermicular, thin, smooth, or with weakly projecting upper angles, the basal lax, yellow, porose, the alar numerous, quadrate; perichaetium not rooting, inner perichaetial leaves much elongate and abruptly subulate: seta moderately long, castaneous, mostly rough, drying twisted; capsule cernuous to horizontal, dorsally gibbous, oblong to oblong-cylindric, more or less curved; annulus present; peristome-teeth basally confluent, linear-subulate, bordered, dorsally cross-striate, thickly lamellate; inner peristome of same length, free, the segments broad and carinately split, cilia strong and nodose; lid conic-acute to thickly short-rostrate; calyptra glabrous.

A genus of about 15 species, confined mainly to temperate regions on soil, bark of trees in woods, or in swamps; a number of species occur in the West, but in our region only the following:

1.   Camptothecium nitens [Schreber] Schimper
(*Hypnum nitens* Schreber)

A striking species by reason of its bright yellow or golden color, silky lustre, strongly plicate leaves, and stems densely covered by a felt of reddish radicles: the stems often reach a length of 10 cm, strong; the elongate-lanceolate leaves entire, strongly plicate, marginally revolute, gradually and evenly narrowed to the slender apex, reaching usually over 3 mm long; median leaf-cells linear, the basal shorter with very thick and porose walls, the alar broader and short-rectangular to sub-quadrate but rather few in number and not forming a very distinct auricle: seta smooth; capsule cylindric, arcuate, contracted below the mouth when dry and empty; peristome well developed; cilia long; spores mature in spring.

In wet meadows, bogs, and swamps; Europe, Asia, and from Arctic America to northern United States.   Occurs in eastern Pennsylvania but not yet reported in our region.

3.   Chamberlainia Grout

Cespitose, mostly glossy green, variously branching; stem-leaves ovate; branch-leaves erect-spreading, imbricate when dry, lanceolate to ovate-lanceolate, concave, more or less serrulate, costate to above middle; median leaf-cells linear to elongate rhomboidal, alar quadrate, often numerous: seta 1-2 cm high, smooth; capsule erect, symmetric, cylindric; operculum conic, apiculate to short rostrate; annulus none; peristome cilia none or single and rudimentary; spores ripe in autumn.

This genus has been segregated from *Brachythecium* by Dr. Grout and named in honor of E. B. Chamberlain (1878-1925), former secretary-treasurer of the Sullivant Moss Society. Three species; two in our region.

1. CHAMBERLAINIA CYRTOPHYLLA (Kindberg) Grout
(*Brachythecium cyrtophyllum* Kindberg)
Plate LIII

Cespitose, lustrous, dark green: stem irregularly branching to sub-pinnate, creeping, up to 4 to 6 cm long; stem-leaves broadly ovate, up to 1 mm long; branch-leaves similar but narrower and smaller, lance-ovate to lanceolate, acute to short-acuminate, 0.6-0.8 x 0.3 mm, rather close, loosely appressed when dry, serrulate at least in the upper half, marginally reflexed at base, not plicate, not decurrent, when moist more or less spreading; costa stout, reaching about two-thirds the length of the leaf; median leaf-cells rhomboid-fusiform, about 4-8:1, the alar sub-quadrate, numerous, sub-inflated, somewhat chlorophyllose; perichaetial leaves ecostate, half-sheathing: seta about 2-2.5 cm long, dextrorse above, erect, flexuous; capsule erect, cylindric, sometimes slightly curved, from 1.5 to 3 mm long, castaneous, smooth; annulus none; peristome-teeth slender, pale castaneous, confluent at base, hyaline and papillose above, the dorsal lamellae closely cross-striolate below, the trabeculae close and strong; segments nearly as long as the teeth, slender, pale yellowish, more or less carinately split, the cilia rudimentary or none; basal membrane about one-fourth the height of the teeth; lid high-conic, usually acutely apiculate; spores papillose, brownish, medium- to thick-walled, .012-.016 mm, mature in autumn. Very closely related to the following species, which it apparently replaces to the west and northwest of our region.

On roots and bases of trees and on old logs, in woods from our region northwestward to Minnesota and Ontario, south to North Carolina.

Uncommon in our region. ALLEGHENY CO.: Fern Hollow, Pittsburgh, on old logs in ravine, January 21, 1906 (figured), and March 8, 1908. O.E.J. McKEAN CO.: Bradford. D.A.B. (Porter's Catalogue).

2. CHAMBERLAINIA ACUMINATA (Hedwig) Grout
(*Leskea acuminata* Hedwig; *Hypnum acuminatum* Beauvois;
Brachythecium acuminatum Kindberg)
Plate LIV

Widely and somewhat densely cespitose, dark to yellowish-green, glossy: stems slender, prostrate, up to 5 to 8 cm long, bearing rhizoids, at least near the perichaetia, rather distantly and unequally branched, the branches two-ranked, plumose to sub-julaceous, acute, not usually more than 1 cm long: stem-leaves close, erect-spreading, lance-ovate to ovate, about 1-1.5 mm long, acuminate, concave, with the borders reflexed below, the upper half serrulate, the leaf non-plicate or but slightly plicate; narrowed and somewhat decurrent at the base; costa usually reaching beyond the middle of the leaf; branch-leaves similar to the stem-leaves but relatively narrower and smaller; median leaf-cells linear-flexuose, about 51-0:1, medium-walled, prosenchymatous with rounded ends, apical cells a little shorter, the basal sub-quadrate or sub-rectangular, the alar numerous and sub-quadrate to quadrate, rather thin-walled and sub-inflated: seta erect, castaneous, flexuous, about 1-1.5 cm long; capsule castaneous, erect, the urn 1.5-3 mm long, symmetric or sometimes slightly curved, cylindric, about 3.5-4.5:1, tapering at base; lid high-conic, acute to apiculate; exothecial cells densely yellowish-incrassate, small, rounded but varying to quite irregular in size and shape but with rounded corners; peristome-teeth narrow, castaneous, margined, numerously trabeculate, hyaline and papillose above, dorsally cross-striate below, the lamellae distinct, teeth confluent at base; segments about as long as the teeth, narrow, carinately split, cilia rudimentary or none, the basal membrane only about one-fourth as high as the teeth; annulus none; spores castaneous, papillose, medium-walled, about .014-.018 mm, mature in late fall or in winter.

On earth, woods-humus, roots and bases of trees, stones, and very often on rotten logs, forming wide mats, in woods from the southeastern part of Canada to the Gulf States and Minnesota.

Rather common in our region. ALLEGHENY CO.: Thirteen pockets determined from various localities, mainly on old logs in ravines. O.E.J. and G.K.J.; Fern Hollow, January 21, 1906. O.E.J. (figured). BEAVER CO.: Eight feet up the trunk of elm tree, Raccoon Creek, 1 mi. s. of Traverse Creek. C.M.B. April 1, 1934. CLEARFIELD CO.: Phillipsburg. T. P. James. (Porter's Catalogue). McKEAN CO.: Gate's Hollow, Bradford, April 29, 1898. D.A.B. Issued as Grout's No. 116, North American Musci Pleurocarpi. WASHINGTON CO.: On decayed wood, near Washington. Linn & Simonton, No. 24. Oct., 1891. WESTMORELAND CO.: Near Apollo, 1902. Miss K. R. Holmes; Greensburg, T. P. James. (Porter's Catalogue).

4. BRACHYTHECIUM Bryologia Europaea

Autoicous or dioicous: slender to robust, mostly widely and flatly cespitose, green or yellowish to whitish, sometimes lustrous: stems creeping or procumbent, sometimes more or less erect, thickly-leaved, irregularly divided, interruptedly pinnate, stolon-like at the apex; stem and branch-leaves unlike, stem-leaves erect-spreading to spreading, more or less concave, mostly plicate, narrowly lanceolate from a narrowed, ovate or triangular-cordate and decurrent base, acuminate, marginally plane, serrate all around or only towards the apex, rarely entire; costa simple, usually long but rarely complete; median leaf-cells narrow to moderately wide, elongate-rhomboid to linear, smooth, the basal more lax, and shorter, the alar quadrate to rectangular or oblong-hexagonal, forming a rather indefinitely bounded group; branch-leaves mostly shorter, narrower, with a somewhat weaker costa; inner perichaetial leaves slenderly and finely acuminate: seta more or less long, smooth to rough; capsule cernuous to horizontal, rarely erect, mostly short-ovoid and dorsally gibbous, rarely oblong-cylindric, slightly arcuate when dry and empty; usually annulate; peristome-teeth strong, basally confluent, dorsally cross-striate, apically papillate, thickly lamellate; inner peristome about the same length, yellow to orange, free, with wide basal membrane, the segments broadly lanceolate, long-acuminate, carinately split and often gaping, cilia complete, nodose to appendiculate, rarely rudimentary or lacking; lid conic-convex, obtuse to acute; calyptra glabrous.

A genus of about 225 species, occurring on various substrata, mostly confined to temperate regions; at least 12 species in our region.

KEY TO THE SPECIES

A. Seta smooth; annulus often present; cilia well-developed ....B
A. Seta rough at least in part ....E
   B. Capsules sub-erect, narrowly cylindric-oblong; usually more than 3:1 ....
   ....1. *B. oxycladon*
   B. Capsules cernuous, usually less than 3:1 C
   C. Leaves narrowed gradually from base to acuminate apex, non-plicate ....5. *B. acutum*
   C. Stem-leaves ovate-lanceolate, more or less plicate ....D
      D. Stem-leaves broad, about 1 mm at base, not falcate-secund ....3. *B. salebrosum*
      D. Stem-leaves narrow, about 0.5-0.6 mm at base, very gradually narrowed to the
      apex ....4. *B. flexicaule*
E. Seta rough only above ....F
E. Seta rough throughout ....H
   F. Costa percurrent or very nearly so ....11. *B. populeum*
   F. Costa ending about in middle of the leaf ....G
   G. Stem-leaves plicate: cilia non-appendiculate ....2. *B. campestre*
   G. Stem-leaves non-plicate: cilia appendiculate ....12. *B. flagellare*
      H. Cilia appendiculate I
      H. Cilia non-appendiculate ....J
I. Costa percurrent or sub-percurrent ....8. *B. reflexum*
I. Costa distinctly incomplete ....9. *B. Starkei*
   J. Stem-leaves very short-acuminate, alar cells abruptly inflated ....7. *B. rivulare*
   J. Leaves gradually acuminate; alar cells not very abruptly enlarged and inflated ....K
K. Slender; leaves lanceolate, often secund ....10. *B. velutinum*
K. Robust; leaves ovate to lance-ovate, not secund ....6. *B. rutabulum*

1. BRACHYTHECIUM OXYCLADON [Bridel] Jaeger and Sauerb
(*B. laetum* Bryologia Europaea; *Hypnum oxycladon* Bridel)
Plate LXIX

Cespitose, bright or yellowish-green: stems prostrate, branching unequally and irregularly, the branchlets attenuate at the apex and erect; leaves close, loosely imbricate, ovate in the stem-leaves (2-2.5 mm) and more lance-ovate in the branch-leaves (1.5-2 mm) rather abruptly acuminate, concave, plicate, finely serrulate all around; costa rather narrow, extending about to mid-leaf or somewhat farther; median leaf-cells long, narrow, about 8-10:1, flexuous, the basal more or less quadrate, the alar numerous, small, rather incrassate, the alar portion strongly decurrent: seta about 2.5 cm long, flexuous, flattened and dextrorse when dry; capsule sub-erect, about 4:1, 3-4 mm long, oblong-cylindric, when dry somewhat arcuate and often inclined; lid conic-acuminate;

annulus none; peristome parts of about equal length, hynoid, the cilia somewhat appendiculate, usually 2 in number; spores mature in fall.

On earth, rocks, roots and bases of trees, in woods, but not so frequently occurring on rotten logs as do some of the other species. From eastern Canada to Tennessee and westward.

ERIE Co.: Entrance to Lily Pond, among trees, Presque Isle, July 13, 1925 and Sand Bank Trail, July 25, 1925. Nelle Ammons. WASHINGTON Co.: On decayed wood near Washington, Oct. 3, and 21 (figured), 1891. A Linn and J. S. Simonton.

2. BRACHYTHECIUM CAMPESTRE (Bruch) Bryologia Europaea

(Hypnum campestre Bruch)

Plate LIV

Very closely resembling B. *salebrosum,* but differing in having the seta smooth at base and slightly rough above; the capsule longer and the leaves longer-acuminate. Otherwise the characters are as given for B. *salebrosum.*

On moist earth, often in grassy places, rocks, or on rotten logs, usually preferring a non-calcareous habitat. Spores mature in autumn or early winter. Europe, Asia, northern Africa, and, in North America from Canada to the northern United States and south to Pennsylvania and New Jersey.

Infrequent in our region. ALLEGHENY Co.: Darlington Hollow, Sharpsburg, October 25, 1908, and Power's Run, on shaded rock, November 30, 1909 (figured). O.E.J. FAYETTE Co.: Ohio Pyle, along Meadow Run Valley, four miles south of village, September 1-3, 1906. O.E.J. and G.K.J. McKEAN Co.: Bennett Brook, August 26, 1894, and Quintuple, September 9, 1896. D.A.B. Both near Bradford.

3. BRACHYTHECIUM SALEBROSUM [Hoffmann] Bryologia Europaea

(Hypnum salebrosum Hoffmann)

Plate LIV

Widely cespitose in glossy, dark yellow-green mats: stems usually 5 or 6 cm or more long, creeping and irregularly branching; stem-leaves lance-ovate, about 1.5-2.5 x 0.6-1.1 mm, in our region apparently somewhat smaller than most descriptions call for; branch-leaves similar, lanceolate, about 1.8-2.2 x 0.5-0.6 mm, abruptly slenderly acuminate, serrate above, entire or sub-serrulate below, concave, the lower margins narrowly reflexed, the narrow insertion decurrent, both kinds of leaves plicate and erect-spreading; costa thin, usually reaching to the middle or a little above; median leaf-cells linear-fusiform, flexuous, about 8-12:1, the basal shorter and broader, usually two or three rows of lax, rather large, oblong or sub-quadrate cells across the whole base of the leaf, the alar more numerous, lax, sub-quadrate, rather thin-walled, the alae quite strongly decurrent; perichaetial leaves filiform-acuminate, ecostate or nearly so: seta smooth, castaneous, about 2-2.5 cm long, flexuous, flattened and twisted when dry; capsule oblong-ovoid, dorsally turgid, inclined to horizontal, usually arcuate, about 2-3:1, castaneous, the urn about 2-2.5 mm long; the lid conic-acuminate, about 1 mm long; annulus narrow; exothecial cells rounded-quadrate at the rim, larger and irregularly oblong or elliptic below, all strongly yellowish-incrassate; peristome-teeth slender, confluent at base, closely trabeculate and lamellate, dorsally cross-striolate and brownish below, hyaline and papillose above, rather prominently margined; segments about as long as the teeth, finely papillose, carinately split and usually gaping; cilia a little shorter, hyaline, nodose, 1 to 3 in number; basal membrane about one-third as high as the teeth; spores mature in late fall or winter, about .015-.020 mm, the walls medium-incrassate, brownish, and somewhat papillose: autoicous.

On earth, stones, roots and bases of trees, rotten wood, etc., in moist, shady woods; said to be especially common in pine or hemlock woods; Europe, Asia, northern Africa, and from eastern Canada southward to North Carolina and Missouri.

Common in our region. Now known from the following counties: Allegheny, Bedford, Butler, Crawford, Clinton, Elk (Porter), Erie, Greene, Indiana, Lawrence, McKean, Somerset, Washington, and Westmoreland. Specimen figured: Douthett, Allegheny Co., April 26, 1908. O.E.J.

4. BRACHYTHECIUM FLEXICAULE Renauld and Cardot

Plate LV

Widely cespitose, yellowish-green: stems usually at least 3-6 cm long, creeping, irregularly pinnate; leaves plicate, erect-spreading, the stem-leaves lanceolate, about 1.8-2.5 x 0.6-0.9 mm; branch-leaves narrower, up to 2.4 x 0.5-0.7 mm, gradually slenderly acuminate from a deeply concave, somewhat decurrent plicate base with often narrowly reflexed basal margins, the margins serrulate above; costa extending to above the middle of the leaf; median leaf-cells linear-fusiform, prosenchymatous, flexuous, about 8-15:1, rather incrassate, the apical shorter, the basal rather abruptly shorter and wider with two to four rows of large oblong to rounded-quadrate cells across the whole median base, the alar cells sub-quadrate, rather incrassate, numerous, the wings decurrent; perichaetial leaves up to 3 mm long with slender flexuous acuminations, partly sheathing, ecostate or nearly so: seta smooth, castaneous, usually sinistrorse, 1.5-2.5 cm long; capsule about 3-4:1, oblong-cylindric, inclined to nearly horizontal, dorsally gibbous, sub-arcuate, pale-castaneous, slightly narrowed below the rim when dry, the urn from 2-4 mm long; lid conic-acuminate, about 1-3 mm long; exothecial cells small and rounded at the rim, below larger and oblong to linear-oblong, all sharply yellowish-incrassate; annulus indistinct; peristome-teeth confluent at base, castaneous and dorsally cross-striolate below, closely trabeculate and lamellate, margined, hyaline towards apex; segments very slender, about as long as teeth, carinately cleft and gaping in median portion, yellowish, papillose, basal membrane one-fourth to one-third as high, the cilia somewhat shorter than the segments, filiform, nodose, hyaline-papillose; spores rather incrassate, smoothish, brown-walled, .013-.016 mm. According to Grout this is probably *B. salebrosum* variety *densum* Bryologia Europaea. In most characters it is quite similar to typical *salebrosum* but differs in having narrow leaves with evenly narrowed and very slender acuminations.

Ranging from Newfoundland, New England and the Adirondacks to New Jersey and Pennsylvania, and occurring also in British Columbia.

Rare in our region. ALLEGHENY CO.: Guyasuta Hollow on clay and stones, October 12, 1908. O.E.J. ERIE CO.: On log in hemlock woods, Presque Isle. Nelle Ammons. McKEAN CO.: Bennett Brook, May 3, 1893. D.A.B. (figured).

5. BRACHYTHECIUM ACUTUM (Mitten) Sullivant
(Hypnum acutum Mitten)

Loosely cespitose, bright glossy green: stems long, flexuous, creeping, basally radiculose, sparsely branched; branchlets short, sometimes reflexed; leaves loose, open-spreading, more imbricate when dry, lanceolate to lance-ovate, non-striate, slightly decurrent, plane-margined, scarcely concave, obscurely serrulate or almost entire, short auriculate at base, the margins tapering gradually and almost in a straight line from base to apex; median leaf-cells linear-vermicular, about 10:1, the basal lax, the alar sub-quadrate, small, numerous and extending down to form a rather strong decurrent portion; costa reaching to somewhat above the middle; stem-leaves wider, triangular-ovate, reaching 2.5 x 1 mm, long and slenderly acuminate: seta smooth, about 1.5-2.5 cm long, flexuous; capsule ovoid-oblong, dorsally turgid, inclined to horizontal, usually slightly arcuate, about 2-3:1; annulus narrow; peristome hypnoid, the cilia 2 or 3, strongly nodose to sub-appendiculate; lid conic-acuminate; spores mature in late fall or winter.

In moist woods on rotten logs and earth; Canada and the northern United States, south to New Jersey, Pennsylvania, and Ohio.

Rare in our region. McKEAN CO.: D.A.B. (Porter's Catalogue).

6. BRACHYTHECIUM RUTABULUM [Linnaeus] Bryologia Europaea
(Hypnum rutabulum Linnaeus)
Plate LV

Widely and loosely cespitose, yellowish-green, glossy: stems prostrate, creeping, often stoloniferous at the end, the branchlets more or less erect and attenuate; stem-leaves large, cordate-ovate to more or less deltoid, or narrower and lance-ovate, the wider ones abruptly and rather shortly acuminate, the narrower ones slenderly acuminate, the leaves varying in size up to 2.5 x 0.7-1.5 mm, decurrent; the branch-leaves ovate to lance-ovate, about 1.7-2.0 x 0.6-1.0 mm, concave, decurrent, the margin slightly serrulate all around, when dry more or less reflexed at base and the leaves then somewhat plicate; costa thin, reaching to the middle or beyond; median leaf-cells acutely elongate-rhomboid or linear-rhomboid, usually about 10-20:1, the apical somewhat shorter, the basal shorter and wider, incrassate especially in the stem-leaves, the alar similar, except that a few are more enlarged, inflated, and oblong-quadrate, but scarcely forming distinct auricles; perichaetial leaves up to 2.5 mm long, slenderly acuminate: seta 2-3 cm long, rough throughout, drying flattened and twisted, castaneous, sinistrorse except sometimes at the very apex; capsule about 2-3 x 1 mm, oval-oblong to sub-cylindric, unsymmetric, inclined or more usually nearly horizontal, dorsally gibbous, arcuate, dark-castaneous; lid conic to conic-acuminate; annulus broad, 2-3-seriate; peristome-teeth slender, castaneous below, the apex hyaline and papillose, basally confluent, the lamellae and trabeculae closely placed, teeth dorsally cross-striolate, margined; segments slender, about as long as the teeth, yellowish, carinately split; basal membrane about one-half as high as the segments, some of the cilia usually as long as segments, hyaline, nodose, usually 2 or 3; spores usually minutely roughened, somewhat incrassate, brownish, about .016-.020 mm, maturing in early winter.

In wet places on earth, stones, rotten wood, bases of trees, etc., in shady woods and thickets; Europe, Asia, northern Africa, and, in North America, from Canada to New Jersey and Pennsylvania.

Rather common in our region. Collected in 11 counties widely distributed in western Pennsylvania: Allegheny, Armstrong, Butler, Erie, Fayette, Greene, Lawrence, McKean, Warren, Washington, and Westmoreland. Specimen figured: Wildwood Road Hollow, Allegheny Co., O.E.J. & G.K.J. Nov. 19, 1908.

7. BRACHYTHECIUM RIVULARE (Bruch) Bryologia Europaea
(*Hypnum rivulare* Bruch)
Plate LVI

Robust, cespitose in wide and thick mats, pale golden green, shining, rigid: stems hard and woody, prostrate, filiform, leafless when old; branches irregular on the ascending or sub-erect and somewhat dendroid secondary stems which usually reach a height of 3 or 4 cm; stem-leaves broadly ovate, rather regularly imbricate when dry, erect-spreading or more open when moist, rather distant, abruptly short-acuminate or acute, concave, decurrent, plicate, denticulate, reaching about 1.8-2.5 x 1.0-1.4 mm; branch-leaves similar to the stem-leaves but usually wider, ovate to lance-ovate, decurrent, about 1.5 x 0.7 mm, quite concave, dentate above, the margins plane or reflexed below, often somewhat plicate; median leaf-cells linear, about 10-15:1, prosenchymatous with rounded ends, rather incrassate, the apical shorter, the basal abruptly laxer, shorter, wider, the median basal usually with incrassate and porose walls, the alar abruptly differentiated, more or less enlarged, inflated, hyaline to orange-pellucid, forming distinct and widely decurrent auricles; costa often forking, reaching to the middle or above; seta 1.5-2.5 cm long, strongly papillose throughout, castaneous; capsule castaneous, turgid- to oblong-ovate, about 2-3 x 1 mm, more or less arcuate, inclined to more or less horizontal; lid conic-acuminate; annulus 2-seriate; exothecial cells at rim small and rounded, below larger and rounded-oblong; peristome-teeth castaneous below, apically hyaline and papillose, basally confluent, strongly trabeculate, distinctly margined by the projecting edges of the cross-striolate dorsal lamellae; segments nearly as long, carinately split and gaping, yellowish, the basal membrane about one-half as high, cilia 2 or 3, nodose, slender, about as long as the segments; spores smoothish, the walls somewhat incrassate and greenish-brown, about 0.16-0.20 mm, maturing in fall.

On wet rocks in or at the margin of streams, swamps, or in wet places in ravines, usually where often submerged; Europe, Asia, and from Canada to Missouri and Virginia. Rather rare in our region. Quite variable with a number of named varieties.

Now known from the following counties: Allegheny, Beaver, Butler, Cambria (Porter), Crawford, Erie, Fayette, McKean, Somerset, Warren, Washington, and Westmoreland. Specimen figured: Pymatuning Swamp, Linesville, Crawford Co., May 10-11, 1906. O.E.J.

8. BRACHYTHECIUM REFLEXUM [Starke] Bryologia Europaea

(Hypnum reflexum Starke; *H. subtenue* James; *Thuidium laxifolium* Macoun)

Very slender, dark green, densely intertwining to form low, flat patches: the branches short, delicate, often curved, more or less pinnately arranged; stem-leaves cordate-triangular, quickly narrowed to a fine, long, often twisted acumen, strongly decurrent, minutely serrulate all around; branch-leaves narrower, lanceolate, strongly decurrent, serrulate, smooth to faintly plicate, margins plane to very narrowly recurved, when dry spreading or imbricate and rendering the branches rather julaceous; costa strong, reaching to apex or even into the acumen; leaf-cells short and broad, about 3-8:1, rhomboid-fusiform, sub-obtuse, rather incrassate, towards the basal angles becoming gradually shorter and broader, the alar large, pellucid, rounded-quadrate to rounded-rectangular, numerous and extending up the sides of the leaf but not forming very clearly distinct auricles: seta slender, about 1-1.5 cm long, rough; capsule small, about 2 mm long, about 2:1, ovate-globose, curved, dorsally turgid, abruptly horizontal, almost black when old; lid convex-conic, apiculate; annulus narrow, 2-seriate; cilia slender and appendiculate; spores mature in winter: autoicous.

On rocks and tree-trunks in mountainous or hilly regions; Europe, Asia, and from Garrett County, Maryland (J. Donnell Smith), and westward.

Rare in our region. McKEAN Co.: Bradford. D. A. Burnett. (Porter's Catalogue).

9. BRACHYTHECIUM STARKEI [Bridel] Bryologia Europaea

(Hypnum Starkei Bridel)

Plate LVI

Dark green, widely and thinly cespitose, the plants usually quite distinctly complanate: stems slender, creeping, radiculose, pinnate with short, curved-ascending, rather distant, slender branches; branch-leaves loose, divergently spreading, often somewhat secund, those from the middle of the branches broadly ovate to broadly triangular-cordate, abruptly and usually rather shortly slender-acuminate, apically twisted, broadly decurrent, marginally serrate above, denticulate below; costa variable but usually about three-fourths as long as the leaf; median leaf-cells about 8-15:1, fusiform-hexagonal to fusiform-rhomboid, sometimes shorter, somewhat incrassate; the basal in one or two rows more or less rectangular-oblong, the alar rather numerous, sub-rectangular, with thick and often brownish or yellowish walls, forming quite disitnct auricles; stem-leaves usually smaller than branch-leaves, broadly ovate and broadly long-acuminate: seta papillose, about 2 cm long, flexuous, slender, castaneous, rough; capsule small, turgid-oval, often blackish when ripe, the urn about 2.5-3 x 1 mm, dorsally gibbous, abruptly more or less horizontal, sub-globose when empty; annulus large; exothecial cells rounded-quadrate and small at the rim, oblong-rectangular and a little larger below, all strongly castaneous or yellowish and incrassate; peristome-teeth castaneous below, set far back from the edge of rim, margined, rather widely confluent at base, lamellate, cross-striolate dorsally below, hyaline and papillose at apex, strongly trabeculate; segments slender, nearly as long as teeth, carinately split and often widely gaping in the middle, yellowish; basal membrane about two-fifths as high as the teeth, the cilia 2 or 3, strongly appendiculate, hyaline granular, a little shorter than the segments; spores about .012-.015 mm, greenish-yellow or brownish, slightly roughened, medium-walled, mature in winter.

On moist, rotten wood, stumps, bases of trees, earth, in moist woods in hilly or mountainous regions; Europe, and from Canada to northern United States as far south as New Jersey and Pennsylvania.

Rather rare in our region. ELK Co.: Benezette. McMinn. (Porter's Catalogue). LAWRENCE Co.: Kennedy's Mills. Kellar Shelar. Nov. 20, 1931. McKEAN Co.: On shaded banks along Marilla Brook, Bradford, April 25, 1897. D.A.B. (figured). WASHINGTON Co.: On stone near creek, Snowden Sta. Dec. 3, 1892. Linn & Simonton, No. 96.

10.   BRACHYTHECIUM VELUTINUM [Linnaeus] Bryologia Europaea

(*Hypnum velutinum* Linnaeus; *H. declivum* Mitten)

Plate LVI

Slender and usually in low, soft, silky mats, bright or yellowish-green, prostrate: stems radiculose; branches numerous, short, in our specimens the branches usually less than 5 mm long, crowded, irregular or curved, more or less sub-pinnate; branch-leaves loosely erect-spreading to falcate-secund at tips of branches, more widely spreading when dry, lanceolate to lance-ovate, in ours mainly 1-1.5 mm long, tapering to a long acumination, serrate, apically often twisted, shortly decurrent, faintly plicate, glossy when dry, marginally plane; costa slender, reaching somewhat beyond the middle; median leaf-cells narrow-linear, rather obtuse, about 8-15:1, the apical similar but a little shorter, the basal shorter, the alar few, rather opaque, incrassate, sub-quadrate; the stem-leaves similar but usually not so large as some of the branch-leaves; perichaetial leaves erect, slenderly acuminate, up to 1.8 mm long; seta about 1.5 cm long, very rough, castaneous, often flattened and twisted when dry; capsule about 2-2.5 mm long, 2-3:1, turgid-oblong, dorsally gibbous to sub-arcuate, castaneous, inclined to horizontally spreading; exothecial cells small and rounded-quadrate at rim, oblong-rectangular below, all densely incrassate; peristome-teeth slender, castaneous and confluent at base, apically hyaline and papillose, dorsally cross-striolate, closely trabeculate and lamellate; segments as long as the teeth, slender, carinately split between the nodes, yellowish, the basal membrane one-third to two-fifths as high; cilia 2 or 3, nodose, hyaline, somewhat shorter than the segments; lid conic-acuminate, about 0.5-0.8 mm long; annulus large; spores mature in winter, faintly roughened, medium-walled, brownish, .013-.016 mm in diameter.

On earth, rocks, bases of trees, rotting wood, etc., in rather dry woods, often on knolls; Europe, Asia, and from Canada south to New Jersey and Pennsylvania and also in the Pacific States.

Thus far reported but once in our region. McKEAN Co.: Langmade, near Bradford, April 25, 1898. D.A.B. (figured).

11. BRACHYTHECIUM POPULEUM (Hedwig) Bryologia Europaea

(*Hypnum populeum* Hedwig)

Slender, densely cespitose in small yellowish-green tufts, lustrous: stems procumbent, branched with numerous, more or less pinnately-arranged, erect or curved-ascending branches; leaves of stem and branches similar except that the branch-leaves are narrower and lanceolate; stem-leaves rather closely imbricated, erect to erect-spreading when dry, ovate-lanceolate, serrate to nearly entire, slenderly and gradually acuminate, non-striate, shortly decurrent; costa strong and reaching the apex; median leaf-cells about 5-8:1, sometimes relatively longer, the basal more or less rectangular, the alar numerous, often yellowish but rather opaque; seta rough except towards the base, where nearly smooth, dark brown; annulus persistent, simple, narrow; capsule about 2:1, cernuous, turgid-ovate to ovoid, mostly dorsally gibbous, glossy, constricted at the mouth when dry; lid short-acuminate; peristome normal, cilia short, usually 1 or 2 and unequal, appendiculate; spores mature in winter; autoicous.

On roots of trees, stones, sometimes on bases of trees, in shady woods, said to be somewhat partial to pine woods; Europe, northern Africa, and from Nova Scotia to North Carolina and in British Columbia.

Rare in our region. McKEAN Co.: "*B. populeum rufescens.*" Bradford. D.A.B. (Porter's Catalogue).

12. BRACHYTHECIUM FLAGELLARE (Hedwig) Jennings

(*Hypnum flagellare* Hedwig; *Hypnum plumosum* Swartz; *B. plumosum* (Sw.) Bryologia Europaea)

Plate LVII

Robust in loose, wide, green mats, brownish below: stems prostrate, up to 5 or 6 or more cm long, with rather densely pinnate branches; the branches stout, ascending to erect, somewhat tumid with the closely imbricate, concave leaves; leaves crowded, erect-spreading when moist, imbricated when dry, often quite strongly falcate-secund, the branch-leaves lanceolate to broadly lance-ovate, abruptly slenderly acuminate, about 1.3-2.0 x 0.4-0.9 mm, decurrent, serrate above to nearly entire, the base very concave somewhat excavate at the alae, narrowed, sometimes striate when dry, margin plane or slightly recurved at the base; costa reaching to the middle or a little farther; median leaf-cells narrow to linear, about 8-15:1, the apical shorter, the basal shorter, the median basal enlarged, rounded to oblong ,incrassate, sometimes porose, the alar somewhat smaller, oblong to sub-quadrate, incrassate and somewhat opaque; stem-leaves similar, rather scattered, usually smaller and narrower, about 1.5 x 0.6-0.7 mm, narrowly triangular-ovate; perichaetial bracts more or less erect, partly sheathing: seta papillose in the upper half, brown to blackish, stout, 1.5-2.0 cm long, sinistrorse below, sometimes dextrorse above; capsule about 1.5-2.5 x 1 mm, turgidly oval-oblong, blackish when old, dorsally gibbous, horizontal to sub-erect, somewhat unsymmetric; lid conic-acute about 0.6-0.8 mm long; annulus simple, persistent; peristome-teeth castaneous, confluent at base, strongly trabeculate and lamellate, prominently margined by the projecting lamellae, dorsally cross-striolate below, hyaline and papillose at apex; segments narrow, carinately split but usually not widely gaping, yellowish, nearly as long as teeth, the basal membrane about one-third as high; cilia 2, nodose, hyaline, appendiculate below, about as long as the segments; spores smooth, medium-walled, brownish, about .013-.017 mm, mature in autumn.

In streams, or on moist rocks, in non-calcareous habitats; Europe, Asia, Hawaiian Islands, and from Newfoundland to British Columbia and south in the mountains to Alabama; Florida. Very common in our region.

Now known from the following counties: Allegheny, Armstrong, Beaver, Bedford, Butler, Centre, Erie, Fayette, Greene, McKean, Washington, and Westmoreland. Specimen figured: Wildwood Hollow, Allegheny Co., Nov. 19, 1908. O.E.J. and G.K.J.

12a.   BRACHYTHECIUM FLAGELLARE var. HOMOMALLUM
(Bryologia Europaea) Jennings
(B. plumosum var. homomallum Bryologia Europaea)
Plate LVII

This variety differs from the type of the species in having the leaves distinctly falcate-secund and branches curved at tip. It is said to be generally smaller with narrower leaves and with the capsule small and ovate. In the same pockets with typical B. flagellare can often be found specimens with characters approaching more or less closely the variety. The following pocket of specimens perhaps typical of the variety:

McKEAN Co.: Gate's Hollow, Bradford, April 18, 1897. D.A.B. (figured).

5.   CIRRIPHYLLUM Grout

Dioicous: robust, widely cespitose, whitish to yellowish-green, rarely darker, mostly lustrous: stem creeping to ascending, often stolon-like, pinnately to fasciculately branched, often with flagellae; branches ascending to erect, more or less densely-leaved and julaceous; leaves uniform, often spreading, often drying imbricate, very concave, somewhat weakly plicate, ovate to oblong from a somewhat narrowed and decurrent base, more or less abruptly lanceolate to piliferous at the apex, plane-margined, serrate to entire; costa simple, ending at or above the middle of the leaf, never ending in a dorsal spine; median leaf-cells narrowly prosenchymatous, smooth, the basal, shorter, thickened, and porose, the alar more or less numerous, short-rectangular to quadrate, mostly green; inner perichaetial leaves from a sheathing base abruptly long and finely acuminate: seta elongate, mostly rough; capsule cernuous to horizontal, oval to oblong-oval, more or less dorsally gibbous, rarely erect and sub-cylindric; annulus present; peristome as in *Brachythecium;* lid usually more or less long-rostrate from a conic base.

A small genus of about 15 species, mostly in temperate regions on rocks and earth; 4 or more species in North America; 2 species in our region.

KEY TO THE SPECIES

A. Stems without stolons, almost regularly pinnate; the acumination about one-half as long as the body of the leaf: seta rough ....1. *C. piliferum*

A. Stem with stolons, irregularly branched; the leaf-acumination short: seta smooth ....2. *C. Boscii.*

1. CIRRIPHYLLUM PILIFERUM [Schreber] Grout

(*Hypnum piliferum* Schreber; *Eurynchium piliferum* Bryologia Europaea)

Robust, in loose straggling patches, glossy yellow-green: stems elongate, up to 10 or 15 cm long, prostrate, creeping, radiculose, more or less pinnate; the ends of the stems and branches of a paler shining green; leaves concave, widely oblong-ovate, spoon-shaped, abruptly hair-pointed from the rounded apex, the piliferous acumination often reaching one-half the length of the main portion of the leaf, towards the apex of the stems and branches the leaves more closely imbricate and forming cuspidate terete points, but with the piliferous leaf-tips flexuous-spreading, leaf-margin usually denticulate, plane or inflexed; when dry the leaves striate; median leaf-cells about 10-15:1, the basal more lax, shorter and wider, the angular forming a well-defined patch, large, oval-rectangular; the branch-leaves somewhat smaller, narrower and more gradually pointed; costa broad at base, reaching to about three-fourths the length of the leaf: seta about 2.5 cm long, rough; capsule ovoid-oblong to turgid, somewhat arcuate, when dry and empty strongly arcuate and constricted below the mouth, about 2 mm long; lid conic with a subulate beak about as long as urn, 2 mm; peristome large, teeth long, the segments about as long, the cilia nodose to sub-appendiculate, 2 or 3, about as long as the segments; spores mature in fall but capsules rarely found.

In wet woods and swampy meadows, on the ground or on the bases of trees; Europe, and from New Brunswick to New Jersey, Pennsylvania, and Ohio; Washington.

Rare in our region. ELK Co.: Benezette. McMinn. (Porter's Catalogue). McKEAN Co.: D. A. Burnett. (Porter's Catalogue).

2. CIRRIPHYLLUM BOSCII (Schwaegrichen) Grout

(*Hypnum Boscii* Schwaegrichen; *Eurynchium Boscii* Jaeger).

SPOON-LEAVED MOSS

Plate LVII

Loosely cespitose in large, golden-green mats, the older portions blackish, robust: stems up to 8-10 cm long, prostrate, somewhat pinnately branching, the branches mostly simple, erect, turgid-terete; leaves closely to loosely imbricate, large, about 1.5-2.5 mm long, spoon-shaped, abruptly acuminate, the acumination filiform and twisted, the leaves oblong-ovate, scarious, shining; costa double and short, or simple and reaching to the leaf-middle or beyond; median leaf-cells narrowly linear-rhomboid, the marginal shorter and mainly rhomboid, the basal short, wide, yellowish-brown, pellucid, irregularly oblong to rectangular, larger but shorter, the alar incrassate, quadrate, forming an indistinct group, the apical shorter and wider than the median, the median about 6-10:1; perichaetial leaves narrowly long-acuminate, the inner erect: seta smooth; capsule oblong, about 2.5-3:1, the urn about 2 mm long, inclined, sub-arcuate; lid sharply obliquely rostrate, about 1 mm long; annulus 2-seriate; peristome normally hypnoid with somewhat split segments and cilia 3, about as long as segments, nodose; spores mature in fall, about .016 mm.

On earth or rocks in moist woods, often at the edges of the woods, or even in the fields; from New England to Florida and westward to Missouri.

Probably fairly common in our region. CAMBRIA Co.: (Porter's Catalogue). HUNTINGDON Co.: Pennsylvania Furnace, July 13, 1909. WASHINGTON Co.: Linn and Simonton. (Porter's Catalogue). WESTMORELAND Co.: Hillside, May 22, 1909. O.E.J. (figured).

6. OXYRHYNCHIUM (Bryologia Europaea) Warnstorf

Mostly dioicous: slender to robust, laxly to densely cespitose, dark to yellowish-green, drying soft or stiff, dull to lustrous: stem creeping or ascending, often stolon-like, often bearing rhizoids, irregularly pinnate to fasciculately branched; branches mostly complanately-leaved, stem-leaves and branch-leaves sometimes different, sometimes similar except in size, non-plicate, little or not concave; stem-leaves erect-spreading to squarrose, from a somewhat narrowed and sometimes decurrent base ovate to triangular oval, with short and broad or somewhat longer apex, plane-margined, somewhat serrate; costa simple, ending at or above the leaf-middle, often ending in a dorsal spine; median leaf-cells narrowly prosenchymatous, smooth, the basal shorter, mostly incrassate and porose, the alar differentiated: seta elongated, mostly red, quite thick, mostly rough; capsule cernuous to horizontal, sometimes sub-erect, thickly oval to oblong-ovate, dorsally gibbous; annulus present; peristome as in *Brachythecium;* lid long and obliquely subulate-rostrate; calyptra glabrous.

A genus of about 20 species, on damp and shaded rocks, stones, or sometimes in water, mostly in temperate regions; 2 species in our region.

KEY TO THE SPECIES

A. Aquatic: alar leaf-cells forming a slightly differentiated group: seta smooth ....1. *O. riparioides*

A. Terrestrial: alar-cells not differentiated: seta roughly papillose ....2. *O. hians*

1. OXYRHYNCHIUM RIPARIOIDES [Hedwig] Jennings

(*Hypnum rusciforme* Necker; *Eurynchium rusciforme* Milde; *Hypnum riparioides* Hedwig; *Rhynchostegium rusciforme* Bryologia Europaea)

Plate LVIII

Robust, in large tufts, dark to blackish below: stems prostrate, woody, and usually denuded below; branches suberect, or ascending, usually more or less rigid and harsh, especially when dry; leaves ovate, loosely ascending or erect-spreading, scarcely decurrent, about 2-2.5 x 1.5 mm, obtuse to acute, plane-margined, denticulate nearly to the base; costa thick below, reaching to one-half or two-thirds the length of the leaf, or occasionally even sub-percurrent, often ending in a dorsal spine; median leaf-cells incrassate, linear-fusiform, about 10-12:1, the apical and basal shorter and broader, but no alar group differentiated, the median and upper slightly dorsally spinose: seta smooth, about 1.5 cm long, castaneous, slightly twisted when dry; capsule castaneous, ovoid-oblong, somewhat constricted below the mouth when dry, about 2-3:1, dorsally turgid but scarcely curved, inclined or nearly horizontal, the urn about 1.5-2 mm long; lid obliquely slenderly rostrate from a conic base, about two-thirds as long as the urn; annulus revoluble, usually 2-seriate; exothecial cells yellowish-incrassate, at the rim small and rounded-quadrate, below rather large and irregularly oblong-rectangular; peristome-teeth slender, apically hyaline-papillose, strongly trabeculate, dorsally plainly lamellate and finely cross-striolate, margined, confluent at base; segments about as long, usually carinate-ly widely gaping but remaining unsplit at apex, the basal membrane about one-half as high; cilia 2-3, subulate, nodose to sub-appendiculate, somewhat shorter than the segments; spores weakly papillose, medium-walled, yellowish, about .010-.013 mm, mature in early fall.

On wet or submerged rocks in streams and rivulets; Europe, Asia, northern Africa, and from Newfoundland to Ontario and southwards in the mountains to Georgia.

Common in our region. Now known from the following counties: Armstrong, Bedford, Butler, Cambria (Porter), Cameron, Centre, Fayette, Lawrence, McKean, Somerset, Warren, Washington, and Westmoreland. Specimen figured: Rachelwood, Mellon's Estate near New Florence, Laurel Hill Mts., Westmoreland Co., Sept. 8-11, 1907. O.E.J.

2. OXYRHYNCHIUM HIANS (Hedwig) Jennings

(*Hypnum hians* Hedwig; *Eurynchium hians* Jaeger and Sauerbeck; *Hypnum praelongum* C. Mueller; *Pterygynandrum apiculatum* Bridel)

Plate LVIII

Rather slender, depressed, cespitose, somewhat shining: stems creeping, rather sparsely branched, slender, usually not over 3 or 4 cm long, the branches short and more or less distichously arranged; leaves of the stem and longer branches rather distant, on some of the short branches sometimes more or less imbricated-julaceous, the stem-leaves about 1-1.6 mm long by three-fourths as wide, ovate, the apex abruptly acute to shortly acuminate, the base clasping but not decurrent, margins sharply serrulate nearly to the base; branch-leaves closely similar; costa distinct, reaching to one-half to four-fifths the length of the leaf, dorsally ending in a spine; median cells about 5-8:1, prosenchymatous, medium-walled, the apical rhomboid, shorter, about 2-4:1, the basal shorter and incrassate, the alar forming an indistinct group of thick-walled quadrate to rectangular cells; perichaetial leaves up to 2 mm long, ovate-oblong, sheathing, acuminate, serrate above: seta dark-castaneous, stout, strongly papillose, 1-1.5 cm long; capsule inclined to horizontal, arcuately oblong-cylindric, narrowed below the rim but slightly when dry, the urn about 2 mm long by 1 mm thick, castaneous; operculum conic and slenderly rostrate, yellowish, about 1 mm long; exothecial cells yellowish-incrassate, at the rim rounded-quadrate in about two series, below larger oblong-rectangular; annulus narrow, 2-seriate; peristome-teeth castaneous, slender, hyaline-papillose at apex, strongly trabeculate, narrowly margined, the dorsal lamellae often in three series towards the base, striolate in various directions; segments about as long as teeth, slender, narrowly carinately gaping between nodes, the basal membrane about two-fifths as high as teeth, the cilia usually two, slender, nodose to shortly appendiculate, nearly as long as segments; spores slightly papillose, yellowish, medium-walled, about .011-.015 mm in diameter, mature in late fall or early winter.

On the ground in moist, shady places in woods, etc., in Europe, Asia, and, in North America from Nova Scotia south to the Gulf east of the Mississippi.

Apparently not common in our region. ALLEGHENY Co.: Clay stream-bank, South Park. H. N. Mozingo. March 11, 1945. ERIE Co.: In woods near Lagoon Boathouse, Presque Isle, Nelle Ammons. July 22, 1933. FAYETTE Co.: Ohio Pyle, September 1-3, 1906. O.E.J. and G.K.J. McKEAN Co.: On shaded banks of rivulet, Bennett Brook, April 9, 1893, Marilla Brook, September 29, 1894 (figured), and on ground over leaf-mold, April 19, 1897. All near Bradford. D.A.B. WASHINGTON Co.: Shady bank, Oak Grove Station, Nov. 5, 1892; on the ground, Oak Grove Station, Dec. 5, 1891; and Snake Woods, Nov. 19, 1892, in the vicinity of Washington; and on stone, Claysville, Dec. 17, 1892 all A. Linn and J. S. Simonton.

7. EURHYNCHIUM Bryologia Europaea

Dioicous and pseudoautoicous: slender to robust, laxly or densely cespitose, green to yellowish, drying stiff and more or less lustrous: stem creeping to ascending, often more or less stolon-like, here and there fasciculate, often bearing flagellae, pinnate to fasciculate or even dendroid; branches more or less densely-leaved; leaves often dimorphic, mostly plicate; stem-leaves spreading to squarrose, more or less concave, ovate-cordate to triangular-cordate from a narrowed and more or less decurrent base, margins plane, serrate, the apex short and broad to long and narrow; costa simple, more or less elongate, often ending as a dorsal spine; median leaf-cells smooth, prosenchymatous, narrow, at base shorter and usually incrassate and porose, the alar differentiated; inner perichaetial leaves with squarrose-reflexed, subulate tips: seta mostly smooth; capsule cernuous, sometimes horizontal, ovate to sub-cylindric, more or less dorsally gibbous; peristome as in *Brachythecium;* lid long and finely rostrate; calyptra glabrous.

A genus of about 14 species, on rocks, earth, or bark, almost entirely in temperate regions; about 6 species in North America; probably only one species in our region.

1. Eurhynchium pulchellum (Hedwig) Jennings

(*Hypnum pulchellum* Hedwig; *H. strigosum* Hoffmann; *Eurhynchium strigosum* Bryologia Europaea)

Specimens collected by Nelle Ammons on Presque Isle may belong to this species, but our region is represented mostly by the following varieties of this species.

1a. Eurhynchium pulchellum var. robustum (Roell) Jennings

(*E. strigosum* var. *robustum* Roell; *Hypnum strigosum* Drummond)

Common Beaked Moss

Plate LVIII

Loosely and widely matted or densely tufted, bright and shining green: stems stoloniferous, creeping, with distant leaves; secondary stems prostrate to erect, often curved, rather robust; leaves on the middle of the branches erect-spreading, lance-ovate, scarcely decurrent, reaching about 1-1.2 x 0.4-0.5 mm, acute to widely obtuse, plane-margined, sharply serrate above, concave, somewhat plicate, costate to about two-thirds, the costa usually ending in a dorsal spine; median leaf-cells about 8-10:1, linear to linear-rhomboid, the apical becoming rhomboid-oblong and about 2-3:1, the basal somewhat shorter than the median, the alar few, rectangular to quadrate or oval; stem-leaves decurrent, rather long-acuminate from an ovate to triangular-ovate base, somewhat larger than the branch-leaves, reaching about 1.2-1.5 mm long, serrate nearly to the base, costate to about two-thirds; paraphyllia small, rounded-ovate; leaves on the stolons ecostate, triangular-ovate, small, acuminate: seta castaneous, smooth, about 1-1.5 cm long, drying dextrorse above; capsule yellowish-brown, oblong-ovate, about 2-3:1, more or less dorsally turgid or sub-arcuate, drying slightly constricted below the mouth, inclined or almost horizontal, the urn about 2 mm long; annulus 2-3-seriate; lid convex, slenderly rostrate, about 1.5 mm long; exothecial cells rounded-quadrate at rim, oblong-hexagonal to rectangular below, incrassate; peristome-teeth hyaline and papillose at apex, below dorsally cross-striolate, margined, plainly lamellate, strongly trabeculate, confluent at base; segments narrow, nearly as long as the teeth, carinately split between the nodes, yellowish, the basal membrane about two-fifths as high: cilia 3, slender, hyaline, nodose, usually one or two of them nearly as long as the segments; spores yellowish, incrassate, papillose, about .012-.014 mm, mature in autumn.

The species occurs on gravelly or sandy soil, rocks, roots of trees, etc., in open woods in Europe, Asia, northern Africa, and from Arctic America to northern United States. The variety *robustum* occurs from eastern Canada south to Louisiana.

Elk Co.: McMinn. (Porter's Catalogue). McKean Co.: Six pockets of specimens collected on the ground or on rocks in woods, near Bradford, May 13, 1893, to September 29, 1896 (figured). D.A.B.

1b. Eurhynchium pulchellum var. praecox (Hedwig) New Combination
(E. strigosum var. praecox Husnot; Hypnum praecox Hedwig)

Loose yellow-green mats; creeping and often stoloniferous; branches erect, julaceous about 4-5 mm long; branch-leaves erect-ascending when moist, imbricate dry, decurrent ovate-cordate, acute to bluntly obtuse, serrulate all around, more or less plicate; costa to $3/4$ length of leaf, ending in dorsal spine; median leaf-cells 6-8:1, apical short and wide, basal and alar numerous and quadrate: seta about 1 cm long; capsule ovoid, somewhat curved, horizontal, about 2:1; lid long-rostrate, 2/3 length of urn; cilia 1-3, nodose; spores .010-.012 mm, ripe in autumn.

Moist shady soil or rocks. New York, New Jersey, and eastern Pennsylvania.

BEDFORD CO.: Sulphur Springs. C.M.B. Sept. 29, 1940.

8. BRYHNIA Kaurin

Dioicous: more or less slender, weak, widely and laxly cespitose, more or less dark green, when old yellowish or brownish, rather dull: stem elongate, procumbent, rhizoids fascicled, branching interruptedly pinnate, some of the shoots in the middle of the tufts often erect and tree-like but later procumbent and giving rise to new shoots; branches usually spreading to recurved, thin, acute, mostly laxly-leaved; paraphyllia none; stem-leaves loosely imbricate, more or less concave, irregularly plicate, triangular-cordate to lance-ovate from a widely decurrent and non-auriculate base; shortly or more slenderly pointed, plane-margined, finely serrate all around; costa simple, ending in or over the leaf-middle, smooth; median leaf-cells incrassate, green, oblong-rhomboid to oblong-hexagonal, the basal lax, a few alar rectangular; branch-leaves mostly dorsally rough by projecting cell-angles, sharply serrate all around; costa often ending dorsally in a spine; inner perichaetial leaves oblong, abruptly narrowed to a reflexed-squarrose, long, serrate acumination: seta 8-15 mm, dark red, very rough; capsule cernuous to horizontal, dorsally gibbous, oval to oblong-cylindric; annulus present; peristomes of equal length, the teeth basally confluent, dorsally cross-striate, normally lamellate, apically papillose; inner peristome yellow, finely papillose, basal membrane high, segments lanceolate, long-subulate, split and finally gaping along the keel, cilia well-developed; lid more or less plainly and thicky sub-rostrate from a conic base; calyptra glabrous.

A small genus of 10 species, occurring on various substrata, confined to the Northern Hemisphere; 3 species in North America; 2 species in our region.

KEY TO THE SPECIES

A. Branch-leaves acute to short-pointed, the apex mostly twisted ....1. B. novae-angliae
A. Branch-leaves acuminate, the apex not twisted ....2. B. graminicolor

1. BRYHNIA NOVAE-ANGLIAE (Sullivant and Lesquereux) Grout

(*Hypnum novae-angliae* Sullivant and Lesquereux; *Brachythecium novae-angliae* Jaeger and Sauerbeck)

Plate LXIX

Widely and loosely matted, bright green outside, dirty green inside, rather rigid: stems prostrate, irregularly sub-pinnately branched, sometimes more or less dendroidal in appearance; branches often indistinctly julaceous; branch-leaves rather loosely imbricate when dry, erect-spreading when moist, broadly ovate, acute to shortly acuminate, concave, decurrent, serrulate, up to 1-1.2 x 0.5-0.6 mm, dorsally papillose by reason of the projecting cell-angles, the leaf-apex often twisted about half-around; median leaf-cells about 5-6:1, oblong-hexagonal, somewhat shorter and broader below and at the basal angles; perichaetial leaves ovate, abruptly long-acuminate, faintly costate; costa of branch- and stem-leaves reaching to the middle or slightly beyond; stem-leaves similar to the branch-leaves but more broadly triangular-ovate and with more distinctly quadrate alar cells, occasionally some inflated, and somewhat excavate: seta short, very rough, dark castaneous; capsule dark-castaneous, blackish when old, about 4-5:1, reaching about 3.5-4.5 mm in length, oblong, erect, slightly curved; lid conic-acuminate or sub-rostellate; peristome normal; annulus double, large; spores mature in winter.

On the ground and on stones in swamps and wet, shady places; Europe, Asia, and from eastern Canada to Maryland and Pennsylvania.

ALLEGHENY Co.: Swampy spot. Deer Creek at Middle Road. C.M.B. Oct. 29, 1949. BUTLER Co.: Swampy soil, Criders Corner. O.E.J. Dec. 29, 1908 (figured): West Liberty Bog outlet. C.M.B. Nov. 26, 1948. FAYETTE Co.: Hollow below Cucumber Falls, Ohiopyle. C.M.B. June 22, 1940. SOMERSET Co.: Wet rock by spring, 1 mi. s. of Bakersville. Aug. 10, 1945; and Beck Spring, Laurel Hill. C.M.B. Aug. 23, 1946; Cranberry Glade Run. C.M.B. June 28, 1942. WARREN Co.: South side Allegheny River, 2 mi. s. of Big Bend. C.M.B. Sept. 2, 1935. WESTMORELAND Co.: On rock, in Meadow Run, Jacobs Creek. C.M.B. Aug. 18, 1945; and Chestnut Ridge s. of Torrance. C.M.B. June 13, 1943.

2. BRYHNIA GRAMINICOLOR [Bridel] Grout

(*Hypnum graminicolor* Bridel; *H. Sullivantii* Spruce; *Eurhynchium graminicolor* Paris)

Plate LIX

Small, much more slender than the preceding species, densely to loosely cespitose, pale green, yellowish below: stems slender, red, usually not over 1-2 cm long, rather irregularly branched with erect branches; branch-leaves reaching about 0.8 x 0.8-0.3 mm, narrowly lance-ovate, long-acuminate, concave, serrulate to the base, marginally reflexed below, the base decurrent, the back strongly papillose by reason of the projecting cell-angles, the costa reaching to above the middle; stem-leaves larger, up to 0.8-1.0 x 0.4-0.5 mm, with a somewhat more slender acumen; median leaf-cells linear-flexuous, incrassate, varying from 4-8:1, obtuse, the alar sub-quadrate, thin-walled, pellucid; perichaetial leaves oblong, basally sheathing, filiform-acuminate, very faintly costate: seta about

1 cm long, rough throughout; capsule oval to oblong or turgid-ovate, dorsally somewhat gibbous about 2-3:1, inclined, about 2 mm long; annulus simple, persistent; lid conic to short-rostrate; peristome normally hypnoid, segments shorter than the teeth, carinately split, the cilia 2, somewhat shorter; rather uncommon, capsules rarely produced.

In moist woods and shady places on rocks or earth; from New Brunswick to Minnesota and south to Georgia.

Rare in our region. HUNTINGDON CO.: Alexandria. T. C. Porter (Porter's Catalogue). MCKEAN CO.: Bolivar and Bennett divide on shaded dripping rocks, April 21, 1895 (figured), and on perpendicular faces of rocks, Lewis Run, April 25, 1895. D.A.B. WARREN CO.: South Fork of Ten-Mile Creek, 2 miles southwest of Jefferson. March 15, 1942. C.M.B.

9. RHYNCHOSTEGIUM Bryologia Europaea

Autoicous: more or less robust to quite slender, mostly soft, cespitose, pale green to dark green, rarely yellowish to golden-brown, more or less lustrous: stem creeping, bearing rhizoids, sometimes stolon-like, irregularly to pinnately branched; branches more or less thickly-leaved, often complanate; leaves spreading, rarely imbricate, shortly or non-decurrent, mostly a little concave, nonplicate, ovate to lance-ovate from a narrowed base, with a short or long point, mostly serrulate, the margin basally reflexed; costa simple or rarely forked, ending in about the middle of the leaf; median leaf-cells mostly narrowly prosenchymatous, smooth, the basal shorter and wider, the alar not differentiated, sometimes short-rectangular or quadrate; inner perichaetial leaves sheathing, abruptly subulate and reflexed from the middle: seta more or less elongate, smooth; capsule cernuous to horizontal, oval and weakly gibbous dorsally to oblong or oblong-cylindric and almost symmetric, often constricted below the mouth when dry and empty: annulus present; peristome as in *Brachythecium;* lid long-rostrate from a convex-conic base; calyptra glabrous.

About 130 species, occurring on earth and stones, mostly in the temperate and sub-tropic regions; about 10 species in North America; probably only the following in our region:

1. RHYNCHOSTEGIUM SERRULATUM (Hedwig) Jaeger
(*Hypnum serrulatum* Hedwig; *Eurynchium serrulatum* Lindberg)
Plate LIX

Loosely matted, bright yellowish-green, when dry sub-lustrous: stems creeping, sub-pinnately branched with long and more or less 2-ranked branches; branch-leaves complanate, 1.5-2 mm long, thin, concave, ovate-lanceolate, acuminate, serrulate from usually below the middle, thin-costate to the middle or beyond, the apex often twisted, the margin plane and not bordered; perichaetial leaves similar but more oblong; stem-leaves similar but relatively wider and more cordate and with more distinct alar cells; median leaf-cells linear, prosenchymatous, about 8-10:1, at base somewhat broader and shorter, the alar not differentiated: seta about 2.5 cm long, smooth, castaneous, sinistrorse when dry; capsule light yellow to dark castaneous, oblong, cernuous, incurved, when dry contracted below the mouth; lid conic, slenderly rostrate, the beak long and recurved; peristome-segments nearly as long as teeth, cilia usually 3, about as long as segments, nodose to weakly appendiculate; basal membrane reaching almost to middle of inner peristome; teeth narrowly lanceolate, yellowish-brown, with distinct divisural, moderately trabeculate; annulus large; exothecial cells rectangular to hexagonal, yellow-incrassate, or brownish; spores yellowish-incrassate, finely papillose, about .009-.012 mm in diameter, mature in September and October.

In shaded woods on leaf-humus, old logs, etc., from New England to the Gulf States and west to Kansas. It often hangs down in wide, thin mats from overhanging ledges.

This is one of the most commonly collected mosses of our area, now represented in the herbarium by specimens from more than sixty localities from 16 counties. It probably occurs in all.

Glossary of Bryological Terms Used in the Manual

Acaulescent, stemless.
Acrocarpous, with the fruit terminal on the stem or branch.
Acumen, a slenderly tapering apex,—acumination.
Acuminate, narrowly and slenderly tapering at the apex.
Acute, rather abruptly sharply pointed.
Alar, applied to the cells at the basal angles of the leaf.
Angular, applied to the alar group of cells.
Annulus, the ring of specialized cells often occurring between the rim of the capsule and the operculum.
Antheridium, the male reproductive organ. See Introduction.
Apiculate, ending in a sharp and short point or apiculus.
Apophysis, the hypophysis or swelling of the seta just below the capsule.
Appendiculate, with reference to the cilia, with short transverse bars.
Archegonium, the more or less flask-shaped female organ.
Arcuate, bent like a bow.
Areolation, the cellular mesh or network of the leaf.
Aristate, awn-like or bristle-like.
Articulate, jointed, or with cross-bars.
Attenuate, long drawn out.
Auriculate, furnished with more or less ear-like lobes at the basal angles, applied to the leaf.
Autoicous, having the archegonia and antheridia in separate clusters on the same plant.
Axillary, situated in the axil or upper angle of the insertion of a leaf.

Beak, the prolonged narrow apex of the operculum.
Bicostate, having a double costa or midrib.
Bifid, two-cleft.
Bifurcate, forked.
Bi-stratose, with two layers of cells.
Bi-striate, with two parallel lines or striae.

Calyptra, the thin and usually more or less membranous hood or cap on top of the capsule.
Campanulate, bell-shaped.
Canaliculate, channeled.
Cancellate, (teeth) lattice-like.
Capsule, the spore-case or so-called "fruit" of a moss.
Carinate, keeled.
Caulescent, furnished with a stem.
Castaneous, chestnut-brown in color.
Central Strand, a central bundle of narrow and elongated cells found in some moss-stems.
Cernuous, somewhat drooping, nodding.
Cespitose, forming mats or tufts.
Chlorophyllose, containing chlorophyll or the green coloring matter of leaves.
Cilia, fine hair-like processes, usually applied to the hair-like structures often occurring between the peristome-segments.
Circinate, coiled inward from the apex.
Cirrate, curling up in drying.
Clavate, club-shaped.
Cleistocarpous, applied to a capsule which bursts open irregularly.
Collum, the more or less tapering neck or base of the capsule.
Columella, the central axis of the capsule around which the spores are produced.
Comose, tufted at the apex, in a coma.
Complanate, flattened.

Confluent, merging together.
Constricted, contracted somewhere below the top or apex.
Cordate, heart-shaped.
Cortex, the outer bark or specialized layer.
Cortical, referring to the cortex.
Costa, the midrib or mid-vein of the leaf.
Crenate, with rounded teeth.
Cribrose, perforated more or less sieve-like.
Crispate, variously curled and bent.
Cucullate, hood-like.
Cultriform, curved like a short, wide scimitar.
Cuneate, wedge-shaped.
Cuspidate, tipped with a sharp and rigid point.
Cuticular, belonging to the outermost skin.
Cygneous, abruptly down-curved like a swan's neck.
Cymbiform, the whole leaf more or less boat-shaped.

Decumbent, reclining but with the apex ascending.
Decurrent (leaves) with the borders extending down the stem below the insertion.
Dehiscent, splitting open.
Dendroid, tree-like in form.
Dentate, toothed with outwardly directed teeth.
Denticulate, minutely toothed.
Deoperculate, (capsule) with the lid fallen off.
Dextrorse, twisted to the right as the threads of the ordinary screw or bolt, used in the opposite sense by some authors.
Dimidiate, split on one side.
Dimorphous, with two forms.
Dioicous, with the antheridia and archegonia on separate plants.
Discoid, disk-shaped as in some male inflorescences.
Distichous, in two opposite rows, two-ranked.
Divaricate, widely diverging or spreading.
Divisural (*Line*), the median line running up and down the teeth of the peristome and often zigzag.
Ducts, applied to the narrow chlorophyllose cells in the leaves of the Sphagnums.

Ecostate, without a costa.
Emarginate, apically notched.
Emergent, applied to capsules rising slightly above the perichaetial leaves.
Exannulate, with no annulus.
Erose, irregularly notched.
Excavate, applied to leaf-insertions hollowed out in a more or less definite curve.
Excurrent, with the costa extending beyond the apex of the leaf.
Exothecial, the outer layer of cells of the capsule-wall.
Exserted, projecting beyond, as a capsule rising beyond the perichaetial leaves.

Falcate, scythe-shaped, flat, gradually tapering and curved.
Falcate-secund, falcate and turned to one side of the stem.
Fasciculate, in close and usually short clusters; usually applied to short, unequal, lateral, bunched branches.
Fastigiate, with branches erect, near together, and more or less equal in height.
Fenestrate, furnished with openings.
Fibrillose, applied to hyaline cells of *Sphagnum* in which the walls are lined with fine fibrils or filaments.
Filiform, thread-like.
Fimbriate, fringed.
Flagelliform, lash-like or whip-like.

Flexuose, wavy or bending alternately back and forward.
Frondose, bearing fronds or frond-like.
Fugacious, falling away very early.
Fusiform, spindle-shaped.

Gametophyte, the sexual stage in the life-history of the moss and resulting from the germination of a spore. Usually begins with a filamentous protonema which eventually gives rise to leafy stems, which finally bear the sexual organs (archegonia and antheridia) and, upon the fertilization of the archegonium, there is produced the other alternating phase, the sporophyte.
Gemmae, small more or less bud-like bodies capable of reproducing the plant.
Gemmiparous, producing gemmae.
Geniculate, bent like a knee.
Gibbous, swollen on one side.
Glabrous, with a smooth surface.
Glaucous, covered or whitened with a bloom.
Granulose, finely roughened as with grains of sand.
Gregarious, growing near together or in groups but not forming tufts or mats.
Gymnostomous, with the mouth of the capsule devoid of peristome.

Hamate, hooked.
Heteroicous, with two or more forms of inflorescence in the same cluster.
Hispid, beset with stiff hairs.
Hispidulous, minutely hispid.
Homomallous, (leaves) bent or curved to one side, all in the same direction.
Hyaline, transparent and colorless like water.
Hygroscopic, altering form or position with changes in moisture.
Hypophysis, an enlarged of the seta immediately below the capsule.

Imbricated, overlapped like the shingles on a roof.
Immersed, (capsule) concealed within the leaves of the perichaetium.
Incrassate, thickened, or thick-walled (cells).
Indehiscent, not splitting open.
Inflorescence, the clusters of reproductive organs, usually with enclosing bracts.
Innovation, a young offshoot from the stem.
Insertion, the point of attachment of the leaf to the stem or branch.
Involucre, a whorl of leaves or bracts around the flower.

Julaceous, worm-like or catkin-like.

Laciniate, deeply slashed or cut into narrow lobes.
Lamellae, thin plates, particularly the flat plates on the dorsal surface of many peristome-teeth; also on ventral surface of many leaves.
Lamina, the leaf-blade.
Lanceolate, lance-shaped.
Lid, the covering of the mouth of the capsule, the operculum.
Ligulate, strap-shaped.
Linear, long and narrow with parallel sides.
Lingulate, tongue-shaped.
Lumen, the cavity of a cell.

Mamillate, tipped with a nipple-shaped projection.
Margin, (of a leaf) a bordering band of peculiar shape or color.
Mitriform, mitre-shaped, or like a peaked cap, symmetric.
Monoicous, with the antheridia and archegonia on the same plant.
Mucronate, with the costa percurrent as a short small abrupt tip, tipped with a mucro.
Muricate, with the surface roughened with short, hard points.
Muticous, not pointed.

Neck, the collum.
Nodose, (cilia) with knots or swollen articulations.

Ob-, a prefix often used to convey the sense of inversion.
Obconic, inversely conic.
Obcordate, inversely cordate.
Obovate, inversely ovate, narrowed towards the base.
Obsolete, scarcely apparent.
Operculum, the lid covering the mouth of the capsule.
Ovate, more or less egg-shaped, with the broader end downward.
Ovoid, more usually applied to a solid with an egg-like outline.

Panduriform, fiddle-shaped.
Papillae, minute nipple-shaped protuberances.
Papillose or *Papillate,* covered with papillae.
Paraphyllia, minute thin leaves or branched organs scattered among the leaves.
Paraphyses, jointed and hyaline hair-like structures growing among reproductive organs.
Parenchymatous, composed of broad cells joined end-to-end with square ends, not dove-tailed.
Paroicous, having the antheridia and archegonia in the same cluster but not mixed, the antheridia being in the axils of the perichaetial leaves below the archegonia.
Patent, spreading.
Pectinate, branched or divided like a comb.
Pedicel, the seta or stalk of the capsule.
Pedicellate, furnished with a pedicel.
Pellucid, translucent but scarcely hyaline.
Pendulous, drooping rather more than when cernuous, hanging down.
Percurrent, (costa) running through the whole length of the leaf.
Perichaetium, the involucre of bracts around the female flower and thus also around the base of the seta or sessile capsule.
Perigonium, the whorl of bracts around the male or antheridial flower.
Peristome, the fringe of teeth, etc., at the mouth of the capsule.
Persistent, not easily nor early deciduous.
Pinnate, with the branches more or less equidistant and arranged on both sides of the stem like a feather.
Piliferous, bearing a hair-like prolongation.
Plane, flat.
Pleurocarpous, with the flowers more or less axillary and the fruit laterally borne.
Plicate, folded longitudinally.
Plumose, plume-like.
Pluriseriate, arranged in several or many series, as of leaves on the stem.
Polygamous, with the antheridia and archegonia variously disposed on the same plant.
Porose, pierced with small holes or pores.
Procumbent, trailing along on the ground.
Proliferous, bearing abnormal shoots, often from the flower cluster.
Prosenchymatous, composed of narrow cells whose ends dove-tail past each other, as opposed to the square-ended parenchymatous cells.
Protonema, the green filamentous phase of the gametophyte which is derived directly from the germination of the spore, and sometimes persisting.
Pseudopodium, in *Sphagnum* the false seta bearing the capsule; in *Aulacomnium,* etc., a leafless seta-like branch bearing gemmae.
Punctate, marked with dots.
Pyriform, pear-shaped.

Quadrate, square.

Radicles, rootlets or rhizoids growing out from the base of the stem.

Radiculose, covered with radicles.
Ramose, branching.
Ramulose, bearing smaller branchlets.
Repand, undulately or wavy-margined.
Reticulate, in the form of a net-work.
Retort Cells, cuticular cells of *Sphagnum* having an outward-curved apex.
Retuse, with the obtuse apex slightly indented.
Revolute, rolled backward from the margin.
Revoluble, curling off, as does the annulus of many mosses.
Rhomboid, diamond-shaped.
Rostellate, short-beaked.
Rostrate, with a more or less long beak.
Rugose, wrinkled.
Rupestral, inhabiting rocks.

Scabrous, rough.
Scarious, thin, dry, membranous, but not green.
Secund, turned to one side.
Segments, the main divisions of the inner peristome.
Serrate, with forward-projecting teeth.
Serrulate, minutely serrate.
Sessile, not stalked.
Seta, the stalk or pedicel bearing the capsule.
Setaceous, bristle-like.
Sheathing, applied to perichaetial leaves which wrap around the seta or ordinary leaves
    wrapping around the stem.
Sinistrorse, twisted to the left, as is the case with the threads of the rather-rare "left-
    handed" screw or bolt. By some authors used in the opposite sense.
Sinuose, wavy.
Spatulate, spatula-like, bluntly and narrowly obovate and quite attenuate downwards.
Spinulose, furnished with small spines.
Sporangium, usually synonymous with capsule.
Sporophyte, the spore-bearing generation of the moss arising from the fertilization of the
    archegonium and known also as the sporogonium,—usually consisting of foot, seta,
    and capsule.
Squarrose, spreading abruptly and widely.
Squarrulose, a lesser degree of squarrose.
Stegocarpous, with the capsule operculate.
Stipitate, mounted on a short stalk.
Stoloniferous, bearing slender, creeping and usually minutely-leaved secondary stems or
    branches.
Stomata, breathing pores, or openings, in the epidermis.
Stomatose, bearing stomata.
Striate, marked with fine longitudinal lines or ridges.
Striolate, being very finely striate.
Strumose, furnished with a struma or unsymmetrical swelling at the base of the capsule,
    goitre-like.
Sub-, as a prefix commonly used to denote the idea of somewhat or slightly.
Subulate, awl-like.
Sulcate, longitudinally grooved.
Synoicous, with the antheridia and archegonia mixed together in the same flower.

Terete, cylindrical or tapering.
Terrestrial, growing on earth.
Tessellate, checkered.
Tomentose, covered with soft matted hairs or tomentum.
Trabeculae, the more or less projecting plates on the inner side of the peristome-teeth.

Trabeculate, furnished with trabeculae.
Truncate, with the apical portion more or less squarely cut off.
Tubulose, tube-like.
Tumid, swollen, turgid.
Turgid, more or less rigidly swollen as from internal pressure, tumid.

Umbonate, with a slight projection in the center like the boss of a shield.
Uncinate, hook-shaped.
Unilateral, one-sided.
Unistratose, (cells) in one layer.
Urceolate, urn-like, contracted at or below the mouth.
Utricles, applied to the large hyaline cells of the leaves of *Sphagnum*.

Vaginate, surrounded by a sheath.
Vaginule, a small sheath, the modified remains of the lower part of the archegonium surrounding the base of the seta.
Ventral, the surface of the leaf facing the stem, as ordinarily situated.
Ventricose, bulging on one side.
Vermicular, worm-shaped.
Verrucose, minutely warty.
Verticil, a whorl.
Verticillate, whorled.
Vesiculose, more or less bladdery, like inflated air-spaces, vesicular.
Villous, covered with long, soft hairs.

INDEX OF PLANT NAMES

* Numbers in brackets refer to plates. Synonyms are italicized.

Plates

To facilitate reference and comparison of the various plates a series of letters and figures has been used which applies uniformly to all plates.

a—Apex
an—Annulus
B—Branch
b—Base
bc—Basal median
c—Central or Median
ci—Cilia
cr—Cross-Section
d—Dorsal
g—Gemmae
lm—Lower Margin
m—Margin
o—Lid or Operculum
P—Plant, habit sketch of, or of a portion
    of a plant

sp—Spores
S—Stem
s—Peristome-segments
t—Teeth
upm—Upper Margin
v—Ventral

1—Stem-Leaf
2—Branch-leaf
3—Perichaetial Leaf
4—Paraphyllia
5—Seta
6—Capsule
7—Calyptra
8—Peristome

The above letters and figures are used in various combinations. 1*a*, for instance, indicates the apex of a stem-leaf; 1*bc*, the median basal portion of a stem-leaf; 2*ad*, dorsal view of branch-leaf; 3*upm*, upper margin of perichaetial leaf, etc.

Plate I

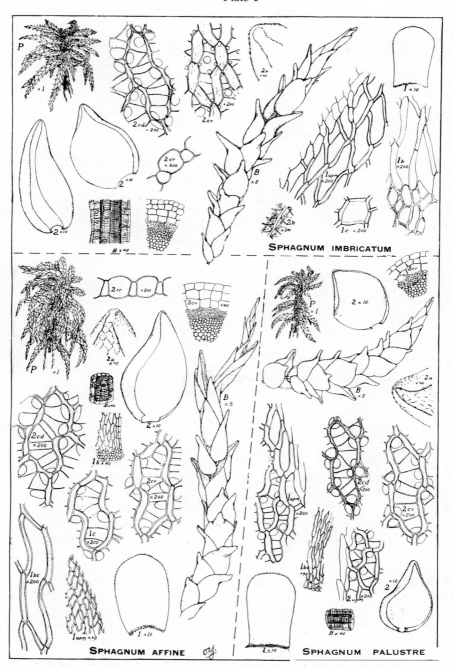

SPHAGNUM IMBRICATUM

SPHAGNUM AFFINE

SPHAGNUM PALUSTRE

Plate II

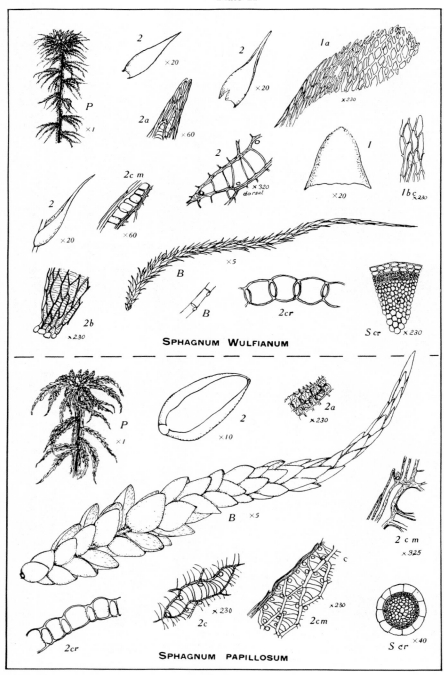

SPHAGNUM WULFIANUM

SPHAGNUM PAPILLOSUM

Plate III

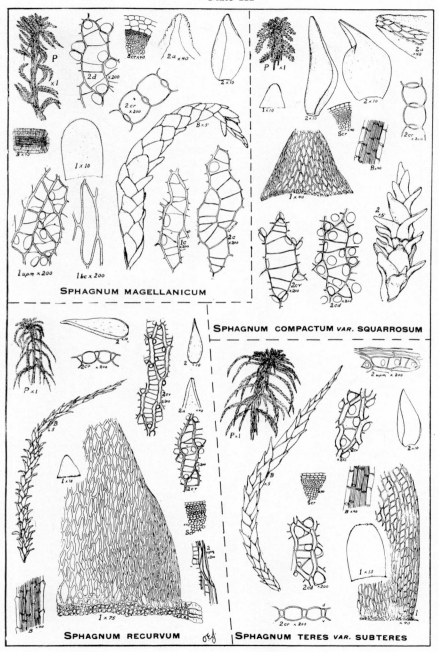

SPHAGNUM MAGELLANICUM

SPHAGNUM COMPACTUM *VAR.* SQUARROSUM

SPHAGNUM RECURVUM

SPHAGNUM TERES *VAR.* SUBTERES

Plate IV

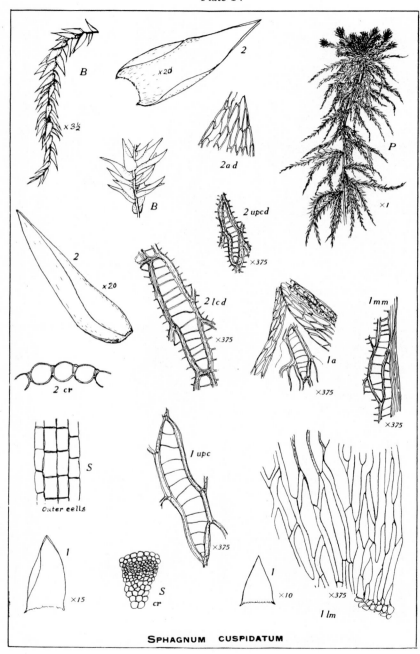

SPHAGNUM CUSPIDATUM

Plate V

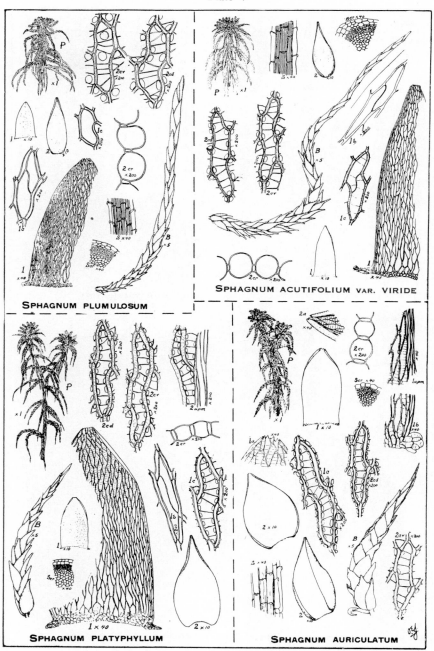

SPHAGNUM PLUMULOSUM

SPHAGNUM ACUTIFOLIUM VAR. VIRIDE

SPHAGNUM PLATYPHYLLUM

SPHAGNUM AURICULATUM

Plate VI

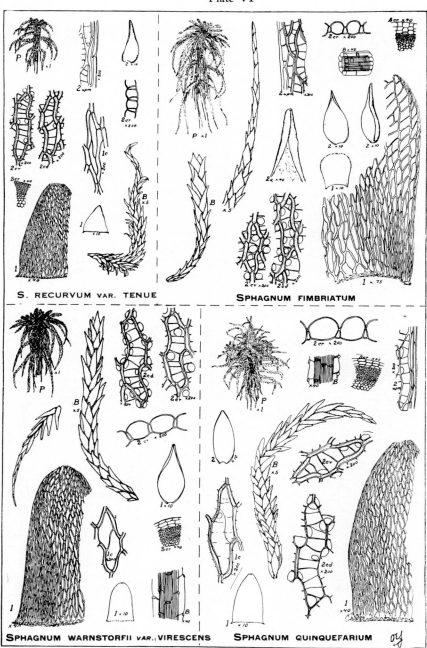

S. RECURVUM VAR. TENUE

SPHAGNUM FIMBRIATUM

SPHAGNUM WARNSTORFII VAR. VIRESCENS

SPHAGNUM QUINQUEFARIUM

Plate VII

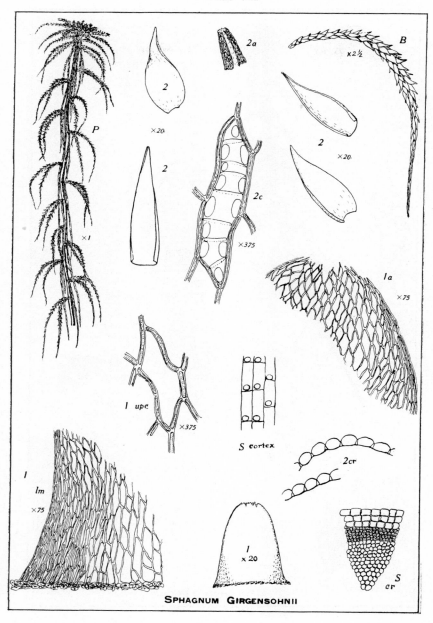

SPHAGNUM GIRGENSOHNII

Plate VIII

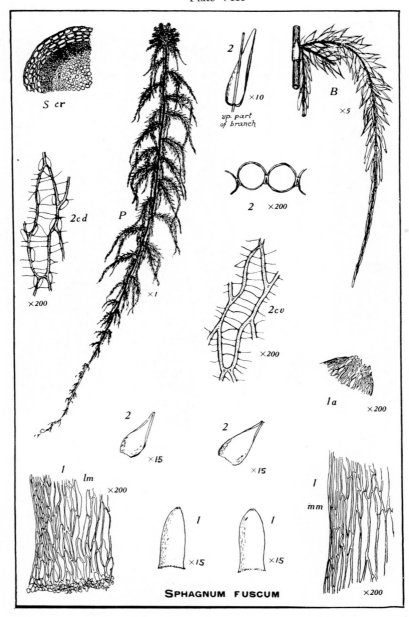

SPHAGNUM FUSCUM

Plate IX

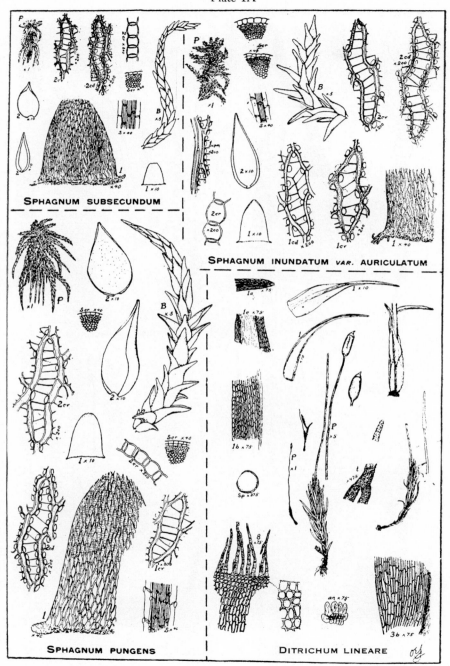

SPHAGNUM SUBSECUNDUM

SPHAGNUM INUNDATUM *VAR.* AURICULATUM

SPHAGNUM PUNGENS

DITRICHUM LINEARE

Plate X

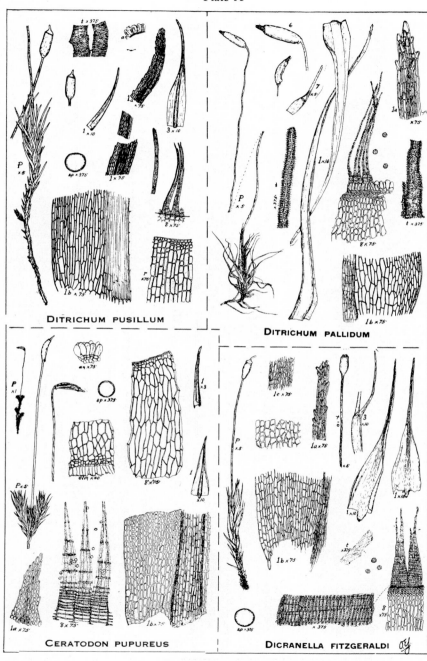

DITRICHUM PUSILLUM

DITRICHUM PALLIDUM

CERATODON PUPUREUS

DICRANELLA FITZGERALDI

Plate XI

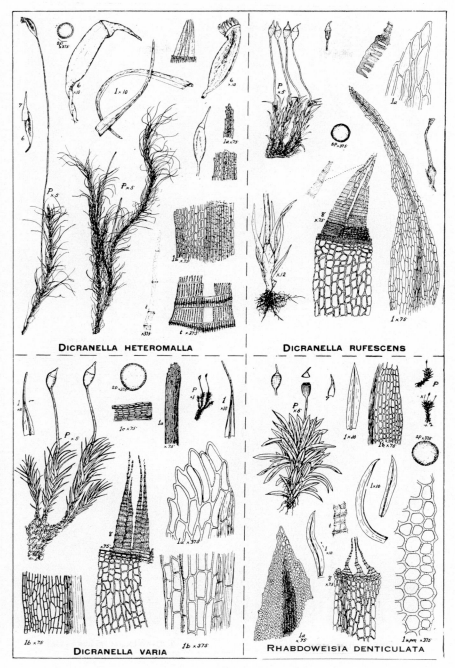

DICRANELLA HETEROMALLA

DICRANELLA RUFESCENS

DICRANELLA VARIA

RHABDOWEISIA DENTICULATA

Plate XII

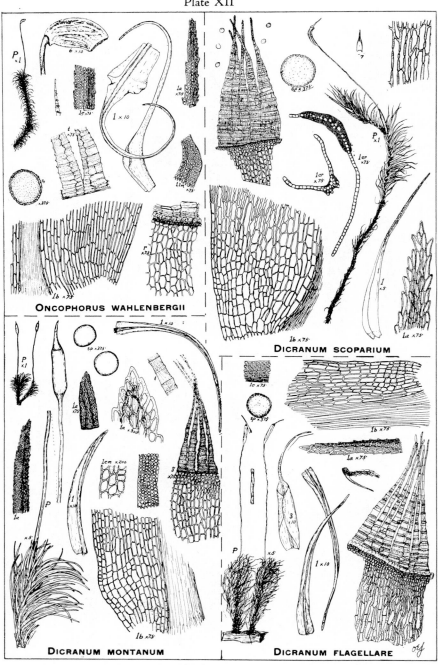

ONCOPHORUS WAHLENBERGII

DICRANUM SCOPARIUM

DICRANUM MONTANUM

DICRANUM FLAGELLARE

Plate XIII

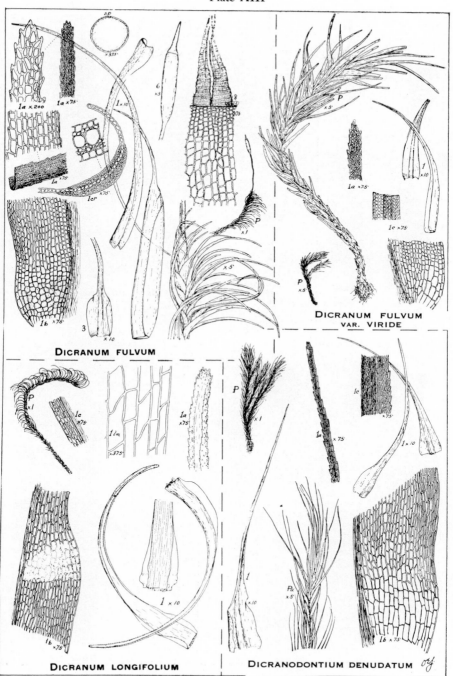

DICRANUM FULVUM

DICRANUM FULVUM
VAR. VIRIDE

DICRANUM LONGIFOLIUM

DICRANODONTIUM DENUDATUM

Plate XIV

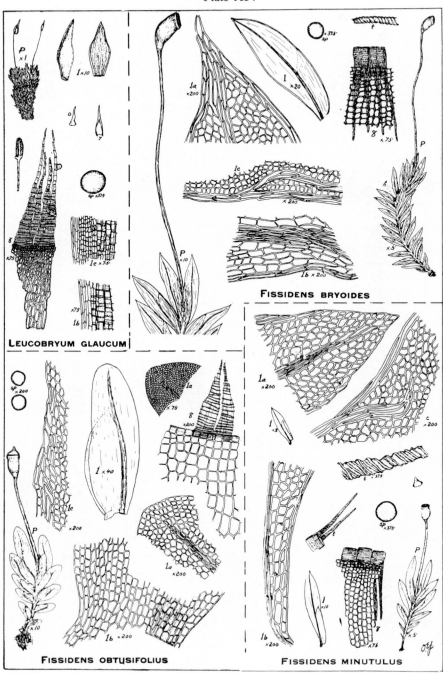

LEUCOBRYUM GLAUCUM

FISSIDENS BRYOIDES

FISSIDENS OBTUSIFOLIUS

FISSIDENS MINUTULUS

Plate XV

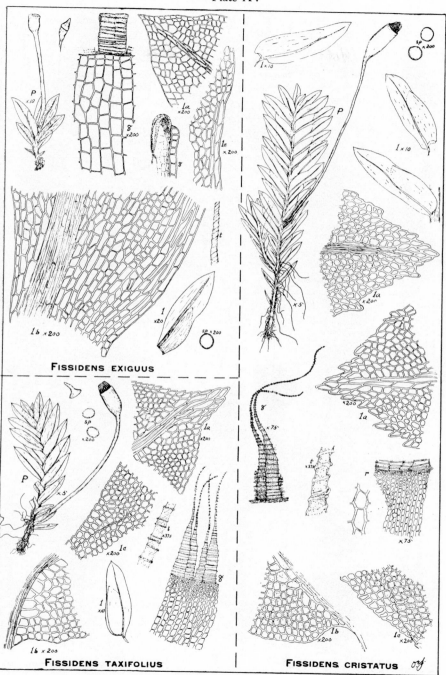

FISSIDENS EXIGUUS

FISSIDENS TAXIFOLIUS

FISSIDENS CRISTATUS

Plate XVI

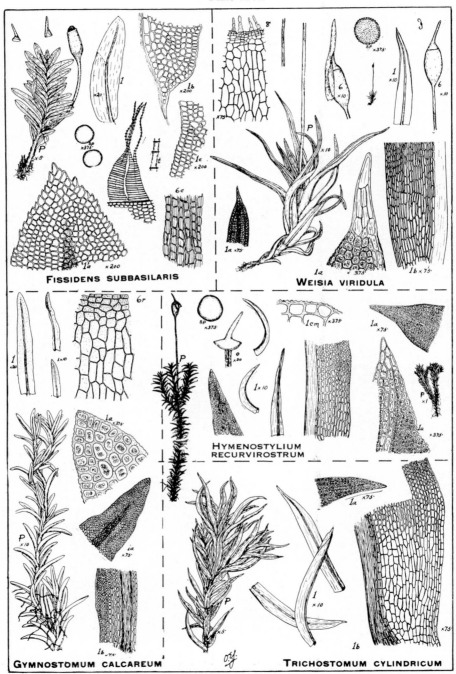

FISSIDENS SUBBASILARIS

WEISIA VIRIDULA

GYMNOSTOMUM CALCAREUM

HYMENOSTYLIUM RECURVIROSTRUM

TRICHOSTOMUM CYLINDRICUM

Plate XVII

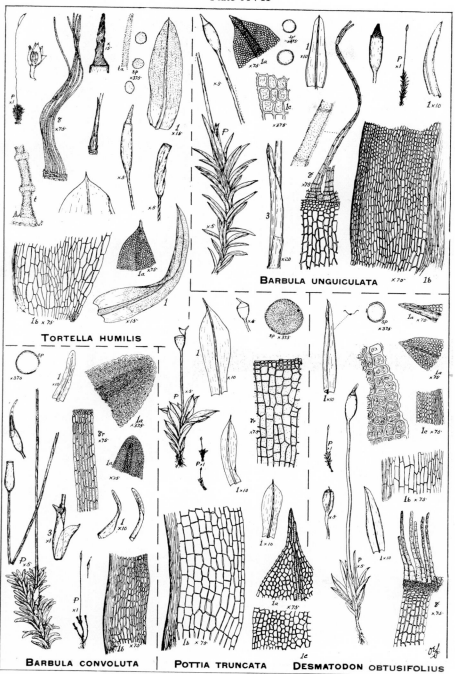

BARBULA UNGUICULATA

TORTELLA HUMILIS

BARBULA CONVOLUTA

POTTIA TRUNCATA

DESMATODON OBTUSIFOLIUS

Plate XVIII

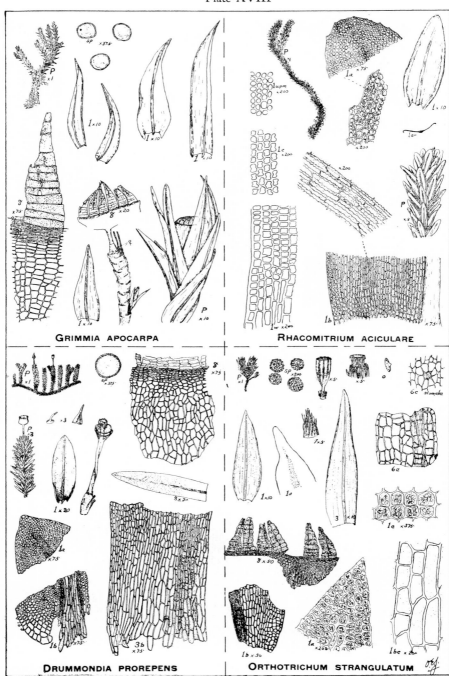

GRIMMIA APOCARPA

RHACOMITRIUM ACICULARE

DRUMMONDIA PROREPENS

ORTHOTRICHUM STRANGULATUM

Plate XIX

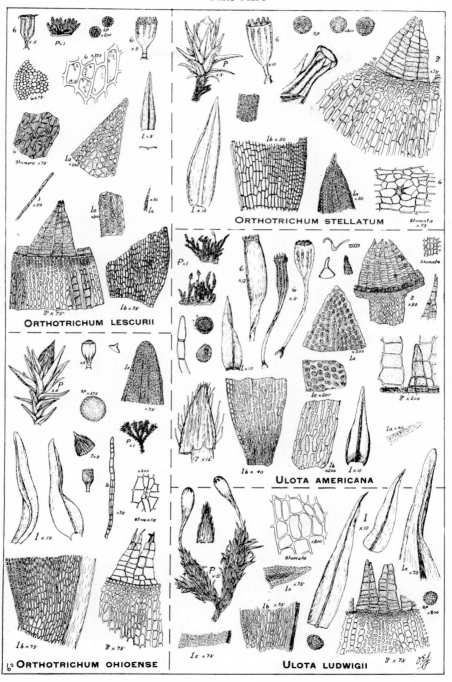

ORTHOTRICHUM STELLATUM

ORTHOTRICHUM LESCURII

ULOTA AMERICANA

ORTHOTRICHUM OHIOENSE

ULOTA LUDWIGII

Plate XX

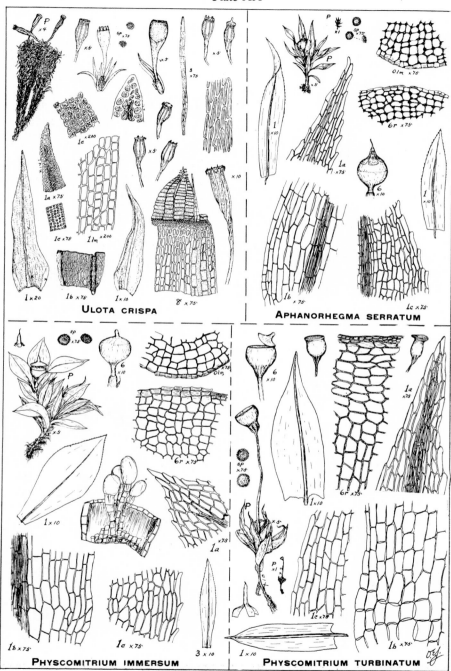

ULOTA CRISPA

APHANORHEGMA SERRATUM

PHYSCOMITRIUM IMMERSUM

PHYSCOMITRIUM TURBINATUM

Plate XXI

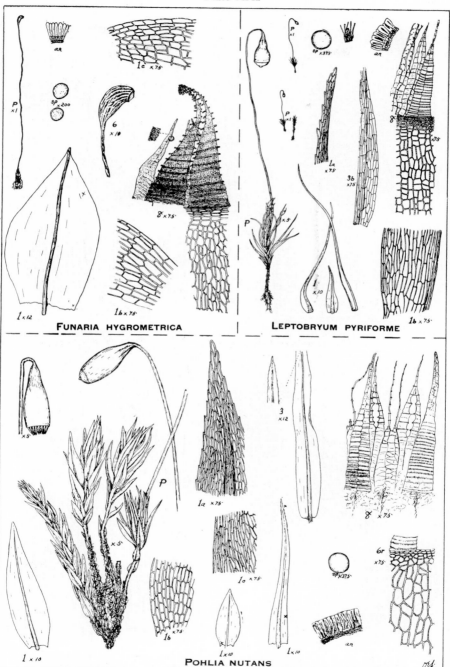

FUNARIA HYGROMETRICA

LEPTOBRYUM PYRIFORME

POHLIA NUTANS

Plate XXII

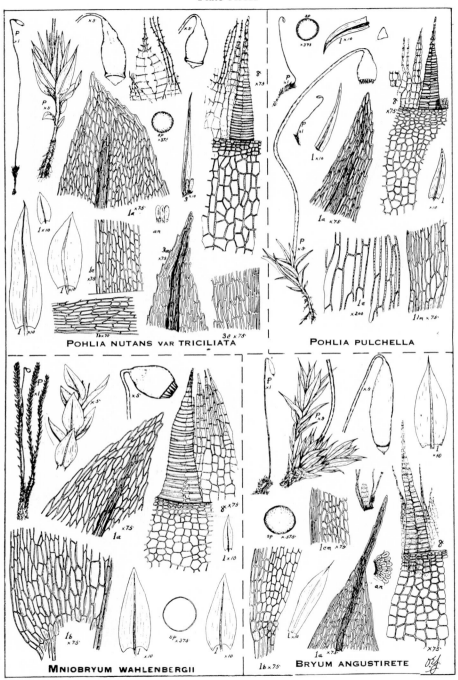

POHLIA NUTANS VAR TRICILIATA

POHLIA PULCHELLA

MNIOBRYUM WAHLENBERGII

BRYUM ANGUSTIRETE

Plate XXIII

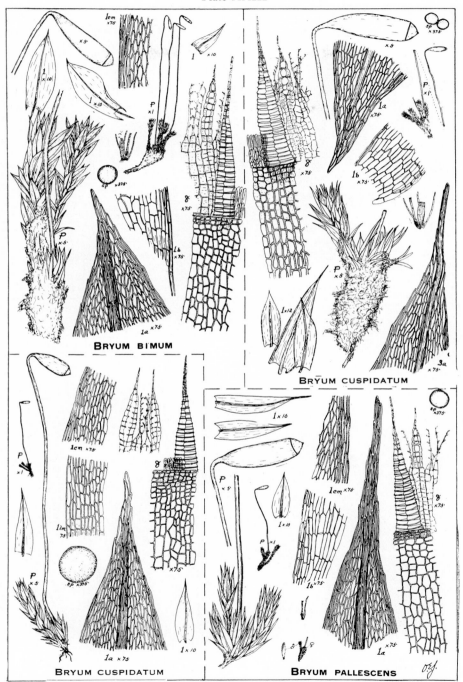

BRYUM BIMUM

BRYUM CUSPIDATUM

BRYUM CUSPIDATUM

BRYUM PALLESCENS

Plate XXIV

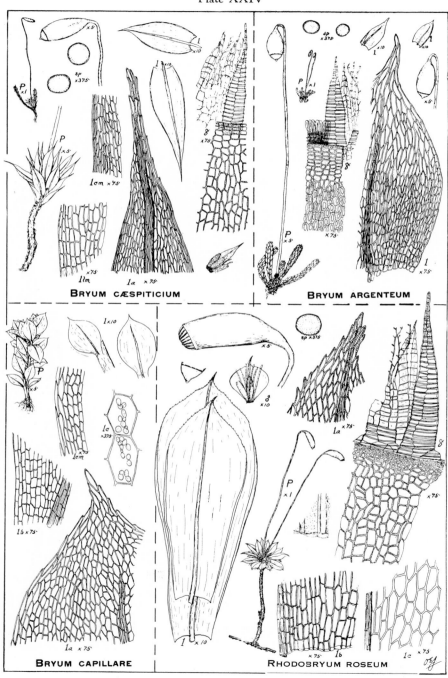

BRYUM CÆSPITICIUM

BRYUM ARGENTEUM

BRYUM CAPILLARE

RHODOSRYUM ROSEUM

Plate XXV

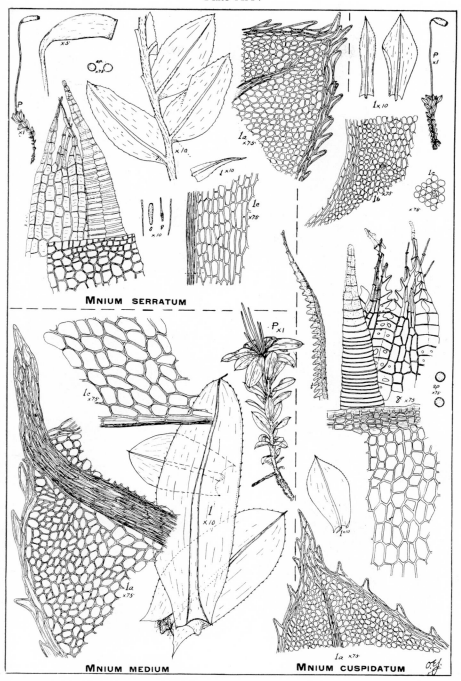

MNIUM SERRATUM

MNIUM MEDIUM

MNIUM CUSPIDATUM

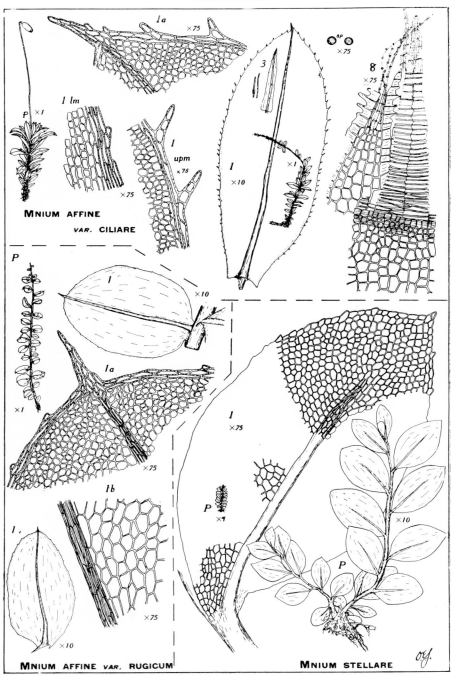

MNIUM AFFINE VAR. CILIARE

MNIUM AFFINE VAR. RUGICUM

MNIUM STELLARE

Plate XXVII

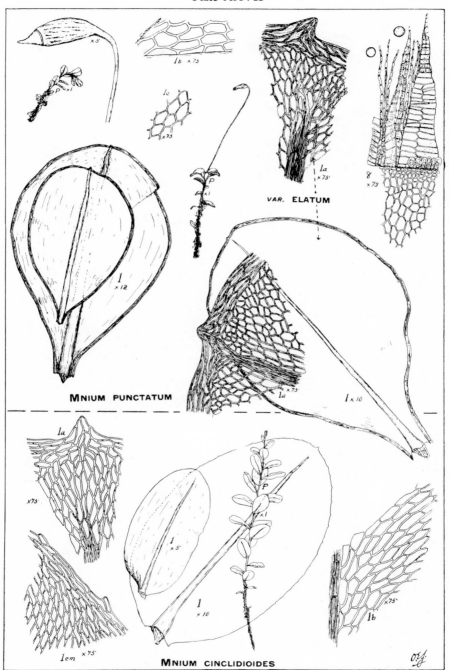

VAR. ELATUM

MNIUM PUNCTATUM

MNIUM CINCLIDIOIDES

Plate XXVIII

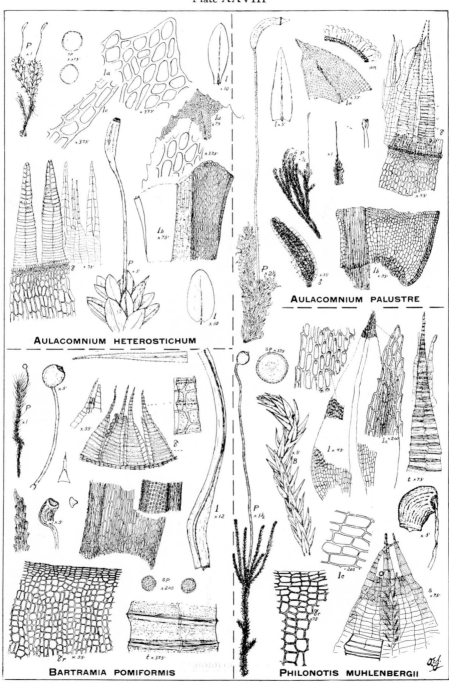

AULACOMNIUM HETEROSTICHUM

AULACOMNIUM PALUSTRE

BARTRAMIA POMIFORMIS

PHILONOTIS MUHLENBERGII

Plate XXIX

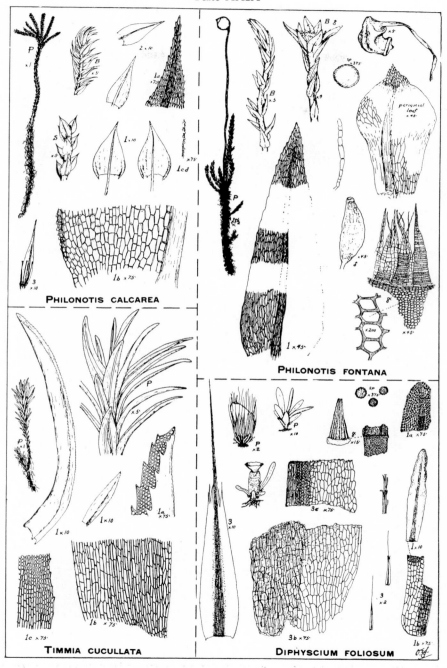

PHILONOTIS CALCAREA

PHILONOTIS FONTANA

TIMMIA CUCULLATA

DIPHYSCIUM FOLIOSUM

Plate XXX

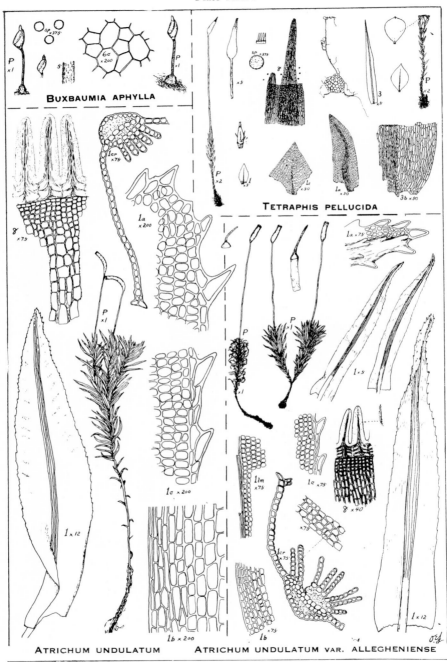

BUXBAUMIA APHYLLA

TETRAPHIS PELLUCIDA

ATRICHUM UNDULATUM   ATRICHUM UNDULATUM VAR. ALLEGHENIENSE

Plate XXXI

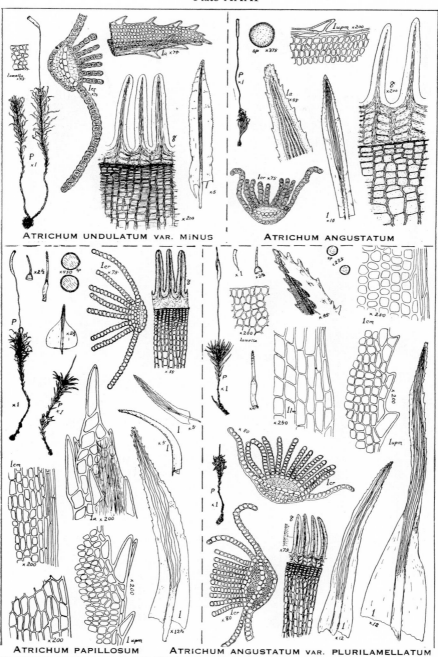

ATRICHUM UNDULATUM VAR. MINUS

ATRICHUM ANGUSTATUM

ATRICHUM PAPILLOSUM

ATRICHUM ANGUSTATUM VAR. PLURILAMELLATUM

Plate XXXII

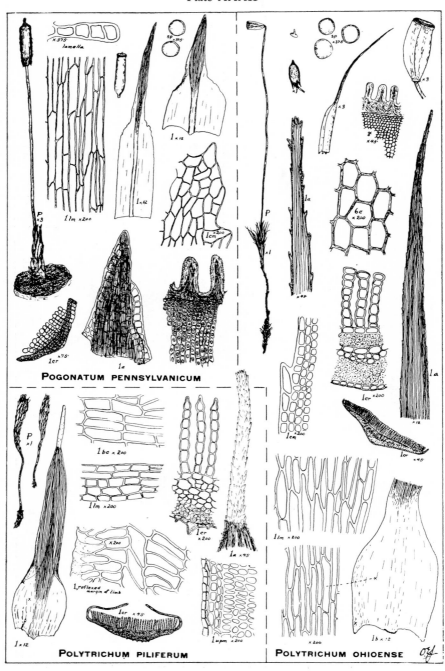

POGONATUM PENNSYLVANICUM

POLYTRICHUM PILIFERUM

POLYTRICHUM OHIOENSE

Plate XXXIII

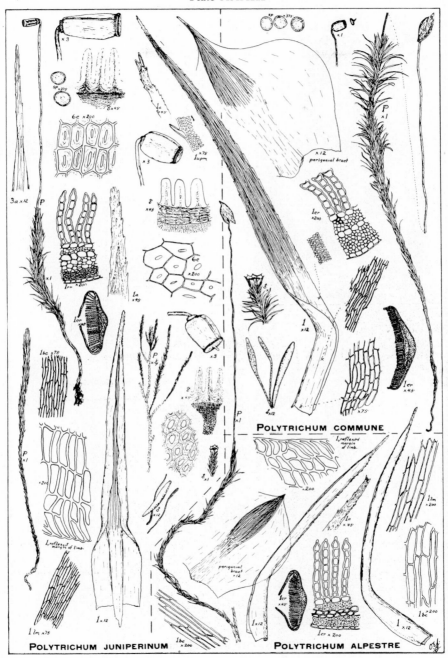

POLYTRICHUM COMMUNE

POLYTRICHUM JUNIPERINUM

POLYTRICHUM ALPESTRE

Plate XXXIV

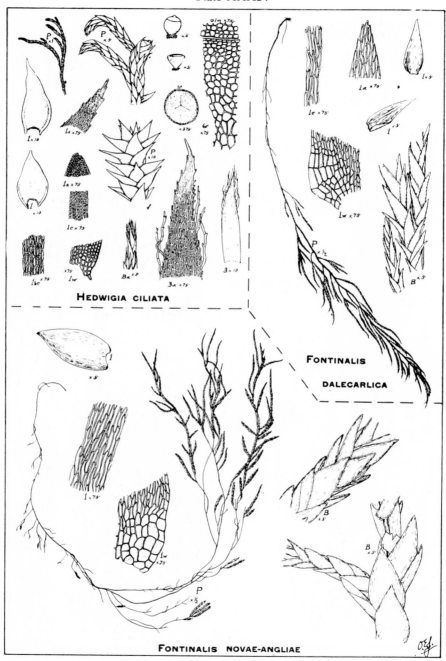

HEDWIGIA CILIATA

FONTINALIS
DALECARLICA

FONTINALIS NOVAE-ANGLIAE

Plate XXXV

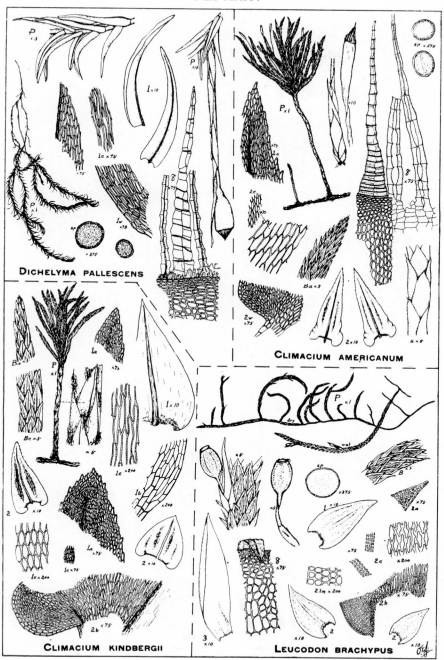

DICHELYMA PALLESCENS

CLIMACIUM AMERICANUM

CLIMACIUM KINDBERGII

LEUCODON BRACHYPUS

Plate XXXVI

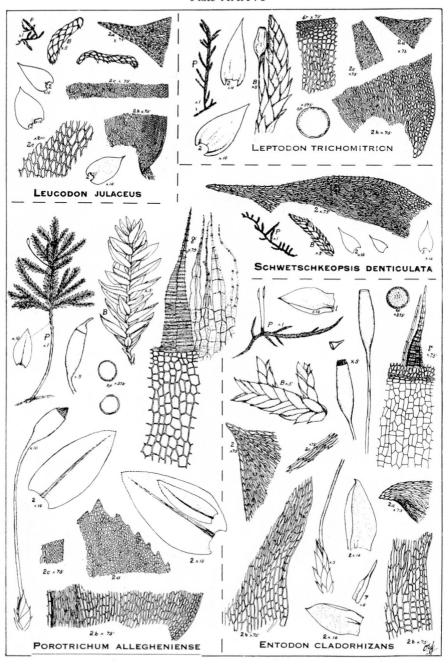

LEUCODON JULACEUS

LEPTODON TRICHOMITRION

SCHWETSCHKEOPSIS DENTICULATA

POROTRICHUM ALLEGHENIENSE

ENTODON CLADORHIZANS

Plate XXXVII

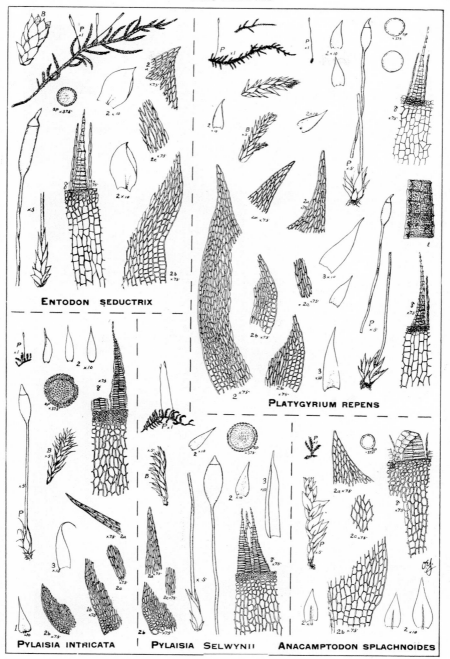

ENTODON SEDUCTRIX

PLATYGYRIUM REPENS

PYLAISIA INTRICATA

PYLAISIA SELWYNII

ANACAMPTODON SPLACHNOIDES

Plate XXXVIII

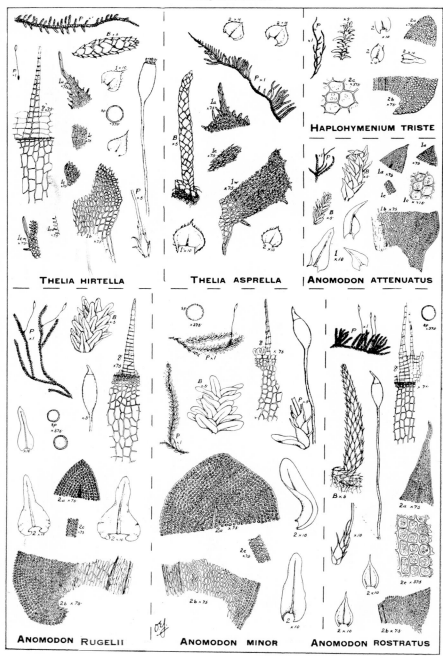

THELIA HIRTELLA

THELIA ASPRELLA

HAPLOHYMENIUM TRISTE

ANOMODON ATTENUATUS

ANOMODON RUGELII

ANOMODON MINOR

ANOMODON ROSTRATUS

Plate XXXIX

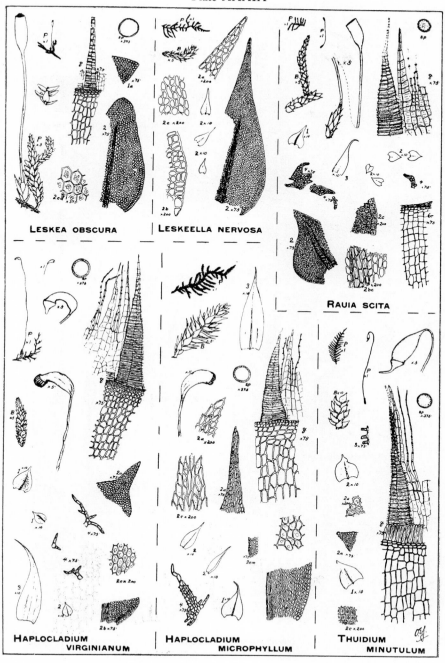

LESKEA OBSCURA

LESKEELLA NERVOSA

RAUIA SCITA

HAPLOCLADIUM
VIRGINIANUM

HAPLOCLADIUM
MICROPHYLLUM

THUIDIUM
MINUTULUM

Plate XL

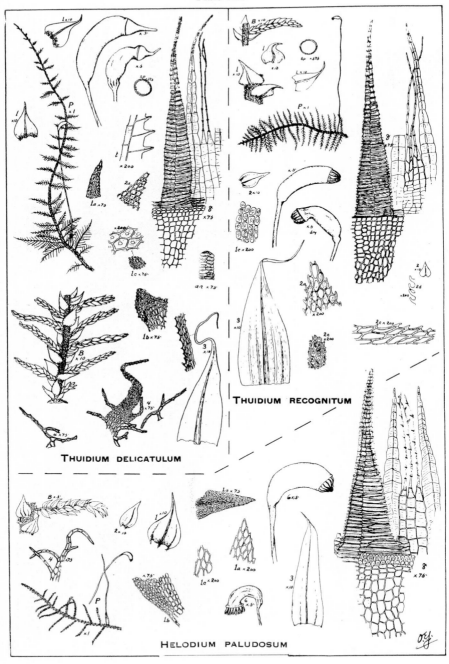

THUIDIUM RECOGNITUM

THUIDIUM DELICATULUM

HELODIUM PALUDOSUM

Plate XLI

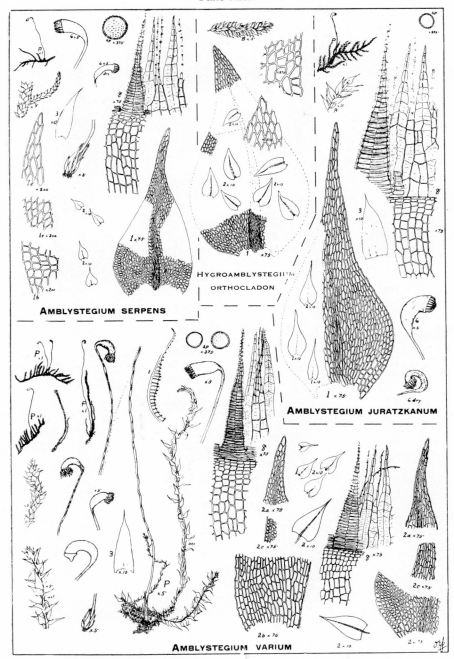

HYGROAMBLYSTEGIUM ORTHOCLADON

AMBLYSTEGIUM SERPENS

AMBLYSTEGIUM JURATZKANUM

AMBLYSTEGIUM VARIUM

Plate XLII

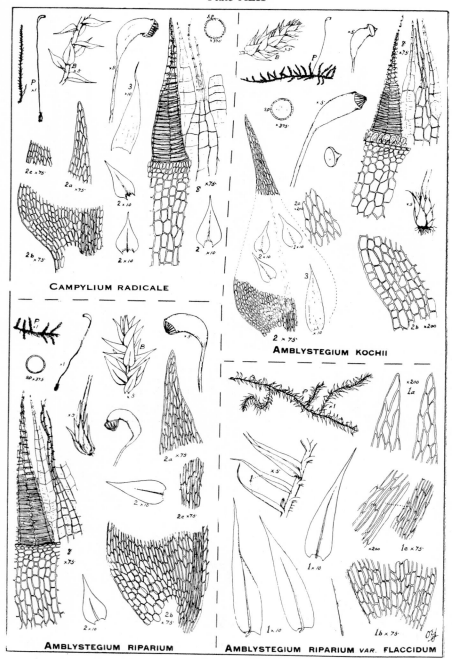

CAMPYLIUM RADICALE

AMBLYSTEGIUM KOCHII

AMBLYSTEGIUM RIPARIUM

AMBLYSTEGIUM RIPARIUM VAR. FLACCIDUM

Plate XLIII

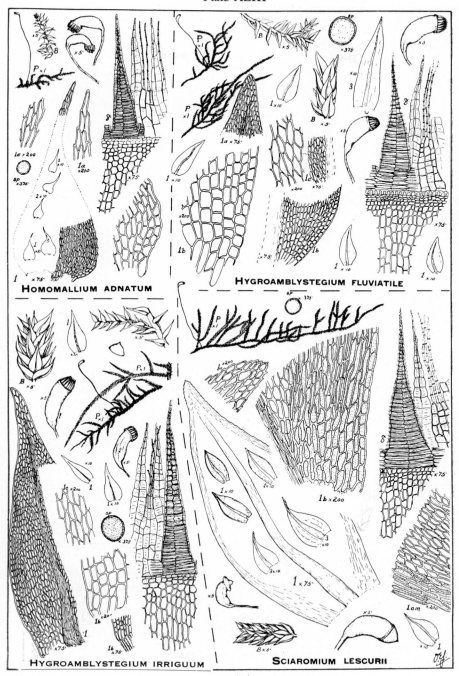

HOMOMALLIUM ADNATUM

HYGROAMBLYSTEGIUM FLUVIATILE

HYGROAMBLYSTEGIUM IRRIGUUM

SCIAROMIUM LESCURII

Plate XLIV

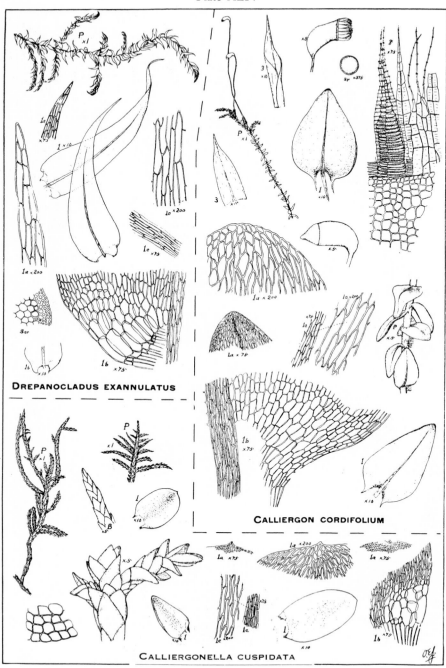

DREPANOCLADUS EXANNULATUS

CALLIERGON CORDIFOLIUM

CALLIERGONELLA CUSPIDATA

Plate XLV

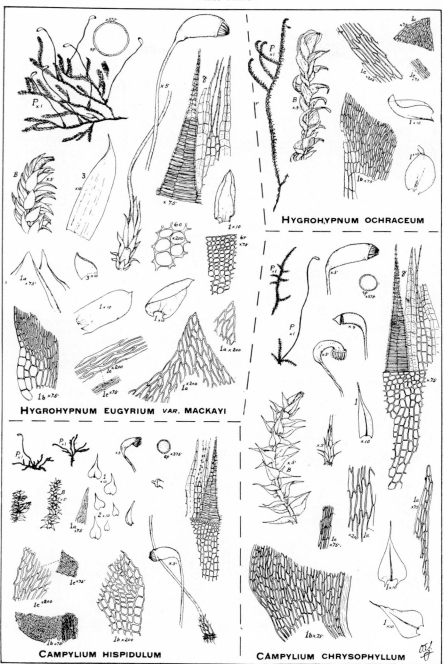

HYGROHYPNUM OCHRACEUM

HYGROHYPNUM EUGYRIUM *VAR.* MACKAYI

CAMPYLIUM HISPIDULUM

CAMPYLIUM CHRYSOPHYLLUM

Plate XLVI

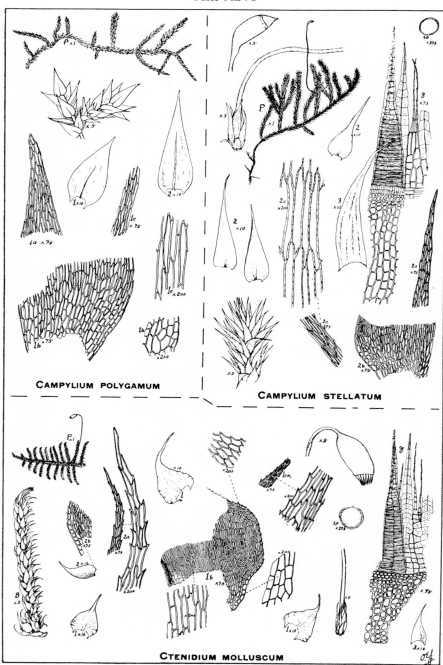

CAMPYLIUM POLYGAMUM

CAMPYLIUM STELLATUM

CTENIDIUM MOLLUSCUM

Plate XLVII

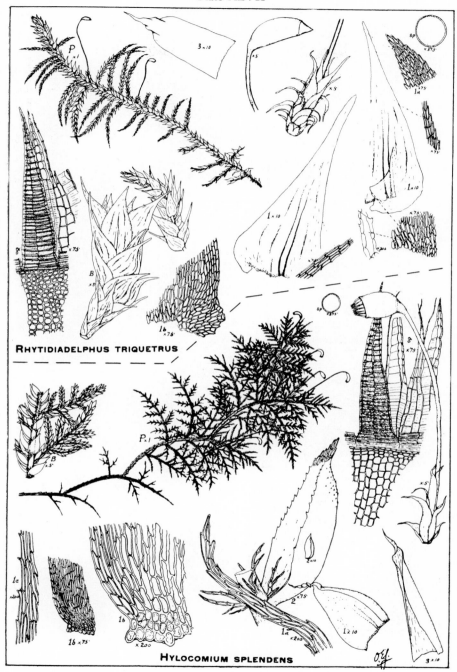

RHYTIDIADELPHUS TRIQUETRUS

HYLOCOMIUM SPLENDENS

Plate XLVIII

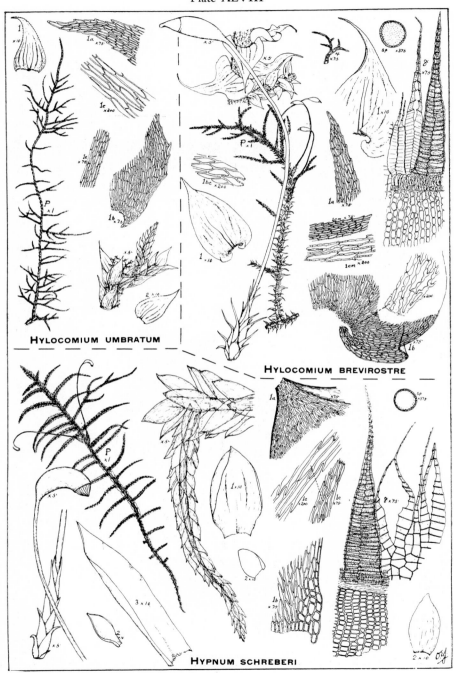

HYLOCOMIUM UMBRATUM

HYLOCOMIUM BREVIROSTRE

HYPNUM SCHREBERI

Plate XLIX

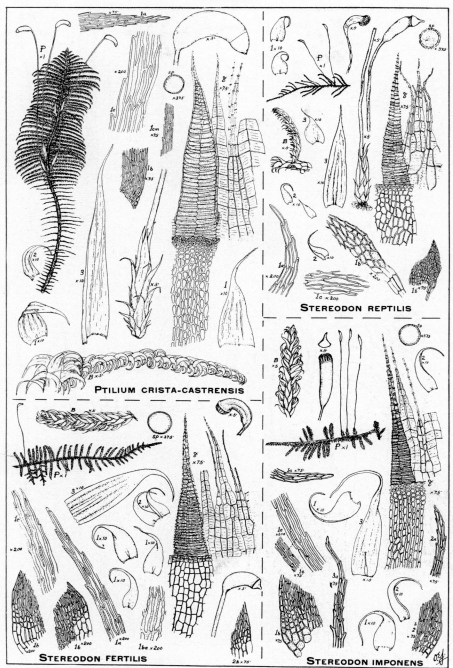

PTILIUM CRISTA-CASTRENSIS

STEREODON REPTILIS

STEREODON FERTILIS

STEREODON IMPONENS

Plate L

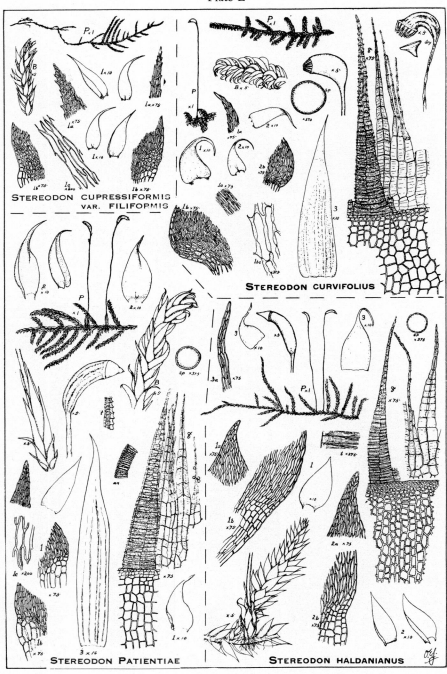

STEREODON CUPRESSIFORMIS
VAR. FILIFORMIS

STEREODON CURVIFOLIUS

STEREODON PATIENTIAE

STEREODON HALDANIANUS

Plate LI

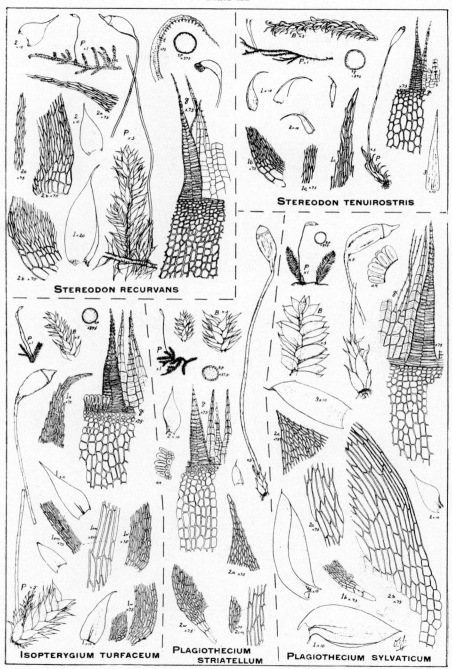

STEREODON TENUIROSTRIS

STEREODON RECURVANS

ISOPTERYGIUM TURFACEUM

PLAGIOTHECIUM STRIATELLUM

PLAGIOTHECIUM SYLVATICUM

Plate LII

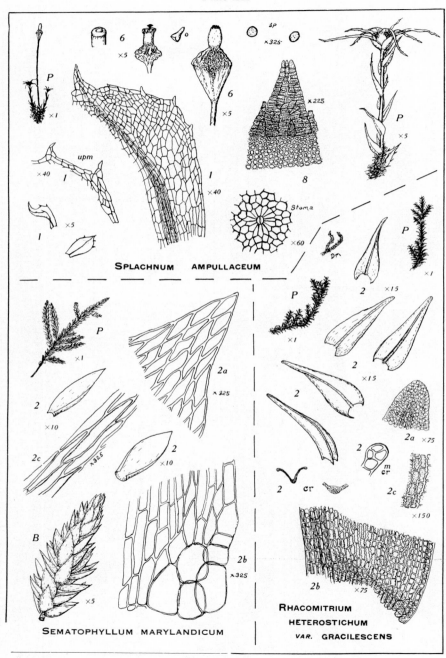

SPLACHNUM AMPULLACEUM

SEMATOPHYLLUM MARYLANDICUM

RHACOMITRIUM
HETEROSTICHUM
VAR. GRACILESCENS

Plate LIII

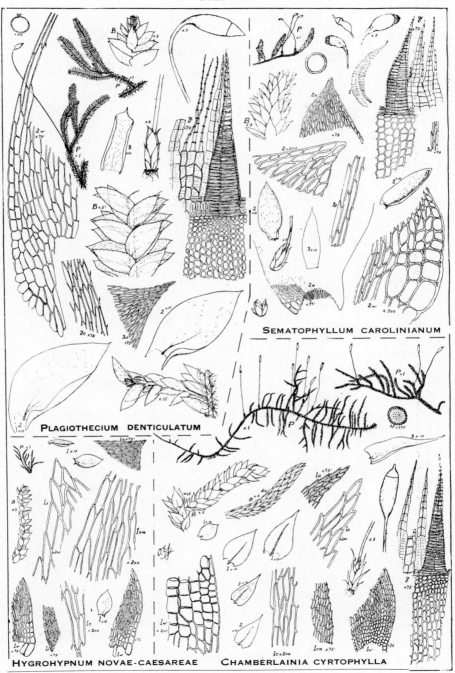

SEMATOPHYLLUM CAROLINIANUM

PLAGIOTHECIUM DENTICULATUM

HYGROHYPNUM NOVAE-CAESAREAE   CHAMBERLAINIA CYRTOPHYLLA

Plate LIV

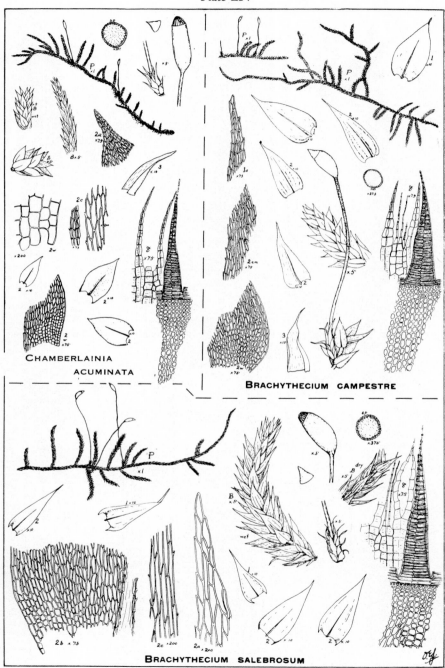

CHAMBERLAINIA
ACUMINATA

BRACHYTHECIUM CAMPESTRE

BRACHYTHECIUM SALEBROSUM

Plate LV

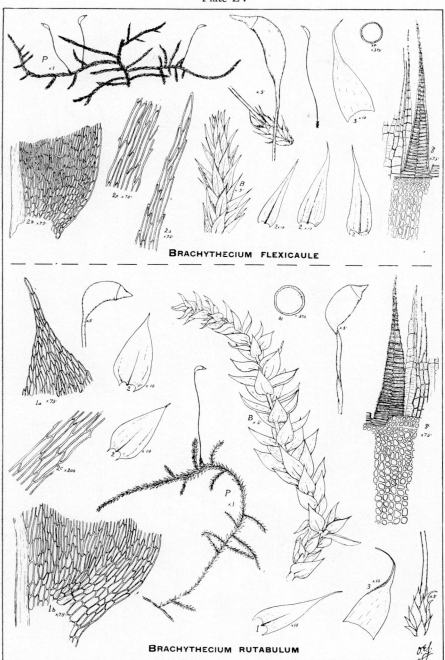

BRACHYTHECIUM FLEXICAULE

BRACHYTHECIUM RUTABULUM

Plate LVI

BRACHYTHECIUM STARKEI

BRACHYTHECIUM RIVULARE

BRACHYTHECIUM VELUTINUM

Plate LVII

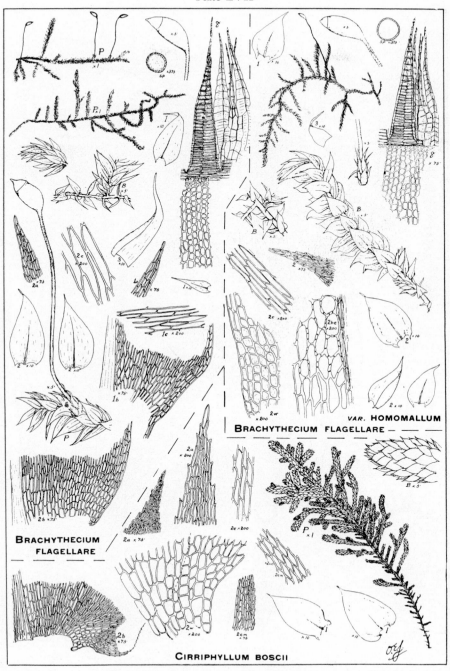

VAR. **HOMOMALLUM**

BRACHYTHECIUM FLAGELLARE —

BRACHYTHECIUM FLAGELLARE

CIRRIPHYLLUM BOSCII

Plate LVIII

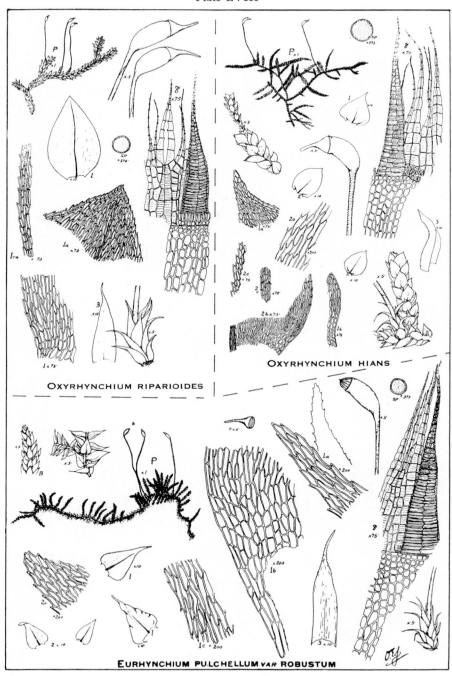

OXYRHYNCHIUM RIPARIOIDES

OXYRHYNCHIUM HIANS

EURHYNCHIUM PULCHELLUM *var* ROBUSTUM

Plate LIX

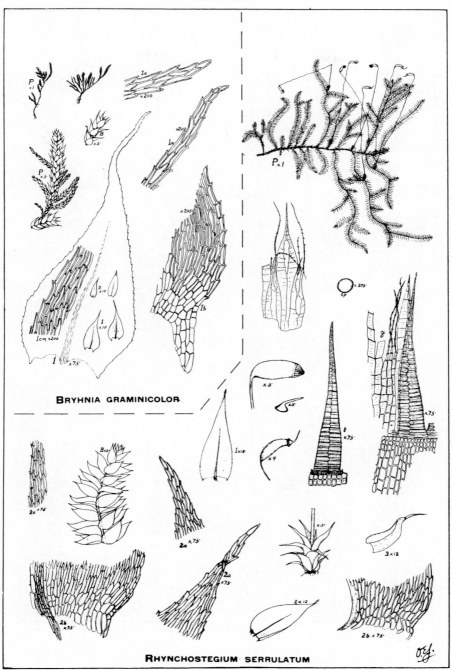

BRYHNIA GRAMINICOLOR.

RHYNCHOSTEGIUM SERRULATUM

Plate LX

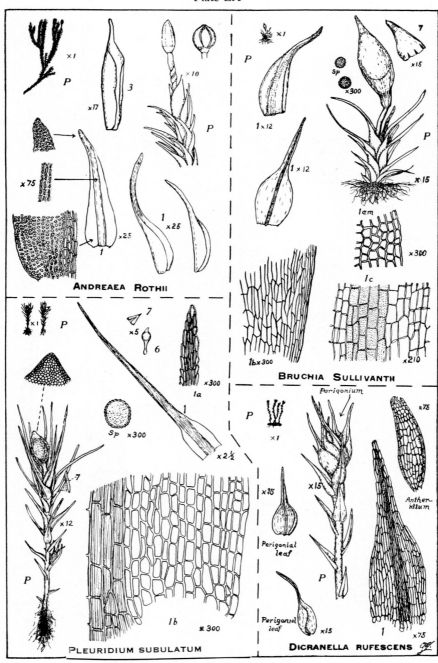

ANDREAEA ROTHII

BRUCHIA SULLIVANTII

PLEURIDIUM SUBULATUM

DICRANELLA RUFESCENS

Plate LXI

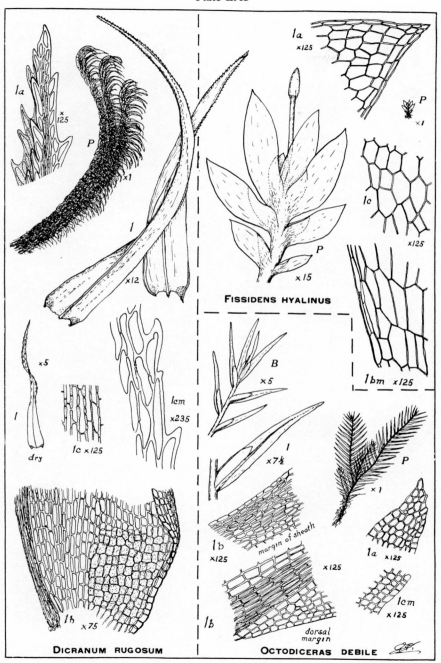

FISSIDENS HYALINUS

DICRANUM RUGOSUM

OCTODICERAS DEBILE

385

Plate LXII

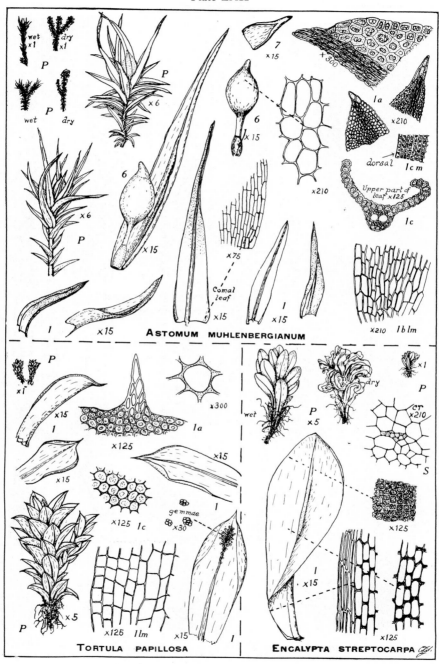

ASTOMUM MUHLENBERGIANUM

TORTULA PAPILLOSA

ENCALYPTA STREPTOCARPA

386

Plate LXIII

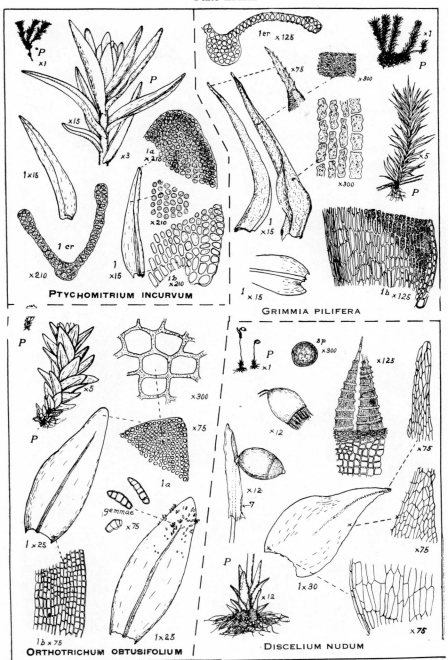

PTYCHOMITRIUM INCURVUM

GRIMMIA PILIFERA

ORTHOTRICHUM OBTUSIFOLIUM

DISCELIUM NUDUM

Plate LXIV

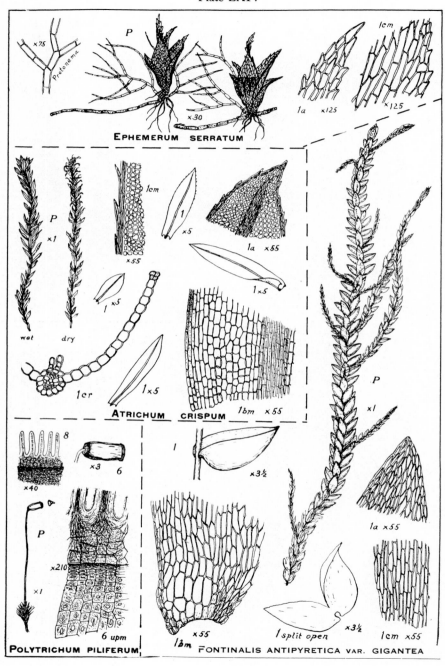

EPHEMERUM SERRATUM

ATRICHUM CRISPUM

POLYTRICHUM PILIFERUM

FONTINALIS ANTIPYRETICA VAR. GIGANTEA

Plate LXV

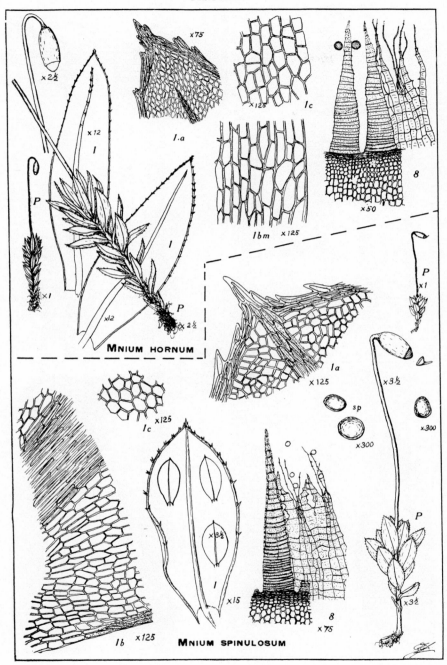

x2½

x12

1

x75

1.a

x125

1c

8

P

1bm x125

x50

P

x1

1a

x125

P

x1

sp

x300

x3½

x300

MNIUM HORNUM

x2½

x12

P

P

x1

1c x125

1b x125

1c x125

x3½

1

x15

8

x75

P

x3½

MNIUM SPINULOSUM

Plate LXVI

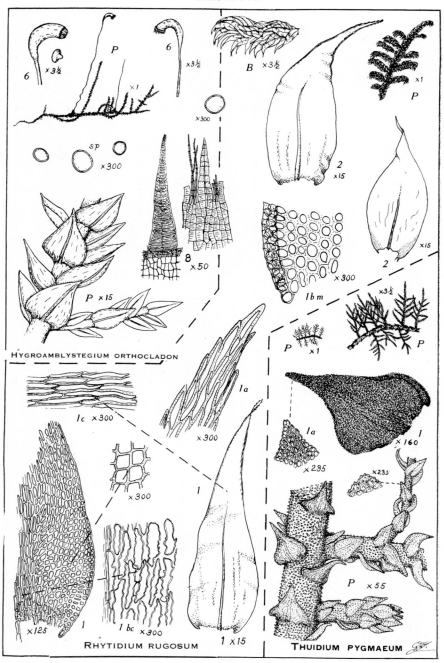

HYGROAMBLYSTEGIUM ORTHOCLADON

RHYTIDIUM RUGOSUM

THUIDIUM PYGMAEUM

Plate LXVII

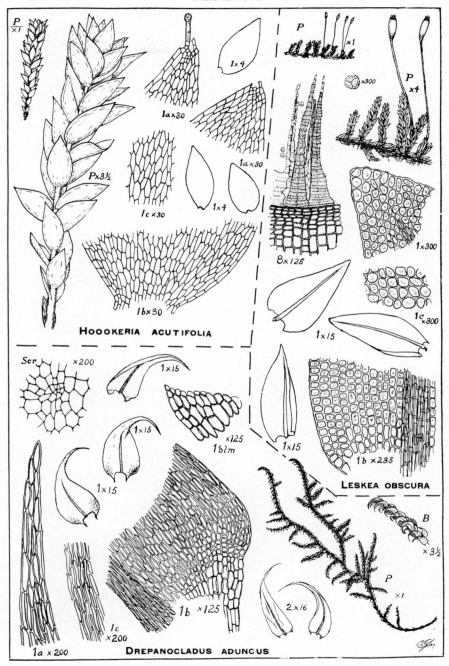

HOOOKERIA ACUTIFOLIA

LESKEA OBSCURA

DREPANOCLADUS ADUNCUS

Plate LXVIII

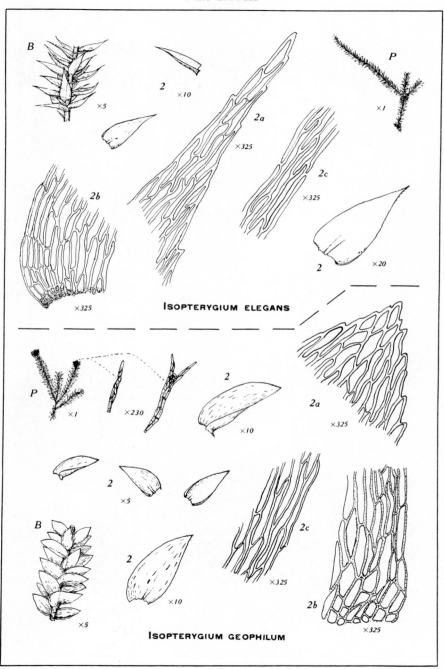

ISOPTERYGIUM ELEGANS

ISOPTERYGIUM GEOPHILUM

Plate LXIX

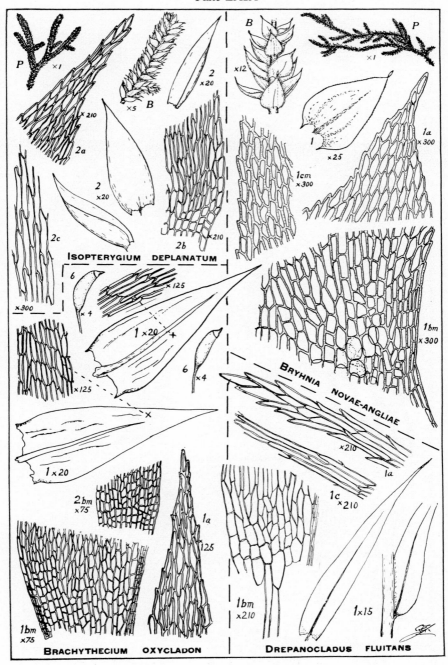

ISOPTERYGIUM DEPLANATUM

BRYHNIA NOVAE-ANGLIAE

BRACHYTHECIUM OXYCLADON

DREPANOCLADUS FLUITANS

Plate LXX

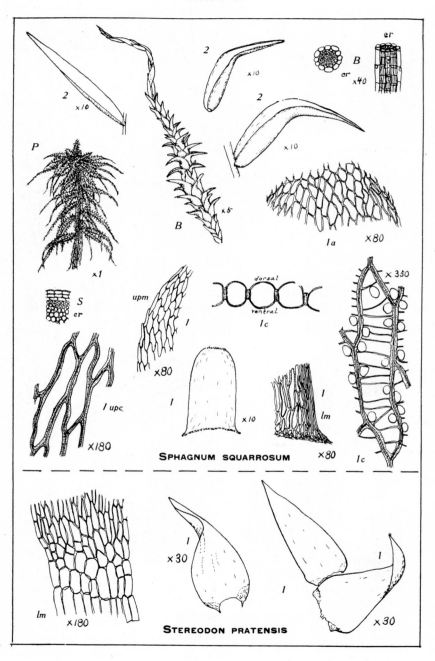

SPHAGNUM SQUARROSUM

STEREODON PRATENSIS

Plate LXXI

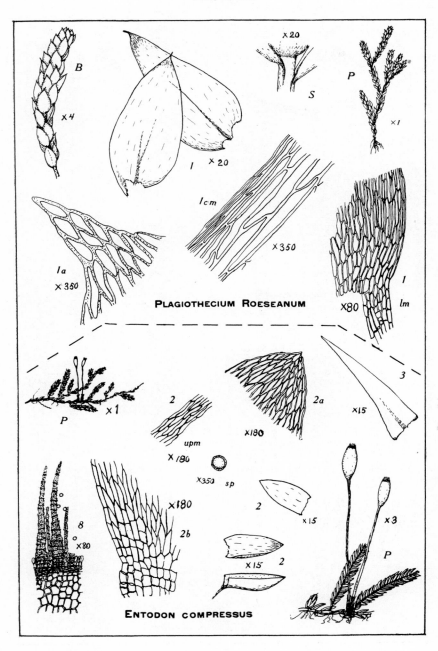

Plate LXXII

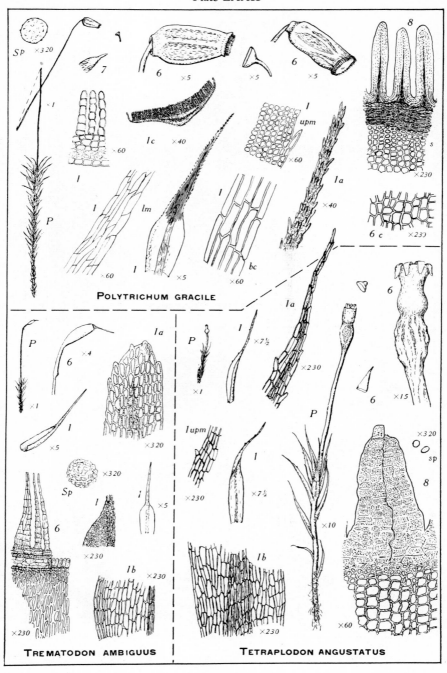

SP ×320

7

6 ×5

×5

6 ×5

8

1c ×40

1 upm ×60

1a ×40

s ×230

6c ×230

P

1 lm ×60

1 ×5

1 bc ×60

POLYTRICHUM GRACILE

P

1a

6 ×4

1 ×5

P

1 ×1

1a ×230

6

×1

1 upm ×230

1 ×7½

×1

6 ×15

Sp ×320

6

1 ×230

1 ×5

1 ×7½

P ×10

×320
sp

8

1b ×230

1b ×230

×60

×230

TREMATODON AMBIGUUS

TETRAPLODON ANGUSTATUS